Lab Safety

Safety symbol	What it means	What to do in the event of an accident
Eye protection	Wear safety goggles anytime there is the slightest chance that your eyes could be harmed.	If anything gets into your eyes, notify your teacher immediately and flush your eyes with running water for 15 minutes.
Hand safety	Wear appropriate protective gloves when working with an open flame, chemicals, or plants. Your teacher will provide the type of gloves necessary for a given activity.	If any chemical gets on your hands, rinse it off immediately with water for at least 5 minutes while calling to your teacher. Report any burn of the hands to your teacher no matter how minor it seems. Wash your hands with soap and hot water at the end of every lab.
Clothing protection	Wear your apron whenever you are working with chemicals or whenever you are instructed to do so.	If you spill a corrosive chemical onto your clothing, rinse it off immediately by using a faucet or the safety shower and remove the affected clothing while calling to your teacher.
Sharp/pointed object safety	Use knives and other sharp objects with extreme care. Place objects on a suitable work surface for cutting.	Notify your teacher immediately in the event of a cut or puncture no matter how minor it seems.
Heating safety	Wear safety goggles when using a heating device or flame. Wear heat-resistant gloves whenever instructed to do so. When heating materials in a test tube, angle the test tube away from yourself and others.	Notify your teacher immediately in the event of a burn or fire no matter how minor it seems.
Electrical safety	Do not place electrical cords where they could trip someone or cause equipment to fall. Do not use equipment with damaged cords. Do not use electrical equipment near water or when your clothing or hands are wet. Make sure that electrical equipment is in the "off" position before plugging it in. Turn off and unplug electrical equipment when you have finished using it.	Notify your teacher immediately if you notice any abnormal or potentially dangerous equipment. In the event of an electric shock, notify your teacher no matter how minor it seems.
Chemical safety	Wear safety goggles, an apron, and gloves whenever working with chemicals.	If a chemical spills onto your skin, rinse it off immediately by using the faucet or safety shower for at least 5 minutes while calling to your teacher.
Animal safety	Handle animals only as your teacher directs. Treat animals carefully and respectfully. Wash your hands thoroughly after handling any animal.	Notify your teacher immediately if you injure yourself or any live specimen no matter how minor the injury seems.
Plant safety	Do not eat any part of a plant or plant seed used in the laboratory. When in nature, do not pick any wild plants unless your teacher instructs you to do so. Wash your hands thoroughly after handling any part of a plant.	Notify your teacher immediately if any potentially dangerous plant material comes into contact with your skin or if any plant matter is inhaled or ingested no matter how minor the event seems.

Common Words with Multiple Meanings

Word	Common meaning	Scientific meaning
concentration	the act of focusing one's attention on something	the amount of a particular substance in a given quantity of a mixture or solution
fluid	smooth; graceful (for example, fluid movement)	a nonsolid state of matter in which the atoms or molecules are free to move past each other, as in a gas or liquid
friction	conflict between people who have opposing views	a force that opposes motion between two surfaces that are in contact
gas	short for gasoline; a liquid fuel used by vehicles, such as cars and buses	a form of matter that does not have a definite volume or shape
gravity	seriousness (for example, the gravity of the situation)	a force of attraction between objects that is due to their masses and that decreases as the distance between the objects increases
group	a number of people gathered together	a vertical column of elements in the periodic table; elements in a group share chemical properties
mass	a quantity of material that has an unspecified shape	a measure of the amount of matter in an object
matter	a subject of concern or topic of discussion	anything that has mass and takes up space
medium	an intermediate measurement between small and large	a physical environment in which phenomena occur
model	a miniature representation of a larger object	a pattern, plan, representation, or description designed to show the structure or workings of an object, system, or concept
organic	describes an organism or object that is produced without the use of synthetic drugs, fertilizers, or hormones	describes a material that is derived from living organisms and that contains carbon
period	a punctuation mark used to indicate the end of a sentence	a horizontal row of elements in the periodic table
pressure	the burden of mental stress	the amount of force exerted per unit area of a surface
product	something available for sale (for example, a computer product)	a substance that forms in a chemical reaction
reaction	a response to a stimulus	the process by which one or more substances change to produce one or more different substances
solution	the answer to a problem	a homogeneous mixture throughout which two or more substances are uniformly dispersed
star	a person who is highly celebrated in a particular field	a large celestial body that is composed of gas and that emits light
table	a piece of furniture that has a flat, horizontal surface	an orderly arrangement of data
theory	an assumption based on limited knowledge	a system of ideas that explains many related observations and is supported by a large body of evidence acquired through scientific investigation
volume	a measure of how loud a sound is	a measure of the size of a body or region in three-dimensional space

Physical Science

HOLT, RINEHART AND WINSTON

A Harcourt Education Company

Orlando • **Austin** • New York • San Diego • London

Acknowledgments

Contributing Authors

Christie Borgford, Ph.D.
Assistant Professor of Chemistry (retired)
Department of Chemistry
University of Alabama
Birmingham, Alabama

Mapi Cuevas, Ph.D.
Professor of Chemistry
Department of Natural Sciences
Santa Fe Community College
Gainesville, Florida

Leila Dumas, MA
Former Physics Teacher
Lago Vista, Texas

Mary Kay Hemenway, Ph.D.
Research Associate and Senior Lecturer
Department of Astronomy
The University of Texas at Austin
Austin, Texas

John Krupczak, Jr., Ph.D.
Associate Professor & Engineering Program Director
Department of Physics and Engineering
Hope College
Holland, Michigan

William G. Lamb, Ph.D.
Winningstad Chair in the Physical Sciences
Oregon Episcopal School
Portland, Oregon

Lee Summerlin, Ph.D.
Professor of Chemistry (retired)
University of Alabama
Birmingham, Alabama

Sally Ann Vonderbrink, Ph.D.
Chemistry Teacher (retired)
Cincinnati, Ohio

Jane Yuster
Department Chair
Hoover Elementary School
Redwood City, California

Consultants

Ellen McPeek Glisan
Special Needs Consultant
San Antonio, Texas

Belinda Dunnick Karge, Ph.D.
Chair, Department of Special Education
California State University, Fullerton
Fullerton, California

Robin Scarcella
California Inclusion Consultant
Irvine, California

Safety Reviewers

Jim Adams
Science Education Technician (retired)
Las Positas College
Livermore, California

Jack Gerlovich, Ph.D.
Associate Professor
School of Education
Drake University
Des Moines, Iowa

Senior Advisors

Susana E. Deustua, Ph.D.
Director of Educational Activities
American Astronomical Society
Washington, D.C.

Frances Marie Gipson, MA
Director of the UCLA and District 3 LAUSD Partnership
Department of Secondary Literacy
University of California, Los Angeles;
  Center X
Los Angeles, California

Ron Hage
Science Partner
University of California, Los Angeles;
  Los Angeles Unified School District
Los Angeles, California

James E. Marshall, Ph.D.
Professor of Science Education
Department of Curriculum and Instruction
California State University, Fresno
Fresno, California

Acknowledgments
continued on page 594

Contents in Brief

UNIT 1 **Introduction to Physical Science** 2

Chapter 1 The Nature of Physical Science 4

Chapter 2 Data in Science 38

UNIT 2 **The Structure of Matter** 72

Chapter 3 Properties of Matter 74

Chapter 4 States of Matter 106

Chapter 5 Elements, Compounds, and Mixtures 130

UNIT 3 **The Atom** 158

Chapter 6 Introduction to Atoms 160

Chapter 7 The Periodic Table 190

UNIT 4 **Interactions of Matter** 220

Chapter 8 Chemical Bonding 222

Chapter 9 Chemical Reactions 252

Chapter 10 Chemical Compounds 278

Chapter 11 The Chemistry of Living Things 306

UNIT 5 **Motion and Forces** 330

Chapter 12 Matter in Motion 332

Chapter 13 Forces and Motion 366

Chapter 14 Forces in Fluids 402

UNIT 6 **Studying the Universe** 430

Chapter 15 Stars, Galaxies, and the Universe 432

Chapter 16 Our Solar System 468

Contents

How to Use Your Textbook xxii

Safety First! xxviii

UNIT 1 Introduction to Physical Science

TIMELINE 2

CHAPTER

1

Chapter Preview 4
Improving Comprehension—Process Chart
Unpacking the Standards 🐻 **8.9.a, 8.9.b, 8.9.c**

The Nature of Physical Science 6

SECTION 1 Science and Scientists 8

SECTION 2 Scientific Methods 14

SECTION 3 Safety in Science 22

Chapter Lab Measuring Liquid Volume 28

Science Skills Activity Testing a Hypothesis 30

Chapter Review 32

Standards Assessment 34

Science in Action 36
  Science Fiction "Inspiration" by Ben Bova
  Science, Technology, and Society Racing with the Sun
  Careers Julie Williams–Byrd (Electronics Engineer)

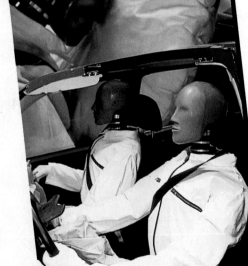

PROPERTY OF
WESTERN CENTER ACADEMY

CHAPTER

2

Chapter Preview 38
Improving Comprehension—Combination Notes
Unpacking the Standards 🐻 **8.9.d, 8.9.e, 8.9.f, 8.9.g**

Data in Science 40

SECTION 1 Tools and Models in Science 42

SECTION 2 Organizing Your Data 50

SECTION 3 Analyzing Your Data 56

Chapter Lab Penny Densities 62

Science Skills Activity Accuracy and Reproducibility of Data 64

Chapter Review 66

Standards Assessment 68

Science in Action 70

    Science, Technology, and Society Using Satellites to
    Track Plate Motion

    Weird Science Dolphins in the Navy

    Careers Evan Forde (Oceanographer)

Contents   **v**

UNIT 2 The Structure of Matter

TIMELINE 72

CHAPTER 3

Chapter Preview 74
Improving Comprehension—Venn Diagram
Unpacking the Standards **8.5.a, 8.5.c, 8.5.d, 8.7.c, 8.8.a, 8.8.b**

Properties of Matter 76

SECTION 1 What Is Matter? 78
SECTION 2 Physical Properties 84
SECTION 3 Chemical Properties 90
Chapter Lab Classifying Substances 96
Science Skills Activity Using a Three-Variable Equation 98
Chapter Review 100
Standards Assessment 102
Science in Action 104
  Scientific Debate Paper or Plastic?
  Science, Technology, and Society Reading a Hidden Text
  Careers Mimi So (Gemologist and Jewelry Designer)

CHAPTER 4

Chapter Preview 106
Improving Comprehension—Comparison Table
Unpacking the Standards  8.3.d, 8.3.e, 8.5.d, 8.7.c

States of Matter 108

SECTION 1 Four States of Matter 110
SECTION 2 Changes of State 114
Chapter Lab Boiling and Temperature 120
Science Skills Activity Linear and
Nonlinear Relationships 122
Chapter Review 124
Standards Assessment 126
Science in Action 128
   Science, Technology, and Society Deep-Sea Diving
      with Helium
   Scientific Discoveries The Fourth State of Matter
   People in Science Andy Goldsworthy (Nature Artist)

CHAPTER 5

Chapter Preview 130
Improving Comprehension—Venn Diagram
Unpacking the Standards  8.3.b, 8.5.a, 8.7.c

Elements, Compounds, and Mixtures 132

SECTION 1 Elements 134
SECTION 2 Compounds 138
SECTION 3 Mixtures 142
Chapter Lab Flame Tests 148
Science Skills Activity Identifying Types of Parameters 150
Chapter Review 152
Standards Assessment 154
Science in Action 156
   Weird Science Dry Cleaning: How Stains Are Dissolved
   Science, Technology, and Society Fireworks Over California
   Careers Aundra Nix (Metallurgist)

UNIT 3 The Atom

TIMELINE 158

CHAPTER 6

Chapter Preview 160
Improving Comprehension—Concept Map
Unpacking the Standards **8.3.a, 8.7.b**

Introduction to Atoms 162

SECTION 1 Development of the Atomic Theory 164

SECTION 2 The Atom 172

Chapter Lab Building Atomic Nuclei 180

Science Skills Activity Testing a Hypothesis 182

Chapter Review 184

Standards Assessment 186

Science in Action 188
   Scientific Discoveries Californium
   Weird Science Mining on the Moon?
   Careers Melissa Franklin (Experimental Physicist)

CHAPTER 7

Chapter Preview 190
Improving Comprehension—Spider Map
Unpacking the Standards **8.3.f, 8.7.a, 8.7.b, 8.7.c**

The Periodic Table 192

SECTION 1 Arranging the Elements 194

SECTION 2 Grouping the Elements 202

Chapter Lab Create a Periodic Table 210

Science Skills Activity Constructing a Line Graph 212

Chapter Review 214

Standards Assessment 216

Science in Action 218
   Weird Science Buckyballs
   Scientific Discoveries Modern Alchemy
   People in Science Glenn T. Seaborg (Making Elements)

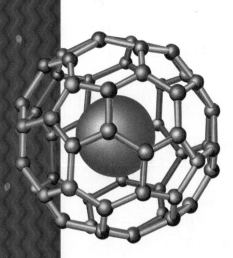

UNIT 4 Interactions of Matter

TIMELINE 220

CHAPTER 8

Chapter Preview 222
Improving Comprehension—Comparison Table
Unpacking the Standards 🐻 **8.3.a, 8.3.b, 8.3.c, 8.3.f, 8.5.a**

Chemical Bonding 224

SECTION 1 Electrons and Chemical Bonding 226

SECTION 2 Ionic Bonds 230

SECTION 3 Covalent and Metallic Bonds 236

Chapter Lab Covalent Marshmallows 242

Science Skills Activity Planning an Investigation 244

Chapter Review 246

Standards Assessment 248

Science in Action 250
   Science, Technology, and Society Superglue Bandages
    and Stitches
   Weird Science How Geckos Stick to Walls
   Careers Michael Fan (Wastewater Manager)

CHAPTER 9

Chapter Preview 252
Improving Comprehension—Cause-and-Effect Map
Unpacking the Standards **8.3.b, 8.3.f, 8.5.a, 8.5.b, 8.5.c**

Chemical Reactions 254

SECTION 1 Forming New Substances 256
SECTION 2 Chemical Formulas and Equations 262
Chapter Lab Putting Elements Together 268
Science Skills Activity Identifying Types of Parameters 270
Chapter Review 272
Standards Assessment 274
Science in Action 276
    Science, Technology, and Society Western Wildfires
    Weird Science Light Sticks
    Careers Larry McKee (Arson Investigator)

CHAPTER 10

Chapter Preview 278
Improving Comprehension—Idea Wheel
Unpacking the Standards **8.3.b, 8.3.c, 8.5.e, 8.7.c**

Chemical Compounds 280

SECTION 1 Ionic and Covalent Compounds 282
SECTION 2 Acids and Bases 286
SECTION 3 Solutions of Acids and Bases 292
Chapter Lab Cabbage Patch Indicators 296
Science Skills Activity Planning an Investigation 298
Chapter Review 300
Standards Assessment 302
Science in Action 304
    Science, Technology, and Society In Hot Water
    Weird Science Silly Putty™
    Careers Jeannie Eberhardt (Forensic Scientist)

CHAPTER

11

Chapter Preview 306
Improving Comprehension—Spider Map
Unpacking the Standards 🐻 **8.3.c, 8.6.a, 8.6.b, 8.6.c**

The Chemistry of Living Things 308

SECTION 1 Elements in Living Things 310

SECTION 2 Compounds of Living Things 314

Chapter Lab Enzymes in Action 320

Science Skills Activity Finding the Slope of a Graph 322

Chapter Review 324

Standards Assessment 326

Science in Action 328
    Science, Technology, and Society Molecular Photocopying
    Scientific Discoveries Skunk Spray Remedy
    Careers Flossie Wong-Staal (Molecular Biologist)

UNIT 5 Motion and Forces
TIMELINE 330

CHAPTER 12

Chapter Preview 332
Improving Comprehension—Cause-and-Effect Map
Unpacking the Standards 🐻 **8.1.a, 8.1.b, 8.1.c, 8.1.d, 8.1.e, 8.1.f, 8.2.a**

Matter in Motion 334

SECTION 1 Measuring Motion 336

SECTION 2 What Is a Force? 344

SECTION 3 Friction: A Force That Opposes Motion 350

Chapter Lab Detecting Acceleration 356

Science Skills Activity Constructing and
  Interpreting Graphs 358

Chapter Review 360

Standards Assessment 362

Science in Action 364
  Science, Technology, and Society GPS Watch System
  Weird Science Jai Alai: The World's Fastest Sport
  Careers Duane Flatmo (Kinetic Sculptor)

CHAPTER 13

Chapter Preview 366
Improving Comprehension—Combination Notes
Unpacking the Standards  8.2.a, 8.2.b, 8.2.c, 8.2.d, 8.2.e, 8.2.f

Forces and Motion 368

SECTION 1 Gravity: A Force of Attraction 370

SECTION 2 Gravity and Motion 376

SECTION 3 Newton's Laws of Motion 384

Chapter Lab Exploring Inertia 392

Science Skills Activity Finding a Missing Quantity 394

Chapter Review 396

Standards Assessment 398

Science in Action 400
    Scientific Discoveries The Millennium Bridge
    Science, Technology, and Society Power Suit for Lifting Patients
    Careers Steve Okamoto (Roller Coaster Designer)

CHAPTER 14

Chapter Preview 402
Improving Comprehension—Idea Wheel
Unpacking the Standards  8.8.a, 8.8.b, 8.8.c, 8.8.d

Forces in Fluids 404

SECTION 1 Fluids and Pressure 406

SECTION 2 Buoyancy and Density 412

Chapter Lab Fluids, Force, and Floating 420

Science Skills Activity Finding a Missing Quantity 422

Chapter Review 424

Standards Assessment 426

Science in Action 428
    Science, Technology, and Society Deep Flight
    Science Fiction "Wet Behind the Ears" by Jack C. Haldeman II
    Careers Alisha Bracken (Scuba Instructor)

Contents   **xiii**

UNIT 6 Studying the Universe

TIMELINE 430

CHAPTER **15**

Chapter Preview 432
Improving Comprehension—Pyramid Chart
Unpacking the Standards 8.2.g, 8.4.a, 8.4.b, 8.4.c, 8.4.d

Stars, Galaxies, and the Universe 434

SECTION 1 Stars 436

SECTION 2 The Life Cycle of Stars 444

SECTION 3 Galaxies 450

SECTION 4 Formation of the Universe 454

Chapter Lab Star Colors: Red Hot, or Not? 458

Science Skills Activity Constructing a line Graph 460

Chapter Review 462

Standards Assessment 464

Science in Action 466
    Weird Science Holes Where Stars Once Were
    Scientific Discoveries The Brightest Star Yet Discovered
    Careers Sandra Faber (Astronomer)

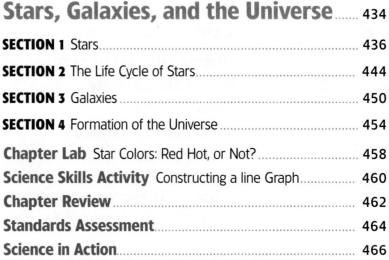

CHAPTER

Chapter Preview 468
Improving Comprehension—Concept Map
Unpacking the Standards  **8.2.g, 8.4.b, 8.4.c, 8.4.d, 8.4.e**

Our Solar System 470

SECTION 1 A Solar System Is Born 472

SECTION 2 The Inner Planets 480

SECTION 3 The Outer Planets 486

SECTION 4 Moons 492

SECTION 5 Small Bodies in the Solar System 500

Chapter Lab Weighing In 506

Science Skills Activity Finding the Slope of a Graph 508

Chapter Review 510

Standards Assessment 512

Science in Action 514
  Science Fiction "The Mad Moon" by Stanley Weinbaum
  Science, Technology, and Society Light Pollution and
    Astronomical Observation
  Careers Adriana C. Ocampo (Planetary Geologist)

Appendix 516
Study Skills 517
  Making and Using FoldNotes 517
  Making and Using Graphic Organizers 521
Understanding Word Parts 530
Common Words with Multiple Meanings 532
Math Refresher 534
Making Graphs 538
Physical Science Refresher 541
Physical Science Laws and Principles 543
Useful Equations 546
  Useful Equations for Heat and Work 549
Scientific Methods 550
SI Measurement 554
Measuring Skills 555
Using the Microscope 556
Periodic Table of the Elements 558
Solar System Data 560
Temperature Scales 562

Glossary 563

Index 577

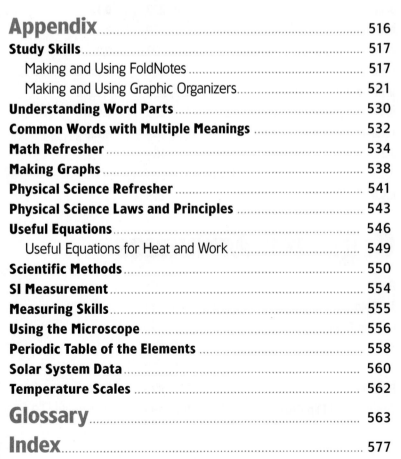

Contents **xv**

Chapter Previews

Improving Comprehension

How to Make a Process Chart 4

How to Make Combination Notes 38, 366

How to Make a Venn Diagram 74, 130

How to Make a Comparison Table 106, 222

How to Make a Concept Map 160, 468

How to Make a Spider Map 190, 306

How to Make a
    Cause-and-Effect Map 252, 332

How to Make an Idea Wheel 278, 402

How to Make a Pyramid Chart 432

Jump-start your learning!

Each chapter starts with a **Chapter Preview** that does two things. The Chapter Preview describes how to make a **Graphic Organizer** to improve your comprehension. And it helps you "unpack" the **California Science Standards,** which will help you better understand what the standards say and mean.

Unpacking the California Standards

Standard

8.1.a–f 333

8.2.a 333, 367

8.2.b–f 367

8.2.g 433, 469

8.3.a 161, 223

8.3.b 131, 223, 253, 279

8.3.c 223, 279, 307

8.3.d–e 107

8.3.f 191, 223, 253

8.4.a 433

8.4.b–d 433, 469

8.4.e 469

8.5.a 75, 131, 223, 253

8.5.b 253

8.5.c 75, 253

8.5.d 75, 107

8.5.e 279

8.6.a–c 307

8.7.a 191

8.7.b 161, 191

8.7.c 75, 107, 131, 191, 279

8.8.a–b 75, 403

8.8.c–d 403

8.9.a–c 5

8.9.d–g 39

Organize Activities

Pyramid 6, 368

Tri-Fold 40, 334

Double Door 76

Table Fold 108

Key-Term Fold 132, 308

Booklet 162, 470

Three-Panel Flip Chart 192, 434

Layered Book 224, 280

Four-Corner Fold 254

Two-Panel Flip Chart 404

Reading Strategies

There are ways to make reading easier.

Reading Strategies at the beginning of each section will help you remember and organize information as you read the chapter.

Asking Questions
Chapter 2 56
Chapter 3 84
Chapter 16 492

Clarifying Concepts
Chapter 8 226

Outlining
Chapter 5 134
Chapter 9 262
Chapter 16 .... 486, 500

Prediction Guide
Chapter 12 336
Chapter 15 454

Summarizing
Chapter 1 8
Chapter 2 42
Chapter 5 138
Chapter 10 292
Chapter 11 310
Chapter 13 370
Chapter 14 406

Graphic Organizers

Cause-and-Effect Map
Chapter 1 14
Chapter 9 256
Chapter 12 .... 344, 350

Combination Notes
Chapter 2 50
Chapter 13 .... 376, 384

Comparison Table
Chapter 4 .... 110, 114
Chapter 7 202
Chapter 8 .... 230, 236
Chapter 15 450
Chapter 16 480

Concept Map
Chapter 6 164
Chapter 16 472

Idea Wheel
Chapter 10 .... 282, 286
Chapter 14 412

Process Chart
Chapter 1 23
Chapter 15 444

Pyramid Chart
Chapter 15 436

Spider Map
Chapter 6 172
Chapter 7 194
Chapter 11 314

Venn Diagram
Chapter 3 .... 78, 90
Chapter 5 142

Math Practice

Effect of Additional Data 19
Calculating the Mean 58
Volume and Density 111
Mass Number Calculations 177
Percentages 200
Calculating Charge 232
Counting Atoms 265
Nucleic Acids 317
Calculating Velocity 377
Starlight, Star Bright 440
Period of Revolution 498

Math Focus

Volume of a Rectangular Solid 80
Calculating Density 86
Calculating Average Speed 338
Pressure, Force, and Area 407
Finding Density 415

Quick Labs

Safety First! xxviii

Chapter

1 Asking a Question 9
  Investigating a Pendulum's Swing 18
  Drawing a Safety Map 24

2 Accuracy of Measurements 44
  Height Vs. Arm Span 52
  Slope and Speed 60

3 Finding Accurate Volumes 79
  Finding Volume by Displacement 81
  Finding the Density of
  Unknown Metals 87
  Physical or Chemical Change? 94

4 Changing Volumes 112
  Boiling Water Without Heating It 118

5 Separating Elements 135
  Identifying Compounds 139
  Identifying Solutes by Solubility 146

6 Mystery Box 167
  Atomic Bead Models 177

7 Heat Conduction 198
  Locating Elements on the Table 208

8 A Model Atom 228
  Growing Crystals 234
  Studying Sugar 238

9 Reaction Ready 259
  Endothermic and Exothermic
  Processes 260
  Conservation of Mass 267

10 Ionic or Covalent? 284
  Blue to Red—Acid! 290
  Neutralization 293

11 What's in the Wax? 312
  Modeling Proteins 316

12 Reference Points and Positions 337
  Changing Average Speed 339
  Graphing Acceleration 342
  Finding Net Force 346
  Identifying Forces 348
  Feeling Friction 351

13 Mass and Weight 374
  Parachutes and Air Resistance 379
  Circling Marbles 382
  First-Law Skateboard 385
  Testing Newton's Second Law 388

14 Forces on Fluids 410
  Finding the Buoyant Force 413
  Will It Sink or Float? 416
  Ship Shape 417

15 Demonstrating Parallax 441
  Making a Star Movie 445
  Modeling Galaxies 451
  The Expanding Universe 455

16 Modeling Fusion 476
  Distances in the Inner Solar System .. 484
  Distances in the Outer Solar System . 490
  Modeling Eclipses 495
  Modeling Crater Formation 502

The more labs, the better!

Take a minute to browse the variety of exciting labs in this textbook. All **labs** are designed to help you experience science firsthand. But please don't forget to be safe. Read the Safety First! section before starting any of the labs.

Chapter Labs

Safety First! xxviii

Chapter

1 Measuring Liquid Volume 28

2 Penny Densities 62

3 Classifying Substances 96

4 Boiling and Temperature 120

5 Flame Tests 148

6 Building Atomic Nuclei 180

7 Create a Periodic Table 210

8 Covalent Marshmallows 242

9 Putting Elements Together 268

10 Cabbage Patch Indicators 296

11 Enzymes in Action 320

12 Detecting Acceleration 356

13 Exploring Inertia 392

14 Fluids, Force, and Floating 420

15 Star Colors: Red Hot, or Not? 458

16 Weighing In 506

Explore Activities

Safety First! xxviii

Chapter

1 Making Observations and Testing Ideas . 7

2 Creating a Scientific Plan 41

3 Similar Size, Different Mass 77

4 A Change of State 109

5 Classifying by Properties 133

6 A Model of Exploring the Atom 163

7 A Tool to Predict Properties 193

8 Bonding and Properties 225

9 A Model Chemical Formula 255

10 A Model of Salt 281

11 Building an Organic Molecule 309

12 The Domino Derby—Measuring Speed 335

13 Gravity and Falling 369

14 Floating and Density Changes 405

15 Exploring the Movement of
Galaxies in the Universe 435

16 Measuring Space 471

Start your engines with an activity!

Get motivated to learn by doing an activity at the beginning of each chapter. The **Explore Activity** helps you gain scientific understanding of the chapter material through hands-on experience.

Internet Activities

Chapter	Keyword
1 Careers in Physical Science	HY7WPSW
2 Careers in Engineering	HY7DISW
3 My New Material	HY7MATW
4 Physical Scientist Biographies	HY7STAW
5 A Physical Science Fairytale	HY7MIXW
6 Atomic Scientist Biography	HY7ATSW
7 The Right Element for You	HY7PRTW
8 Atomic Attraction	HY7BNDW
9 Middle Ages Chemistry	HY7REAW
10 Physicist Biography	HY7CMPW
11 My New Sandwich	HY7BD7W
12 Biographies of Physical Scientists	HY7MOTW
13 Newton's Rap	HY7FORW
14 Trapped With No Bottle	HY7FLUW
15 Astronomer Biographies	HY7UNVW
16 Planetary Exploration	HY7FAMW

Learn and practice the skills of a scientist!
The **Science Skills Activity** in each chapter helps you build investigation and experimentation skills. These skills are essential to learning science.

Science Skills Activities

Testing a Hypothesis	30
Accuracy and Reproducibility of Data	64
Using a Three-Variable Equation	98
Linear and Nonlinear Relationships	122
Identifying Types of Parameters	150
Testing a Hypothesis	182
Constructing a Line Graph	212
Planning an Investigation	244
Identifying Types of Parameters	270
Planning an Investigation	298
Finding the Slope of a Graph	322
Constructing and Interpreting Graphs	358
Finding a Missing Quantity	394
Finding a Missing Quantity	422
Constructing a Line Graph	460
Finding the Slope of a Graph	508

School-to-Home Activities

Nonscientific Topics	11
Weather Forecasting	47
Twenty Questions	86
Your Music Catalogue	136
Atomic Diagrams	176
Patterns of Symbols	199
Studying Salt	231
Acids and Bases at Home	288
Water in Fruits	318
Comparing Friction	352
Newton Ball	389
Floating Fun	414
Stargazing	439
Observing the Phases of the Moon	496

Science in Action

Careers

Julie Williams–Byrd
(Electronics Engineer) 37

Evan Forde (Oceanographer) 71

Mimi So
(Gemologist and Jewelry Designer) 105

Aundra Nix (Metallurgist) 157

Melissa Franklin (Experimental Physicist) 189

Michael Fan (Wastewater Manager) 251

Larry McKee (Arson Investigator) 277

Jeannie Eberhardt
(Forensic Scientist) 305

Flossie Wong-Staal
(Molecular Biologist) 329

Duane Flatmo (Kinetic Sculptor) 365

Steve Okamoto
(Roller Coaster Designer) 401

Alisha Bracken (Scuba Instructor) 429

Sandra Faber (Astronomer) 467

Adriana C. Ocampo
(Planetary Geologist) 515

People in Science

Andy Goldsworthy (Nature Artist) 129

Glenn T. Seaborg (Making Elements) 219

Science Fiction

"Inspiration" by Ben Bova 36

"Wet Behind the Ears"
by Jack C. Haldeman II 428

"The Mad Moon" by Stanley Weinbaum 514

Scientific Discoveries

The Fourth State of Matter 128

Californium 188

Modern Alchemy 218

Skunk Spray Remedy 328

The Millennium Bridge 400

The Brightest Star Yet Discovered 466

Scientific Debate

Paper or Plastic? 104

Science moves beyond the classroom!

Read **Science in Action** articles to learn more about science in the real world. These articles will give you an idea of how interesting, strange, helpful, and action-packed science is. And if your thirst is still not quenched, go to **go.hrw.com** for details about each article.

Science, Technology, and Society

Racing with the Sun 36

Using Satellites to Track Plate Motion 70

Reading a Hidden Text 104

Deep-Sea Diving with Helium 128

Fireworks Over California 156

Superglue Bandages and Stitches 250

Western Wildfires 276

In Hot Water 304

Molecular Photocopying 328

GPS Watch System 364

Power Suit for Lifting Patients 400

Deep Flight 428

Light Pollution and
Astronomical Observation 514

Weird Science

Dolphins in the Navy 70

Dry Cleaning: How Stains Are Dissolved 156

Mining on the Moon? 188

Buckyballs 218

How Geckos Stick to Walls 250

Light Sticks 276

Silly Putty™ 304

Jai Alai: The World's Fastest Sport 364

Holes Where Stars Once Were 466

How to Use Your Textbook

Your textbook may seem confusing at first. But with a little introduction, you'll realize that your science textbook can be a big help. In the next few pages, you'll learn how this textbook can help you become a successful science student. You will also learn how interesting and exciting science can be.

Jump-Start Your Learning

The Chapter Preview helps you brush up on your learning skills and helps you focus on what is important.

Each chapter starts with instructions on how to make a **Graphic Organizer,** a tool for organizing the information that you read. A sample Graphic Organizer gives you a sneak preview of the major concepts in the chapter.

California has important **Science Standards** that guide your learning. Use this page to get to know the standards better. The chart contains **Academic Vocabulary** found in the standards. Also, **What It Means** describes each standard in basic terms.

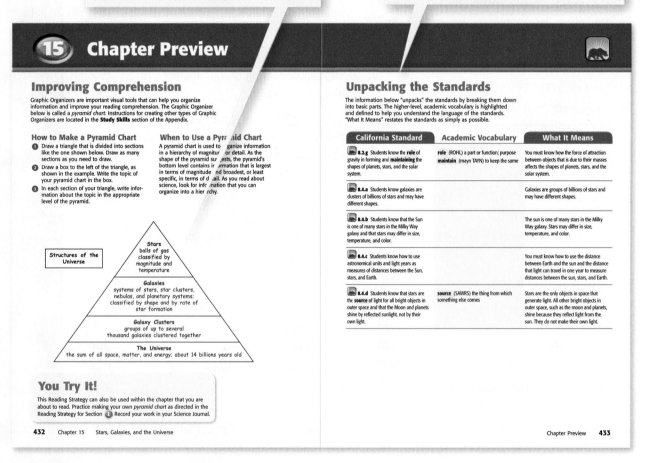

15 Chapter Preview

Improving Comprehension

Graphic Organizers are important visual tools that can help you organize information and improve your reading comprehension. The Graphic Organizer below is called a *pyramid chart*. Instructions for creating other types of Graphic Organizers are located in the **Study Skills** section of the Appendix.

How to Make a Pyramid Chart
1. Draw a triangle that is divided into sections like the one shown below. Draw as many sections as you need to draw.
2. Draw a box to the left of the triangle, as shown in the example. Write the topic of your pyramid chart in the box.
3. In each section of your triangle, write information about the topic in the appropriate level of the pyramid.

When to Use a Pyramid Chart
A pyramid chart is used to organize information in a hierarchy of magnitude or detail. As the shape of the pyramid suggests, the pyramid's bottom level contains information that is largest in terms of magnitude and broadest, or least specific, in terms of detail. As you read about science, look for information that you can organize into a hierarchy.

| Structures of the Universe |

Stars
balls of gas classified by magnitude and temperature

Galaxies
systems of stars, star clusters, nebulas, and planetary systems; classified by shape and by rate of star formation

Galaxy Clusters
groups of up to several thousand galaxies clustered together

The Universe
the sum of all space, matter, and energy; about 14 billions years old

You Try It!

This Reading Strategy can also be used within the chapter that you are about to read. Practice making your own *pyramid chart* as directed in the Reading Strategy for Section 1. Record your work in your Science Journal.

Unpacking the Standards

The information below "unpacks" the standards by breaking them down into basic parts. The higher-level, academic vocabulary is highlighted and defined to help you understand the language of the standards. "What It Means" restates the standards as simply as possible.

California Standard	Academic Vocabulary	What It Means
8.2.g Students know the **role** of gravity in forming and **maintaining** the shapes of planets, stars, and the solar system.	**role** (ROHL) a part or function; purpose **maintain** (mayn TAYN) to keep the same	You must know how the force of attraction between objects that is due to their masses affects the shapes of planets, stars, and the solar system.
8.4.a Students know galaxies are clusters of billions of stars and may have different shapes.		Galaxies are groups of billions of stars and may have different shapes.
8.4.b Students know that the Sun is one of many stars in the Milky Way galaxy and that stars may differ in size, temperature, and color.		The sun is one of many stars in the Milky Way galaxy. Stars may differ in size, temperature, and color.
8.4.c Students know how to use astronomical units and light years as measures of distances between the Sun, stars, and Earth.		You must know how to use the distance between Earth and the sun and the distance that light can travel in one year to measure distances between the sun, stars, and Earth.
8.4.d Students know that stars are the **source** of light for all bright objects in outer space and that the Moon and planets shine by reflected sunlight, not by their own light.	**source** (SAWRS) the thing from which something else comes	Stars are the only objects in space that generate light. All other bright objects in outer space, such as the moon and planets, shine because they reflect light from the sun. They do not make their own light.

Step into Science

The beginning of each chapter is designed to get you involved with science. You will immediately see that science is cool!

> Check out the **Big Idea** to see the focus of the chapter. The entire chapter supports this Big Idea.

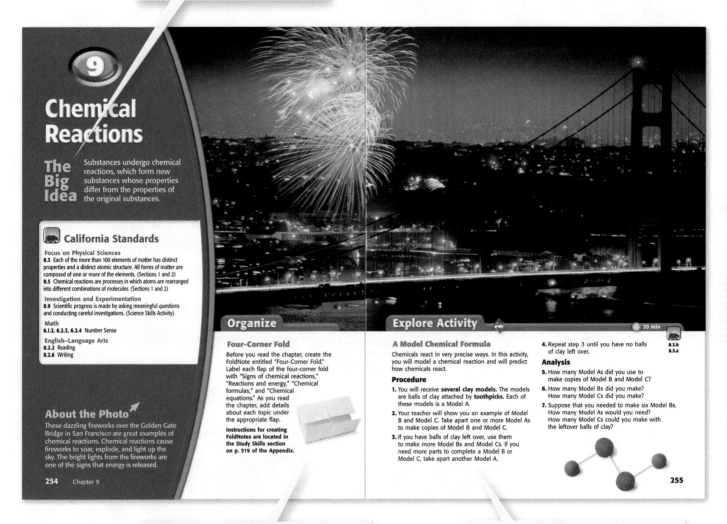

9

Chemical Reactions

The Big Idea Substances undergo chemical reactions, which form new substances whose properties differ from the properties of the original substances.

California Standards

Focus on Physical Sciences
8.3 Each of the more than 100 elements of matter has distinct properties and a distinct atomic structure. All forms of matter are composed of one or more of the elements. (Sections 1 and 2)
8.5 Chemical reactions are processes in which atoms are rearranged into different combinations of molecules. (Sections 1 and 2)

Investigation and Experimentation
8.9 Scientific progress is made by asking meaningful questions and conducting careful investigations. (Science Skills Activity)

Math
6.1.2, 6.2.3, 6.2.4 Number Sense

English–Language Arts
8.2.2 Reading
8.2.6 Writing

About the Photo

These dazzling fireworks over the Golden Gate Bridge in San Francisco are great examples of chemical reactions. Chemical reactions cause fireworks to soar, explode, and light up the sky. The bright lights from the fireworks are one of the signs that energy is released.

254   Chapter 9

Organize

Four-Corner Fold
Before you read the chapter, create the FoldNote entitled "Four-Corner Fold." Label each flap of the four-corner fold with "Signs of chemical reactions," "Reactions and energy," "Chemical formulas," and "Chemical equations." As you read the chapter, add details about each topic under the appropriate flap.

Instructions for creating FoldNotes are located in the Study Skills section on p. 519 of the Appendix.

Explore Activity   20 min

A Model Chemical Formula
Chemicals react in very precise ways. In this activity, you will model a chemical reaction and will predict how chemicals react.

Procedure
1. You will receive **several clay models.** The models are balls of clay attached by **toothpicks.** Each of these models is a Model A.
2. Your teacher will show you an example of Model B and Model C. Take apart one or more Model As to make copies of Model B and Model C.
3. If you have balls of clay left over, use them to make more Model Bs and Model Cs. If you need more parts to complete a Model B or Model C, take apart another Model A.

4. Repeat step 3 until you have no balls of clay left over.   8.3.b 8.5.a

Analysis
5. How many Model As did you use to make copies of Model B and Model C?
6. How many Model Bs did you make? How many Model Cs did you make?
7. Suppose that you needed to make six Model Bs. How many Model As would you need? How many Model Cs could you make with the leftover balls of clay?

255

> You can't be organized enough when learning science. The **FoldNote** provided here gives you note-taking options. These FoldNotes are fun to make and help you understand and remember what you have learned.

> It is never too early for exploration in science. The **Explore Activity** gives you a chance to get some hands-on experience right away. Each activity is a lot of fun and introduces you to one or more California Science Standards from the chapter.

Read for Meaning

You want to get the most out of your reading. One way to do so is to take a minute to learn how the sections are organized.

The **Key Concept** sets the stage for your understanding of the section. Read it carefully, and notice how it relates to the chapter's Big Idea. Together, the Big Idea and the Key Concepts give you an excellent overview of the chapter.

Be sure to start each section by reading the information in the margin. This information tells you **What You Will Learn** and **Why It Matters.** Believe it or not, knowing these things will improve your learning.

Don't skip the **Reading Strategy.** Each strategy provides tips on how to take better notes and how to read for better understanding.

SECTION 3

Chemical Properties

Key Concept A chemical property describes the ability of a substance to change into a new substance.

What You Will Learn
- Examples of chemical properties are reactivity and flammability.
- A chemical change is the process by which a substance changes into a new substance.
- Chemical changes usually liberate or absorb heat.

Why It Matters
Understanding the chemical properties of matter can help you understand how new substances form from other substances.

Vocabulary
- chemical property
- chemical change

READING STRATEGY

Graphic Organizer In your **Science Journal,** create a Venn Diagram that compares types of changes that matter can undergo.

Wordwise flammability
The root *flamm-* means "to burn" or "flame."

► How would you describe a piece of wood before and after it is burned? Did burning change the wood's color? Did burning change the wood's texture? The piece of wood changed, and physical changes alone do not account for all of the ways in which the wood changed.

Identifying Chemical Properties

Physical properties are not the only properties that describe matter. **Chemical properties** describe matter based on its ability to change into new matter, ⊙ from the identity of the origin⊙ is reactivity. *Reactivity* is the ⊙ into one or more new substa in **Figure 1** shows reactivity a⊙

A kind of reactivity is fla⊙ ity of a substance to burn ⊙o flammability. When woo⊙ is bu⊙ other substances. The ⊙roperti⊙ from the properties ⊙f the wood. Ash and smoke cannot burn, so they have the chemical property of nonflammability.

Do you understand what you are reading? Don't wait until test time to find out. The **Standards Checks** help you see if you are understanding the standards.

Standards Check Why is reactivity not a physical property?
🐻 8.5.a

Figure 1 Reactivity with Oxygen

The ⊙umper on this car still looks new becau⊙e it is coated with chromium. Chrom⊙m has the chemical property of nonr⊙activity with oxygen.

The iron used in this old car has the chemical property of **reactivity with oxygen.** When iron is exposed to oxygen, the iron rusts.

8.5.a Students know reactant atoms and molecules interact to form products with different chemical properties.
8.5.c Students know chemical reactions usually liberate heat or absorb heat.
8.5.d Students know physical processes include freezing and boiling, in which a material changes form with no chemical reaction.

Notice how vocabulary is treated in the margins. All vocabulary terms are defined in the margins for quick reference. Also look for **Wordwise** items, which help you understand how prefixes and suffixes are used in scientific words.

Keep an Eye on the Headings

Notice how the headings in the textbook are different sizes and different colors. The headings help you organize your reading and form a simple outline, as shown below.

Blue: section title

Red: major subheads

Light blue: minor subheads

One good way to study is to write down the headings in outline form in your notes. Reviewing this outline will give you a good idea of the main concepts in the chapter and will show you how they are related.

Science Is Doing

You get many opportunities throughout the textbook to actually do science.

Each section has at least one **Quick Lab** to help you get real experience doing science. Also look for **School-to-Home Activities** for cool activities that you can do at home.

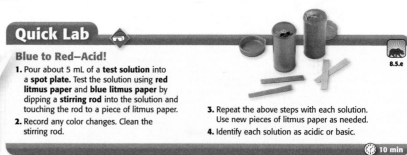

Quick Lab

Blue to Red—Acid!

1. Pour about 5 mL of a **test solution** into a **spot plate.** Test the solution using **red litmus paper** and **blue litmus paper** by dipping a **stirring rod** into the solution and touching the rod to a piece of litmus paper.

2. Record any color changes. Clean the stirring rod.

3. Repeat the above steps with each solution. Use new pieces of litmus paper as needed.

4. Identify each solution as acidic or basic.

8.5.e

10 min

The **Chapter Lab** at the end of each chapter helps you build your understanding of scientific methods. These labs reinforce the California Science Standards with a hands-on activity.

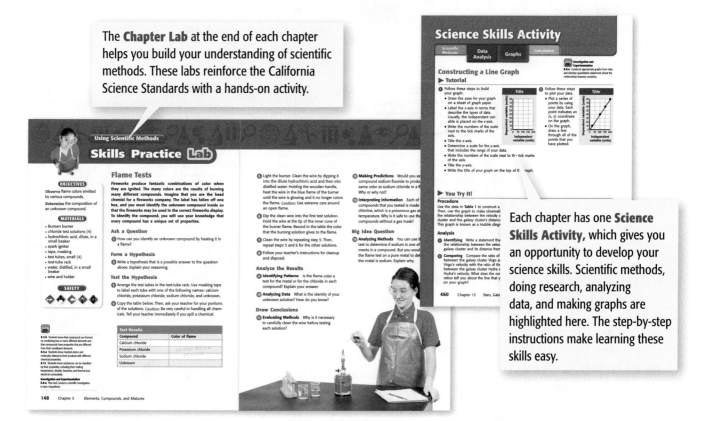

Each chapter has one **Science Skills Activity,** which gives you an opportunity to develop your science skills. Scientific methods, doing research, analyzing data, and making graphs are highlighted here. The step-by-step instructions make learning these skills easy.

Review What You Have Learned

You can't review too much when you are learning science. To help you review, a **Section Review** appears at the end of every section and a **Chapter Summary** and **Chapter Review** appear at the end of every chapter. These reviews not only help you study for tests but also help further your understanding of the content.

Just a few clicks away, each **Super Summary** gives you even more ways to review and study for tests.

Internet Resources let you link to interesting topics and activities related to the section's content.

Be sure to read the **Big Ideas** and the **Key Concepts** to see how they fit together.

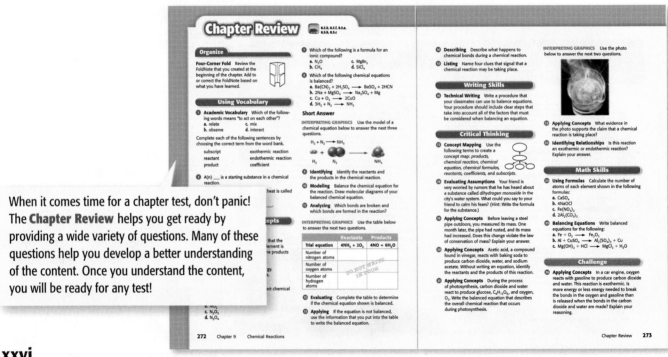

When it comes time for a chapter test, don't panic! The **Chapter Review** helps you get ready by providing a wide variety of questions. Many of these questions help you develop a better understanding of the content. Once you understand the content, you will be ready for any test!

Review the Standards

Mastering the California Science Standards takes practice and more practice! The **Standards Assessment** helps you review the California Science Standards covered in the chapter. The multiple-choice questions also give you some additional practice with standardized tests.

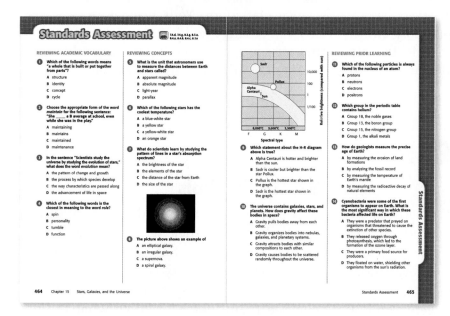

Test-Drive Your Understanding

How well can you use the book now? Use Chapter 1 to answer the questions below and to find out!

1. Which type of Graphic Organizer is used in the Chapter Preview?
2. Which California Science Standards are covered in Chapter 1?
3. What is the Big Idea of this chapter?
4. What will you be doing in the Explore Activity?
5. What is the Key Concept of Section 2?
6. What is the Reading Strategy for Section 1?
7. What new vocabulary terms are introduced in Section 2?
8. How many Standards Checks are in Section 1?
9. What is the name of the Quick Lab in Section 3?
10. On what page does the Chapter Summary appear?
11. How many Standards Assessment questions are there?
12. What is the Super Summary code for Chapter 1?

↗ Be Resourceful—Use the Web!

Internet Resources for Each Section

A box on the Section Review page for each section takes you to resources that you can use for science projects, reports, and research papers. To find information on a topic, go to **scilinks.org** and type in the code provided.

Current Events in Science

Check out the online magazine articles and other materials that go with your textbook at **go.hrw.com**. Click on the textbook icon and the Table of Contents to see all of the resources for each chapter.

Your Online Textbook

If your teacher gives you a special password to log onto the **Holt Online Learning** site, you'll find your complete textbook on the Web. In addition, you'll find some great learning tools and practice quizzes. You'll be able to see how well you know the material from your textbook.

SAFETY FIRST!

Exploring, inventing, and investigating are essential to the study of science. However, these activities can also be dangerous. To make sure that your experiments and explorations are safe, you must be aware of a variety of safety guidelines. You have probably heard of the saying "It is better to be safe than sorry." This is particularly true in a science classroom where experiments and explorations are being performed. Being uninformed and careless can result in serious injuries. Don't take chances with your own safety or with anyone else's.

The following pages describe important guidelines for staying safe in the science classroom. Your teacher may also have safety guidelines and tips that are specific to your classroom and laboratory. Take the time to be safe.

Safety Rules!

Start Out Right

Always get your teacher's permission before attempting any laboratory exploration. Read the procedures carefully, and pay particular attention to safety information and caution statements. If you are unsure about what a safety symbol means, look it up or ask your teacher. You cannot be too careful when it comes to safety. If an accident does occur, inform your teacher immediately no matter how minor the event seems.

If you are instructed to note the odor of a substance, wave the fumes toward your nose with your hand. Never put your nose close to the source.

Safety Symbols

All of the experiments and investigations in this book and their related worksheets include important safety symbols to alert you to particular safety concerns. Become familiar with these symbols so that when you see them, you will know what they mean and what to do. It is important that you read this entire safety section to learn about specific dangers in the laboratory.

Eye protection

Clothing protection

Hand safety

Heating safety

Electric safety

Chemical safety

Animal safety

Sharp object

Plant safety

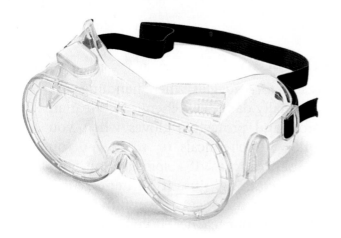

Eye Safety

Wear safety goggles when working around chemicals, acids, bases, or any type of flame or heating device. Wear safety goggles anytime there is the slightest chance that your eyes could be harmed. If anything gets into your eyes, notify your teacher immediately and flush your eyes with running water for at least 15 minutes. Treat any unknown chemical as if it were a dangerous chemical. Never look directly into the sun. Doing so could cause permanent blindness.

Avoid wearing contact lenses in a laboratory situation. Even if you are wearing safety goggles, chemicals can get between the contact lenses and your eyes. If your doctor requires that you wear contact lenses instead of glasses, wear eye-cup safety goggles in the lab.

Safety Equipment

Know the locations of the nearest fire alarms and any other safety equipment, such as fire blankets and eyewash fountains, as identified by your teacher. And know the procedures for using the equipment.

Neatness

Keep your work area free of all unnecessary books and papers. Tie back long hair, and secure loose sleeves or other loose articles of clothing, such as ties and bows. Remove dangling jewelry. Don't wear open-toed shoes or sandals in the laboratory. Never eat, drink, or apply cosmetics in a laboratory setting. Food, drink, and cosmetics can easily become contaminated with dangerous materials.

Certain hair products (such as aerosol hair spray) are flammable and should not be worn while working near an open flame. Avoid wearing hair spray or hair gel on lab days.

Sharp/Pointed Objects

Use knives and other sharp instruments with extreme care. Never cut objects while holding them in your hands. Place objects on a suitable work surface for cutting.

Be extra careful when using any glassware. When adding a heavy object to a graduated cylinder, tilt the cylinder so that the object slides slowly to the bottom.

Heat

Wear safety goggles when using a heating device or a flame. Whenever possible, use an electric hot plate as a heat source instead of using an open flame. When heating materials in a test tube, angle the test tube away from yourself and others. To avoid burns, wear heat-resistant gloves whenever instructed to do so.

Electricity

Be careful with electrical cords. When using a microscope with a lamp, do not place the cord where it could trip someone. Do not let cords hang over a table edge in a way that could cause equipment to fall if the cord is accidentally pulled. Do not use equipment with damaged cords. Do not use electrical equipment near water or when your clothing or hands are wet. Make sure that electrical equipment is in the "off" position before plugging it in. Turn off and unplug electrical equipment when you have finished using it.

Chemicals

Wear safety goggles when handling any potentially dangerous chemicals. Wear an apron and protective gloves when you work with chemicals or whenever you are told to do so. If a spill gets on your skin or clothing, rinse it off immediately with water for at least 5 minutes while calling to your teacher. If you spill a corrosive chemical onto your clothing, rinse it off immediately by using a faucet or the safety shower and remove the affected clothing while calling to your teacher.

Never mix chemicals unless your teacher tells you to do so. Never taste, touch, or smell chemicals unless you are specifically directed to do so. Before working with a flammable liquid or gas, check for the presence of any source of flame, spark, or heat.

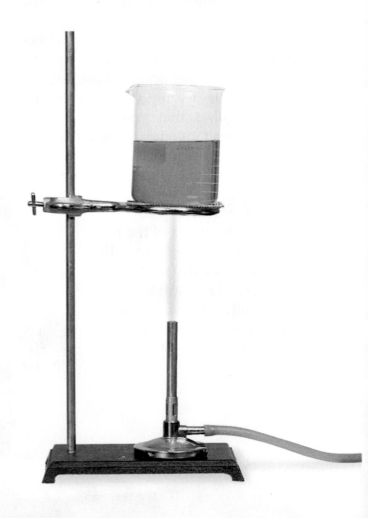

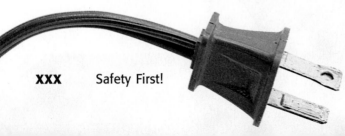

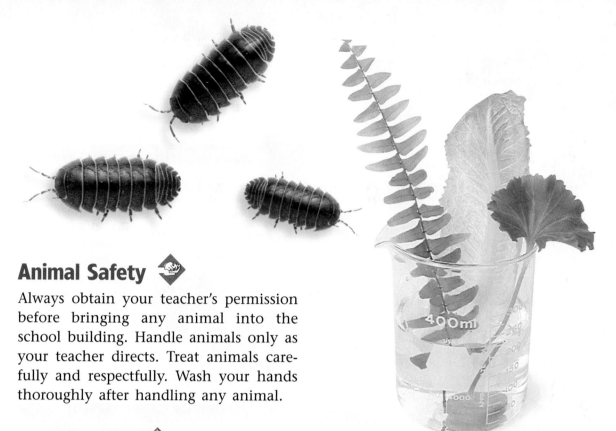

Animal Safety

Always obtain your teacher's permission before bringing any animal into the school building. Handle animals only as your teacher directs. Treat animals carefully and respectfully. Wash your hands thoroughly after handling any animal.

Plant Safety

Do not eat any part of a plant or plant seed used in the laboratory. Wash your hands thoroughly after handling any part of a plant. When in nature, do not pick any wild plants unless your teacher instructs you to do so.

Glassware

Examine all glassware before use. Be sure that glassware is clean and free of chips and cracks. Report damaged glassware to your teacher. Glass containers used for heating should be made of heat-resistant glass.

Introduction to Physical Science

Physical science is the scientific study of nonliving matter. In this unit, you will learn about how scientific progress is made and how scientists conduct investigations. Scientists ask meaningful questions to guide their investigations. Scientists use a variety of tools to collect, analyze, and understand their results. This timeline identifies some events that were the result of scientific investigations.

1751

Benjamin Franklin attaches a key to a kite and flies the kite in a thunderstorm to demonstrate that lightning is a form of electricity.

1903

Willem Einthoven, a Dutch physician, develops the first electrocardiograph machine to record the tiny electric currents in the body's tissues.

1947

The transistor is invented.

1958

The invention of the integrated circuit, which uses millions of transistors, revolutionizes electronic technology.

1773
American colonists hold the Boston Tea Party and dump 342 chests of British tea into Boston Harbor.

1831
Michael Faraday, a British scientist, and Joseph Henry, an American physicist, separately demonstrate the principle of electromagnetic induction, in which magnetism is used to generate electricity.

1876
Alexander Graham Bell officially invents the telephone when he beats Elisha Gray to the patent office by only a few hours.

1911
Superconductivity is discovered. Superconductivity is the ability of some metals and alloys to carry electric current without resistance under certain conditions.

1945
Grace Murray Hopper, a pioneer in computers and computer languages, coins the phrase "debugging the computer" after removing a moth from the wiring of her computer. The moth had caused the computer to fail.

1984
The first portable CD player is introduced.

1997
Garry Kasparov, reigning world chess champion, loses a historic match to a computer named Deep Blue.

2003
One of the largest electricity blackouts in North American history started in the afternoon on August 14, 2003. The blackout left several large cities—including New York City; Detroit, Michigan; and Toronto, Canada—in the dark. Several days passed before electrical energy was fully restored to the millions of people affected in eight U.S. states and Canada.

Improving Comprehension

Graphic Organizers are important visual tools that can help you organize information and improve your reading comprehension. The Graphic Organizer below is called a *process chart*. Instructions for creating other types of Graphic Organizers are located in the **Study Skills** section of the Appendix.

How to Make a Process Chart

1 Draw a box. In the box, write the first step of a process, chain of events, or cycle.

2 Under the box, draw another box, and draw an arrow to connect the two boxes. In the second box, write the next step of the process or the next event in the timeline.

3 Continue adding boxes until each step of the process, chain of events, or cycle is written in a box. For cycles only, draw an arrow to connect the last box and the first box.

When to Use a Process Chart

Science is full of processes. A process chart shows the steps that a process takes to get from one point to another point. Timelines, chains of events, and cycles are examples of the kinds of information that can be organized well in a process chart. As you read, look for information that is described in steps or in a sequence, and draw a process chart that shows the progression of the steps or sequence.

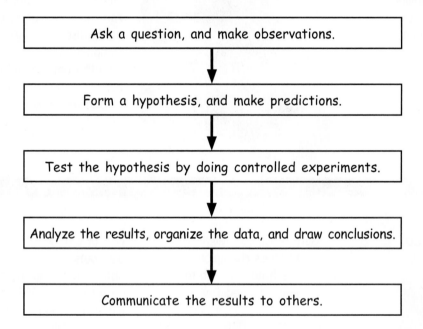

Ask a question, and make observations.

↓

Form a hypothesis, and make predictions.

↓

Test the hypothesis by doing controlled experiments.

↓

Analyze the results, organize the data, and draw conclusions.

↓

Communicate the results to others.

You Try It!

This Reading Strategy can also be used within the chapter that you are about to read. Practice making your own *process chart* as directed in the Reading Strategy for Section **3**. Record your work in your **Science Journal.**

Unpacking the Standards

The information below "unpacks" the standards by breaking them down into basic parts. The higher-level, academic vocabulary is highlighted and defined to help you understand the language of the standards. "What It Means" restates the standards as simply as possible.

California Standard	Academic Vocabulary	What It Means
8.9.a Plan and **conduct** a scientific **investigation** to test a hypothesis.	**conduct** (kuhn DUHKT) to carry out; to do **investigation** (in VES tuh GAY shuhn) a detailed search for answers	Organize and do a methodical experiment to test a possible explanation for an observation.
8.9.b **Evaluate** the **accuracy** and reproducibility of data.	**evaluate** (ee VAL yoo AYT) to judge the worth of **accuracy** (AK yur uh see) the quality or state of being correct; free of error	Judge whether the information collected during an experiment is correct and can be repeated.
8.9.c Distinguish between **variable** and controlled **parameters** in a test.	**variable** (VER ee uh buhl) a factor that changes in an experiment in order to test a hypothesis **parameter** (puh RAM uht uhr) any factor that sets the limit of a possible value	Be able to identify which factors of an experiment are being changed and which factors are being kept the same.

1

The Nature of Physical Science

The Big Idea Scientific progress is made by asking meaningful questions and conducting careful investigations.

California Standards

Investigation and Experimentation
8.9 Scientific progress is made by asking meaningful questions and conducting careful investigations. (Sections 1, 2, and 3; Science Skills Activity)

Math
6.1.2 Statistics, Data Analysis, and Probability
7.1.2 Number Sense
7.1.2 Mathematical Reasoning

English–Language Arts
8.2.2 Reading
8.1.1 Writing

About the Photo

Flippers work great to help penguins move through the water. But could flippers help ships, too? Two scientists have been trying to find out. By using scientific methods, they are asking questions such as, "Would flippers use less energy than propellers do?" As a result of these investigations, ships may someday have flippers like those of penguins!

Organize

Pyramid

Before you read this chapter, create the FoldNote entitled "Pyramid." Label each side of the pyramid with the title of one of the sections in the chapter. As you read the chapter, add details from each section on the appropriate side of the pyramid.

Instructions for creating FoldNotes are located in the Study Skills section on p. 517 of the Appendix.

Explore Activity

20 min

8.9.a

Making Observations and Testing Ideas

In this activity, you will make observations and use them to solve a puzzle, just as scientists do.

Procedure

1. Get the **five shapes** shown here from your teacher.

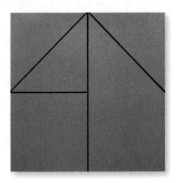

2. Observe the drawing at right. Predict how the five shapes could be arranged to make the fish.

3. Test your idea. You may have to try several times. (Hint: Shapes can be turned over.)

Analysis

4. Did you solve the puzzle just by making observations? What observations helped the most?

5. How did testing your ideas help?

Science and Scientists

Key Concept Scientists benefit society in many ways by asking questions and carefully investigating to find the answers.

What is science? You may already be more of a scientist than you think! To be a scientist, you start by observing the world around you. Then you ask questions about your observations. And that's part of what science is all about.

Starting with a Question

The knowledge gained about the natural world by investigation is called **science.** Asking a question is often the first step in the process of gathering knowledge. The world around you is full of things that can lead you to ask questions, such as those in **Figure 1.**

In Your Own Neighborhood

Take a look around your school and around your neighborhood. Most of the time, you take things that you use or see every day for granted. However, one day you might look at something in a new way. That's when a question hits you! The student in **Figure 1** didn't have to look very far to realize that she had some questions to ask.

The World and Beyond

Do you think you might get tired of asking questions about things in your neighborhood? Then just remember that the world is made up of many different places. You could ask questions about deserts, forests, or sandy beaches. Many different plants and animals live in each of these places. And then there are the rocks, soil, and flowing water in these environments.

But Earth is not the only place to look for questions. You can look outward to the moon, the sun, and the planets in our solar system. And beyond that, you have the rest of the universe! There seem to be enough questions to keep scientists busy for a long time.

Figure 1 *Part of science is asking questions about the world around you.*

Investigation: The Search for Answers

Once you ask a question, it's time to find an answer. Scientific progress is made by asking meaningful questions and conducting careful investigations. There are several different methods that you can use to start your investigation.

Standards Check What are two key steps needed to make scientific progress? **8.9.a**

Research

You can find answers to some of your questions by doing research. You can look up information in books, on the Internet, and in other sources. You can find information by reading about an experiment that someone did. Be sure to think about where the information you find comes from. You want to use information only from reliable sources.

Observation

You can find answers to questions by making careful observations. For example, if you want to know if cloud type and weather are associated, you could make daily observations. By recording the types of clouds that you see each day and that day's weather, you may find associations between the two.

Experimentation

You can answer some of your questions by doing an experiment, as shown in **Figure 2.** A well-planned experiment will put a *hypothesis*, which is a trial explanation, to the test.

Research, observation, and experimentation all go together. Your research might help you plan your experiment. And you'll need to make careful observations. What do you do if you can't do the experiment yourself? For example, what do you do if you want to see how a rat runs through a maze while in space? Don't give up! Do more research, and try to find the results from someone else's experiment!

Investigation and Experimentation
8.9.a Plan and conduct a scientific investigation to test a hypothesis.

Quick Lab

Asking a Question 8.9.a

1. Examine a **ball** that your teacher gives you.
2. Think of a question about the properties of the ball.
3. Propose a hypothesis that answers your question, and plan an experiment that you could carry out to test the hypothesis.

⏱ 10 min

Figure 2 *This student is doing an experiment to find out how her reflection changes in different mirrors.*

Applying the Answers

Although people cannot use science to answer every question, they do find some interesting answers. But do any of the answers really matter? Absolutely! As you study science, you will see how it affects you and everything around you.

Saving Lives

Using science, people have come up with several answers to the question, How can people be protected during an automobile accident? One answer is to require people to wear seat belts. Other answers include designing and building cars that are made of stronger materials and that have air bags. **Figure 3** shows how air bags are tested under scientific conditions. In this way, science helps make cars safer.

Figure 3 *The results of this test are used to improve air bags.*

Saving Resources

Science has also helped answer the question, How can resources be made to last longer? Recycling is one answer. Science has helped people invent ways to recycle a variety of materials. For example, when a car becomes worn out or is wrecked, its steel can be recycled and used to make new products. And recycling steel saves more than just the steel, as shown in **Figure 4.** Using science, people develop more-efficient methods and better equipment for recycling steel, aluminum, paper, glass, and even some plastics. In this way, science helps make resources last longer.

Figure 4 **Resources Saved Through Recycling**

Compared with producing the steel originally, recycling 1 metric ton (1.1 tons) of steel:

uses 60 kg (132 lb) less limestone

uses 2,700,000 kcal less energy

uses 1.25 metric tons (1.38 tons) less ore

produces 76 percent less water pollution

uses 0.70 metric tons (0.77 tons) less coal

produces 86 percent less air pollution

Protecting the Environment

Science has helped answer the question, How can the ozone layer be protected? Scientists have found that substances called chlorofluorocarbons (KLAWR oh FLUR uh KAHR buhnz) (CFCs), which can be found in aerosols (spray-can products), have had a role in damaging the ozone layer. Also using science, people have made other substances that can take the place of CFCs. These substances do not harm the ozone layer.

Why does the loss of this layer matter? The ozone that makes up this layer protects everything on the planet from a harmful type of light called ultraviolet (UV) light. Without the protection of the ozone layer, higher levels of UV light would reach the ground. Higher rates of skin cancer could result. By finding ways to reduce the use of these chemicals, we can help protect the environment and make the world a healthier place.

Standards Check Give three examples of important questions that scientists have asked. 8.9.a

Nonscientific Topics
Although science can be used to answer many questions about the world around us, there are some topics that cannot be examined usefully in a scientific way. With an adult, discuss two or three possible topics that may not be explainable by science. In your **Science Journal**, write down some notes on what you discuss.

ACTIVITY

Scientists Everywhere

Believe it or not, scientists work in many different places. Any person who asks questions and investigates how things work could be called a scientist. Keep reading to learn about a few jobs that use science.

Meteorologist

A *meteorologist* (MEE tee uhr AHL uh jist) is a person who studies the atmosphere. One of the most common careers that meteorologists have is that of weather forecaster. But some meteorologists specialize in—and even chase—tornadoes! These meteorologists predict where a tornado is likely to form. Then, they drive very near the site to gather data, as shown in **Figure 5.** These data help meteorologists and other scientists understand tornadoes better. A better understanding of tornadoes helps scientists more accurately predict the behavior of these violent storms. The ability to make more-accurate predictions allows scientists to give earlier warnings of storms, which helps reduce injuries and deaths caused by storms.

Figure 5 *These meteorologists are risking their lives to gather data about tornadoes.*

Figure 6 *This geochemist takes rock samples from the field. Then, she studies them in her laboratory.*

INTERNET ACTIVITY

Careers in Physical Science

Would you like to be a physical scientist? Write an essay on your investigation of an interesting career. Go to **go.hrw.com,** and type in the keyword HY7WPSW.

Figure 7 *Volcanologists study volcanoes. Many volcanologists study volcanic patterns in order to predict when a volcano will erupt.*

Geochemist

Look at **Figure 6.** A *geochemist* (JEE oh KEM ist) is a person who specializes in the chemistry of rocks, minerals, and soil. Geochemists determine the economic value of these materials. Many geochemists work for oil companies. They also try to find out what the environment was like when these materials formed and what has happened to the materials since they first formed.

Ecologist

To understand the behavior of living things, you need to know about their surroundings. An *ecologist* (ee KAHL uh jist) is a person who studies a community of living things and their nonliving environment. Ecologists work in many fields, such as wildlife management, agriculture, forestry, and conservation.

Volcanologist

Imagine working right at the edge of a 1,000°C pool of lava, as seen in **Figure 7.** That's where you might work if you were a volcanologist! A *volcanologist* (VAHL kuh NAHL uh jist) is a scientist who studies volcanoes. Volcanologists must know the structure and the chemistry of Earth and its rocks. They must also understand how volcanic materials such as lava interact with air and water. This knowledge helps volcanologists learn how and why volcanoes erupt. If volcanologists can predict when a volcano will erupt, they can help save lives.

Science Illustrator

You may be surprised to learn that there is a career that uses both art and science skills. *Science illustrators* draw scientific diagrams, such as the one in **Figure 8.** Good science illustrators are needed in areas like biology and medicine, where accurate and clear diagrams are important.

Science illustrators often have a background in art and a variety of sciences. However, some science illustrators focus on one area of science. For example, some science illustrators draw only medical diagrams. These diagrams are used in medical textbooks or in brochures that patients receive from their doctors.

Figure 8 *A science illustrator drew this diagram so that students can learn about the digestive system in birds.*

SECTION Review

 8.9.a

Summary

- Scientific progress is made by asking meaningful questions and conducting careful investigations.
- Three methods of investigation are research, observation, and experimentation.
- Science affects people's daily lives. Science can help save lives and resources and can help improve the environment.
- There are several types of scientists and many jobs that use science.

Using Vocabulary

1. Write an original definition for *science.*

Understanding Concepts

2. **Listing** What are three methods of investigation?

3. **Describing** Describe three jobs that use science.

4. **Summarizing** Explain how science can help people save resources such as coal.

Critical Thinking

5. **Making Inferences** The slogan for a package delivery service is "For the fastest shipping from port to port, call Holt Speedy Transport!" Describe how science could help you figure out whether this service really ships packages faster than other services do.

6. **Applying Concepts** Your friend wants to know the amount of salt added to her favorite fast-food French fries. What would you recommend that she do to find out the amount of salt?

Math Skills

7. **Making Calculations** A slow flow of lava is traveling at a rate of 3 m per day. How far will the lava have traveled at the end of 30 days?

Challenge

8. **Identifying Bias** Imagine someone says to you, "Nonscientific questions aren't meaningful because they can't be investigated carefully like scientific questions can!" Why is this statement false overall? Explain what is true and what is false about the claim this person makes.

Internet Resources

For a variety of links related to this chapter, go to www.scilinks.org

Topic: Scientific Investigations; Scientists in California

SciLinks code: HY71358; HY7C11

Scientific Methods

Key Concept Scientists use scientific methods to answer questions and to solve problems.

What You Will Learn

● Scientific methods are based on six steps, which may be followed in different ways based on the kind of question being asked.
● Scientific investigations begin with a question and proceed by forming a hypothesis and then testing it.
● Scientists use a variety of methods to analyze and report their data.

Why It Matters

Scientific methods provide a framework for conducting careful investigations and understanding the natural world.

Vocabulary

• scientific methods
• observation
• hypothesis
• data

READING STRATEGY

Graphic Organizer In your **Science Journal,** create a Cause-and-Effect Map that shows the steps used in the scientific method.

▶ Two scientists from the Massachusetts Institute of Technology (MIT) thought that studying penguins was a great way to improve ships! James Czarnowski (zahr NOW SKEE) and Michael Triantafyllou (tree AHN ti FEE loo) used scientific methods to develop *Proteus* (PROH tee uhs), the penguin boat. Can you imagine how and why they did that? In the next few pages, you will learn how these scientists used scientific methods to answer their questions. Scientific methods require knowledge and creativity. And they are very useful in answering some difficult questions.

What Are Scientific Methods?

Scientific methods are the ways in which scientists answer questions and solve problems. As scientists look for answers, they often use the same steps. But there is more than one way to use the steps. Look at **Figure 1.** This figure is an outline of the six steps on which scientific methods are based. Scientists may use all of the steps or just some of the steps during an investigation. They may even repeat some of the steps or do the steps in a different order. How they choose to use the steps depends on what works best to answer their question.

Figure 1 **Steps of Scientific Methods**

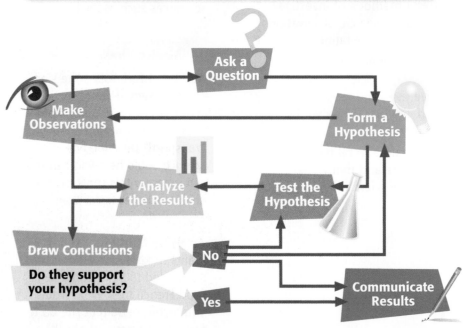

Ask a Question

Make Observations

Form a Hypothesis

Analyze the Results

Test the Hypothesis

Draw Conclusions
Do they support your hypothesis?

No

Yes

Communicate Results

Investigation and Experimentation
8.9.a Plan and conduct a scientific investigation to test a hypothesis.
8.9.b Evaluate the accuracy and reproducibility of data.
8.9.c Distinguish between variable and controlled parameters in a test.

Figure 2 *James Czarnowski (left) and Michael Triantafyllou (right) made observations about how boats work in order to develop* Proteus.

Asking a Question

Asking a question helps focus the purpose of an investigation. Scientists often ask a question after making many observations. **Observation** is any use of the senses to gather information. Noting that the sky is blue or that a cotton ball feels soft is an observation. Measurements are observations that are made with tools. Observations can be made (and should be accurately recorded) at any point during an investigation.

Standards Check In science, what is the purpose of asking questions?
8.9.a

A Real-World Question

Czarnowski and Triantafyllou, shown in **Figure 2,** are engineers—scientists who put scientific knowledge to practical use. Czarnowski was a graduate student at the Massachusetts Institute of Technology. He and Triantafyllou, his professor, worked together to observe boat propulsion (proh PUHL shuhn) systems. Then, they investigated how to make these systems work better. A propulsion system is what makes a boat move. Most boats have propellers to move them through the water.

Czarnowski and Triantafyllou began their investigation by studying the efficiency (e FISH uhn see) of boat propulsion systems. *Efficiency* compares energy output (the energy used to move the boat forward) with energy input (the energy supplied by the boat's engine). From their observations, Czarnowski and Triantafyllou learned that boat propellers are not very efficient.

scientific methods (SIE uhn TIF ik METH uhdz) a series of steps followed to solve problems

observation (AHB zuhr VAY shuhn) the process of obtaining information by using the senses

Figure 3 *Penguins use their flippers to "fly" underwater. As they pull their flippers toward their bodies, they push against the water, which propels them forward.*

The Importance of Boat Efficiency

Most boats that have propellers are only about 70% efficient. Boat efficiency is important because it saves many resources. Making only a small fraction of U.S. boats and ships just 10% more efficient would save millions of liters of fuel per year. Based on their observations and all of this information, Czarnowski and Triantafyllou were ready to ask a question: How can boat propulsion systems be made more efficient? This is a good example of a question that can start a scientific investigation because it is a question that can be answered by observation.

Forming a Hypothesis

Once you've asked your question and made observations, you are ready to form a hypothesis. A **hypothesis** is a possible explanation or answer to a question. You can use what you already know and what you have observed to form a hypothesis.

A good hypothesis is testable. In other words, information can be gathered or an experiment can be designed to test the hypothesis. A hypothesis that is not testable isn't necessarily wrong. But there is no way to show whether the hypothesis is right or wrong.

A Possible Answer from Nature

Czarnowski and Triantafyllou wanted to base their hypothesis on an example from nature. Czarnowski had made observations of penguins swimming. He observed how quickly and easily the penguins moved through the water. **Figure 3** shows how penguins propel themselves. Czarnowski also observed that penguins, like boats, have rigid bodies. These observations led to a hypothesis: A propulsion system that imitates the way that a penguin swims will be more efficient than a propulsion system that uses propellers.

hypothesis (hie PAHTH uh sis) a testable idea or explanation that leads to scientific investigation
Wordwise The prefix *hypo-* means "under." The root *thesis* means "proposition." Other examples are *hypodermic* and *hypoallergenic.*

Making Predictions

Before scientists test a hypothesis, they often predict what they think will happen when they test the hypothesis. Scientists usually state predictions in an if-then statement. The engineers at MIT might have made the following prediction: *If* two flippers are attached to a boat, *then* the boat will be more efficient than a boat powered by propellers.

Testing the Hypothesis

After you form a hypothesis, you must test it. You must find out if it is a reasonable answer to your question. Testing helps you find out if your hypothesis is pointing you in the right direction or if it is way off the mark. If your hypothesis is way off the mark, you may have to change it.

Controlled Experiments

A controlled experiment is a good way to test a hypothesis. A *controlled experiment* compares the results from a control group with the results from experimental groups. All factors remain the same except for one. The factors that are kept the same between the groups are called *controlled parameters*. These factors are held constant. The one factor that changes between the groups is called a *variable parameter*. The results will show the effect of the variable parameter.

Czarnowski and Triantafyllou thought the best way to test their hypothesis was to build a device to test. So, they built *Proteus,* the penguin boat, shown in **Figure 4.** It had flippers like a penguin so that the scientists could test their hypothesis.

Figure 4 Proteus, *a 3.4 m long and 50 cm wide specially built boat model, was used to test the "flippers" hypothesis.*

Standards Check What is the difference between the controlled and the variable parameters in an experiment? 🐻 **8.9.c**

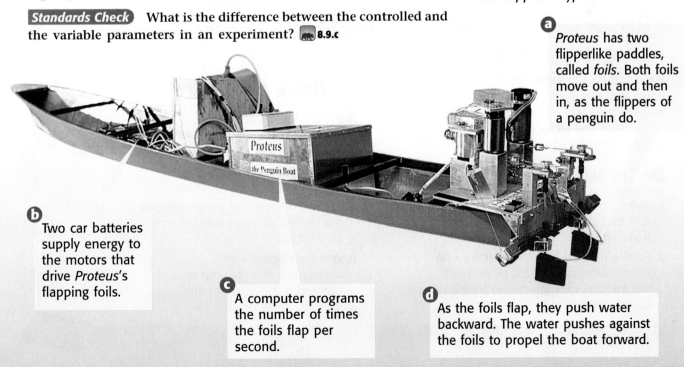

ⓐ *Proteus* has two flipperlike paddles, called *foils.* Both foils move out and then in, as the flippers of a penguin do.

ⓑ Two car batteries supply energy to the motors that drive *Proteus*'s flapping foils.

ⓒ A computer programs the number of times the foils flap per second.

ⓓ As the foils flap, they push water backward. The water pushes against the foils to propel the boat forward.

Figure 5 Proteus, *the "penguin boat," was tested in the Charles River in Boston.*

Testing *Proteus*

Czarnowski and Triantafyllou took *Proteus* out into the open water of the Charles River in Boston, shown in **Figure 5,** when they were ready to collect data. **Data** are any pieces of information gotten through experimentation. For each test, data such as the flapping rate, the energy used by the motors, and the speed achieved by the boat were carefully recorded. But the only parameter the scientists changed was the flapping rate. That way, they could tell what effect the flapping rate had on *Proteus's* efficiency. The efficiency was the ratio of output energy to input energy. The input energy was determined by how much energy was used. The output energy was determined from the speed that *Proteus* reached.

data (DAYT uh) any pieces of information acquired through observation or experimentation

Quick Lab

Investigating a Pendulum's Swing

Have you ever thought about what makes a pendulum swing the way it does? In this lab, you will plan and conduct an investigation to examine one factor and test whether the factor affects the speed of a pendulum.

▶ Try It!

1. Make a pendulum by tying a **piece of string** to a **ring stand.** Hang a **small weight** from the string.

2. Form a testable hypothesis about one factor (such as the mass of the small weight) that may affect how long it takes for the pendulum to swing 10 times.

▶ Think About It!

3. Predict the results as you change this factor.

4. Test your hypothesis. For each trial, record the time it takes for the pendulum to swing 10 times.

5. Identify the variable parameter and the controlled parameters in your experiment.

6. Was your hypothesis supported? Analyze your results, evaluating the accuracy and reproducibility of your data.

8.9.a
8.9.b
8.9.c

15 min

Figure 6 Graphs of the Test Results

This line graph shows that *Proteus* was most efficient when its foils were flapping about 1.7 times per second.

This bar graph shows that *Proteus* is 17% more efficient than a propeller-driven boat.

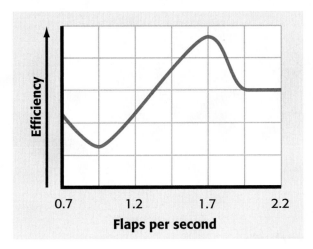

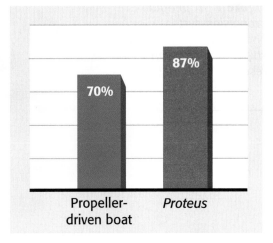

Analyzing the Results

After you collect your data, you must analyze them. Organizing data into tables and graphs makes relationships between information easier to see. Analyzing and organizing data from repeated tests can help you tell if your data were accurate. It can also help you evaluate your data's reproducibility. Data are reproducible when you get similar data from many tests.

Analyzing *Proteus*

Czarnowski and Triantafyllou used the data for input energy and output energy to calculate *Proteus's* efficiency for different flapping rates. These data are graphed in **Figure 6.** The scientists compared *Proteus's* highest level of efficiency with the average efficiency of a propeller-driven boat. As you can see, the data support the scientists' hypothesis that penguin propulsion is more efficient than propeller propulsion.

Standards Check What is a good way to evaluate the accuracy and reproducibility of data?  8.9.b

Drawing Conclusions

At the end of an investigation, you must draw a conclusion. You might conclude that your results support your hypothesis. Or you could conclude that your results do *not* support your hypothesis. If so, you could change the procedure, gather more information, or ask new questions. Whether or not your hypothesis was supported, the results are always important.

MATH PRACTICE

Effect of Additional Data

Flip a coin 3 times. Record the results in your **Science Journal.** Then, flip a coin 30 times and record the results.

1. What was the ratio of heads to tails when you flipped the coin 3 times?
2. What was the ratio of heads to tails when you flipped the coin 30 times?
3. Which of the two ratios is closer to the actual statistical mean of heads to tails in flipping a coin? What does this tell you about collecting statistical data?

Figure 7 *A penguin propulsion system may one day be used on large ships. Would it work? The research continues!*

The *Proteus* Conclusion

Czarnowski and Triantafyllou found that the penguin propulsion system was more efficient than a propeller propulsion system. They concluded that their hypothesis was supported.

The scientists were able to reach this conclusion because of repeated tests of variable and controlled parameters. Valid—that is, trustworthy—conclusions require that your data are reproducible. In other words, you can demonstrate the same relationship many times. This helps make sure the data of your experiment were not accidental. Reaching a valid conclusion usually leads to more questions that can be investigated, as **Figure 7** shows. In this way, the process of scientific progress continues!

Standards Check Why is it important to establish the reproducibility of data? **8.9.b**

Communicating Results

One of the most important steps in any investigation is communicating your results. You can write a scientific paper, make a presentation, or create a Web site. Telling others what you learned keeps science going. Other scientists can then conduct their own tests based on your results.

Czarnowski and Triantafyllou published their results in academic papers, science magazines, and newspapers. They also displayed the results of their project on the Internet. Sharing your results allows other scientists to continue your work or to verify your results by doing their own experiments.

Summary

- Scientific methods are the ways in which scientists answer questions and solve problems.
- Asking a question usually results from making an observation. Questioning is often the first step in using scientific methods.
- A hypothesis is a possible explanation or answer to a question. A good hypothesis is testable by an experiment.
- After performing an experiment, you should analyze your results. Analyzing is usually done by using calculations, tables, and graphs.
- After analyzing your results, you should draw conclusions about whether your hypothesis is supported.
- Communicating your results allows others to check or continue your work. You can communicate through reports, posters, and the Internet.

Using Vocabulary

Correct each statement by replacing the underlined term.

1 Observations are the ways in which scientists answer questions and solve problems.

2 Hypotheses are pieces of information that are gathered through experimentation.

3 Data are possible explanations or answers to a question.

Understanding Concepts

4 Listing Name the steps that can be used in scientific methods.

5 Describing After an experiment has been done and data have been collected, what is the next thing that should be done with the data?

6 Analyzing If a scientist performed an experiment only once, why would the results not be valid?

INTERPRETING GRAPHICS Use the graph below to answer the next two questions.

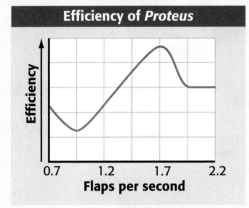

7 Identifying At what number of flaps per second is *Proteus* most efficient? least efficient?

8 Analyzing At approximately what point does the efficiency appear neither to increase nor to decrease?

Math Skills

9 Analyzing Ideas If a hypothesis that you test is not supported by the results of your experiment, was your investigation therefore a failure? Explain.

10 Applying Concepts You want to test different shapes of kites to see which shape results in the strongest lift, or upward force, in the air. List some factors that need to be the same for each trial so that the only variable is the shape of the kite.

Challenge

11 Analyzing Methods Imagine that you perform an experiment repeatedly but you get different results each time. Name three possible reasons why the results do not match. For each reason that you name, describe what you could do to solve the problem.

Internet Resources

For a variety of links related to this chapter, go to www.scilinks.org

Topic: Scientific Methods; Science Museums in California

SciLinks code: HY71359; HY7C14

Safety in Science

Key Concept To conduct a careful investigation, you must take care to keep yourself and others safe.

▶ Accidents can happen to anyone. But taking responsibility for your safety by taking some simple safety precautions makes accidents much less likely.

Keeping Yourself Safe

When you are working in a science lab, taking responsibility for your safety is very important. You should take every precaution to prevent accidents. You must wear appropriate safety equipment. And you should use all lab materials, such as those shown in **Figure 1,** safely and correctly.

Avoiding Accidents

You can help avoid accidents by being aware of what is going on around you. Pay attention, and follow directions. Watch what you are doing. When you put materials on the lab bench, be sure that they are placed securely and will not tip or fall over. If you walk around the lab area, avoid bumping into anyone and watch for anyone who might bump into you.

Reporting Accidents

No matter how careful we try to be, accidents sometimes happen anyway. If you have an accident, no matter how minor it may seem, you should let your teacher know about the accident immediately.

Figure 1 *When you work in a science lab, your lab materials can include chemicals, heat sources, animals, and plants. All must be handled safely.*

22

Figure 2 Safety Symbols

Eye
protection

Clothing
protection

Hand
safety

Heating
safety

Electrical
safety

Chemical
safety

Animal
safety

Sharp
objects

Plant
safety

For more safety tips, read the Safety First! section at the front of your book.

Elements of Safety

Safety precautions help prevent accidents at home, at school, or at play. But working in a science lab sometimes requires working with special materials and equipment. So, you need to know what special precautions to take to ensure your safety when you are in the science lab. In this section, some of the special precautions that apply to working in the lab will be discussed.

Understanding Safety Symbols

Scientists use symbols that quickly alert them to the particular dangers that they face when performing experiments and doing activities in science. These symbols are shown in **Figure 2.** You will see these symbols in experiments in this book. Learn to recognize these symbols and to understand what they mean. When you see one of these symbols, you will know that specific precautions should be taken when you do that lab or activity. Take those precautions!

Following Safety Symbols

Your teacher will explain in detail the meaning of each safety symbol and the precautions that each symbol requires. For example, imagine that you see the symbol for heating safety. You know to clear your work area of flammable materials. You should be careful with long sleeves and should tie back long hair. If you see the symbol for animal safety, you should follow your teacher's instructions on how to handle small animals properly. This includes wearing gloves and washing your hands thoroughly afterward. **Figure 3** shows the care that you should use when handling animals in the laboratory.

Standards Check What role do safety symbols have in helping you plan a scientific investigation? 8.9.a

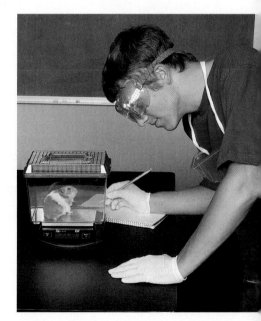
Investigation and Experimentation
8.9.a Plan and conduct a scientific investigation to test a hypothesis.

Figure 3 *The handling of animals in the science laboratory always requires special care so that neither animals nor students are injured.*

Section 3 Safety in Science **23**

Following Directions

The most common cause of accidents in the laboratory is the failure to read and follow directions carefully. Be sure to follow procedures exactly. The directions given by your teacher have been carefully worked out to produce the best results in the safest possible way. You should always read directions before beginning a lab activity. Ask your teacher to explain anything that you do not understand about the activity. And ask your teacher to approve anything that you want to do differently from what the directions say.

Be sure to gather all of the materials that you will need before doing an experiment. Measure chemicals precisely. Never use a greater amount of a chemical than your directions call for. And always pay special attention to safety symbols.

Neatness

As **Figure 4** shows, neatness is important when you work in a science lab. Working in a cluttered area is both awkward and unsafe. Before beginning any activity, be sure to clear your work area of unnecessary objects, such as books, backpacks, hats, and coats. Neatness is also important when you are doing your experiment. Clean up any spills of solid chemicals or liquids as soon as they happen. Keep flammable objects away from Bunsen burners and other heat sources.

Standards Check What are some of the procedures that you should follow to make your laboratory work area neat? 🐻 **8.9.a**

Figure 4 *You can keep your lab area neat by removing unnecessary objects, such as books that you aren't using. Personal neatness, including tying back long hair, also helps keep you safe.*

Figure 5 *Proper safety equipment should be used in a science laboratory.* **Why are safety gloves being used in the experiment shown in this picture?**

Using Proper Safety Equipment

Being safe in the science laboratory requires using protective safety equipment. Note how different pieces of safety equipment are being used by the students in **Figure 5.** Even if you think that you are going to do a short experiment, be sure to use all of the safety equipment that you need.

Don't forget to wear safety goggles. And be sure to use the type of safety goggles required by your school. Goggles should fit snugly over your eyes. If your goggles are scratched or cloudy or if they fit improperly, tell your teacher.

Not everything you encounter in the laboratory will harm your skin, but you need to wear gloves if you are handling plants, small animals, or chemicals. When handling warm objects or when using a hot plate or an open flame, you may need to use special heat-resistant gloves.

Cleaning Up

Cleaning up is an important part of a science activity. After you finish a science experiment, return all materials and chemicals to their original locations. The lids should be tight on all containers of chemicals. Give any damaged glassware to your teacher. Dispose of all wastes as directed by your teacher. Check that all burners and hot plates are turned off. Finally, clean your work area by wiping it with a damp paper towel, and wash your hands thoroughly with soap and water.

Figure 6 *Make sure that you can locate and use the first-aid supplies and special safety equipment in your science lab. Your teacher can help familiarize you with these supplies and equipment.*

first aid (FUHRST AYD) emergency medical care for someone who has been hurt or who is sick

Responding to Accidents

Accidents can happen in the lab, even when safety precautions are taken. Always tell your teacher if an accident happens.

Many labs have special emergency equipment, such as the equipment shown in **Figure 6,** that should be used in the event of an accident. Know where this equipment is located in your lab. After an accident happens, your teacher may need you to get emergency equipment. Learning to cope with accidents is one way to take responsibility for your safety.

Proper Accident Procedures

The school lab is generally a very safe place to work. However, accidents that require immediate attention happen sometimes. If you see an accident happen, there are some procedures that you should follow.

First, make sure that you are safe. If someone has slipped on a spill, be careful not to slip yourself. If someone has been cut by broken glass, don't touch the glass.

Then, tell your teacher about the accident. Your teacher will know what to do. Your teacher may send the injured student to the school nurse or to a doctor. However, if an injury requires immediate attention, your teacher may have to perform first aid. **First aid** is emergency treatment for someone who is hurt or sick. First aid is *not* complete medical treatment for an injury. It is only temporary care to be given until more complete medical care can be given. You should not perform first aid unless you have received special training to do so.

Procedures for Accidental Injuries

The procedures for treating an accidental injury depend on the type of injury that happens. If someone gets a heat burn, the burned area should be held in cold water for at least 15 minutes, as shown in **Figure 7.** If someone gets a chemical burn, the chemical should be rinsed from the burned area. The burned area should then be held under cold, running water. Your classroom probably has an eye bath. If a chemical gets into someone's eyes, the eyes should be washed in an eye bath for 15 minutes. Then, the eyes should be covered with a clean cloth. If someone gets cut, the cut should be rinsed gently. Then, slight pressure should be applied to the cut with a clean paper towel.

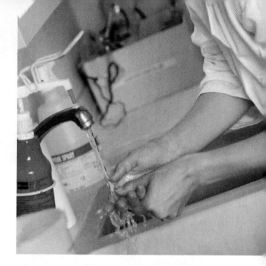

Figure 7 *If you burn your hand while in the lab, you should rinse the area in cold water.*

SECTION Review

 8.9.a

Summary

- Appropriate safety precautions must always be taken when conducting scientific investigations.
- Scientists use symbols to alert them to particular dangers that they face when performing experiments in science.
- Goggles, gloves, and aprons are proper safety equipment that should be used in a science laboratory.
- If you suffer any injury during an experiment, inform your teacher immediately.
- Proper first-aid procedures must be followed when an accident occurs in the lab.

Using Vocabulary

1. Write an original definition for *first aid.*

Understanding Concepts

2. **Describing** Explain how to take responsibility for your safety in the lab.

3. **Summarizing** Summarize how safety symbols, following directions, neatness, proper cleanup procedures, and safety equipment keep people safe in the lab.

4. **Listing** Describe three procedures that you would follow if an accident were to happen in the science lab.

5. **Summarizing** Explain the first-aid procedures that should be followed for heat burns, chemical burns, and cuts.

6. **Justifying** Why is it so important to be prepared for an experiment by taking the appropriate safety precautions?

Critical Thinking

7. **Applying Concepts** What safety icons would you expect to see on a lab that asks you to pour acid into a beaker?

8. **Applying Concepts** What safety equipment would you use when heating a test tube full of liquid over a burner?

Challenge

9. **Making Comparisons** You already take safety precautions in your everyday activities. Give three examples of safety precautions you take outside of the laboratory. Tell how they are similar to precautions that you would take in the laboratory.

Internet Resources

For a variety of links related to this chapter, go to www.scilinks.org

Topic: Safety in the Laboratory
SciLinks code: HY71341

Skills Practice Lab

Measuring Liquid Volume

In this lab, you will use a graduated cylinder to measure and transfer precise amounts of liquids. Remember that to accurately measure liquids in a graduated cylinder, you should first place the graduated cylinder flat on the lab table. Then, at eye level, read the volume of the liquid at the bottom of the meniscus, which is the curved surface of the liquid.

OBJECTIVES

Measure accurately different volumes of liquids with a graduated cylinder.

Transfer exact amounts of liquids from a graduated cylinder to a test tube.

MATERIALS

- beakers, filled with colored liquid (3)
- funnel, small
- graduated cylinder, 10 mL
- marker
- tape, masking
- test-tube rack
- test tubes, large (6)

SAFETY

Ask a Question

1 Will each mixture of colored liquids produce the same new color each time that mixture is made?

Form a Hypothesis

2 Write a hypothesis that is a possible answer to the question above. Explain your reasoning.

Test the Hypothesis

3 Using the masking tape and marker, label the test tubes "A," "B," "C," "D," "E," and "F." Place them in the test-tube rack.

4 Make a data table as shown on the next page.

5 Using the graduated cylinder and the funnel, pour 14 mL of the red liquid into test tube A. (To do this, first measure out 10 mL of the liquid in the graduated cylinder, and pour it into the test tube. Then, measure an additional 4 mL of liquid in the graduated cylinder, and add this liquid to the test tube.)

6 Use the graduated cylinder and funnel in steps 7–11 to transfer liquids. Rinse them out after you transfer each liquid.

Investigation and Experimentation
8.9.a Plan and conduct a scientific investigation to test a hypothesis.
8.9.b Evaluate the accuracy and reproducibility of data.

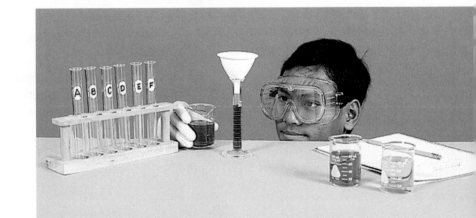

Data Table

Test tube	Initial color	Initial volume	Final color	Final volume
A				
B				
C				
D				
E				
F				

DO NOT WRITE IN BOOK

7 Measure 13 mL of the yellow liquid, and pour it into test tube C.

8 Measure 13 mL of the blue liquid, and pour it into test tube E. Record the initial color and the volume of the liquid in each test tube.

9 Transfer 4 mL of liquid from test tube C into test tube D. Transfer 7 mL of liquid from test tube E into test tube D.

10 Measure 4 mL of blue liquid out of the beaker, and pour it into test tube F. Measure 7 mL of red liquid from the beaker, and pour it into test tube F.

11 Transfer 8 mL of liquid from test tube A into test tube B. Transfer 3 mL of liquid from test tube C into test tube B.

Analyze the Results

12 Analyzing Data Record your final color observations in your data table.

13 Examining Data What is the final volume of all of the liquids? Use the graduated cylinder to measure the volume of liquid in each test tube. Record the volumes in your data table.

14 Organizing Data Record your final color observations and final volumes in a table of class data prepared by your teacher.

Draw Conclusions

15 Interpreting Information Did all of your classmates report the same colors? Does this result support the hypothesis you made in step 2? Explain.

16 Evaluating Methods Why should you not fill the graduated cylinder to the top?

Big Idea Question

17 Evaluating Methods How do the results of your class demonstrate the importance of conducting careful investigations so as to get valid results?

Science Skills Activity

Investigation and Experimentation

8.9.a Plan and conduct a scientific investigation to test a hypothesis.

Testing a Hypothesis

▶ Tutorial

Scientific progress is made by asking meaningful questions and conducting careful investigations. The first step in this process is asking a question. Asking a question leads directly to the next step, which is proposing an answer, or a hypothesis, that you can test. Then, you are ready to plan and conduct a scientific investigation.

1 Ask a question that you would like to answer through scientific investigation.

2 Propose a hypothesis, or an answer to your question, that you will be able to test.

3 Plan an experiment that will test your hypothesis. Include the materials that you will need, the procedure that you will use, and the safety precautions that you should follow. When planning an experiment, it is important to think about factors such as controls and reproducibility. This will allow you to get valid results.

4 If your teacher approves your plan, conduct your experiment. Analyze your data and communicate your findings in writing.

1

Question: What brand of paper towel absorbs the most water?

2

Question: What brand of paper towel absorbs the most water?
Hypothesis: "Sop-It-Up" brand

3

Materials:
Procedure, with controls and number of trials:
Safety:

4

Data:
Conclusion:

▶ You Try It!

Procedure

Ask a question that can be answered by scientific methods, as described in the Tutorial. Propose a hypothesis, and plan an experiment to test it.

Analysis

1 **Evaluating Hypotheses** What was the hypothesis that you planned to test? How does your hypothesis show that your question is one that can be answered by scientific methods?

2 **Evaluating Assumptions** What assumptions did you make in planning your experiment? How did those assumptions guide the design of your experiment?

3 **Evaluating Methods** What controlled parameters did you plan for in your procedure? Explain how these controlled parameters help you answer your question.

Chapter Summary

The Big Idea
Scientific progress is made by asking meaningful questions and conducting careful investigations.

Section	Vocabulary

1 Science and Scientists

Key Concept Scientists benefit society in many ways by asking questions and carefully investigating to find the answers.

- Methods of scientific investigation include research, observation, and experimentation.
- The work of scientists benefits society in a number of different ways.
- Scientists work in all kinds of jobs.

Experimentation can help answer questions about how things work.

science p. 8

2 Scientific Methods

Key Concept Scientists use scientific methods to answer questions and to solve problems.

- Scientific methods are based on six steps, which may be followed in different ways based on the kind of question being asked.
- Scientific investigations begin with a question and proceed by forming a hypothesis and then testing it.
- Scientists use a variety of methods to analyze and report their data.

Two scientists got an idea about boat propulsion after noticing how penguins swim. Then they tested it!

scientific methods p. 14
observation p. 15
hypothesis p. 16
data p. 18

3 Safety in Science

Key Concept To conduct a careful investigation, you must take care to keep yourself and others safe.

- You can take responsibility for your own safety in the laboratory.
- Following directions, taking safety precautions, and following proper cleanup procedures help keep you safe.
- If an accident happens in the laboratory, first make sure that you are safe and then tell your teacher about the accident.

 Eye protection
 Clothing protection
 Hand safety

 Heating safety
 Electrical safety
 Chemical safety

 Animal safety
 Sharp objects
 Plant safety

first aid p. 26

Chapter Review

 8.9.a, 8.9.b, 8.9.c

Organize

Pyramid Review the FoldNote that you created at the beginning of the chapter. Add to or correct the FoldNote based on what you have learned.

Using Vocabulary

① **Academic Vocabulary** Which of the following words means "the degree to which a measurement is precise and reliable"?
   a. variable
   b. accuracy
   c. parameter
   d. constant

For each pair of terms, explain how the meanings of the terms differ.

② *science* and *scientific methods*

③ *observation* and *data*

Understanding Concepts

Multiple Choice

④ The statement "Sheila has a stain on her shirt" is an example of a(n)
   a. question.
   b. hypothesis.
   c. observation.
   d. prediction.

⑤ A hypothesis is a(n)
   a. question.
   b. piece of information acquired by experimentation.
   c. possible answer to a question.
   d. observation.

⑥ A variable parameter
   a. does not affect the result.
   b. is the factor that changes in an experiment.
   c. cannot change.
   d. is rarely included in experiments.

⑦ Organizing data into a graph is an example of
   a. collecting data.
   b. forming a hypothesis.
   c. asking a question.
   d. analyzing data.

⑧ In a scientific investigation, the purpose of an experiment is to
   a. test a hypothesis.
   b. communicate results.
   c. ask a meaningful question.
   d. organize data.

Short Answer

⑨ **Describing** Explain how variable and controlled parameters are used in scientific experiments.

⑩ **Summarizing** What does it mean for data to be *reproducible?* How would you conduct an experiment in such a way as to get data that are reproducible?

⑪ **Evaluating** If a hypothesis is not testable, is the hypothesis therefore wrong? Explain.

INTERPRETING GRAPHICS Use the safety symbols below to answer the next three questions.

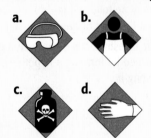

⑫ **Identifying** Explain in your own words what each of the safety symbols above means.

⑬ **Applying** If you were doing a laboratory experiment in which you needed to use chemicals that would cause burns if you spilled them on your skin, which symbol(s) would you expect to see in the instructions for the experiment?

⑭ **Comparing** Which symbol(s) represent(s) the use of safety equipment to be used for an experiment?

Writing Skills

15 Communicating Concepts Write a clear and coherent essay in which you describe the different ways in which science benefits society. Give examples from the text that support your conclusion.

Critical Thinking

16 Concept Mapping Use the following terms to create a concept map: *science, scientific methods, hypothesis, observations,* and *data.*

17 Analyzing Methods Imagine that during a scientific investigation, you perform the same experiment several times but you get different results each time. What might cause your results to be different each time? How might you change your experiment so that it will have reproducible results?

18 Analyzing Ideas Imagine that you are conducting an experiment. You are testing the effects of the height of a ramp on the speed at which a toy car goes down the ramp. What is the variable parameter in this experiment? What parameters must be controlled?

19 Evaluating Hypotheses You build a model boat that you predict will float. However, your tests show that the boat sinks. What would be a reasonable next step in your investigation?

20 Evaluating Sources Suppose that you are doing research on a scientific topic. You decide to use the World Wide Web to find information. You find a page that does not seem to be associated with any research institution and does not cite any sources for its information. Should you use this information? Explain.

INTERPRETING GRAPHICS Use the diagram below to answer the next two questions.

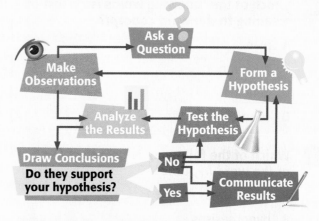

21 Analyzing Methods What are two different steps you can take after forming a hypothesis? Describe the circumstances in which you might take each step.

22 Analyzing Methods What step should you always take before drawing a conclusion? Explain why this step is so important.

Math Skills

23 Solving Problems Suppose that you read the following results from a scientific investigation. Object 1: mass = 12 g, volume = 3 cm^3, density = 4 g/cm^3. Object 2: mass = 9 g, volume = 3 cm^3, density = 3 g/cm^3. Object 3: mass = 12 g, volume = 2 cm^3, density = 6 g/cm^3. Based on these findings, what is the general formula for density?

Challenge

24 Evaluating Assumptions Suppose that a classmate says, "I don't need to study science because I'm not going to be a scientist, and scientists are the only people who use science." How would you respond? In your answer, give several examples of ways in which people who are not scientists may use physical science. (Hint: Think about the definition of *science* given in this chapter.)

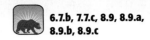
REVIEWING ACADEMIC VOCABULARY

1 Which of the following words is closest in meaning to the word *concept*?

A plan

B question

C idea

D solution

2 Which of the following is the plural form of the word *hypothesis*?

A hypothesis

B hypothesises

C hypotheses

D hypothesa

3 Which of the following words best completes this sentence: "Scientists must always be certain of the _____ of their data."?

A accurate

B accuracy

C accurately

D accurateness

4 Which of the following words means "a factor that changes in an experiment in order to test a hypothesis"?

A variable

B control

C data

D prediction

5 In the sentence "Scientists include both constant and changing parameters in their experiments," what does the word *parameter* mean?

A limit or boundary

B value used to define something

C environment or surroundings

D procedure in an investigation

REVIEWING CONCEPTS

6 Which of the following steps might come first in a scientific investigation?

A applying results

B making careful observations

C forming a hypothesis

D conducting an experiment

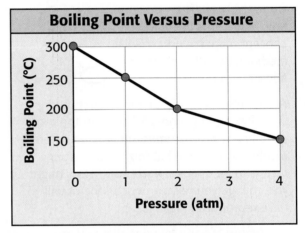

7 The above graph shows data from an experiment on a liquid. Which of the following questions might have led a scientist to conduct this experiment?

A How does the boiling point of this liquid compare to that of other liquids?

B Why does a liquid's boiling point decrease as pressure increases?

C How does the pressure applied to a liquid affect its temperature?

D How does the boiling point of this liquid change as pressure increases?

8 What is the first step you should take if someone is cut with broken glass during an experiment?

A Apply first aid.

B Clean up the glass.

C Complete the experiment.

D Make sure you are safe.

9 Which of the following might be a part of a successful scientific investigation?

A conducting an experiment that does not produce reproducible results

B asking a question that cannot be answered by science

C drawing conclusions that are not based on the results

D producing results that do not support a hypothesis

10 A scientist wants to test the ability of different detergents to clean a shirt. Which of the following variables and controls will the scientist use in the experiment?

A The detergents and type of washing machines are variables, while the shirt material is controlled.

B The shirt material and type of washing machines are variables, while the detergent is controlled.

C The type of washing machine is variable, while the shirt material and detergent is controlled.

D The detergent is variable, while the type of washing machine and shirt material are controlled.

11 Which of the following should be avoided in the area where an experiment is taking place?

A tying long hair back in a ponytail

B keeping information from previous experiments on the work area

C wearing safety goggles that fit snugly over one's eyes

D wearing heat-resistant gloves if an open flame is used

REVIEWING PRIOR LEARNING

12 What tools might a scientist use for an experiment about the mass of objects?

A graduated cylinder

B thermometer

C balance

D meterstick

13 What observations might people have used long ago to disprove the theory that the sun and planets revolve around Earth?

A Other planets appear to revolve around the sun.

B The sun appears to rise in the morning and set at night.

C Earth is the most important place in the universe.

D The sun provides energy to Earth.

Food Eaten by Rabbits Over 8 Hours		
Time	Carrots eaten	Food pellets eaten
10 A.M.	20 g	25 g
12 P.M.	10 g	12 g
2 P.M.	5 g	7 g
4 P.M.	3 g	1 g
6 P.M.	21 g	20 g

14 An experiment was conducted in which a group of rabbits were fed carrots and food pellets every two hours. The results of this experiment are shown in the table above. Which of the following conclusions might a scientist draw from these observations?

A Rabbits prefer food pellets to carrots.

B Rabbits eat mostly in the morning and evening.

C Rabbits eat a wide range of foods.

D Rabbits will not eat at 3 p.m.

Science in Action

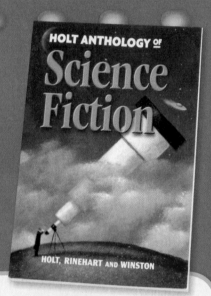

Science Fiction

"Inspiration" by Ben Bova

What if you were able to leap back and forth through time? Novelist H. G. Wells imagined such a possibility in his 1895 novelette *The Time Machine*. Most physicists said that time travel was against all the laws of physics. But what if Albert Einstein, then 16 and not a very good student, had met Wells and had an inspiration? Ben Bova's story "Inspiration" describes such a possibility. Young Einstein meets Wells and the great physicist of the time, Lord Kelvin. But was the meeting just a lucky coincidence or something else entirely? Escape to the *Holt Anthology of Science Fiction*, and read "Inspiration."

Social Studies ACTIVITY

Research the life of Albert Einstein from high school through college. Make a poster that describes some of his experiences during this time. Be sure to include information about how he matured as a student.

Science, Technology and Society

Racing with the Sun

The California Energy Commission has set some goals in exploring many different sources of energy. One of those sources is solar energy, a clean alternative to fossil fuels that pollute the atmosphere and that may contribute to global warming. One way that students in California can learn about solar energy is by participating in the Junior Solar Sprint, a competition run by the U.S. Department of Energy. Competitors build their own solar-powered model cars and race them. Over 100,000 students participate every year in this nationwide event.

Math ACTIVITY

A group of solar-powered model cars participate in a race that is 250 m long. The fastest car finishes the race in 2 min. What was the winning car's average speed, in meters per second? Write your answer in your **Science Journal**.

Julie Williams-Byrd

Electronics Engineer Julie Williams-Byrd uses her knowledge of physics to develop better lasers. She started working with lasers when she was a graduate student at Hampton University in Virginia. Today, Williams-Byrd works as an electronics engineer in the Laser Systems Branch (LSB) of NASA. She designs and builds lasers that are used to study wind and ozone in the atmosphere. Williams-Byrd uses scientific models to predict the nature of different aspects of laser design. For example, laser models are used to predict output energy, wavelength, and efficiency of the laser system.

Her most challenging project has been building a laser transmitter that will be used to measure winds in the atmosphere. This system, called *Lidar,* is very much like radar except that it uses light waves instead of sound waves to bounce off objects. Although Williams-Byrd works with high-tech lasers, she points out that lasers are a part of daily life for many people. For example, lasers are used in scanners at many retail stores. Ophthalmologists use lasers to correct vision problems. Some metal workers use them to cut metal. And lasers are even used to create spectacular light shows!

Language Arts AcTiViTY

Research lasers and the ways that they can be used in everyday life. Then, write a one-page essay in your **Science Journal** on how lasers have made life easier for people.

Internet Resources

- To learn more about careers in science, visit **www.scilinks.org** and enter the SciLinks code HY70225.

- To learn more about these Science in Action topics, visit **go.hrw.com** and type in the keyword HY7WPSF.

- Check out articles related to this chapter by visiting **go.hrw.com**. Just type in the keyword HY7WPSC.

Improving Comprehension

Graphic Organizers are important visual tools that can help you organize information and improve your reading comprehension. The Graphic Organizer below is called *combination notes*. Instructions for creating other types of Graphic Organizers are located in the **Study Skills** section of the Appendix.

How to Make Combination Notes

1 Draw a table like the one shown below. Draw the columns to be as long as you want them to be.

2 Write the topic of your notes in the section at the top of the table.

3 In the left column, write important phrases or sentences about the topic. In the right column, draw diagrams or pictures that illustrate the information in the left column.

When to Use Combination Notes

Combination notes let you express scientific information in words and pictures at the same time. Use combination notes to express information that a picture could help explain. The picture could be a diagram, a sketch, or another useful visual representation of the written information in your notes.

Data in Science

Data that are collected in various ways, including by using tools of measurement or technology, can also be displayed and analyzed in various ways:

- **Models** Physical, conceptual, and mathematical models can be used to help people understand objects, systems, or concepts that are not easily understood in other ways.
- **Tables** Data tables, made of rows and columns, are useful ways to organize information during an experiment.
- **Graphs** Line graphs help scientists identify patterns in data.

Models:
Models such as the ones below help explain how the idea of an atom's structure has changed over time.

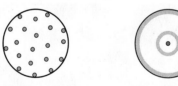

1897 model   Current model

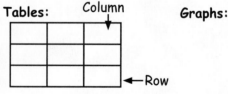

Tables: Column

←Row

Graphs:

You Try It!

This Reading Strategy can also be used within the chapter that you are about to read. Practice making your own *combination notes* as directed in the Reading Strategy for Section **2**. Record your work in your **Science Journal**.

Unpacking the Standards

The information below "unpacks" the standards by breaking them down into basic parts. The higher-level, academic vocabulary is highlighted and defined to help you understand the language of the standards. "What It Means" restates the standards as simply as possible.

California Standard	Academic Vocabulary	What It Means
8.9.d Recognize the slope of the linear graph as the **constant** in the relationship $y = kx$ and apply this **principle** in **interpreting** graphs **constructed** from data.	**constant** (KAHN stuhnt) a quantity whose value does not change **principle** (PRIN suh puhl) basic law, rule, or belief **interpret** (in TUHR pruht) to figure out the meaning of **construct** (kuhn STRUHKT) to build; to make from parts	Be able to tell that the rise over run of the line in a graph is the factor that stays the same in the equation $y = kx$. Use this understanding to figure out what graphs based on data mean.
8.9.e Construct appropriate graphs from data and develop quantitative statements about the relationships between **variables.**	**appropriate** (uh PROH pree it) correct for the use; proper **variable** (VER ee uh buhl) a factor that changes in an experiment in order to test a hypothesis	Make the correct type of graph to show your facts and figures. Then, write a statement that explains how one variable changes relative to the other variable.
8.9.f Apply simple mathematical relationships to determine a missing quantity in a mathematic expression, given the two remaining terms (including speed = distance/time, density = mass/volume, force = pressure × **area,** volume = **area** × height).	**area** (ER ee uh) a measure of the size of a surface or a region	Use simple mathematical equations to find a missing value in a mathematical equation when given the other two values. You should be able to solve problems by using the following equations: *speed = distance ÷ time, density = mass ÷ volume, force = pressure × area,* and *volume = area × height.*
8.9.g Distinguish between linear and nonlinear relationships on a graph of data.		Be able to use graphs to tell the difference between variables that have a simple mathematical relationship and variables that have more-complex relationships.

The following list identifies other standards that are covered in this chapter and indicates where you can go to see them unpacked: **8.9.b** (Chapter 1) and **8.9.c** (Chapter 1).

2

Data in Science

The Big Idea

Scientists use tools to collect, organize, and analyze data while conducting investigations.

 ## California Standards

Investigation and Experimentation
8.9 Scientific progress is made by asking meaningful questions and conducting careful investigations. (Sections 1, 2, and 3; Science Skills Activity)

Math
6.1.1 Statistics, Data Analysis, and Probability
7.4.2 Algebra and Functions

English–Language Arts
8.2.2 Reading
8.2.6 Writing

About the Photo

How would you investigate the possible effects of a meteor hitting Earth? This scientist is studying impact craters using the Light Gas Gun Chamber located in the NASA Ames Research Center in Mountain View, California. To collect data, the scientist shoots an aluminum pellet at 1.8 km/s to hit a sand target covered with red paint, forming an impact crater.

Organize

Tri-Fold

Before you read this chapter, create the FoldNote entitled "Tri-Fold." Write what you know about organizing and analyzing data in the column labeled "Know." Then, write what you want to know about organizing and analyzing data in the column labeled "Want." As you read the chapter, write what you learn about organizing and analyzing data in the column labeled "Learn."

Instructions for creating FoldNotes are located in the Study Skills section on p. 520 of the Appendix.

Explore Activity

20 min

Creating a Scientific Plan

In this activity, you will use observations to form a question or hypothesis. Then, you will develop a plan for testing your hypothesis.

Procedure

1. Get a **picture** or **drawing** from your teacher.

2. Make a list of observations about the picture or drawing. From your list, develop a question or hypothesis that you could investigate.

3. Plan a scientific investigation to answer the question or hypothesis. Decide which factors you want to test (variables, such as brand or usage) and which factors you need to keep the same.

4. Describe the data you would gather and the tools you would need during your investigation.

Analysis

8.9.a
8.9.c

5. How did your initial observations influence the question that you developed?

6. Would a graph of your data help you draw a conclusion more easily? Explain your reasoning.

7. Why is it important for scientists to have a plan for answering a scientific question before they begin their work?

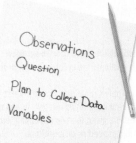

41

Tools and Models in Science

Key Concept Scientists use tools and models to increase their ability to investigate the natural world.

What You Will Learn

- Tools are used to make accurate measurements while collecting data.
- The International System of Units (SI) is a system of measurement used by most scientists.
- A model uses familiar things to describe unfamiliar things. Physical, conceptual, and mathematical models are commonly used in science.
- Models help scientific progress through their use in theories and laws.

Why It Matters

Understanding how scientists use tools and models can help you use them better in your own investigations.

Vocabulary

- mass
- volume
- density
- temperature
- model
- theory
- law

READING STRATEGY

Summarizing Read this section silently. In pairs, take turns summarizing the material. Stop to discuss ideas and words that seem confusing.

▶ To dig a hole, you need the correct tools. A *tool* is anything that helps you do a task. Scientists use many different tools to help them in their experiments.

Tools in Science

One way to collect data is to take measurements. To get the most accurate measurements, you must use the proper tools to gather data. For example, you can use a meterstick to measure length. You can use a thermometer to observe changes in temperature. Two other tools and their uses are shown in **Figure 1**.

After you collect data, you need to evaluate and analyze the data. Calculators are handy tools to help you do calculations quickly. Or you might show your data in a graph or a figure. A computer that has the correct software can help you display your data. A pencil and graph paper are also tools you can use to display your data.

Standards Check Why is it important to use the proper tools for gathering data? **8.9.b**

Making Measurements

Many years ago, different countries used different systems of measurement. In England, the standard for an inch used to be three grains of barley placed end to end. Other units were originally based on parts of the body, such as the foot.

Investigation and Experimentation
8.9.b Evaluate the accuracy and reproducibility of data.
8.9.f Apply simple mathematical relationships to determine a missing quantity in a mathematic expression, given the two remaining terms (including speed = distance/time, density = mass/volume, force = pressure × area, volume = area × height).

Figure 1 Measurement Tools

You can use a stopwatch to measure time.

You can use a spring scale to measure force.

Table 1   Common SI Units

	SI Units	Conversions
Length	**meter (m)**	
	kilometer (km)	1 km = 1,000 m
	decimeter (dm)	1 dm = 0.1 m
	centimeter (cm)	1 cm = 0.01 m
	millimeter (mm)	1 mm = 0.001 m
	micrometer (μm)	1 μm = 0.000001 m
	nanometer (nm)	1 nm = 0.000000001 m
Volume	**cubic meter (m³)**	
	cubic centimeter (cm³)	1 cm³ = 0.000001 m³
	liter (L)	1 L = 1 dm³ = 0.001 m³
	milliliter (mL)	1 mL = 0.001 L = 1 cm³
Mass	**kilogram (kg)**	
	gram (g)	1 g = 0.001 kg
	milligram (mg)	1 mg = 0.000001 kg
Temperature*	**kelvin (K)**	0°C = 273 K
		100°C = 373 K

*The Celsius (°C) scale is a commonly used non-SI temperature scale.

The International System of Units

In the late 1700s, the French Academy of Sciences set out to make a simple and reliable measurement system. Over the next 200 years, the metric system was formed. This system is now the International System of Units (SI). Because all SI units are expressed in multiples of 10, changing from one unit to another is easy. Prefixes are used to express SI units that are larger or smaller than basic units such as a meter and a gram. For example, *kilo-* means 1,000 times, and *milli-* indicates 1/1,000 times. **Table 1** shows common SI units.

Length

To describe the length of a large classroom, a scientist would use meters (m). A *meter* is the basic SI unit of length. Other SI units of length are larger or smaller than the meter by multiples of 10. For example, if you divide 1 m into 1,000 parts, each part equals 1 millimeter (mm). So, 1 mm is one-thousandth of a meter.

Mass

Mass is the amount of matter in an object. The *kilogram* (kg) is the basic SI unit for mass. The kilogram is used to describe the mass of large objects, such as a suitcase. One kilogram equals 1,000 g. So, the gram is more often used to describe the mass of small objects. Masses of very large objects, such as cars or airplanes, are often expressed in metric tons. A metric ton equals 1,000 kg.

mass (MAS) a measure of the amount of matter in an object

Quick Lab

Accuracy of Measurements

8.9.b

1. Pick an object to use as a unit of measure. You can pick a **pencil**, your **hand**, a **chalkboard eraser**, or anything else.

2. Measure the width of your desk using your chosen unit. Record your answer.

3. Choose a partner in class, and measure each other's desks using your chosen unit of measure. Record your answers, and compare your measurements.

4. Use a **meterstick** to determine the exact length of your chosen unit of measure. Make a conversion factor using your results. For example, 1 pencil equals 18 cm.

5. Measure your desk with a meterstick, and record your answer.

6. Using your conversion factor, compare the measurements made using your chosen unit of measure to the measurements made using the meterstick. How accurate were the measurements made with your chosen unit of measure?

7. Were your partner's measurements more accurate than your measurements? Why is it important to use the proper tools to get accurate measurements?

⏱ 20 min

---

volume (VAHL yoom) a measure of the size of an object or region in three-dimensional space

density (DEN suh tee) the ratio of the mass of a substance to the volume of the substance

temperature (TEM puhr chuhr) a measure of how hot (or cold) something is; specifically, a measure of the average kinetic energy of the particles in an object

model (MAHD'l) a pattern, plan, representation, or description designed to show the structure or workings of an object, system, or concept

Volume

Imagine that you need to move some lenses to a laser laboratory. How many lenses will fit into a crate? The answer depends on the volume of the crate and the volume of each lens. **Volume** is the amount of space that something occupies.

Liquid volume is expressed in *liters* (L). Liters are based on the meter. A cubic meter (1 m³) is equal to 1,000 L. So, 1,000 L will fit perfectly into a box that is 1 m on each side. A milliliter (mL) will fit perfectly into a box that is 1 cm on each side. So, 1 mL = 1 cm³. Graduated cylinders are used to measure the volume of liquids. The volume of solid objects is usually expressed in cubic meters (m³). The volume of smaller objects can be expressed in cubic centimeters (cm³). To find the volume of a crate—or any other rectangular shape—multiply the length by the width by the height.

Density

If you measure the mass and the volume of an object, you have the information you need to find the density of the object. **Density** is the amount of matter in a given volume. You cannot measure density directly. But after you measure the mass and the volume, you can calculate density by dividing the mass by the volume, as shown in the following equation:

$$D = \frac{m}{V}$$

Standards Check What is the density of an object if its mass is 15 g and its volume is 3 cm³? 8.9.f

Temperature

The **temperature** of a substance is a measurement of how hot (or cold) the substance is. Degrees Fahrenheit (°F) and degrees Celsius (°C) are used to describe temperature. However, the *kelvin* (K), the SI unit for temperature, is also used. Notice that the degree sign (°) is not used with the Kelvin scale. The thermometer in **Figure 2** shows how the Celsius and Fahrenheit scales compare.

Models in Science

A **model** is a representation of an object or system. A model uses something familiar to help you understand something that is not familiar. For example, models of individual systems in the human body, such as the nervous system, can help you understand how the body works. Models can also be used to explain the past or to predict future events. There are three common kinds of scientific models. They are physical, conceptual (kuhn SEP choo uhl), and mathematical models. However, models have limitations because they are never exactly like the real thing.

Physical Models

Model airplanes, dolls, and drawings are examples of physical models. Other kinds of physical models can help you understand certain concepts. For example, look at the model space shuttle and the real space shuttle in **Figure 3.** Launching a model like the one on the right can help you understand how a real space shuttle blasts off into space.

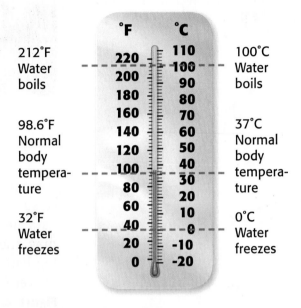

Figure 2 *Some common temperature measurements are shown here in degrees Fahrenheit and degrees Celsius.*

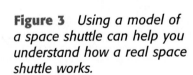

Figure 3 *Using a model of a space shuttle can help you understand how a real space shuttle works.*

Figure 4 *The big bang theory says that 12 billion to 15 billion years ago, an event called the* big bang *sent matter in all directions. This matter eventually formed the galaxies and planets.*

Conceptual Models

The second kind of model is a conceptual model. A conceptual model tries to put many ideas together to explain or summarize something. After a conceptual model is formed, data are sometimes found that do not fit the model. The model may then be revised to fit the new data. For example, the big bang theory is a conceptual model that explains why the universe seems to be expanding. This model is described in **Figure 4.** Although the big bang theory is widely accepted by astronomers, some data do not fit the model. So, conceptual models may not take certain data into account. Or the models may include certain ideas but not others.

Mathematical Models

Every day, people try to predict the weather. One way to predict the weather is to use mathematical models. A mathematical model is made up of mathematical equations and data. Some mathematical models are simple. These models allow you to calculate things such as force and acceleration. But other mathematical models, like those that predict the weather, are so complex that only computers can handle them. Some of these very complex models have many variables. Using the wrong value for even a single variable could cause the model to make highly inaccurate predictions.

Standards Check Why is having accurate data important when working with a mathematical model? 🐻 8.9.b

Models: The Right Size

Models are often used to represent things that are very small or very large. The solar system is too large to view all at once. So, a model can help you picture the thing in your mind. Sometimes, models are used to learn about things you cannot see, such as sound waves. Look at **Figure 5.** A coiled spring toy is often used as a model of sound waves because the spring toy behaves similarly to the way sound waves do.

Figure 5 *The compressed coils on the spring toy can be used to model the way air particles are crowded together in a sound wave.*

The Limits of Models

Models are an important tool for scientists. Mathematical models can help scientists analyze complex systems quickly and efficiently. For example, scientists can use models to study how certain drugs might fight diseases without scientists having to test the drugs on animals or people.

But it is important for a scientist to remember the limitations of the models that he or she uses. A model is not exactly the same as the real object or system. To make sense of the information gathered, a scientist must know the ways in which a model does not act exactly as the real thing does.

Using Models for Scientific Progress

Models can represent scientific ideas and objects. Models can also be tools to help you summarize and learn new information. When scientists need to communicate information that would be difficult to explain, they often create a model. **Figure 6** shows a model of a protein molecule. Molecules are too small to be seen with your eyes. And some molecules are made of a large number of atoms. So, a drawing of a molecule that tries to show the location of every single atom would be very confusing to look at. But by using a model, you can see the shape of the molecule from any side.

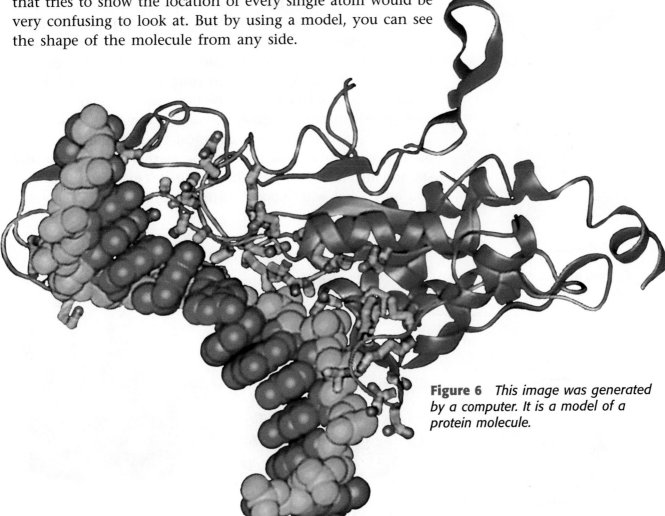

Figure 6 *This image was generated by a computer. It is a model of a protein molecule.*

Scientific Theories

Models are often used to help illustrate and explain scientific theories. In science, a **theory** is an explanation for many hypotheses and observations. Usually, these hypotheses have been supported by repeated tests. A theory not only explains an observation you've made but also can predict what might happen in the future.

Scientists use models to help guide their search for new information. This information can help support a theory or can show that the theory is wrong. Keep in mind that models can be changed or replaced. These changes happen when scientists make new observations. Because of these new observations, scientists may have to change their theories. **Figure 7** compares an old model with a current model.

Standards Check Why is having accurate data important during the development and testing of a theory? 🐻 **8.9.b**

Scientific Laws

What happens when a model correctly predicts the results of many different experiments? A scientific law can be constructed. In science, a **law** is a summary of many experimental results and observations. A law tells you how things work. Laws are not the same as theories. Laws tell you only what happens, not why it happens. Look at **Figure 8.** A chemical change took place when the flask was turned over. A light blue solid and a dark blue solution formed. Notice that the mass did not change, which demonstrates the *law of conservation of mass.* This law says that during a chemical change, the total mass of the materials formed is the same as the total mass of the starting materials. However, the law doesn't explain why. It tells you only what will happen during every chemical change.

Figure 7 *These models show how the theory about an atom's structure has changed over time.*

1897 atomic model

Current atomic model

Figure 8 *The total mass before the chemical change is always the same as the total mass after the change.*

Summary

- Tools are used to make observations, take measurements, and analyze data.
- The International System of Units (SI) is the standard system of measurement.
- Length, mass, volume, density, and temperature are common measurements.
- A model uses familiar things to describe unfamiliar things.
- Physical, conceptual, and mathematical models are commonly used in science.
- A scientific theory is an explanation for many hypotheses and observations.

Using Vocabulary

1 Use *volume*, *density*, and *mass* in separate sentences.

2 Write an original definition for the term *model*.

Understanding Concepts

3 **Identifying** Which SI unit would you use to express the height of your desk?

4 **Summarizing** Explain the relationship between mass and density.

5 **Listing** What is normal body temperature in degrees Fahrenheit and degrees Celsius?

6 **Applying** What kind of model would you use to represent the human heart?

7 **Comparing** Explain the difference between a theory and a law.

Critical Thinking

8 **Analyzing Methods** Both a globe and a flat world map can model features of Earth. Give an example of when you would use each of these models.

INTERPRETING GRAPHICS Use the image below showing water temperature variations to answer the next three questions.

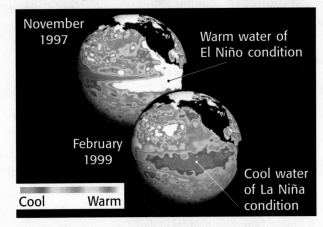

November 1997 — Warm water of El Niño condition

February 1999 — Cool water of La Niña condition

Cool   Warm

9 **Applying Concepts** These models were created with data from satellite images. What are some possible uses for these models?

10 **Evaluating Sources** How accurately could you predict water temperature for a specific location on the California coast?

11 **Analyzing Processes** What is a possible limitation of these models?

Math Skills

12 **Using Equations** What is the density of an object whose mass is 36 g and whose volume is 12 cm³?

Challenge

13 **Identifying Relationships** For a science fair, you want to make a model of the moon orbiting Earth by using two different balls. The diameter of the ball that will represent Earth will be about 62 cm. You want your model to be to scale. If Earth is about four times wider than the moon is, what should the diameter of the ball that represents the moon be?

Organizing Your Data

Key Concept Scientists organize data to make quantitative statements about the relationships between the variables in an investigation.

▶ It's Tuesday night, and you are studying for a test. You have a notebook, the textbook, and flashcards. You have so much information that you feel overwhelmed! In the same way, you—like the student in **Figure 1**—could be easily overwhelmed by all of the data gathered from scientific investigations. To be useful, data must be organized. But how? In this section, you will learn some of the same methods that scientists use to make information easier to interpret and understand.

Creating a Data Table

For several years, a teacher has been investigating the amount of exercise his students get weekly. The students gather information about the total hours of exercise they get each week. The first step that the teacher and the students take in organizing the data is to fill in a data table.

Organizing: The First Step

It's important to determine what information you are going to gather and to create a data table before the experiment starts. Then, you can be as organized as possible and can be sure not to miss any information that might be important.

Figure 1 *When conducting research, you can collect so much information that you become overwhelmed, as this student has.*

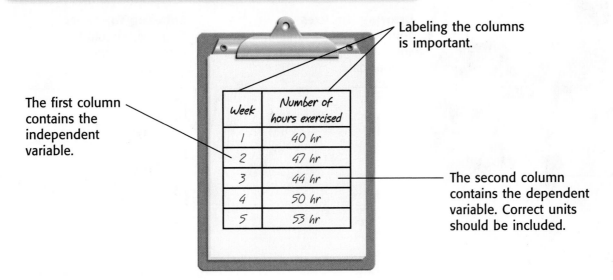

Figure 2 Creating a Data Table

Labeling the columns is important.

The first column contains the independent variable.

Week	Number of hours exercised
1	40 hr
2	47 hr
3	44 hr
4	50 hr
5	53 hr

The second column contains the dependent variable. Correct units should be included.

Independent and Dependent Variables

A data table has two columns, as shown in **Figure 2.** The first column lists the **independent variable,** the factor or parameter that the investigator can change. In this case, the class chose to study the total number of hours exercised each week for five weeks. So, the independent variable is the week. If the class chose to study the total number of hours exercised each month, the independent variable would be a month.

The second column in the data table lists the dependent variable. The **dependent variable** is the factor that changes in response to the independent variable. It is the variable that the scientist measures. In **Figure 2,** the dependent variable is the total number of hours exercised. It changes with the independent variable. So, the hours exercised change every week.

Variable and Controlled Parameters

When you design an experiment, you have controlled parameters and variable parameters. *Controlled parameters* are factors that stay constant throughout the experiment. *Variable parameters* are factors that change, or vary, throughout the experiment. If you want to explore the relationship between two factors, such as mass and volume, then those factors are your variable parameters. All other factors, such as temperature and the material you study, should be kept constant and are your controlled parameters.

Standards Check Explain the difference between variable and controlled parameters. **8.9.c**

independent variable
(IN dee PEN duhnt VER ee uh buhl)
in an experiment, the factor that is deliberately manipulated
Wordwise The prefix *in-* means "not." Other examples are *ineffective* and *insane.*

dependent variable
(dee PEN duhnt VER ee uh buhl)
in an experiment, the factor that changes as a result of manipulation of one or more other factors (the independent variables)

Investigation and Experimentation
8.9.c Distinguish between variable and controlled parameters in a test.
8.9.e Construct appropriate graphs from data and develop quantitative statements about the relationships between variables.
8.9.g Distinguish between linear and nonlinear relationships on a graph of data.

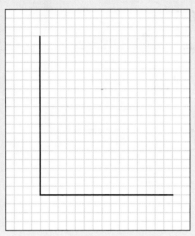

Figure 3 **Creating a Data Graph**

Drawing the Axes
Your horizontal and vertical axes should be long enough to fit all of your data.

Labeling Your Axes
Each axis should have a label and, when needed, the correct unit.

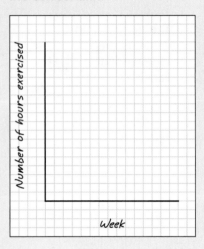

Number of hours exercised

Week

axis (AK sis) one of two or more reference lines that mark the borders of a graph

Creating a Graph

Data tables help you organize data. Graphs help you understand and use that data. Graphs make it easy to identify trends and make predictions. Students studying the amount of exercise they get each week used their data table to graph the total number of hours exercised over a five-week period.

Axes

Figure 3 shows how to make a graph. First, use a data table to determine the graph's axes (singular, *axis*). An **axis** is a reference line that forms one side of a graph. A graph has a horizontal *x*-axis and a vertical *y*-axis. The *x*-axis usually represents the independent variable in the data table. The *y*-axis usually represents the dependent variable. In a graph of the number of hours exercised in a five-week period, the *x*-axis represents the week, and the *y*-axis represents the number of hours exercised. Each axis is labeled with the name of the variable that is represented.

Range

Each axis has its own range. To find the range, subtract the smallest value of a single variable from the largest value of the same variable. For the exercise data, the range of the independent variable, the week, is 5 weeks. Therefore, the *x*-axis must cover at least 5 weeks. The range of the dependent variable, the number of hours, is $53 - 40 = 13$. Thus, the *y*-axis must have room for at least 13 hours.

Quick Lab

Height Vs. Arm Span   8.9.e
                              8.9.g

1. Create a data table with height as the independent variable and arm span as the dependent variable.
2. Use a **meterstick** to measure the height and arm span of five classmates.
3. Graph your data.
4. Does your graph show a linear or nonlinear relationship?

 15 min

Determining Range and Scale
Each axis on a graph can have its own scale so that the data can be seen easily.

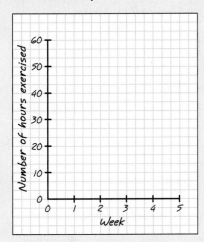

Plotting the Data Points
The easiest part of creating a graph is taking pairs of data and putting them where they belong.

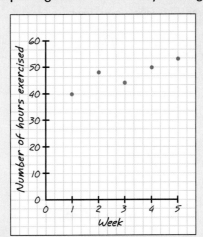

Labeling the Graph
Every graph needs an appropriate title. A good title tells a reader what the graph is all about.

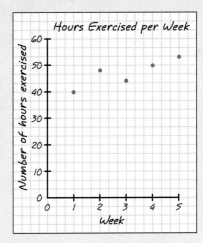

Scale

The next step is to decide the scale of the graph. Each axis has its own scale. The scale is the size that is used for each box or grid mark on the graph. For the exercise data, we can choose a scale of 1 week for each grid mark on the x-axis. For the y-axis, the grid marks can be placed at intervals of 10. The scale should be chosen such that the graph spreads out to fill most of the available space.

Data Points

Now, the data points need to be plotted. You plot the data points by putting a dot on the graph for each pair of data in the data table. Sometimes, a "line of best fit" is needed. Most graphs of data or observations are not drawn dot to dot through the data points. A line of best fit, such as the one in **Figure 4,** is a smooth line that is drawn to "fit," or to include, some but not all of the data points. The smooth line without sharp turns or sudden bends shows the pattern described by the data. The line of best fit also shows how the data differ from the pattern.

Labels

The last step is to give the graph a title. The title helps people recognize what the graph describes. Scientists often include the independent and dependent variables in the title.

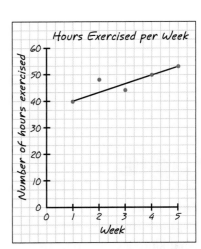

Figure 4 *The line of best fit shows the general relationship between the two variables in the graph. It also shows how data vary from the overall relationship.*

Standards Check Why is an appropriate title for a graph important?
8.9.e

Figure 5 Trends in Nonlinear Graphs

Direct Nonlinear Relationship
The dependent variable increases as the independent variable increases.

Inverse Nonlinear Relationship
The dependent variable decreases as the independent variable increases.

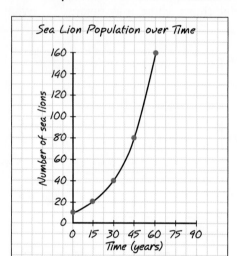

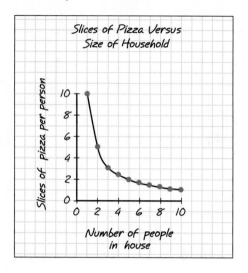

Patterns Shown by Graphs

When you graph data, you can identify what the pattern, or *trend,* of the data is. A trend shows the relationship between the two variables studied in the experiment. Graphs make it easy to tell if something is increasing, decreasing, or staying the same.

A straight line can sometimes be used to show the trend of data on a graph. A graph in which the relationship between the independent variable and dependent variable can be shown with a straight line is called a *linear graph.* Sometimes, the relationship between the variables studied is not a straight line but a smooth curve. Any graph in which the relationship between the variables cannot be shown with a straight line is called a *nonlinear graph.*

Graphs allow scientists to determine if the relationship between the variables is direct or inverse. If a graph shows that the dependent variable increases as the independent variable increases, the relationship between the variables is direct. If one variable increases while the other variable decreases, the relationship between the variables is inverse. **Figure 5** shows two nonlinear graphs, one of which has a direct relationship and one of which has an inverse relationship.

Standards Check Describe the difference between linear and nonlinear relationships on a graph. 8.9.g

Careers in Engineering
What kind of work do engineers do? Write about different kinds of engineers and the fields in which they work. Go to **go.hrw.com,** and type in the keyword HY7DISW.

Using Computers to Create Graphs

Computer technology can be used to make organizing data easier. Computers help scientists collect, organize, process, and display large amounts of data. In **Figure 6,** a doctor is recording data on her hand-held computer. With this tool, she is able to gather data rapidly and as needed. Specially designed software makes appropriate graphs from lists of data. These graphs can be quickly examined to find patterns and relationships between the variables. The instant feedback provided by computer technology allows scientists to make mathematical representations of large amounts of data as they are collected.

Standards Check How can technology help scientists create and interpret graphs from data? 🐻 **8.9.e**

Figure 6 *This doctor uses a hand-held computer to help her keep track of patient information and her demanding schedule.*

SECTION Review

 8.9.c, 8.9.e, 8.9.g

Summary

- Scientists use data tables to organize information.
- Labels and units are important parts of data tables and graphs.
- The independent variable is the factor that the investigator changes.
- The dependent variable is the factor that the investigator measures.
- The line of best fit shows the trend of a linear graph.
- Graphs help show patterns, or trends, in data.
- Linear and nonlinear graphs show different relationships between variables.

Understanding Concepts

❶ **Demonstrating** Why is it important to organize a data table before doing an experiment?

❷ **Identifying** Alfonso is conducting an experiment to determine whether temperature affects how fast earthworms move. Identify the dependent variable and the independent variable.

INTERPRETING GRAPHICS
Use the table below to answer the next two questions.

Time (min)	Temperature (°C)
0	25
3	28
5	31

❸ **Applying** While studying how long it takes milk to warm, Marissa makes the observations shown in the table. Use her data to create a graph.

❹ **Describing** Does your graph show an inverse linear relationship or a direct linear relationship? Explain your answer.

Critical Thinking

❺ **Analyzing Processes** Why does an investigator change the value of a variable parameter during an investigation?

❻ **Identifying Relationships** As computer technology becomes faster, how does the ability of scientists to collect and organize data change?

Challenge

❼ **Interpreting Statistics** After an experiment, Monica creates a graph that shows a direct linear relationship between the size of a fish and the amount of oxygen the fish uses. Describe this trend in terms of the amount of oxygen that a fish would use as it grows from being very small to very large.

Internet Resources

For a variety of links related to this chapter, go to www.scilinks.org

Topic: Computer Technology
SciLinks code: HY70334

Analyzing Your Data

Key Concept Scientists analyze data in order to answer questions, understand results, and make predictions.

What You Will Learn

● Mathematics is an important tool for understanding and summarizing large quantities of information.

● The accuracy and reproducibility of data affect the results and conclusions of scientific studies.

● The mean, median, and mode are terms used to describe and analyze an entire set of data.

● Slope is the degree of slant, or steepness, of a straight line. The slope of a linear graph represents a constant that can be used to help analyze a set of data.

Why It Matters

Knowing how to analyze data can help you understand the results and predictions made in scientific studies.

Vocabulary

• mean   • mode
• median   • slope

READING STRATEGY

Asking Questions Read this section silently. In your **Science Journal,** write down questions that you have about this section. Discuss your questions in a small group.

One way to analyze data is to use mathematics. Mathematical models in the form of computer simulations can answer questions about how rockets, such as the one in **Figure 1,** will fly and react to different conditions before the rockets even leave the ground.

Why Mathematics?

Just like making observations, conducting experiments, and organizing data, mathematics is used to answer questions. Mathematics helps determine important properties of substances, such as area, volume, and density. Mathematics also allows scientists to understand and sum up a lot of information. As a result, scientists can make predictions. For example, a meteorologist gathers data on hurricane movement. Mathematics helps her to see patterns in the data. Then, she uses these patterns to predict where future hurricanes might hit land.

There are scientists in every country around the world. They speak many different languages. Mathematics is often called the *language of science* because it allows scientists to easily share their findings with each other in a language that everyone understands: numbers!

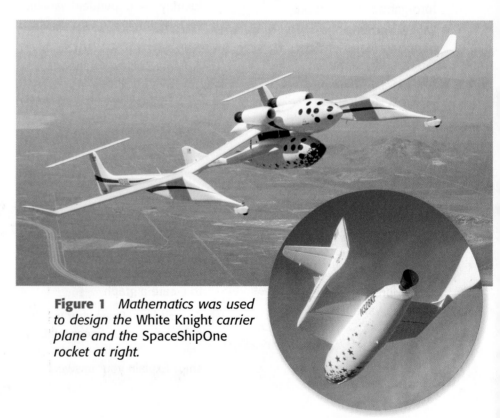

Figure 1 *Mathematics was used to design the* White Knight *carrier plane and the* SpaceShipOne *rocket at right.*

Investigation and Experimentation
8.9.b Evaluate the accuracy and reproducibility of data.
8.9.d Recognize the slope of the linear graph as the constant in the relationship $y = kx$ and apply this principle in interpreting graphs constructed from data.

Figure 2 **Using Tools Correctly**

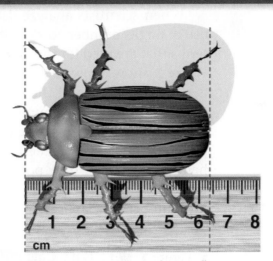

The most accurate reading of the beetle's length is from directly overhead. *If you make your measurement when you are slightly to the right of the beetle rather than directly overhead, how would your measurement compare with the actual length of the beetle?*

Accuracy of Data

When scientists conduct experiments, they want to collect accurate data. In other words, they want the values to be correct. If you place 525 g on a balance and get a mass reading of 450 g, your reading is not accurate. Some reasons why a value is inaccurate include using broken equipment, using the wrong tool, or using a tool incorrectly.

Choosing Tools and Using Them Correctly

You have probably made measurements using the tools shown in **Figure 2.** Using a graduated cylinder to measure volume can provide a more accurate measurement than using a measuring cup found in a kitchen. But your data will still be inaccurate if you do not read the volume at the bottom of the meniscus at eye level. Likewise, to get an accurate reading using a ruler, you should look straight down on the end of the thing you are measuring. If you move your head to either side, you will get a slightly different measurement.

Reproducibility of Data

Imagine that you and a friend do an experiment using the same procedure and equipment. You'd expect to get data that are very similar. When scientists conduct investigations, they want their results to be able to be repeated, or reproduced, by other scientists. If the data are not reproducible, then there is no way for the results of the experiment to be supported and accepted by other scientists. Data must be reproducible in order for other people to agree with your conclusions.

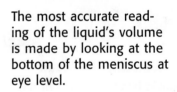

The most accurate reading of the liquid's volume is made by looking at the bottom of the meniscus at eye level.

Standards Check Explain what it means to say that the data from a scientific investigation are reproducible. **8.9.b**

Describing the Entire Set of Data

When scientists analyze data, they often find it helpful to use a single number to describe the entire set of data. Three terms that are used for this purpose are *mean, median,* and *mode.* **Figure 3** shows how to find each one. The **mean,** or average, is found by adding all the data points together, then dividing the sum by the total number of data points. The **median** is the value of the data point in the middle when the data are placed in order from smallest to largest. The median is especially helpful when one data point is much smaller or larger than the rest of the data points, as in Week 9 below. The **mode** is the number that appears most often in a data set.

mean (MEEN) the number obtained by adding up the data for a given characteristic and dividing this sum by the number of individuals

median (MEE dee uhn) the value of the middle item when data are arranged in order by size

mode (MOHD) the most frequently occurring value in a data set

slope (SLOHP) a measure of the slant of a line; the ratio of rise over run

Calculating the Mean

David has test scores of 85, 76, 82, and 90. What is his mean test score?

Figure 3 **Analyzing the Entire Set of Data**

A class of students recorded the total number of hours they exercised during Weeks 6–10.

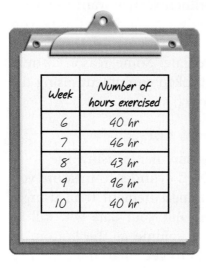

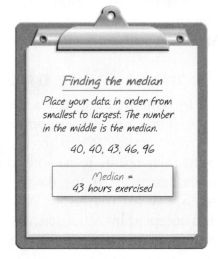

Slope of a Line

What do you think of when you hear the word *slope*? You might think of how something slants uphill or downhill. **Figure 4** shows a skier moving down a slanted mountainside. Imagine drawing a straight line under the skier that runs along the mountainside. The steepness of the line representing the slant of the mountainside is called the slope of the line. In math, **slope** is defined as the degree of slant of a line.

Calculating Slope

To calculate the slope of a line, it is helpful to use the terms *rise* and *run*, as shown in **Figure 4.** The rise represents a vertical change. The run represents a horizontal change. For a line on the coordinate plane, the change in y, or the rise, indicates the number of units moved up or down. The change in x, or the run, is the number of units moved to the right or left. Slope is calculated by dividing the vertical change (the change in y) by the horizontal change (the change in x). In other words, the slope of a straight line is found by dividing the rise by the run, often described as "rise over run."

Using Slope to Analyze Data

The slope of a line graphed from data can help you analyze the data. Look at **Figure 5.** Three sets of data result in three different lines, each with a different slope. For each line, the value of the slope between any two points on that line will be a constant number. Here, the slope (rise over run) represents the speed (meters over seconds) of an object moving at a constant rate. **Figure 5** shows that slope can have a positive, negative, or zero value. The slope of all horizontal lines is zero.

Standards Check Define the slope of a straight line using the terms *rise* and *run*. 🐻 **8.9.d**

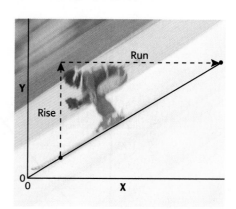

Figure 4 *In skiing, the term* slope *refers to a slanted mountainside. The steeper a slope is, the higher its difficulty rating will be for a skier. In math, slope is calculated by dividing the rise by the run.*

Figure 5 *The results from three sets of data can be graphed to analyze the data. Here, the slope of a line on a position versus time graph represents the speed of the object.*

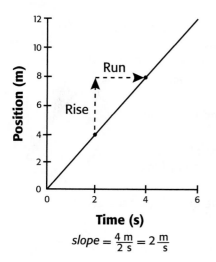

$$slope = \frac{4\,m}{2\,s} = 2\,\frac{m}{s}$$

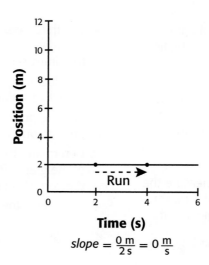

$$slope = \frac{0\,m}{2\,s} = 0\,\frac{m}{s}$$

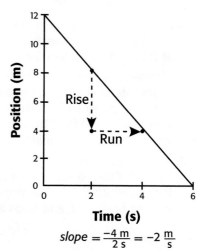

$$slope = \frac{-4\,m}{2\,s} = -2\,\frac{m}{s}$$

Density of Lead

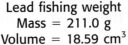

(Graph titled "Density of Lead" with Mass (g) on the vertical axis from 0 to 220, and Volume (cm³) on the horizontal axis from 0 to 20. A straight line passes through the origin.)

Lead fishing weight
Mass = 211.0 g
Volume = 18.59 cm^3

Lead fishing weight
Mass = 4.2 g
Volume = 0.37 cm^3

Figure 6 *The line in the graph at left represents the constant density of lead. When plotting the mass and volume measurements for the two lead fishing weights above, the data points fall on the line shown in the graph.*

Slope as the Constant in $y = kx$

Scientists sometimes find that their data form a straight line that includes the point that has x and y values of zero. They can then use the equation $y = kx$ to represent their data. **Figure 6** is a graph representing the density of lead. Here, y represents measurements of mass. And x represents measurements of volume. Then, k represents the constant term, which is the slope of the line. The slope of this line (rise divided by run) represents the density (mass divided by volume) of lead. If you rearrange the formula for density into the form $y = kx$, the equation is $m = DV$. So, density is the constant, k, which is the slope of the line.

Quick Lab

Slope and Speed

8.9.d

1. Put a piece of **tape** 3 m long on the floor. Use tape and a **meterstick** to mark the line at 0 m, 1 m, 2 m, and 3 m.

2. Choose one person to be the walker. The walker starts at 0 m, walks forward on the line for 3 m, stops for a short time, and then walks backward for 2 m. The whole trip should take about 1 min.

3. Choose a second person to be the timer. The timer uses a **stopwatch** to measure the time at which the walker stops at 3 m, starts moving backward, and stops again at 1 m.

4. The third person in your group is the recorder. The recorder writes down the times called out by the timer.

5. Conduct the procedure, and collect your data.

6. Plot the position and time data on a graph.

7. Determine the slope of each part of the graph. Be sure to include the correct units.

8. What does the slope of each part represent?

20 min

Comparing Linear and Nonlinear Graphs

The lines on a graph can help you draw conclusions about your data. The slope of a straight line shows how much one factor (*y*) always changes in relation to another factor (*x*). A straight line shows that a constant linear relationship exists between the factors you are studying. In other words, *y* always changes the same amount in relation to *x*. But what if your data do not form a straight line? Many relationships that scientists study are not linear. In a nonlinear graph, each unit change in one factor (*y*) does not always bring about the same change in another factor (*x*). The graph of this relationship will be a curve instead of a straight line. So, there is a nonlinear relationship between the factors you are studying.

SECTION Review

8.9.b, 8.9.d

Summary

- Mathematics is an important tool for understanding and summarizing data.
- The accuracy and reproducibility of data used in scientific investigations affect the results.
- Mean, median, and mode summarize an entire set of data.
- Slope is the degree of slant of a straight line.
- The slope of a straight line represents a constant that can be used to understand and analyze data.
- Linear and nonlinear graphs result from different relationships in the data.

Using Vocabulary

1 Write an original definition for *slope.*

Understanding Concepts

2 **Applying** A scientific study is repeated by four different groups. Only two groups get the same results. Are the data reproducible? Explain.

3 **Analyzing** What does the phrase "rise over run" refer to when defining slope?

4 **Summarizing** Why is mathematics an important tool for scientists?

Critical Thinking

5 **Applying Concepts** Describe a situation in which the median of a data set would be more useful than the mean.

6 **Analyzing Methods** A scientist is measuring the height of water hyacinths on 30 ponds. How important is the degree of accuracy of the measurements he gathers? Explain your answer.

Math Skills

7 **Analyzing Data** Rachel has gathered information about the guppy population in her fish tank. She has counted the number of living guppies once per month for five months. Her data are as follows: 5, 15, 35, 35, and 55. Calculate the mean, median, and mode.

Challenge

8 **Identifying Relationships** You are gathering data about factor *y* and factor *x*. A graph of your data results in a straight line. What does this tell you about the relationship between *y* and *x*? What would the slope of this line represent? Explain your answers in terms of *y* and *x*.

Internet Resources

For a variety of links related to this chapter, go to www.scilinks.org

Topic: Science and Technology in California

SciLinks code: HY7C10

Skills Practice Lab

Penny Densities

All pennies are exactly the same, right? Probably not! After all, each penny was made in a certain year at a specific mint, and each has traveled a unique path to reach your classroom. But all pennies are similar. In this lab, you will conduct an investigation to gather data about the differences and similarities among a group of pennies.

OBJECTIVES

Determine the mass, volume, and density of objects.

Identify patterns and trends in data.

Construct graphs from data.

Recognize the slope of a linear graph to be the constant in the relationship $y = kx$.

MATERIALS

- balance, metric
- graduated cylinder, 100 mL
- paper, notebook (3 sheets)
- paper towels
- pennies (10)
- water

SAFETY

Procedure

1. Write the numbers 1 through 10 on a sheet of paper, and place a penny next to each number.

2. Use the metric balance to find the mass of each penny to the nearest 0.1 g. Return each penny to its place on the paper and record each measurement next to the number of that penny.

3. On a table that your teacher will provide, make a mark in the correct column of the table for each penny you measured.

4. Separate your pennies into two piles, based on the class data. Label a sheet of paper Pile 1 and place the pile of lower-mass pennies on the sheet. Label a second sheet of paper Pile 2 and place the pile of higher-mass pennies on the sheet.

5. Measure and record the mass of each pile. Write the mass on the paper you are using to identify the pile.

6. Fill a graduated cylinder halfway with water. Carefully measure the volume in the cylinder, and record it.

7. Carefully place the pennies from one pile into the graduated cylinder. Measure and record the new volume.

Investigation and Experimentation

8.9.d Recognize the slope of the linear graph as the constant in the relationship $y = kx$ and apply this principle in interpreting graphs constructed from data.

8.9.e Construct appropriate graphs from data and develop quantitative statements about the relationships between variables.

8.9.f Apply simple mathematical relationships to determine a missing quantity in a mathematic expression, given the two remaining terms (including speed = distance/time, density = mass/volume, force = pressure × area, volume = area × height).

8.9.g Distinguish between linear and nonlinear relationships on a graph of data.

8 Carefully pour out the water into the sink, and remove the pennies from the graduated cylinder. With a paper towel, dry off the pile of pennies.

9 Repeat steps 6 through 8 for the other pile.

Analyze the Results

10 **Analyzing Data**   Determine the volume of the displaced water by subtracting the initial volume from the final volume. This amount is equal to the volume of the pennies. Record the volume of each pile of pennies.

11 **Organizing Data**   On tables that your teacher will provide, record the mass and volume of each pile of pennies. Copy each table containing all of the data collected by your class.

12 **Analyzing Data**   Calculate the density of each pile by dividing the total mass of the pennies by the volume of the pennies.

13 **Constructing Graphs**   Construct a graph of mass versus volume for each pile of pennies using the data collected by your class.

14 **Recognizing Patterns**   Do your graphs show a linear or nonlinear relationship between mass and volume? Explain your reasoning.

Draw Conclusions

15 **Analyzing Graphs**   Determine the slope of the line on each graph.

16 **Evaluating Data**   Compare the two values for density that you found for each pile.

17 **Defending Conclusions**   The slope of a line on a graph of mass versus volume represents the density of the material. Show how the formula for calculating density can be rearranged into the form $y = kx$ to support this claim.

Big Idea Question

18 **Evaluating Methods**   By analyzing your data and the pennies, can you identify any patterns that would allow you to separate the pennies into the same groups without conducting an investigation? Explain your answer.

Science Skills Activity

Scientific Methods	Data Analysis	Graphs	Calculation

Accuracy and Reproducibility of Data

▶ Tutorial

When you perform an investigation, the tool you choose to collect data affects the accuracy of your measurements. Accuracy has to do with the correctness of a measurement. In other words, accurate measurements are free of errors. Reproducibility has to do with the ability to repeat, or reproduce, the same data. If you repeat an experiment done by someone else and you get the same results, then the data are reproducible.

Procedure

1 The following data were collected to investigate accuracy and reproducibility using two different triple-beam balances and a 1.0 kg mass.

	Balance 1	**Balance 2**
Group 1	1.0 kg	1.4 kg
Group 2	1.0 kg	1.4 kg
Group 3	1.0 kg	1.4 kg

Analysis

2 Identifying Analyze the data table to evaluate the accuracy of the data. Because the mass is known to be 1.0 kg, you can see that the data collected using Balance 1 are accurate. You can also see that the data collected using Balance 2 are not accurate.

3 Applying Analyze the data table again to evaluate the reproducibility of the data. Each group obtained the same data on each balance. So, the data are reproducible. However, Balance 2 is showing reproducible, but inaccurate, results.

▶ You Try It!

Procedure

The data table below shows mass and volume measurements for four pieces of lead. Construct a graph of mass versus volume from these data. Use the graph to help determine the accuracy of the data.

	Mass (g)	**Volume (cm³)**
Piece 1	40	3.52
Piece 2	70	6.17
Piece 3	100	4.11
Piece 4	20	1.76

Analysis

1 Identifying Do the data points for the measurements of each piece of lead all fall on a straight line? If not, which piece is not on the line?

2 Applying On your graph of mass versus volume, what does the slope of the line represent? Explain why all of the points should fall on this line.

3 Evaluating Explain how your graph helps you evaluate the accuracy of the data.

4 Concluding What is a possible reason for the inaccurate measurement?

5 Evaluating What would you need to evaluate the reproducibility of the data?

Chapter Summary

The Big Idea
Scientists use tools to collect, organize, and analyze data while conducting investigations.

Section		Vocabulary

1 Tools and Models in Science

Key Concept Scientists use tools and models to increase their ability to investigate the natural world.

- Tools are used to make accurate measurements while collecting data.
- The International System of Units (SI) is a system of measurement used by most scientists.
- A model uses familiar things to describe unfamiliar things. Physical, conceptual, and mathematical models are commonly used in science.
- Models help scientific progress through their use in theories and laws.

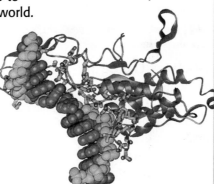
Scientists use models to help understand and explain data.

mass p. 43
volume p. 44
density p. 44
temperature p. 45
model p. 45
theory p. 48
law p. 48

2 Organizing Your Data

Key Concept Scientists organize data to make quantitative statements about the relationships between the variables in an investigation.

- Scientists use data tables and graphs to organize information.
- The independent variable is the factor or parameter that the investigator can change.
- The dependent variable is the factor or parameter that the investigator measures.
- Graphs help show patterns in data. Linear and nonlinear graphs show different relationships between the variables.

Organizing your data helps you see trends and draw conclusions.

independent variable p. 51
dependent variable p. 51
axis p. 52

3 Analyzing Your Data

Key Concept Scientists analyze data in order to answer questions, understand results, and make predictions.

- Mathematics is an important tool for understanding and summarizing large quantities of information.
- The accuracy and reproducibility of data affect the results and conclusions of scientific studies.
- The mean, median, and mode are terms used to describe and analyze an entire set of data.
- Slope is the degree of slant, or steepness, of a straight line. The slope of a linear graph represents a constant that can be used to help analyze a set of data.

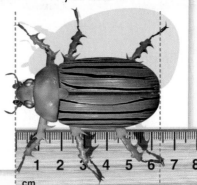
The accuracy of measurements affects your data.

mean p. 58
median p. 58
mode p. 58
slope p. 59

Chapter Review

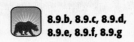

8.9.b, 8.9.c, 8.9.d,
8.9.e, 8.9.f, 8.9.g

Organize

Tri-Fold   Review the FoldNote that you created at the beginning of the chapter. Add to or correct the FoldNote based on what you have learned.

Using Vocabulary

1 **Academic Vocabulary**   Choose the appropriate form of the word *accurate* for the following sentence: "The degree of ___ of the data used in a scientific investigation affects the results."
a. accurate
b. accuracy
c. accuracies
d. being accurate

Complete each of the following sentences by choosing the correct term from the word bank.

slope   independent variable
axis   dependent variable
density   median

2 The ___ is the factor that the experimenter changes.

3 A reference line that forms one side of a graph is called a(n) ___.

4 In math, ___ is defined as the degree of slant of a line.

5 The ___ changes in response to the independent variable.

6 The ratio of the mass of a substance to the volume of the substance is ___.

Understanding Concepts

Multiple Choice

7 The slope of all horizontal lines is
a. positive.
b. negative.
c. zero.
d. undefined.

8 In an experiment, the mass of each of five apples is measured. The results are 95 g, 85 g, 90 g, 85 g, and 100 g. Identify the mode.
a. 85 g
b. 90 g
c. 92 g
d. 95 g

9 What do scientists often create when they cannot easily study the real thing?
a. a theory
b. a model
c. a trend
d. a dependent variable

10 What is the value of the data point in the middle of a set of data when the data are arranged in order from smallest to largest?
a. the mode
b. the median
c. the mean
d. the average

Short Answer

11 **Applying**   How would you determine the volume of an object if you were given its mass and density?

12 **Identifying**   A data table shows the height of a person on his birthday each year for 10 years. What is the dependent variable?

13 **Demonstrating**   Several scientists are working together to study the change in the number of whales born each year along the northern coast of California. What is the controlled parameter?

Writing Skills

14 **Technical Writing**   A group of scientists is studying the change in the amount of pesticides found in ocean water over a 20-year period. Outline the steps for constructing an appropriate graph for the data from the investigation. Be sure to clearly identify the sequence of steps to follow and the variables to consider in order to create a graph that would help the scientists analyze their results.

Critical Thinking

15 **Concept Mapping** Use the following terms to create a concept map: *slope, linear graphs, density, independent variable, axes,* and *dependent variable.*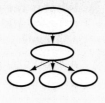

16 **Applying Concepts** Describe three kinds of models used in science. Give an example and explain one limitation of each model.

17 **Identifying Relationships** If you have the masses and volumes of a set of objects, what would a graph of these values represent?

18 **Applying Concepts** A tailor is someone who makes or alters items of clothing. Why might a standard system of measurement be helpful to a tailor? How would the degree of accuracy of a tailor's measurements affect the quality of the clothes?

INTERPRETING GRAPHICS Use the table below to answer the next two questions.

Age (months)	Mass (kg)
0	3.2
1	4.2
2	5.1
4	6.7
5	7.3
6	7.8

19 **Applying Concepts** A baby's mass was measured when the baby was born and then every month for 6 months. At 3 months of age, the baby was sick, so the baby's mass was not measured. Create a graph by using the data table above. Use the graph to find the likely mass of the baby at 3 months.

20 **Evaluating Conclusions** Does your graph show a linear or a nonlinear relationship? Explain your answer.

INTERPRETING GRAPHICS Use the image below to answer the next three questions.

21 **Making Comparisons** How similar is this model to a real object?

22 **Evaluating Sources** Describe one possible limitation of this model.

23 **Applying Concepts** How might this model be useful?

Math Skills

24 **Analyzing Data** Find the mean, median, and mode of the following data set: 8.9 cm, 7.2 cm, 15.7 cm, 5.2 cm, and 15.7 cm.

25 **Using Equations** A box of cereal has a mass of 340 g. Its dimensions are 27 cm × 19 cm × 6 cm. What is the volume of the box? What is its density?

Challenge

26 **Making Inferences** You and a friend each decide to build the same model airplane. After the airplanes are built, you decide to conduct an investigation to determine which airplane can glide through the air the longest. Outline a plan to conduct your investigation. Identify the controlled and variable parameters. What are some possible reasons for finding that one airplane glides much farther than the other airplane?

Standards Assessment

6.7.a, 6.7.e, 7.7.c, 7.7.d,
8.9.a, 8.9.b, 8.9.c, 8.9.d,
8.9.e, 8.9.f, 8.9.g

REVIEWING ACADEMIC VOCABULARY

1 Which of the following words means "to judge the worth of"?

A relate

B evaluate

C ponder

D squander

2 Which of the following words means the same as the word *accuracy*?

A correctness

B reality

C honesty

D conversion

3 What is the meaning of *variable* in the sentence "Ashley listed the variable in the first column of her data table"?

A the factor that changes in Ashley's experiment

B the symbol that represents a known quantity in algebra

C the characteristic in a species that tends to differ

D the factor that always equals zero in Ashley's experiment

4 What is the meaning of *construct* in the sentence "Mateo and Teresa constructed a graph based on the data they collected in their experiment"?

A to form a concept or idea

B to copy or match

C to build or make from parts

D to measure the size of a surface

REVIEWING CONCEPTS

5 What is the density of an object with a mass of 100.8 g and a volume of 144 cm³?

A 700 g/cm³

B 70 g/cm³

C 7 g/cm³

D 0.7 g/cm³

6 If the data points on a graph can be connected with a straight line, which of the following is most likely true?

A The slope of the line on the graph represents the mass of the substance being measured.

B The factor represented by the *y*-axis always changes the same amount in relation to the factor represented by the *x*-axis.

C There is an inverse nonlinear relationship between the factors in the data table.

D There is a direct nonlinear relationship between the factors in the data table.

Rainfall in Sacramento	
Month	**Rainfall (cm)**
September	1.2
October	3.5
November	6.25
December	6.8
January	8.75

7 The data table above shows the results of an eighth grade class measuring monthly rainfall. Which column in the data table represents the dependent variable?

A Month

B Rainfall (cm)

C both columns

D neither column

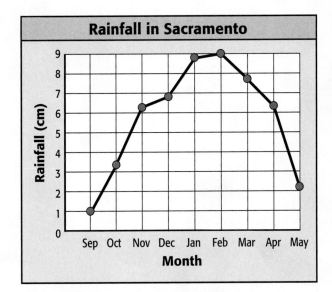

Rainfall in Sacramento

Month

8 The graph above shows centimeters of rainfall in Sacramento over a nine-month period. Study the trend established by the graph. What is the most reasonable prediction you can make by looking at the graph?

A There will be less than 2.3 cm of rain in June.

B The level of rainfall will rise slightly in June.

C There will be more rainfall in June than in January.

D The level of rainfall will be 0 cm in June.

9 Bethany collected data to determine how quickly her puppy was growing. The puppy steadily gained weight over eight months. When Bethany graphs her data, what kind of relationship will it show between the variables?

A a linear relationship

B a nonlinear relationship

C an inverse nonlinear relationship

D a direct nonlinear relationship

REVIEWING PRIOR LEARNING

10 A shampoo advertised in your favorite magazine claims to have a secret ingredient that will make your hair thicker and shinier. How could you test that claim?

A by conducting lab experiments with the shampoo

B by researching the ingredients in the product

C by comparing the results of washing with that shampoo and your regular shampoo

D by researching the number of advertising claims that are actually true

11 How do scientists test their hypotheses?

A by forming theories

B by asking questions

C by making predictions

D by gathering data

12 A Punnett square shows how traits are passed along from parents to offspring. A Punnett square is an example of

A a mathematical model.

B a diagram.

C a conceptual model.

D a map.

13 The symbols below represent some safety cautions to follow when conducting lab experiments. Which of these safety symbols would you most likely find on a science lab sheet that requires working with chemicals?

A   B   C   D

Science in Action

![California state outline]

Science, Technology, and Society

Using Satellites to Track Plate Motion

When you think of laser beams firing, you may think of science fiction movies. However, scientists have developed a system called *satellite laser ranging,* or SLR, that uses laser beams to measure the rate and direction of motion of tectonic plates. SLR is used to monitor movement at faults in Southern California. From ground stations on Earth, laser beams are fired at satellites orbiting 5,900 km above Earth. From the satellites, the laser beams are reflected back to ground stations. Differences in the time it takes signals to be reflected from targets are used to calculate the amount of movement.

Weird Science

Dolphins in the Navy

Did you know that some dolphins work for the navy? One way that dolphins help the navy's Marine Mammal Program is by detecting underwater mines. Underwater mines are bombs that drift underwater. Most mines explode when a large object bumps into them. Dolphins can find mines safely by using *echolocation,* a natural sonar system that allows dolphins to sense their surroundings, even in murky waters. When a dolphin finds a mine and alerts a person, experts can deactivate the mine.

Language Arts ACTIVITY

Research a society that lives on an active plate boundary. Write a short story describing how the people prepare for the possibility of earthquakes and volcanic eruptions.

This scientist is using a laser to test one of the satellites that will be used to track plate motion.

Math ACTIVITY

Suppose that each dolphin in the navy's program is trained for 5 years and each trained dolphin works for 25 years. If 10 dolphins begin training each year for 10 years, how many would be working at the end of those 10 years? How many would still be in training?

Evan Forde

Oceanographer You're 2 mi below the water's surface, trapped in a tiny submarine. A small, underwater landslide has partially buried your sub. Ten minutes crawl by. The submarine finally breaks free, and you notice that your heartbeat and breathing begin to slow. You are just 28 years old, but you're already an expert on undersea canyons. When you were a high school student, you never thought that your work would include such exciting experiences!

Evan Forde survived his submarine scare and continues to enjoy being an oceanographer, a scientist who studies oceans. Forde and other oceanographers use a variety of tools to help them explore and understand the oceans. Forde works for the National Oceanic and Atmospheric Association (NOAA), a scientific branch of the U.S. government. His current specialty is using satellites and computers to improve early-warning systems for detecting hurricanes. Forde is part of NOAA's Atlantic Oceanographic and Meteorological Laboratory.

Social Studies ACTIVITY

Research an oceanographer of your choice, and prepare a class presentation on your findings. Focus on the accomplishments of the scientist and the ways that the scientist used technology to study the oceans.

Internet Resources

- To learn more about careers in science, visit www.scilinks.org and enter the SciLinks code HY70225.

- To learn more about these Science in Action topics, visit go.hrw.com and type in the keyword HY7DISF.

- Check out articles related to this chapter by visiting go.hrw.com. Just type in the keyword HY7DISC.

UNIT 2

TIMELINE

The Structure of Matter

In this unit, you will explore a basic question that people have been pondering for centuries: What is the structure of matter? You will learn how to define the word *matter* and the ways to describe matter and the changes it goes through. You will also learn about the different states of matter and how to classify different arrangements of matter as elements, compounds, or mixtures. This timeline shows some of the events and discoveries that have occurred as scientists have sought to understand the structure of matter.

1661
Robert Boyle, a chemist in England, determines that elements are substances that cannot be broken down into anything simpler by chemical processes.

1712
Thomas Newcomen invents the first practical steam engine.

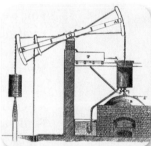

1937
The *Hindenburg* explodes while docking in Lakehurst, New Jersey. To make it lighter than air, the airship was filled with flammable hydrogen gas.

1971
The first commercially available "pocket" calculator is introduced. It has a mass of nearly 1 kg and a price of about $400, hardly the kind of pocket calculator that exists today.

1766

English chemist Henry Cavendish discovers and describes the properties of a highly flammable substance now known as hydrogen gas.

1800

Current from an electric battery is used to separate water into the elements hydrogen and oxygen for the first time.

1920

American women win the right to vote with the ratification of the 19th Amendment to the Constitution.

1950

Silly Putty™ is sold in a toy store for the first time. The soft, gooey substance quickly becomes popular because of its strange properties, including the ability to "pick up" the print from a newspaper page.

1957

The space age begins when the Soviet Union launches *Sputnik I*, the first artificial satellite to circle Earth.

1989

An oil tanker strikes a reef in Prince William Sound, Alaska, and spills nearly 11 million gallons of oil. The floating oil injures or kills thousands of marine mammals and seabirds and damages the Alaskan coastline.

2000

The World's Fair, an international exhibition featuring exhibits and participants from around the world, is held in Hanover, Germany. The theme is "Humankind, Nature, and Technology."

2003

Sally Ride, the first American woman in space, is inducted into the Astronaut Hall of Fame.

Improving Comprehension

Graphic Organizers are important visual tools that can help you organize information and improve your reading comprehension. The Graphic Organizer below is called a *Venn diagram*. Instructions for creating other types of Graphic Organizers are located in the **Study Skills** section of the Appendix.

How to Make a Venn Diagram

1 Draw a diagram like the one shown below. Draw one circle for each topic. Make sure that each circle partially overlaps the other circles.

2 In each circle, write a topic that you want to compare with the topics in the other circles.

3 In the areas of the diagram where circles overlap, write the characteristics that the topics in the overlapping circles share.

4 In the areas of the diagram where circles do not overlap, write the characteristics that are unique to the topic of the particular circle.

When to Use a Venn Diagram

A Venn diagram is a useful tool for comparing two or three topics in science. A Venn diagram shows which characteristics the topics share and which characteristics are unique to each topic. Venn diagrams are ideal when you want to illustrate relationships in a pair or small group of topics. As you read, look for topics that have both shared and unique characteristics, and draw a Venn diagram that shows how the topics are related.

Physical Properties
- can be observed or measured without changing the identity of a substance
- color, odor, mass, volume, weight, density, strength, flexibility, magnetism, and electrical conductivity

- help describe and define matter
- can be characteristic properties

Chemical Properties
- describe matter based on its ability to change into new matter that has different properties
- cannot always be observed
- reactivity, including flammability

You Try It!

This Reading Strategy can also be used within the chapter that you are about to read. Practice making your own *Venn diagram* as directed in the Reading Strategies for Section 1 and Section 3. Record your work in your **Science Journal.**

Unpacking the Standards

The information below "unpacks" the standards by breaking them down into basic parts. The higher-level, academic vocabulary is highlighted and defined to help you understand the language of the standards. "What It Means" restates the standards as simply as possible.

California Standard	Academic Vocabulary	What It Means
8.5.a Students know reactant atoms and molecules **interact** to form products with different **chemical** properties.	**interact** (IN tuhr AKT) to act upon one another **chemical** (KEM i kuhl) of or having to do with the properties or actions of substances	When atoms and molecules are put together, they can interact to form new substances whose chemical properties differ from the properties of the original substances.
8.5.c Students know **chemical reactions** usually **liberate** heat or absorb heat.	**reaction** (ree AK shuhn) a response or change **liberate** (LIB uhr AYT) to release; to set free	When new substances are formed, thermal energy is usually either given off or absorbed.
8.5.d Students know **physical processes** include freezing and boiling, in which a material changes form with no **chemical reaction.**	**physical** (FIZ i kuhl) of or having to do with matter or the body **process** (PRAH SES) a set of steps, events, or changes	Changes of matter that do not change the composition of the matter include the changes from a liquid to a solid and from a liquid to a gas.
8.7.c Students know substances can be classified by their properties, including their melting temperature, density, hardness, and thermal and electrical conductivity.		Different kinds of matter can be grouped by their characteristics, including the temperature at which they melt, the amount of mass per unit volume, their hardness, and their ability to transfer thermal energy or electrical energy.
8.8.a Students know density is mass per unit volume.		Density is the amount of matter in a given amount of space.
8.8.b Students know how to calculate the density of substances (regular and irregular solids and liquids) from measurements of mass and volume.		You must know how to figure out the density of substances—including solids that have uniform shapes, solids that vary in shape, and liquids—from measurements of mass and volume.

The following list identifies other standards that are covered in this chapter and indicates where you can go to see them unpacked: **8.8.d** (Chapter 14).

3

Properties of Matter

The Big Idea

Matter is described by its properties and may undergo changes.

California Standards

Focus on Physical Sciences

8.5 Chemical reactions are processes in which atoms are rearranged into different combinations of molecules. (Section 3)

8.7 The organization of the periodic table is based on the properties of the elements and reflects the structure of atoms. (Section 2)

8.8 All objects experience a buoyant force when immersed in a fluid. (Sections 1 and 2)

Investigation and Experimentation

8.9 Scientific progress is made by asking meaningful questions and conducting careful investigations. (Section 1; Science Skills Activity)

Math

6.1.2 Algebra and Functions
8.8.0 Geometry

English–Language Arts

8.2.2 Reading
8.2.6 Writing

About the Photo

This giant ice dragon began as a 1,700 kg block of ice! Making the blocks of ice takes six weeks. The artist has to work at –10°C to keep the ice from melting. An ice sculptor has to be familiar with the many properties of water, including its melting point.

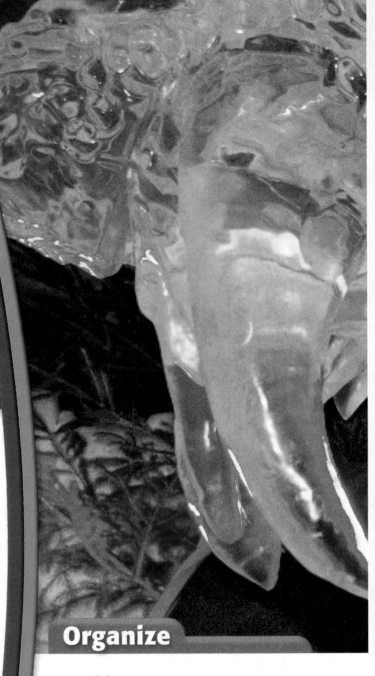

Organize

Double Door

Before you read this chapter, create the FoldNote entitled "Double Door." Write "Physical changes" on one flap of the double door and "Chemical changes" on the other flap. As you read the chapter, compare the two topics, and write characteristics of each topic on the inside of the appropriate flap.

Instructions for creating FoldNotes are located in the Study Skills section on p. 517 of the Appendix.

Explore Activity

🕐 **25 min**

Similar Size, Different Mass

In this activity, you will compare the physical properties of two objects that are similar in size and shape.

Procedure

1. Examine a **table-tennis ball** and a **golf ball.**

2. Use a **triple-beam balance** to determine the mass of each ball. Record your observations.

3. Compare the volume of the balls. For each ball, identify properties other than mass and volume by observing the ball for five minutes. List the properties that you identify.

Analysis

4. Five minutes after observing the two balls, discuss your findings with the class.

5. What units did you use to express the mass of each ball? What can you conclude about the amount of matter in each ball?

8.7.c

6. For any two objects that are similar in size, are both objects made up of the same amount of matter? Explain your answer.

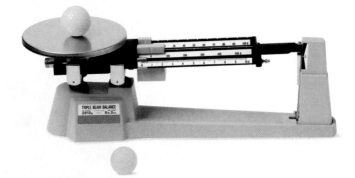

SECTION 1

What Is Matter?

Key Concept Matter is anything that has mass and takes up space. Matter can be described in terms of its volume, mass, and weight.

What You Will Learn

- All matter has volume and mass.
- Volume is the amount of space taken up by an object.
- Mass is a measure of the amount of matter in an object.
- Weight is a measure of the gravitational force exerted on an object.

Why It Matters

Understanding what matter is and how units are used to describe matter can help you understand the structure of the physical world.

Vocabulary

- matter
- mass
- volume
- weight
- meniscus

READING STRATEGY

Graphic Organizer In your **Science Journal,** create a Venn Diagram that compares volume and mass.

matter (MAT uhr) anything that has mass and takes up space

volume (VAHL yoom) a measure of the size of a body or region in three-dimensional space

8.8.b Students know how to calculate the density of substances (regular and irregular solids and liquids) from measurements of mass and volume.

What do you have in common with a toaster, a steaming bowl of soup, or a bright neon sign? You might think that this is a trick question. It is hard to believe that a person has anything in common with a kitchen appliance, hot soup, or a neon sign.

Matter

From a scientific point of view, you have at least one characteristic in common with a toaster, a bowl, soup, steam, and the glass tubing and glowing gas of a neon sign. You and these items are each made of matter. But exactly what is matter? **Matter** is anything that has mass and takes up space.

Matter and Volume

All matter takes up space. The amount of space that an object takes up, or occupies, is known as the object's **volume.** Your fingers, the continent of Africa, and a cloud have volume. And because these things have volume, they cannot occupy the same space at the same time. Even the tiniest piece of dust takes up space. Another piece of dust cannot fit into that space without somehow bumping the first piece out of the way. **Figure 1** shows an example of how two objects cannot be in the same space at the same time.

Figure 1 *Because CDs are made of matter, they have volume. Once your CD storage rack is filled with CDs, you cannot fit another CD in the rack.*

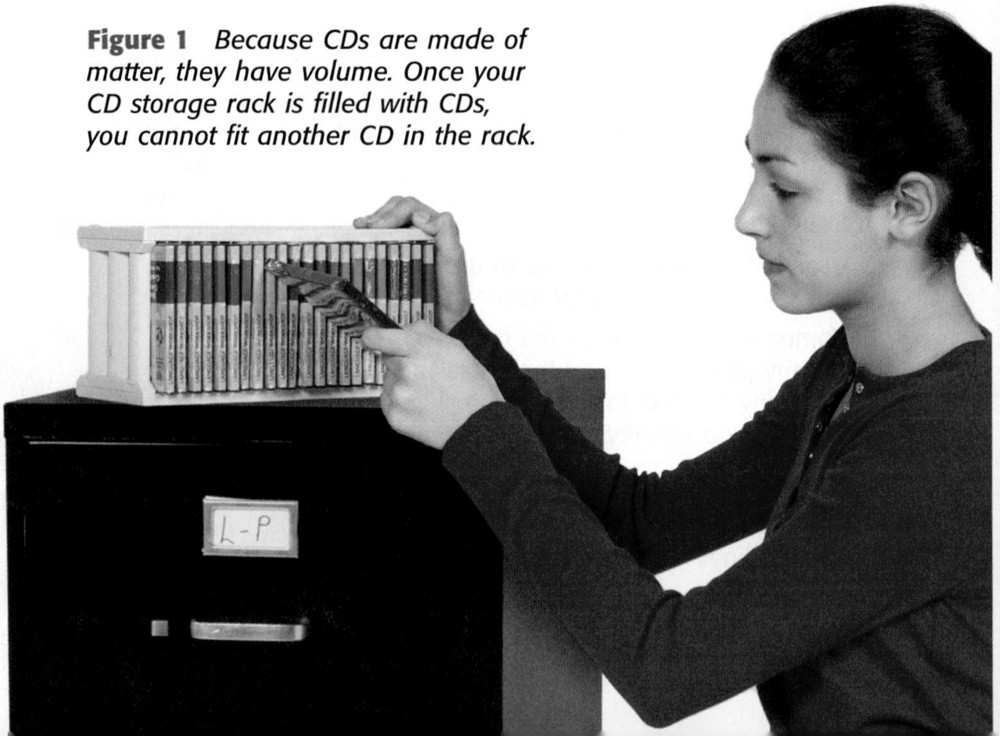

Liquid Volume

Lake Erie, the smallest of the Great Lakes, has a volume of about 483 trillion liters (483,000,000,000,000 L) of water. Can you picture that much water? Think of a 1.5 L bottle of water. The water in Lake Erie could fill more than 322 trillion 1.5 L bottles. On a smaller scale, an ordinary canned drink has a volume of only 0.355 L, which is about one-third of a liter. You can estimate the volume of the can by using a large measuring cup to measure the amount of liquid that a full can holds.

The liter (L) is the SI unit for volume. Often, small volumes of liquid are expressed in milliliters (mL). Remember that 1 L equals 1,000 mL. Any volume of liquid, from one drop of rain to a bottle of water to an ocean, can be expressed in liters or milliliters.

Standards Check What are two units that are used to express volume? 🐻 **8.8.b**

Measuring the Volume of Liquids

In class, you may use a graduated cylinder instead of a measuring cup to measure a liquid's volume. Graduated cylinders are used to measure liquid volume when accuracy is needed. The surface of a liquid in any container is curved. The curve at the surface of a liquid is called a **meniscus.** For most liquids, including water, volume should be measured from the lowest point of the meniscus, as **Figure 2** shows. So, you would measure volume by noting where on the container's scale the lowest point of the meniscus is. Because the meniscus curves only slightly, water's meniscus looks flat in a wide-mouthed container.

meniscus (muh NIS kuhs) the curve at a liquid's surface by which one measures the volume of the liquid

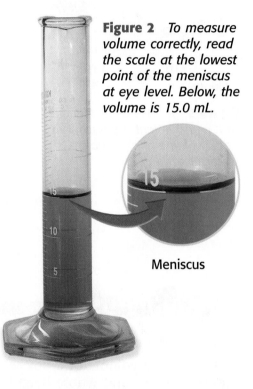

Figure 2 *To measure volume correctly, read the scale at the lowest point of the meniscus at eye level. Below, the volume is 15.0 mL.*

Meniscus

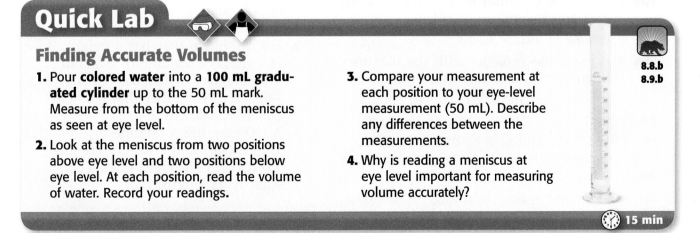

Quick Lab

Finding Accurate Volumes

1. Pour **colored water** into a **100 mL graduated cylinder** up to the 50 mL mark. Measure from the bottom of the meniscus as seen at eye level.

2. Look at the meniscus from two positions above eye level and two positions below eye level. At each position, read the volume of water. Record your readings.

3. Compare your measurement at each position to your eye-level measurement (50 mL). Describe any differences between the measurements.

4. Why is reading a meniscus at eye level important for measuring volume accurately?

8.8.b
8.9.b

⏱ 15 min

Volume of a Regularly Shaped Solid Object

The volume of any solid object is expressed in cubic units. The word *cubic* means "having three dimensions." In science, cubic meters (m^3) and cubic centimeters (cm^3) are the units most often used for the volume of solid things. The 3 in these unit symbols shows that three quantities, or dimensions, were multiplied to get the final result. You can see the three dimensions of a cubic meter in **Figure 3.**

You can use formulas to find the volume of regularly shaped objects. For example, to find the volume (*V*) of a cube or another rectangular object, use the length (*l*), width (*w*), and height (*h*) of the object in the following equation:

$$V = l \times w \times h$$

But you don't need to know all three measurements to find volume. The area of the base of a cube or another rectangular object is equal to length times width. So, if you know the area (*A*) and height (*h*) of the object, you can find the volume (*V*) of the object by using the following equation:

$$V = A \times h$$

Standards Check What two equations can you use to find the volume of a rectangular object? 🐻 **8.9.f**

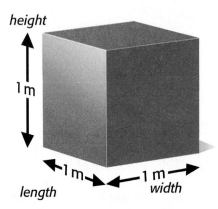

$V = 1\,m \times 1\,m \times 1\,m = 1\,m^3$

height

1 m

length   width

1 m   1 m

Figure 3 *A cube whose length, width, and height are each 1 m has a volume of one cubic meter (1 m³).*

![MATH FOCUS]

Volume of a Rectangular Solid

What is the volume of a box whose base has an area of 5 cm^2 and whose height is 2 cm?

Step 1: Write the equation for volume by using area and height.

volume = area × height

Step 2: Replace the variables with the measurements given, and solve for volume.

volume = 5 cm^2 × 2 cm = 10 cm^3

The equation for volume can also be rearranged to find area or height, as shown.

area = volume ÷ height (Rearrange by dividing by height.)

height = volume ÷ area (Rearrange by dividing by area.)

Now It's Your Turn

1. The cover of a book has an area of 450 cm^2. The book has a height of 4 cm. What is the book's volume? Use the correct unit for volume in your answer.
2. For a suitcase that has a height of 20 cm and a volume of 0.095 m^3, find the area of the base of the suitcase. (Remember that 0.095 m^3 equals 95,000 cm^3.)
3. A CD case has a volume of 176.08 cm^3. If the case's height is 1.0 cm and its width is 12.4 cm, what is its length?

Volume of an Irregularly Shaped Solid Object

How do you find the volume of a solid that does not have a regular shape? One way to find the volume of an irregularly shaped solid object is to use water displacement.

Using Displacement to Find Volume

In **Figure 4,** when a 12-sided object is added to the water in a graduated cylinder, the water level rises. The level rises because the object pushes water out of the way. This process of pushing water out of the way is called *displacement*. The volume of water displaced by the object is equal to the object's volume. Because 1 mL is equal to 1 cm^3, you can give the volume of the water displaced by the object in cubic centimeters. Volumes of liquids can be given in cubic units, but volumes of solids should not be given in liters or milliliters.

Using displacement to find the volume of an object that floats is more difficult. To do so, you must use another object to hold the floating object underwater. Then, you must subtract the volume of the object holding the floating object. Displacement cannot be used to find the volume of something that dissolves in water.

Standards Check Explain how you would measure the volume of a brick that contains holes. **8.8.b**

Quick Lab

Finding Volume by Displacement

8.8.b

1. Fill a **100 mL graduated cylinder** to about the 50 mL mark with **colored water.** Read the volume at the meniscus, and record your reading.

2. Tip the graduated cylinder, and slide a **metal key** into the cylinder.

3. Carefully read the new level of water in the cylinder, and record your results.

4. Calculate the volume of water displaced by the key.

5. Using your results, calculate the volume of the key.

⏱ **15 min**

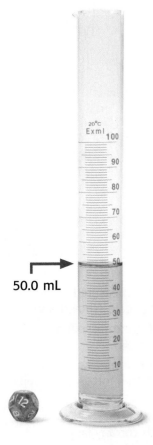

50.0 mL

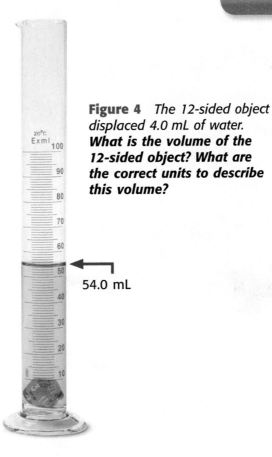

54.0 mL

Figure 4 *The 12-sided object displaced 4.0 mL of water.* **What is the volume of the 12-sided object? What are the correct units to describe this volume?**

Matter and Mass

mass (MAS) a measure of the amount of matter in an object

weight (WAYT) a measure of the gravitational force exerted on an object; its value can change with the location of the object in the universe

Another characteristic of all matter is mass. **Mass** is a measure of the amount of matter that makes up an object. For example, you and a peanut are made of matter. But you are made up of more matter than a peanut is, so you have greater mass. The mass of an object does not change when the object's location changes. The mass of an object changes only when the amount of matter that makes up the object changes.

The Difference Between Mass and Weight

The terms *mass* and *weight* are often used as though they mean the same thing, but they do not. **Weight** is a measure of the gravitational (GRAV i TAY shuhn uhl) force on an object. Gravitational force keeps objects on Earth from floating into space. The gravitational force between an object and Earth depends partly on the object's mass. The greater the mass of an object, the greater the gravitational force on the object and the greater the object's weight. But an object's weight can change depending on the object's location. An object would weigh less on the moon than it does on Earth because the moon has less mass—and therefore less gravitational force—than Earth does. **Figure 5** explains the differences between mass and weight.

Figure 5 Differences Between Mass and Weight

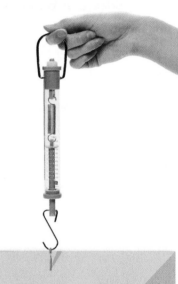

Mass
- Mass is measured by using a balance (shown below).
- Mass is expressed in kilograms (kg), grams (g), and milligrams (mg).
- Mass is a measure of the amount of matter in an object.
- Mass is constant for an object no matter where the object is located.

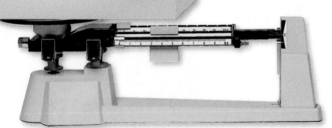

Weight
- Weight is measured by using a spring scale (shown above).
- Weight is expressed in newtons (N).
- Weight is a measure of the gravitational force on an object.
- Weight varies depending on where the object is in relation to Earth (or any large body).

Measuring Mass and Weight

The brick and the sponge in **Figure 6** have the same volume. But because the brick has greater mass, a greater gravitational force acts on the brick than on the sponge. As a result, the brick weighs more than the sponge.

The SI unit of mass is the kilogram (kg). Mass is also expressed in grams (g) and milligrams (mg). These units can be used to express the mass of any object. Weight is a measure of gravitational force. The SI unit of force is the newton (N). One newton is equal to the weight on Earth of an object whose mass is about 100 g.

Standards Check What units are often used to express mass?
 8.8.b

Figure 6 *The brick and the sponge take up the same amount of space. But the brick contains more matter, so its mass—and thus its weight—is greater.*

SECTION Review

8.8.b, 8.9.f

Summary

- Two properties of matter are volume and mass.
- Volume is the amount of space taken up by an object.
- Mass is a measure of the amount of matter in an object.
- The SI unit of volume is the liter (L). The SI unit of mass is the kilogram (kg).
- Weight is a measure of the gravitational force on an object, usually in relation to Earth. Weight is expressed in newtons (N).

Using Vocabulary

① Use *volume* and *meniscus* in the same sentence.

② Write an original definition for *matter, mass,* and *weight.*

Understanding Concepts

③ **Identifying** What units can be used to express the volume of a solid?

Critical Thinking

④ **Evaluating Data** A nugget of gold is placed in a graduated cylinder that contains 85 mL of water. The water level rises to 225 mL after the nugget is added to the cylinder. What is the volume of the gold nugget?

⑤ **Identifying Relationships** Do objects that have large masses always have large weights? Explain your answer.

Math Skills

INTERPRETING GRAPHICS The table below lists measurements for three blocks of wood. Use the table to answer the next two questions.

Wood block	Area of the base (m²)	Height (m)
B1	36	4
B2	16	9
B3	*A*	12

⑥ **Analyzing Shapes** Find the volume of B1 and of B2.

⑦ **Analyzing Shapes** If the three blocks have equal volumes, what is *A*, the area of the base of B3?

Challenge

⑧ **Applying Concepts** Compare an elephant's weight on the moon with its weight on Earth. Explain your answer.

Internet Resources

For a variety of links related to this chapter, go to www.scilinks.org

Topic: What Is Matter?

SciLinks code: HY71662

Physical Properties

Key Concept Physical properties of matter can be observed or measured without changing the matter's identity.

What You Will Learn

- Examples of physical properties are melting temperature, density, hardness, thermal conductivity, and electrical conductivity.
- Density is the amount of matter in a given space or volume.
- A physical change does not change the identity of the matter that undergoes the change.
- Melting, freezing, cutting, bending, and dissolving are physical changes.

Why It Matters

Understanding the physical properties of matter can help you understand the physical changes that you observe in the matter around you.

Vocabulary

- physical property
- density
- physical change

READING STRATEGY

Asking Questions Read this section silently. In your **Science Journal,** write down questions that you have about this section. Discuss your questions in a small group.

▶ Have you ever played the game called *20 Questions?* The goal of this game is to figure out what object a person is thinking of by asking him or her no more than 20 yes-or-no questions.

What should you ask about? You may want to ask about the physical properties of the object. Knowing about the physical properties of an object can help you identify the object.

Identifying Physical Properties

The questions in **Figure 1** ask about four characteristics of an object: color, odor, mass, and volume. These characteristics are physical properties of matter. A **physical property** of matter is a characteristic that can be observed or measured without changing the matter's identity. For example, you can see an apple's color or measure an apple's volume without changing the apple's identity. **Figure 2** shows six physical properties.

Other physical properties—such as magnetism, electrical conductivity, strength, and flexibility—can help you identify ways to use a substance. Think of a scooter that has an electric motor. The magnetism produced by the motor is used to convert energy stored in the scooter's battery into energy that turns the scooter's wheels.

Standards Check List four physical properties. **8.7.c**

Figure 1 *Asking questions about the physical properties of an object can help you identify it.*

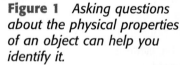

COULD I HOLD IT IN MY HAND? **YES.**
DOES IT HAVE AN ODOR? **YES.**
IS IT SAFE TO EAT? **YES.**
IS IT ORANGE? **No.**
IS IT YELLOW? **No.**
IS IT RED? **YES.**
IS IT AN APPLE? **YES!**

8.7.c Students know substances can be classified by their properties, including their melting temperature, density, hardness, and thermal and electrical conductivity.

8.8.a Students know density is mass per unit volume.

8.8.b Students know how to calculate the density of substances (regular and irregular solids and liquids) from measurements of mass and volume.

8.8.d Students know how to predict whether an object will float or sink.

Figure 2   Examples of Physical Properties

Thermal conductivity
(KAHN duhk TIV uh tee) is the
rate at which a substance
transfers heat. Plastic foam
is a poor conductor of heat.

Malleability (MAL ee uh BIL uh tee)
is the ability of a substance to be
rolled or pounded into various
shapes without breaking. Aluminum can be rolled into foil sheets.

Ductility (duhk TIL uh tee) is
the ability of a substance to
be pulled and made into wire.
Because it is ductile, copper is
often used to make wire.

Solubility (SAHL yoo BIL uh tee)
is the ability of a substance to
dissolve in another substance.
Flavored drink mix dissolves
in water.

State is the physical form in
which a substance exists, such
as a solid, liquid, or gas. Ice is
water in the solid state.

Density is the mass per unit
volume of a substance. Lead is
very dense, so it makes a good
sinker for a fishing line.

Density

Density is a physical property that describes the relationship
between mass and volume. **Density** is the amount of matter in
a given space or volume. A golf ball and a table-tennis ball
have similar volumes, as **Figure 3** shows. But a golf ball has
more mass than a table-tennis ball does. So, the golf ball has
a greater density than the table-tennis ball does.

To find an object's density (*D*), first measure its mass (*m*)
and volume (*V*). Then, use the equation below.

$$D = \frac{m}{V}$$

Units for density consist of a mass unit divided by a volume
unit. The density units most often used are grams per cubic
centimeter (g/cm³) for solids and grams per milliliter (g/mL)
for liquids. The density of a given substance remains the same
no matter how much of the substance you have. That is, the
density of 1 cm³ of a substance is equal to the density of 1 km³
of that substance.

Standards Check   What is density, and how do you calculate it?
🐻 8.8.a, 8.8.b

physical property (FIZ i kuhl
PRAHP uhr tee) a characteristic of
a substance that does not involve
a chemical change, such as density,
color, or hardness

density (DEN suh tee) the ratio of
the mass of a substance to the volume of the substance

mass = 46 g

mass = 3 g

Figure 3   *A golf ball is denser
than a table-tennis ball because
the golf ball contains more
matter in a similar volume.*

Calculating Density

What is the density of an object whose mass is 25 g and whose volume is 10 cm^3?

Step 1: Write the equation for density.

$$D = \frac{m}{V}$$

Step 2: Replace m and V with the measurements given in the problem, and solve.

$$D = \frac{25 \text{ g}}{10 \text{ cm}^3} = 2.5 \text{ g/cm}^3$$

The equation for density can also be rearranged to find mass or volume, as shown.

$m = D \times V$ (Rearrange by multiplying by V.)

$V = \frac{m}{D}$ (Rearrange by dividing by D.)

Now It's Your Turn

1. Find the density of a substance that has a mass of 36 g and a volume of 5 cm^3. (Hint: Make sure that your answer's units are units of density.)
2. Suppose that you have a lead ball whose mass is 454 g. What is the ball's volume? (Hint: Use **Table 1** below.)
3. What is the mass of a 15 mL sample of mercury?
4. Find the density of an unknown sample of rock that has a mass of 11 g and displaces 20 mL of water.

Twenty Questions

Play the game *20 Questions* with an adult. Have one person think of an object, and have the other person ask yes-or-no questions about it. Write the questions in your **Science Journal** as you play. Put a check mark next to the questions asked about physical properties. When the object is identified or when 20 questions have been asked, switch roles.

Using Density to Identify Substances

Density is a useful physical property for identifying substances. At a given temperature and pressure, a substance maintains a constant density. **Table 1** shows the densities of several substances.

Density of Solids

Which would you rather carry around all day: 1 kg of lead or 1 kg of feathers? They have the same mass, so their masses do not make one easier to carry than the other. But lead is denser than feathers. A kilogram of lead has a volume smaller than a stick of butter. A kilogram of feathers has the volume of a bed pillow. This difference in volume makes the lead less awkward to carry than the feathers.

Table 1	Densities of Common Substances*		
Substance	**Density* (g/cm^3)**	**Substance**	**Density* (g/cm^3)**
Helium (gas)	0.0001663	Zinc (solid)	7.13
Oxygen (gas)	0.001331	Silver (solid)	10.50
Water (liquid)	1.00	Lead (solid)	11.35
Pyrite (solid)	5.02	Mercury (liquid)	13.55

*at 20°C and 1.0 atm

Density, Floating, and Sinking

Knowing the density of a substance can tell you if the substance will float or sink in water. If the density of an object is less than the density of water, the object will float. Cork, most woods, and some plastics are less dense than water. So, they float in water. On the other hand, an object whose density is greater than the density of water will sink in water. Most rocks and metals are denser than water. So, they sink.

Standards Check How can you use density to predict whether an object will float or sink? 🐻 **8.8.d**

Liquid Layers

What do you think causes the liquids in **Figure 4** to look the way they do in the graduated cylinder? Does trick photography make them look that way? No, differences in density do! Six liquids are in the graduated cylinder. Each liquid has a different density. If the liquids are carefully poured into the cylinder, they form six layers because of the differences in density. The densest layer is on the bottom. The least dense layer is on the top. The order of the layers helps you see how the liquids' densities compare with one another.

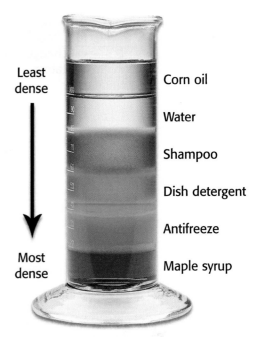

Least dense
Corn oil
Water
Shampoo
Dish detergent
Antifreeze
Most dense
Maple syrup

Figure 4 *This graduated cylinder contains six liquids that form six layers because of the densities of the liquids. The layers are in order of increasing density from the top to the bottom.*

Quick Lab

Finding the Density of Unknown Metals

8.8.a
8.8.b
8.9.f

In this activity, you will use measurements of mass and volume to calculate the density of several metal objects.

▶ **Try It!**

1. Examine a **small metal object,** and record the properties that you observe.

2. Measure the mass of the object by using a **triple-beam balance.** Record the mass.

3. Fill a **graduated cylinder** about halfway with **water.** Read the volume at the meniscus, and record your reading.

4. Tip the cylinder, and gently slide the metal object into the cylinder. Read the new volume, and record your reading.

5. Calculate the volume of the object. Record your results.

6. Repeat steps 1–5 for each metal object.

▶ **Think About It!**

7. Use your data to calculate the density of each metal object.

8. List the objects in order of least to greatest density.

9. Is one or more of the objects most likely made of lead? Explain your answer. (Hint: Lead has a density of 11.35 g/cm³.)

 20 min

Figure 5   Examples of Physical Changes

A change from a solid to a liquid is a physical change. All changes of state are physical changes.

This aluminum can has gone through the physical change of being crushed. The identity of the can has not changed.

Physical Changes: No New Substances

A change that affects one or more physical properties of a substance is a **physical change.** Imagine that a piece of silver is pounded and made into a heart-shaped charm. This change is a physical one because only the shape of the silver has changed. The piece of silver is still silver. The identity of the substance is the same. **Figure 5** shows more examples of physical changes.

physical change (FIZ i kuhl CHAYNJ) a change of matter from one form to another without a change in chemical properties

Standards Check   How are a substance and its physical properties affected during a physical change? 8.7.c

Examples of Physical Changes

Water freezing to become ice cubes and a piece of wood changing shape as a result of being sanded are examples of physical changes. Such changes do not change the identities of the substances. Ice is still water. And sawdust is still wood. Also, an interesting physical change takes place when one substance dissolves in another substance. For example, when sugar dissolves in water, the sugar seems to disappear. But if the mixture is heated, the water evaporates, and the sugar is still there in the pan. So, sugar dissolving is a physical change.

Reversibility of Physical Changes

Because physical changes do not change the identity of a substance, they are sometimes easy to undo. If you make a bowl from a lump of clay, you change the clay's shape and thus cause a physical change. But because the identity of the clay does not change, you can crush your bowl and form the clay into its original shape.

Matter and Physical Changes

Physical changes do not change the identity of the matter. A stick of butter can be melted and poured over a bowl of popcorn, as shown in **Figure 6.** Although the shape of the butter has changed, the butter is still butter, so a physical change has happened. In the same way, if you cut the shape of a star out of a piece of paper, you change the paper's shape and cause a physical change. But the identity of the paper does not change. The star and the piece of paper have the same identity—both are paper.

Figure 6 *When it melts, butter for popcorn undergoes a physical change.*

Summary

- Physical properties of matter can be observed without changing the identity of the matter.

- Examples of physical properties are melting temperature, density, hardness, thermal conductivity, and electrical conductivity.

- Density is the amount of matter in a given space.

- Density can be used to identify substances because the density of a substance is constant at a given pressure and temperature.

- When a substance undergoes a physical change, its identity stays the same.

- Physical changes include dissolving, cutting, bending, freezing, and melting.

Using Vocabulary

1. Use *physical property* and *physical change* in separate sentences.

Understanding Concepts

2. **Comparing** Explain why a golf ball is heavier than a table-tennis ball even though the balls are the same size.

3. **Describing** Explain what happens to a substance when it goes through a physical change.

INTERPRETING GRAPHICS Use the table below to answer the next two questions.

Substance	Density* (g/cm³)
Zinc (solid)	7.13
Silver (solid)	10.50
Lead (solid)	11.35

*at 20°C and 1.0 atm

4. **Identifying** Suppose that 273 g of one of the substances listed above displaces 26 mL of water. What is the substance?

5. **Evaluating** How many milliliters of water would be displaced by 408 g of lead?

Critical Thinking

6. **Applying Concepts** How can you determine that a coin is not pure silver if you know the mass and volume of the coin?

7. **Identifying Relationships** What physical property do water, oil, mercury, and alcohol share?

Math Skills

8. **Using Equations** What is the density of an object that has a mass of 350 g and a volume of 95 cm³? Will the object float in water?

Challenge

9. **Analyzing Processes** Write a step-by-step process for finding the density of an unknown liquid. List the laboratory equipment needed for each step.

Internet Resources

For a variety of links related to this chapter, go to www.scilinks.org

Topic: Physical Changes
SciLinks code: HY71142

Chemical Properties

Key Concept A chemical property describes the ability of a substance to change into a new substance.

What You Will Learn

- Examples of chemical properties are reactivity and flammability.
- A chemical change is the process by which a substance changes into a new substance.
- Chemical changes usually liberate or absorb heat.

Why It Matters

Understanding the chemical properties of matter can help you understand how new substances form from other substances.

Vocabulary

- chemical property
- chemical change

READING STRATEGY

Graphic Organizer In your **Science Journal,** create a Venn Diagram that compares types of changes that matter can undergo.

Wordwise **flammability**
The root *flamm-* means "to burn" or "flame."

How would you describe a piece of wood before and after it is burned? Did burning change the wood's color? Did burning change the wood's texture? The piece of wood changed, and physical changes alone do not account for all of the ways in which the wood changed.

Identifying Chemical Properties

Physical properties are not the only properties that describe matter. **Chemical properties** describe matter based on its ability to change into new matter, or matter whose identity differs from the identity of the original matter. One chemical property is reactivity. *Reactivity* is the ability of a substance to change into one or more new substances. The photo of the old car in **Figure 1** shows reactivity and nonreactivity.

A kind of reactivity is flammability. *Flammability* is the ability of a substance to burn. Wood has the chemical property of flammability. When wood is burned, it becomes ash, smoke, and other substances. The properties of these new substances differ from the properties of the wood. Ash and smoke cannot burn, so they have the chemical property of nonflammability.

Standards Check Why is reactivity not a physical property?
 8.5.a

Figure 1 **Reactivity with Oxygen**

The bumper on this car still looks new because it is coated with chromium. Chromium has the chemical property of **nonreactivity with oxygen.**

The iron used in this old car has the chemical property of **reactivity with oxygen.** When iron is exposed to oxygen, the iron rusts.

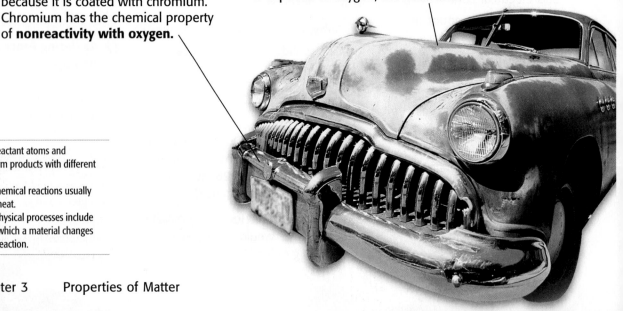

8.5.a Students know reactant atoms and molecules interact to form products with different chemical properties.
8.5.c Students know chemical reactions usually liberate heat or absorb heat.
8.5.d Students know physical processes include freezing and boiling, in which a material changes form with no chemical reaction.

Figure 2 Physical Properties Versus Chemical Properties

Physical property

Chemical property

Shape Bending an iron nail will change its shape.

Reactivity with Oxygen An iron nail can react with oxygen in the air to form iron oxide, or rust.

State Rubbing alcohol is a clear, colorless liquid at room temperature.

Flammability Rubbing alcohol is able to burn easily.

Comparing Physical and Chemical Properties

How can you tell that a property is a physical property and not a chemical property? If the property is a physical property, you can observe that property of a substance without changing the identity of the substance. For example, you can find the density and hardness of wood without changing the wood into another substance.

Chemical properties, however, are not as easy to observe. For example, you can see that wood is flammable only while it is burning. And you can observe that gold is nonflammable only when you try to burn it and it does not burn. But a substance always has chemical properties. A piece of wood is flammable even when it is not burning. **Figure 2** shows kinds of physical properties and chemical properties.

Characteristic Properties

Properties that are most useful in identifying a substance are called *characteristic properties*. Such properties are constant even if the sample size changes. Characteristic properties can be physical properties, such as density, or chemical properties, such as reactivity. Scientists rely on characteristic properties to identify and classify substances.

chemical property (KEM i kuhl PRAHP uhr tee) a property of matter that describes a substance's ability to participate in chemical reactions

Chemical Changes and New Substances

chemical change (KEM i kuhl CHAYNJ) a change that occurs when one or more substances change into entirely new substances with different properties

A **chemical change** happens when one or more substances change into new substances that have new and different properties. Chemical *changes* and chemical *properties* are not the same. The chemical properties of a substance describe which chemical changes can happen and which chemical changes cannot happen to that substance. But chemical changes are processes by which substances change into new substances. You can learn about a substance's chemical properties by observing which chemical changes that substance can undergo.

You see chemical changes more often than you may think. For example, a chemical change happens every time a battery is used. Chemical changes also take place within your body when the food you eat is digested. **Figure 3** describes other chemical changes.

Standards Check How does a chemical change differ from a chemical property? 8.5.a

---

Figure 3 **Examples of Chemical Changes**

Effervescent tablets bubble when the citric acid and baking soda in them react in water.

Soured milk smells bad because bacteria have formed smelly new substances in it.

Hot gas that forms when hydrogen and oxygen join to make water helps blast the space shuttle into orbit.

The **Statue of Liberty** is made of copper, which is orange-brown. But this copper is green because of its interactions with moist air. These interactions are chemical changes that form copper compounds. Over time, the compounds turn the statue green.

Figure 4 *Each of the original ingredients has different physical and chemical properties than the final product, the cake, does.*

What Happens During a Chemical Change?

A fun way to see what happens during chemical changes is to bake a cake. You combine eggs, flour, sugar, and other ingredients, as shown in **Figure 4.** When you bake the batter, you end up with a substance that is very different from the batter. The heat of the oven and the interaction of the ingredients cause a chemical change. The result is a cake that has properties that differ from the properties of the raw ingredients.

Signs of Chemical Changes

Look back at **Figure 3.** In each picture, at least one sign indicates a chemical change. These signs include a change in color or odor, fizzing and foaming, and sound or light being given off. Also, chemical changes usually liberate or absorb heat. *Liberate* means "to release." An increase in temperature takes place when a chemical change liberates heat. But a decrease in temperature occurs when a chemical change absorbs heat.

Standards Check Why do changes in temperature often happen during chemical changes? 🐻 **8.5.c**

Matter and Chemical Changes

When matter undergoes a chemical change, its identity changes. So, most chemical changes in ordinary tasks, such as baking a cake, are irreversible. Imagine *un*baking a cake! But some chemical changes can be reversed by other chemical changes. For example, when an electric current is applied to water formed from hydrogen and oxygen in a space shuttle's rockets, the water again splits into hydrogen and oxygen.

INTERNET ACTIVITY

My New Material
Can you think of a new and useful material? Create a new substance, and describe its properties. Go to **go.hrw.com,** and type in the keyword HY7MATW.

Figure 5 Physical and Chemical Changes

Change in Texture
Grinding baking soda into a fine, powdery substance is a physical change.

Reactivity with Vinegar
A chemical change happens and gas bubbles are produced when vinegar is poured into baking soda.

Physical Versus Chemical Changes

When trying to decide if an object has undergone a physical or chemical change, ask yourself, Did the object's composition change? *Composition* is the type of matter that makes up the object and the arrangement of the matter in the object. **Figure 5** shows a physical change and a chemical change.

Physical changes do not change matter's composition. Water is composed of two hydrogen atoms and one oxygen atom. When water freezes or boils, its composition does not change. So, freezing and boiling are physical changes. But chemical changes do alter the composition of a substance. A chemical change would change water into another substance.

Standards Check Explain why freezing and boiling are physical changes. 🐻 **8.5.d**

Quick Lab

Physical or Chemical Change?

1. Watch as your teacher places a burning **wooden stick** into a **test tube.** Record your observations.

2. Place a mixture of **sand** and **iron filings** in a **plastic bag,** and seal the bag. Place a **bar magnet** on top of the bag, and try to separate the iron from the sand.

3. Drop an **effervescent tablet** into a **beaker of water.** Record your observations.

🐻 **8.5.a**

4. For each step, identify which kind of change happens: a physical change or a chemical change. Explain your answers.

🕐 **15 min**

Reversing Changes

Can physical and chemical changes be reversed? Many physical changes are easily reversed. They do not change the composition of a substance. If an ice cube melts, you could freeze the liquid water to make another ice cube. But composition does change during a chemical change. So, most chemical changes are not easily reversed. Look at **Figure 6.** The chemical changes that happen when a firework explodes would be almost impossible to reverse, even if you collected all of the materials made in the chemical changes.

Figure 6 *This display of fireworks represents many chemical changes happening at the same time.*

SECTION Review

Summary

- Chemical properties describe the ability of a substance to change into a new substance.
- The chemical properties of a substance describe how the substance will behave under conditions that favor a chemical change.
- Reactivity and flammability are chemical properties.
- New substances form as a result of a chemical change.
- Chemical changes usually liberate or absorb heat.
- Chemical changes alter the composition of a substance.

Using Vocabulary

1. Write an original definition for *chemical property* and *chemical change.*

Understanding Concepts

2. **Comparing** Explain why rusting is a chemical change and not a physical change.

3. **Describing** Write two examples of chemical properties, and explain why they are chemical properties.

4. **Applying** Originally, the Statue of Liberty was copper colored. After being exposed to air, she turned green. What kind of change happened? Explain.

5. **Summarizing** What are two ways that heat can be involved in a chemical change?

Critical Thinking

6. **Making Comparisons** Describe the difference between physical and chemical changes in terms of what happens to the matter involved in each kind of change.

7. **Applying Concepts** Is melting a physical change or a chemical change? Explain your answer.

Math Skills

8. **Evaluating Data** The temperature of an acid solution is 25°C. A strip of magnesium is added to the solution, and the temperature rises 2°C per min for the first 3 min. After an additional 5 min, the temperature has risen another 2°C. What is the final temperature of the solution?

Challenge

9. **Analyzing Processes** As a candle burns, chemical changes take place. Describe two of these changes, and explain how you know that these changes are chemical changes and not physical changes.

Internet Resources

For a variety of links related to this chapter, go to www.scilinks.org

Topic: Describing Matter
SciLinks code: HY70391

Skills Practice Lab

Classifying Substances

You have learned how to describe matter based on its physical and chemical properties. You have also learned signs that can help you determine whether a change in matter is a physical change or a chemical change. In this lab, you will use what you have learned to describe four substances and their properties based on the changes that the substances undergo.

Procedure

1. Copy Table 1 and Table 2 shown on the next page. Be sure to leave plenty of room in each box to write down your observations.

2. Use a spatula to place a small amount of baking powder into three cups of your egg carton. Use just enough baking powder to cover the bottom of each cup. Record your observations about the baking powder's appearance, such as color and texture, in Table 1 in the column labeled "Unmixed."

3. Use an eyedropper to add 60 drops (about 3 mL) of water to the baking powder in the first cup. Stir with the stirring rod. Record your observations in Table 1 in the column labeled "Mixed with water." Clean your stirring rod.

8.5.a Students know reactant atoms and molecules interact to form products with different chemical properties.
8.7.c Students know substances can be classified by their properties, including their melting temperature, density, hardness, and thermal and electrical conductivity.

4 Use a clean dropper to add 20 drops of vinegar to the second cup of baking powder. Stir. Record your observations in Table 1 in the column labeled "Mixed with vinegar." Clean your stirring rod.

5 Use a clean dropper to add 5 drops of iodine solution to the third cup of baking powder. Stir. Record your observations in Table 1 in the column labeled "Mixed with iodine solution." Clean your stirring rod. **Caution:** Be careful when using iodine. Iodine will stain your skin and clothes.

6 Repeat steps 2–5 for each of the other substances (baking soda, cornstarch, and sugar). Use a clean spatula for each substance.

Analyze the Results

7 **Analyzing Data** In Table 2, write the type of change that you observed for each substance (physical or chemical). State the property that the change demonstrates.

Draw Conclusions

8 **Making Predictions** Suppose that you have a mixture of two substances. The mixture turns black when it is mixed with iodine and bubbles when it is mixed with water and vinegar. What two substances are in the mixture?

Big Idea Question

9 **Drawing Conclusions** How can you describe each of the four substances in terms of the chemical property of reactivity?

Table 1 Observations

Substance	Unmixed	Mixed with water	Mixed with vinegar	Mixed with iodine solution
Baking powder				
Baking soda				
Cornstarch				
Sugar				

Table 2 Changes and Properties

Substance	Mixed with water		Mixed with vinegar		Mixed with iodine solution	
	Change	Property	Change	Property	Change	Property
Baking powder						
Baking soda						
Cornstarch						
Sugar						

Science Skills Activity

Investigation and Experimentation
8.9.f Apply simple mathematical relationships to determine a missing quantity in a mathematic expression, given the two remaining terms (including speed = distance/time, density = mass/volume, force = pressure × area, volume = area × height).

Using a Three-Variable Equation

▶ Tutorial

Procedure

A three-variable equation can be rearranged and used to solve for any of the variables in the equation. The equation for density is an example of a three-variable equation.

1 The equation for density is arranged to calculate density.

$$D = \frac{m}{V}$$

2 To rearrange the equation to solve for mass, multiply both sides of the equation by volume.

$$m = D \times V$$

3 To rearrange the equation to solve for volume, divide both sides of the equation for mass by density.

$$V = \frac{m}{D}$$

Analysis

4 **Using Equations** To determine which form of the equation you should use to solve a problem, read the question carefully. The question will ask you to find one of the variables. Choose the form of the equation that is used to solve for that variable.

▶ You Try It!

Procedure

Use the equation for density to answer the following questions. Show all of your work, including the work that you do to rearrange the equation, if necessary.

Analysis

1 **Using Equations** If a 16.9 cm³ cube of ice has a mass of 15.5 g, what is the density of the ice?

2 **Using Equations** A piece of metal has a density of 11.3 g/cm³ and a volume of 6.7 cm³. What is the mass of this piece of metal?

3 **Using Equations** Tin has a density of 7.31 g/cm³. What is the volume of a piece of tin whose mass is 18.3 g?

4 **Using Equations** Suppose that the 12-sided object shown in the image at right has a mass of 5.4 g. What is the density of the object?

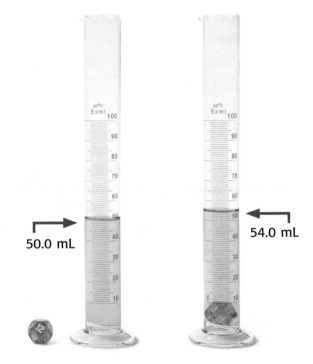

50.0 mL

54.0 mL

Chapter Summary

The Big Idea Matter is described by its properties and may undergo changes.

Section

Vocabulary

1 What Is Matter?

Key Concept Matter is anything that has mass and takes up space. Matter can be described in terms of its volume, mass, and weight.

- All matter has volume and mass.
- Volume is the amount of space taken up by an object.
- Mass is a measure of the amount of matter in an object.
- Weight is a measure of the gravitational force exerted on an object.

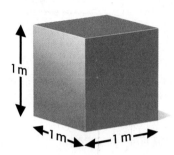

A box whose sides are 1 m long has a volume of 1 m³.

matter p. 78
volume p. 78
meniscus p. 79
mass p. 82
weight p. 82

2 Physical Properties

Key Concept Physical properties of matter can be observed or measured without changing the matter's identity.

- Examples of physical properties are melting temperature, density, hardness, thermal conductivity, and electrical conductivity.
- Density is the amount of matter in a given space or volume.
- A physical change does not change the identity of the matter that undergoes the change.
- Melting, freezing, cutting, bending, and dissolving are physical changes.

The physical property of density allows liquids to form layers.

physical property p. 84
density p. 85
physical change p. 88

3 Chemical Properties

Key Concept A chemical property describes the ability of a substance to change into a new substance.

- Examples of chemical properties are reactivity and flammability.
- A chemical change is the process by which a substance changes into a new substance.
- Chemical changes usually liberate or absorb heat.

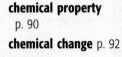

Rubbing alcohol is a clear liquid that has the chemical property of flammability.

chemical property p. 90
chemical change p. 92

Chapter Review

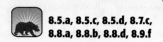

8.5.a, 8.5.c, 8.5.d, 8.7.c, 8.8.a, 8.8.b, 8.8.d, 8.9.f

Organize

Double Door Review the Fold-Note that you created at the beginning of the chapter. Add to or correct the FoldNote based on what you have learned.

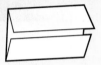

Using Vocabulary

1 Academic Vocabulary In the sentence, "Chemical changes usually liberate or absorb heat," what does the word *liberate* mean?

2 Use *physical property, chemical property, physical change,* and *chemical change* in separate sentences.

For each pair of terms, explain how the meanings of the terms differ.

3 *mass* and *weight*

4 *volume* and *density*

Understanding Concepts

Multiple Choice

5 Which of the following properties is a physical property?
a. reactivity with oxygen
b. malleability
c. flammability
d. reactivity with acid

6 Volume can be expressed in any of the following units EXCEPT
a. grams.
b. liters.
c. milliliters.
d. cubic centimeters.

7 What is the SI unit for mass?
a. gram
b. liter
c. milliliter
d. kilogram

8 The best way to measure the volume of an irregularly shaped solid is to use
a. a ruler to measure the length of each side of the object.
b. a balance.
c. the water displacement method.
d. a spring scale.

9 Which of the following statements about density is true?
a. Density is expressed in grams.
b. Density is mass per unit volume.
c. Density is expressed in milliliters.
d. Density is a chemical property.

Short Answer

10 Listing List two characteristic properties of matter.

11 Comparing Explain how the process of measuring a liquid's volume differs from the process of measuring a solid's volume.

INTERPRETING GRAPHICS Use the image below to answer the next two questions.

Corn oil

Water

Shampoo

Dish detergent

Antifreeze

Maple syrup

12 Analyzing How does the density of dish detergent compare with the density of water and maple syrup?

13 Applying How would the layers appear in a graduated cylinder that contained only shampoo, corn oil, and antifreeze?

INTERPRETING GRAPHICS Use the photograph below to answer the next four questions.

14 **Listing** List three physical properties of this aluminum can.

15 **Classifying** When this can was crushed, did it undergo a physical change or a chemical change?

16 **Analyzing** How does the density of the metal in the crushed can compare with the metal's density before the can was crushed?

17 **Concluding** Can you determine the can's chemical properties by looking at the picture? Explain your answer.

Writing Skills

18 **Technical Writing** Write a set of instructions that describe how to find the density of an object. Write the instructions so that they work for a regularly shaped object and for an irregularly shaped object. List the materials needed and the sequence of steps to follow.

Critical Thinking

19 **Concept Mapping** Use the following terms to create a concept map: *matter, mass, volume, milliliters,* and *cubic centimeters.*

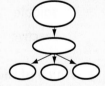

20 **Making Inferences** You mix two substances in a beaker and expect them to undergo a chemical change. The temperature of the mixture does not change. Has a chemical change occurred? Explain your answer.

INTERPRETING GRAPHICS Use the graph below to answer the next two questions.

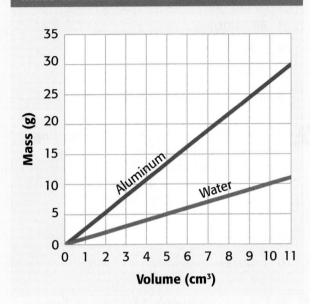

Mass Vs. Volume for Aluminum and Water

21 **Identifying Relationships** What do the slopes of each line represent?

22 **Applying Concepts** Which substance has the greater density?

Math Skills

23 **Using Equations** What is the volume of a book that has a width of 10 cm, a length that is 2 times the width, and a height that is half the width? Express your answer in cubic units.

24 **Using Equations** A jar contains 30 mL of glycerin (whose mass is 37.8 g) and 60 mL of corn syrup (whose mass is 82.8 g). Which liquid is on top? Explain your answer.

Challenge

25 **Analyzing Processes** You are making breakfast for your friend Filbert. When you take the scrambled eggs to the table, he asks, "Would you please poach these eggs instead?" Use the ideas of chemical change and physical change to give Filbert a scientific reason that you are unable to poach the eggs.

Standards Assessment

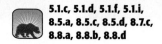

5.1.c, 5.1.d, 5.1.f, 5.1.i,
8.5.a, 8.5.c, 8.5.d, 8.7.c,
8.8.a, 8.8.b, 8.8.d

REVIEWING ACADEMIC VOCABULARY

1 **Which of the following words is the closest in meaning to "size"?**

A amount

B density

C volume

D mass

2 **In the sentence "The process of burning wood liberates heat," what does the word *liberates* mean?**

A steals

B releases

C creates

D imitates

3 **In the sentence "Ash is formed by the chemical reaction between wood and fire," what does the term *chemical reaction* mean?**

A a process that changes the molecular composition of a substance

B a process of igniting something, burning it, and recording the results

C a process that affects the appearance but not the molecular structure

D a process of using chemicals to break down molecular structures

4 **In the sentence "Density is a physical property," what does the term *physical* mean?**

A having to do with chemicals

B having to do with volume

C having to do with the body

D having to do with matter

REVIEWING CONCEPTS

5 **Which physical property of an object can be determined by dividing its mass by its volume?**

A weight

B density

C ductility

D state

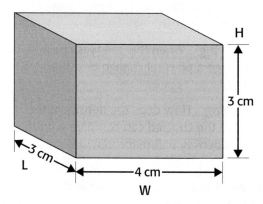

6 **What is the volume of the solid pictured above?**

A 12 cm²

B 12 cm³

C 36 cm²

D 36 cm³

7 **Which of the following is a chemical property that describes copper?**

A conductive

B ductile

C soluble

D reactive

8 **Which of the following describes signs that a chemical change is occurring?**

A A substance changes shape or state.

B A substance gives off or absorbs heat.

C A substance is dense and malleable.

D A substance is flammable and reactive.

Densities of Common Substances*

Substance	Density* (g/cm³)	Substance	Density* (g/cm³)
Helium (gas)	0.0001663	Zinc (solid)	7.13
Oxygen (gas)	0.001331	Silver (solid)	10.50
Water (liquid)	1.00	Lead (solid)	11.35
Pyrite (solid)	5.02	Mercury (liquid)	13.55

*at 20°C and 1.0 atm

9 A solid sample has a mass of 22.5 g and displaces 30 mL of water. Use the table above to determine which sentence best describes the solid sample.

A It is denser than mercury.

B It is less dense than water.

C It is less dense than helium.

D It is denser than zinc.

10 Substances can undergo physical changes or chemical changes. What is the difference between these two kinds of changes?

A A chemical change can often be undone, and a physical change cannot.

B A physical change cannot be observed easily, and a chemical change can.

C A chemical change affects only the physical properties of a substance. A physical change changes the molecular structure of a substance.

D A physical change does not affect the identity of a substance. A chemical change changes the molecular structure of a substance.

11 Which physical property can you use to determine if a substance will float in water?

A density

B volume

C malleability

D conductivity

REVIEWING PRIOR LEARNING

12 What properties do the metals aluminum, copper, silver, and gold have in common?

A They conduct heat and electricity well.

B They are brittle and do not bend easily.

C They do not chemically react.

D They are liquid at room temperature.

13 A student pours a material through a filter. Some particles get caught in the filter and some pass through. This material can be best described as a

A nonmetal.

B mixture.

C metal.

D compound.

14 Which of the following sentences best describes table salt, NaCl?

A Table salt is a compound made from two gases.

B Table salt is a compound made from a solid and a liquid.

C Table salt is a compound made from two metals.

D Table salt is a compound made from a metal and a nonmetal.

15 An element is made up of

A two kinds of atoms.

B one kind of molecule.

C one kind of atom.

D two kinds of molecules.

Science in Action

Scientific Debate

Paper or Plastic?

What should you choose at the grocery store: paper bags or plastic bags? Plastic bags are waterproof and take up less space. They can be used to line waste cans and to pack lunches and can be recycled. But making 1 ton of plastic bags uses 11 barrels of oil, which can't be replaced, and produces polluting chemicals. On the other hand, making 1 ton of paper bags destroys 13 to 17 trees, which take years to replace. Paper bags can be used for lining waste cans and wrapping packages. Recycling paper pollutes less than recycling plastic does. What is the answer? Maybe we should reuse both!

Language Arts ACTiViTY

There are advantages and disadvantages of each kind of bag. In your **Science Journal**, write a one-page essay defending your position on this subject. Support your opinion with facts.

Science, Technology, and Society

Reading a Hidden Text

It seemed like an ordinary old book. But the parchment pages in the book had once contained a copy of some writings of Archimedes, a mathematician in ancient Greece. Sadly, these remarkable mathematical writings had been erased and written over.

Scientists at the Stanford Linear Acceleration Center (SLAC) in Menlo Park, California, used special equipment to help them read the erased writings. The ink used in the writings contained iron. A physical property of iron is that iron glows when struck with X rays. So, the SLAC scientists carefully scanned the parchment with X rays and made images of the writings from the glowing ink.

Social Studies ACTiViTY

Do some research on Archimedes. Who was he, and what were his most important discoveries? Create a poster that summarizes the information that you find.

Mimi So

Gemologist and Jewelry Designer   For gemologist and jewelry designer Mimi So, a typical day includes deciding which materials she will work with. When she chooses a gemstone for a piece of jewelry, she must consider the size, hardness, color, grade, and cut of the stone. When choosing a metal to use as a setting for a stone, she must look at the hardness, melting point, color, and malleability of the metal. She needs to choose a metal that not only looks good with a particular stone but also has physical properties that will work with that stone. For example, So says that emeralds are soft and fragile. A platinum setting would be too hard and could damage the emerald. Therefore, emeralds are usually set in a softer metal, such as 18-karat gold.

The chemical properties of stones must also be considered. Heating can burn or discolor some gemstones. So says that because a pearl is not a stone, you cannot use pearls in a design that requires you to heat the metal in the design. Heating would destroy the pearl.

Math Activity

Gold that is 24-karat (24K) gold is pure gold. Gold that is 18 parts gold plus 6 parts other metals is 18-karat (18K) gold. To find the percentage of gold in 18K gold, divide the number of parts gold (18) by the total number of parts metal (24) and multiply by 100%. So, 18/24 = 0.75, and 0.75 × 100% = 75%. Thus, 18K gold is 75% gold. Find the percentage of gold in 10K gold and 14K gold.

Internet Resources

- To learn more about careers in science, visit www.scilinks.org and enter the SciLinks code HY70225.

- To learn more about these Science in Action topics, visit go.hrw.com and type in the keyword HY7MATF.

- Check out articles related to this chapter by visiting go.hrw.com. Just type in the keyword HY7MATC.

Improving Comprehension

Graphic Organizers are important visual tools that can help you organize information and improve your reading comprehension. The Graphic Organizer below is called a *comparison table*. Instructions for creating other types of Graphic Organizers are located in the **Study Skills** section of the Appendix.

How to Make a Comparison Table

1 Draw a table like the one shown below. Draw as many columns and rows as you want to draw.

2 In the top row, write the topics that you want to compare.

3 In the left column, write the general characteristics that you want to compare. As you read the chapter, fill in the characteristics for each topic in the appropriate boxes.

When to Use a Comparison Table

A comparison table is useful when you want to compare the characteristics of two or more topics in science. Organizing information in a table helps you compare several topics at one time. In a table, all topics are described in terms of the same list of characteristics, which helps you make a thorough comparison. As you read, look for topics whose characteristics you may want to compare in a table.

	Solid	Liquid	Gas	Plasma
Definite volume	yes	yes	no	no
Definite shape	yes	no	no	no
Possible changes of state	melting, sublimation	freezing, evaporation	condensation	

You Try It!

This Reading Strategy can also be used within the chapter that you are about to read. Practice making your own *comparison table* as directed in the Reading Strategies for Section **1** and Section **2**. Record your work in your **Science Journal.**

Unpacking the Standards

The information below "unpacks" the standards by breaking them down into basic parts. The higher-level, academic vocabulary is highlighted and defined to help you understand the language of the standards. "What It Means" restates the standards as simply as possible.

California Standard	Academic Vocabulary	What It Means
8.3.d Students know the states of matter (solid, liquid, gas) depend on molecular motion.		The motion of atoms or molecules that make up a substance determines whether the substance is a solid, a liquid, or a gas.
8.3.e Students know that in solids the atoms are closely locked in position and can only vibrate; in liquids the atoms and molecules are more loosely connected and can collide with and move past one another; and in gases the atoms and molecules are free to move independently, colliding frequently.		In solids, the atoms are held in position and can only vibrate. In liquids, the atoms and molecules are more loosely held together and can bump into and move past one another. In gases, the atoms and molecules are free to move around and bump into each other frequently.
8.5.d Students know **physical processes** include freezing and boiling, in which a material changes form with no **chemical reaction.**	**physical** (FIZ i kuhl) of or having to do with matter or the body **process** (PRAH ses) a set of steps, events, or changes **chemical** (KEM i kuhl) of or having to do with the properties or actions of substances **reaction** (ree AK shuhn) a response or change	Changes of matter that do not change the composition of the matter include the changes from a liquid to a solid and from a liquid to a gas.
8.7.c Students know substances can be classified by their properties, including their melting temperature, density, hardness, and thermal and electrical conductivity.		Different kinds of matter can be grouped by their characteristics, including the temperature at which they melt, the amount of mass per unit volume, their hardness, and their ability to transfer thermal energy or electrical energy.

4

States of Matter

The Big Idea

Matter exists in various physical states, which are determined by the movement of that matter's particles.

California Standards

Focus on Physical Sciences
8.3 Each of the more than 100 elements of matter has distinct properties and a distinct atomic structure. All forms of matter are composed of one or more of the elements. (Sections 1 and 2)
8.5 Chemical reactions are processes in which atoms are rearranged into different combinations of molecules. (Section 2)
8.7 The organization of the periodic table is based on the properties of the elements and reflects the structure of atoms. (Section 2)

Investigation and Experimentation
8.9 Scientific progress is made by asking meaningful questions and conducting careful investigations. (Science Skills Activity)

Math
6.1.4 Statistics, Data Analysis, and Probability
7.1.2 Number Sense

English–Language Arts
8.2.2 Reading
8.2.1 Writing

About the Photo

This beautiful glass creation by artist Dale Chihuly is entitled *Mille Fiori* (A Thousand Flowers). The pieces that form the sculpture were not always solid. Each individual piece started as a blob of melted glass on the end of a hollow pipe. The artist quickly formed each shape before the molten glass cooled and became a solid again.

Organize

Table Fold

Before you read the chapter, create the FoldNote entitled "Table Fold." Label the columns of the table fold with "Shape" and "Volume." Label the rows with "Solid," "Liquid," and "Gas." As you read the chapter, write what can happen to the shape and volume of each state of matter.

Instructions for creating FoldNotes are located in the Study Skills section on p. 520 of the Appendix.

Explore Activity

⏱ 10 min

A Change of State

In this activity, you will use rubbing alcohol (isopropyl alcohol) to investigate a change of state.

Procedure

1. Pour **rubbing alcohol** into a **small plastic cup** until the alcohol just covers the bottom of the cup.

2. Moisten the tip of a **cotton swab** by dipping it into the alcohol in the cup.

3. Rub the cotton swab on the palm of your hand. Make sure that there are no cuts or abrasions on your hand.

4. Record your observations.

5. Wash your hands thoroughly.

Analysis

8.3.d
8.3.e

6. Explain what happened to the alcohol after you rubbed the swab on your hand.

7. Did you feel a sensation of hot or cold? If so, how do you explain what you observed?

8. Describe the change in the alcohol based on what happened to its particles.

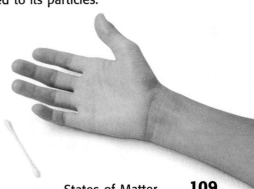

Four States of Matter

Key Concept   Each state of matter has a characteristic way in which its particles interact.

What You Will Learn
- All matter is made of particles that are in constant motion.
- Each state of matter depends on the motion of its particles.
- In solids, particles can only vibrate; in liquids, particles can collide with and move past one another; in gases, particles are free to move independently, colliding frequently.
- In plasmas, particles move independently and are broken apart.

Why It Matters
Understanding the states of matter will help you understand natural processes in the world around you.

Vocabulary
- states of matter
- solid
- liquid
- gas
- plasma

READING STRATEGY

Graphic Organizer   In your **Science Journal,** make a Comparison Table that compares the motion of particles in each state of matter.

You get home from school and decide to make yourself a snack. There are some leftovers in the refrigerator from your dinner last night. So, you heat some up in the microwave oven. As the food heats up, you begin to smell the food. You're also thirsty, so you put some ice in a glass—*clink!*—and fill the glass with water. You take a big gulp—*ahhh!*

Matter: Moving Particles

The scene described above has examples of the three most familiar states of matter. Those states of matter are solid, liquid, and gas. The **states of matter** are the physical forms of a substance. The states of matter depend on the motion of particles.

Matter is made up of very tiny particles called *atoms* and *molecules* (MAHL i KYOOLZ). Atoms and molecules are in constant motion and are always bumping into each other. The motion of particles is different for each state of matter. The way that the particles interact with each other also helps determine the state of the matter. **Figure 1** describes three states of matter—solid, liquid, and gas—in terms of the motion and attraction of the particles.

Standards Check   In terms of particles, how does each state of matter differ from the others? **8.3.d**

8.3.d Students know the states of matter (solid, liquid, gas) depend on molecular motion.
8.3.e Students know that in solids the atoms are closely locked in position and can only vibrate; in liquids the atoms and molecules are more loosely connected and can collide with and move past one another; and in gases the atoms and molecules are free to move independently, colliding frequently.

Figure 1   **Models of a Solid, a Liquid, and a Gas**

Particles of a solid have a strong attraction between them. The particles are closely locked in position and can only vibrate.

Particles of a liquid are more loosely connected than those of a solid and can collide with and move past one another.

Particles of a gas move fast enough so that they overcome the attractions between them. The particles move independently and collide frequently.

Solids

Imagine dropping a marble into a bottle. Would anything happen to the shape or size of the marble? Would the shape or size of the marble change if you put it in a larger bottle?

A marble keeps its original shape and volume no matter where it is placed because it is a solid. A **solid** is the state of matter that has a definite shape and volume.

The particles of a substance in a solid state are very close together. They have a strong attraction between them. The particles in a solid move, but they do not move fast enough to overcome the attraction between them. Therefore, each particle is closely locked in position and can only vibrate in place.

Liquids

What do you think would change about orange juice if you poured the juice from a can into a glass? Would the volume of juice be different? Would the taste of the juice change?

The only thing that would change when the juice is poured into the glass is the shape of the juice. The shape changes because juice is a liquid. **Liquid** is the state of matter that has a definite volume but takes the shape of its container. The particles in liquids move fast enough to overcome some of the attractions between them. The particles collide with and slide past each other. But the particles remain close together.

Because the juice is a liquid, its volume stays the same whether you pour the juice into a large container or into a small one. **Figure 2** shows the same volume of liquid in two different containers.

Standards Check What are a liquid's particles able to do that a solid's particles cannot? 🐻 **8.3.e**

states of matter (STAYTS uhv MAT uhr) the physical forms of matter, which include solid, liquid, and gas

solid (SAHL id) the state of matter in which the volume and shape of a substance are fixed

liquid (LIK wid) the state of matter that has a definite volume but not a definite shape

Volume and Density

A substance's density is the mass per unit volume for the substance. So, the formula for calculating density is $D = m/V$.

1. The mass of 300 mL of water is 300 g. What is the density of water?
2. The density of isopropyl alcohol is 0.79 g/mL. Calculate the mass of 85 mL of isopropyl alcohol.

Figure 2 *Although their shapes are different, the beaker and the graduated cylinder each contain 345 mL of juice.*

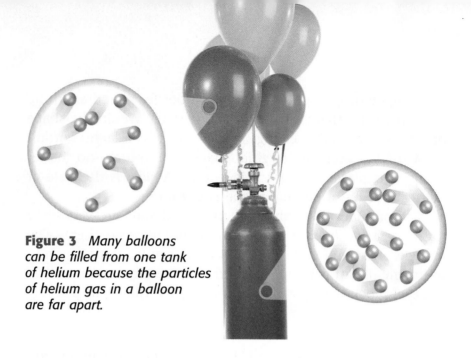

Figure 3 *Many balloons can be filled from one tank of helium because the particles of helium gas in a balloon are far apart.*

Gases

Would you believe that one tank of helium can fill several hundred balloons? How is this possible? After all, the tank is only as big as about five filled balloons.

Helium is a gas. **Gas** is a state of matter that has no definite volume or shape. The particles of a gas have little attraction between them. The particles move about freely and collide randomly with each other.

Because gas particles move about freely, the amount of empty space between them can change. Look at **Figure 3.** The particles of helium in the balloons are farther apart than the particles of helium in the tank. As helium particles fill the balloon, they spread apart. The greater amount of empty space between the particles makes the volume of the gas larger.

gas (GAS) a form of matter that does not have a definite volume or shape

plasma (PLAZ muh) in physical science, a state of matter that starts as a gas and then becomes ionized; it consists of free-moving ions and electrons, it takes on an electric charge, and its properties differ from the properties of a solid, liquid, or gas

Standards Check Describe the motion of particles of a gas. 🐻 8.3.e

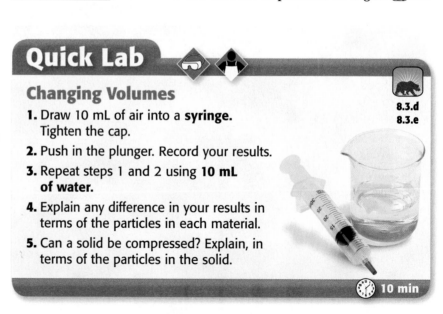

Quick Lab

Changing Volumes

8.3.d
8.3.e

1. Draw 10 mL of air into a **syringe.** Tighten the cap.

2. Push in the plunger. Record your results.

3. Repeat steps 1 and 2 using **10 mL of water.**

4. Explain any difference in your results in terms of the particles in each material.

5. Can a solid be compressed? Explain, in terms of the particles in the solid.

⏱ 10 min

Plasmas

The sun and other stars are made of the most common state of matter in the universe, called plasma. **Plasma** is the state of matter that does not have a definite shape or volume and whose particles have broken apart. More than 99% of the matter in the universe is plasma.

Plasmas have some properties that are quite different from the properties of gases. Plasmas conduct electric current, but gases do not. Electric and magnetic fields affect plasmas but do not affect gases. In fact, strong magnetic fields are sometimes used to contain very hot plasmas that would destroy a solid container.

Here on Earth, natural plasmas are found in lightning and fire. Plasma sometimes forms during storms on Earth by the electrical energy in lightning, as shown in **Figure 4.** Artificial plasmas, found in fluorescent lights and plasma balls, are created by passing electric charges through gases.

Figure 4 *One place that plasma forms is in the electric discharge of a lightning bolt. A lightning bolt is made of plasma.*

SECTION Review

 8.3.d, 8.3.e

Summary

- Particles of matter are in constant motion. The states of matter depend on the motion of particles.

- A solid has a definite shape and volume. A liquid has a definite volume but not a definite shape.

- A gas does not have a definite volume or shape. Plasma, a fourth state of matter, does not have a definite shape or volume, and its particles are broken apart.

Using Vocabulary

1. Write an original definition for *gas* and *plasma*.

Understanding Concepts

2. **Describing** Describe the difference in particle motion between solids, liquids, and gases.

INTERPRETING GRAPHICS Use the image below to answer the next two questions.

3. **Identifying** Identify the state of matter shown in the jar.

4. **Concluding** Can the individual particles inside the jar move? If so, describe how they move.

Critical Thinking

5. **Analyzing Processes** The volume of a gas can change, but the volume of a solid cannot. Explain in terms of particles why this is true.

Challenge

6. **Evaluating Hypotheses** Tommy is planning an experiment to explore particle motion for two different substances. He hypothesizes that particle motion will be the same for each substance under the same conditions. What important factor has he not taken into account?

Internet Resources

For a variety of links related to this chapter, go to www.scilinks.org
Topic: Solids, Liquids, and Gases
SciLinks code: HY71420

Changes of State

Key Concept A change of state, which is a physical change, occurs when matter changes from one physical state to another.

What You Will Learn

● A change of state is a physical process in which a material changes form with no chemical reaction.

● Changes of state include melting, freezing, evaporation, condensation, and sublimation and involve either gain or loss of energy by a material's particles.

● Every material has a characteristic melting point and freezing point.

Why It Matters

Learning about changes of state will help you understand changes you see every day, such as cooking and the weather.

Vocabulary

• change of state
• melting
• evaporation
• boiling
• condensation
• sublimation

READING STRATEGY

Graphic Organizer In your **Science Journal,** make a Comparison Table that compares various characteristics of state changes.

It can be tricky to eat a frozen juice bar outside on a hot day. In just minutes, the juice bar will start to melt. Soon, the solid juice bar becomes a liquid mess. As the juice bar melts, it goes through a change of state. In this section, you will learn about the four changes of state shown in **Figure 1** as well as a fifth change of state called *sublimation* (SUHB luh MAY shuhn).

Energy and Changes of State

A **change of state** is the change of a substance from one physical form to another. All changes of state are physical changes rather than chemical changes. In a physical change, the identity of a substance does not change. In **Figure 1,** the ice, liquid water, and steam are all the same substance—water.

The particles of a substance move differently depending on the state of the substance. The particles also have different amounts of energy when the substance is in different states. For example, particles in liquid water have more energy than particles in ice. To change a substance from one state to another, you must add or remove energy.

Standards Check In terms of energy, what must happen to the particles of a substance for it to change state? **8.3.e**

8.3.d Students know the states of matter (solid, liquid, gas) depend on molecular motion.

8.3.e Students know that in solids the atoms are closely locked in place and can only vibrate; in liquids the atoms and molecules are more loosely connected and can collide with and move past one another; and in gases the atoms and molecules are free to move independently, colliding frequently.

8.5.d Students know physical processes include freezing and boiling, in which a material changes form with no chemical reaction.

8.7.c Students know substances can be classified by their properties, including their melting temperature, density, hardness, and thermal and electrical conductivity.

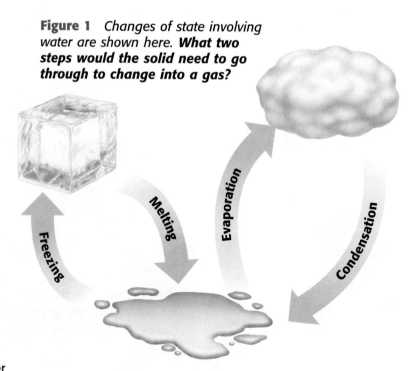

Figure 1 *Changes of state involving water are shown here.* **What two steps would the solid need to go through to change into a gas?**

Melting: Solid to Liquid

One change of state that happens when you add energy to a substance is melting. **Melting** is the change of state from a solid to a liquid. This change of state is what happens when ice melts.

Melting Point

As the temperature of a solid increases, the particles of the solid move faster. When a certain temperature is reached, the solid will melt. The temperature at which a substance changes from a solid to a liquid is the *melting point,* or melting temperature, of the substance. Melting point is a physical property that is characteristic of the material. For example, gallium melts at about 30°C. Because your normal body temperature is about 37°C, gallium will melt in your hand! This is shown in **Figure 2.** Table salt, however, has a melting point of 801°C, so it will not melt in your hand. Melting points and other physical properties reflect the chemical composition of the material and can be used to classify substances.

Standards Check What is melting point, and what does it reflect about a substance? 🐾 **8.7.c**

Adding Energy

For a solid to melt, particles must absorb energy to overcome some of their attractions to each other. The particles acquire enough energy to slide past one another so that the material, which has melted and become a liquid, can flow.

Freezing: Liquid to Solid

The change of state from a liquid to a solid is called *freezing.* For a liquid to freeze, the attractions between a liquid's particles must overcome the motion of the particles. Then, the particles will become closely locked in position.

Removing Energy

The temperature at which a liquid changes into a solid is the liquid's *freezing point.* Freezing is the reverse process of melting. Thus, freezing and melting happen at the same temperature, as shown in **Figure 3.**

Figure 2 *Gallium is a metal that can melt in your hand. Even though gallium is a metal, it would not be very useful as jewelry!*

change of state (CHAYNJ UHV STAYT) the change of a substance from one physical state to another

melting (MEHLT ing) the change of state in which a solid becomes a liquid by adding heat

Figure 3 *Liquid water freezes at the same temperature at which ice melts: 0°C.*

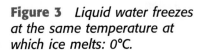
If energy is added at 0°C, the ice will melt.

If energy is removed at 0°C, the liquid water will freeze.

Figure 4 Boiling and Evaporation

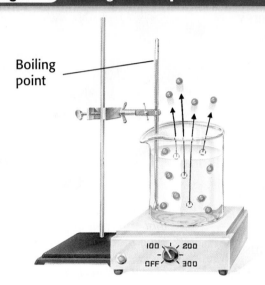

Boiling
point

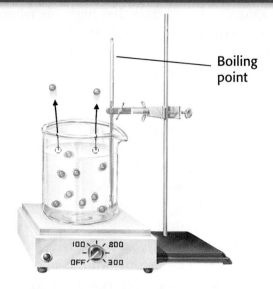

Boiling
point

Boiling happens in a liquid at its boiling point. As energy is added to the liquid, particles throughout the liquid move faster. When they move fast enough to break away from other particles, they evaporate and become a gas.

Evaporation can happen in a liquid below its boiling point. Some particles at the surface of the liquid move fast enough to break away from the particles around them and become a gas.

Evaporation: Liquid to Gas

One way to make evaporation happen is to iron a shirt by using a steam iron. Steam comes up from the iron as the wrinkles disappear. This steam forms when the liquid water in the iron becomes hot and changes to gas.

Evaporation and Boiling

evaporation (ee VAP uh RAY shuhn) the change of state from a liquid to a gas

Wordwise The prefix e- means "out" or "from."
The root *vapor* means "gaseous form of any substance that is usually a liquid or solid."

boiling (BOYL ing) the conversion of a liquid to a vapor when the vapor pressure of the liquid equals the atmospheric pressure

Evaporation is the change of state from a liquid to a gas. Evaporation can happen at the surface of a liquid. For example, when you sweat, your body is cooled through evaporation. Your sweat is mostly water. Water absorbs energy from your skin as the water evaporates. You feel cooler because your body transfers energy to the water.

Figure 4 explains the difference between boiling and evaporation. **Boiling** is the change of a liquid to a vapor, or gas, throughout the liquid. The temperature at which this change happens is the boiling point of the liquid. When liquid water is heated to temperatures of 100°C, molecular motion increases until large groups of water molecules overcome the attractive forces between them. Bubbles of water vapor escape from the liquid water as the water boils.

Standards Check What happens to the particles of a liquid as the liquid boils? 8.3.d

Effects of Pressure on Boiling Point

Earlier, you learned that water boils at 100°C. In fact, this is true only at sea level. The reason is that atmospheric pressure varies depending on where you are in relation to sea level. Atmospheric pressure is caused by the weight of the gases that make up the atmosphere.

Atmospheric pressure is lower at higher elevations. The higher you go above sea level, the fewer air particles there are above you. So, the atmospheric pressure is lower. Think about boiling water at the top of a mountain. The boiling point would be lower than 100°C, because water boils more easily if the atmospheric pressure is lower. For example, Denver, Colorado, is 1.6 km above sea level. In Denver, water boils at about 95°C.

Condensation: Gas to Liquid

Look at the spider web in **Figure 5.** Notice the beads of water that have formed on it. They form because of condensation of gaseous water in the air. **Condensation** is the change of state from a gas to a liquid. Condensation and evaporation are the reverse of each other. The *condensation point* of a substance is the temperature at which the gas becomes a liquid. The condensation point is the same temperature as the boiling point at a given pressure.

For a gas to become a liquid, large numbers of particles must clump together. Particles clump together when the attraction between them overcomes their motion keeping them apart. For this to happen, energy must be removed from the gas to slow the movement of the particles.

INTERNET ACTIVITY

Physical Scientist Biographies

What are some of the greatest advances in physical science, and who made them? Write a biography about a physical scientist. Go to **go.hrw.com,** and type in the keyword HY7STAW.

condensation (KAHN duhn SAY shuhn) the change of state from a gas to a liquid

Figure 5 *Beads of water form when water vapor in the air contacts a cool surface, such as this spider web.*

Changes of State **117**

Sublimation: Solid to Gas

The solid in **Figure 6** is dry ice. Dry ice is carbon dioxide in a solid state. It is called *dry ice* because it goes through sublimation instead of melting into a liquid. **Sublimation** is the change of state in which a solid changes directly to a gas.

For a solid to change directly to a gas, the particles of the substance must go from being very tightly packed to being spread far apart. So, the attractions between the particles must be completely overcome. The substance must gain energy for the particles to overcome their attractions.

Standards Check What do the particles of a solid do when the solid sublimes? 8.5.d

Temperature and Changes of State

When most substances lose or gain energy, one of two things happens to the substance: its temperature changes or its state changes. When temperature changes, the speed of the particles also changes. But when a substance is undergoing a change of state, its temperature does not change until the change of state is complete. For example, continued heating of a liquid at its boiling point will change the liquid entirely into vapor instead of raising its temperature. Only after all of the liquid is turned into gas will the temperature rise. **Figure 7** on the next page shows the effects of adding energy to ice.

Figure 6 *Dry ice is a substance that will change directly from a solid to a gas at atmospheric pressure.*

sublimation (SUHB luh MAY shuhn) the process in which a solid changes directly into a gas

---

Quick Lab

Boiling Water Without Heating It

You have seen water boil when it is heated. However, air pressure above the water plays a role, too. In this activity, you will explore the connection between pressure and boiling point.

8.5.d
8.7.c

▶ Try It!

1. Remove the **cap** from a **syringe**.
2. Place the tip of the syringe in the **warm water** that is provided by your teacher. Pull the plunger out until you have 10 mL of water in the syringe.
3. Place the cap tightly on the syringe. Hold the syringe, and slowly pull the plunger out.
4. Record any changes you see in the water.

▶ Think About It!

5. If the temperature stays the same, what must happen to the atmospheric pressure in order to cause the liquid to boil?
6. What happened to the air inside the syringe above the water as you pulled the plunger out of the syringe?
7. How did this cause the water to boil?
8. When you normally see water boil, what is different about the conditions under which that happens, compared with what you just saw?

🕐 15 min

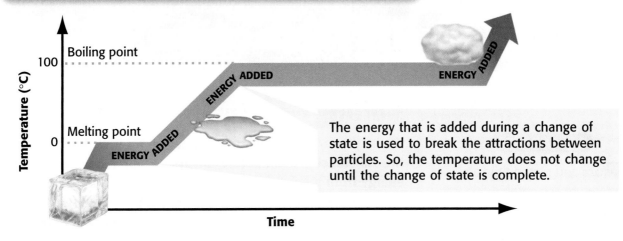

Figure 7 Changing the State of Water

Boiling point

100

Melting point

0

Temperature (°C)

ENERGY ADDED

ENERGY ADDED

ENERGY ADDED

ENERGY ADDED

Time

The energy that is added during a change of state is used to break the attractions between particles. So, the temperature does not change until the change of state is complete.

SECTION Review

8.3.d, 8.3.e,
8.5.d, 8.7.c

Summary

- A change of state is the conversion of a substance from one physical form to another.

- A change of state requires a loss or gain of energy by a substance's particles.

- Melting is the change from a solid to a liquid, and freezing is the change from a liquid to a solid.

- Both boiling and evaporation result in a liquid changing to a gas.

- Condensation is the change of a gas to a liquid. It is the reverse of evaporation.

- Sublimation changes a solid directly to a gas.

- The temperature of a substance does not change during a change of state.

Using Vocabulary

For each pair of terms, explain how the meanings of the terms differ.

1 *boiling* and *melting*

2 *condensation* and *evaporation*

Understanding Concepts

3 **Describing** Describe how the motion and arrangement of particles in a substance change as the substance freezes.

4 **Comparing** How are boiling and evaporating similar? How are they different?

Critical Thinking

5 **Making Inferences** Imagine that bubbles begin to form in a sample of liquid, but the temperature did not change. What must have happened to cause this change?

6 **Analyzing Ideas** When a solid melts, its density does not change very much. So, why do a liquid and a solid have such different physical properties?

INTERPRETING GRAPHICS

Use the two pictures below to answer the next question.

7 **Analyzing Processes** Describe two ways by which the particles in the picture on the left could end up like the particles in the picture on the right.

Math Skills

8 **Making Calculations** If the volume of a substance in the gaseous state is 1,000 times the volume of that substance in the liquid state, how much space would 18 mL of that substance in the liquid state take up if it evaporated?

Internet Resources

For a variety of links related to this chapter, go to www.scilinks.org

Topic: Changes of State
SciLinks code: HY70254

Skills Practice Lab

Boiling and Temperature

When you add energy to a substance through heating, does the substance's temperature always go up? When you remove energy from a substance through cooling, does the substance's temperature always go down? In this lab, you'll investigate these important questions with a very common substance—water.

8.5.d Students know physical processes include freezing and boiling, in which a material changes form with no chemical reaction.
8.7.c Students know substances can be classified by their properties, including their melting temperature, density, hardness, and thermal and electrical conductivity.

Investigation and Experimentation
8.9.d Recognize the slope of the linear graph as the constant in the relationship $y = kx$ and apply this principle in interpreting graphs constructed from data.
8.9.e Construct appropriate graphs from data and develop quantitative statements about the relationships between variables.

OBJECTIVES

Measure and record time and temperature accurately.

Graph the temperature change of water as it changes state.

Analyze and interpret graphs of changes of state.

MATERIALS

- beaker, 250 mL or 400 mL
- coffee can, large
- gloves, heat-resistant
- graduated cylinder, 100 mL
- graph paper
- hot plate
- ice, crushed
- rock salt
- wire-loop stirring device
- stopwatch
- thermometer
- water

SAFETY

Procedure

1 Fill the beaker about one-third to one-half full with water.

2 Put on heat-resistant gloves. Turn on the hot plate, and put the beaker on it. Put the thermometer in the beaker. **Caution:** Be careful not to touch the hot plate.

3 Make a copy of the data table below. Record the temperature of the water every 30 s. Continue doing this until about one-fourth of the water boils away. Note the first temperature reading at which the water is steadily boiling.

Data Table								
Time (s)	30	60	90	120	150	180	210	etc.
Temperature (°C)			DO NOT WRITE IN BOOK					

4 Turn off the hot plate.

5 While the beaker is cooling, make a graph of temperature (y-axis) versus time (x-axis). Draw an arrow pointing to the first temperature at which the water was steadily boiling.

6 After you finish the graph, use heat-resistant gloves to pick up the beaker. Pour the warm water out, and rinse the warm beaker with cool water. **Caution:** Even after cooling, the beaker is still too warm to handle without gloves.

7 Put approximately 20 mL of water in the graduated cylinder.

8 Put the graduated cylinder in the coffee can, and fill in around the graduated cylinder with crushed ice. Pour rock salt on the ice around the graduated cylinder. Place the thermometer and the wire-loop stirring device in the graduated cylinder.

9. As the ice melts and mixes with the rock salt, the level of ice will decrease. Add ice and rock salt to the can as needed.

10. Make another copy of the data table. Record the temperature of the water in the graduated cylinder every 30 s. Stir the water with the stirring device. **Caution:** Do not stir with the thermometer.

11. Once the water begins to freeze, stop stirring. **Caution:** Do not try to pull the thermometer out of the solid ice in the cylinder.

12. Note the temperature when you first notice ice crystals forming in the water. Continue taking readings until the water in the graduated cylinder is completely frozen.

13. Make a graph of temperature (*y*-axis) versus time (*x*-axis). Draw an arrow to the temperature reading at which the first ice crystals form.

Analyze the Results

14. **Describing Events** What happens to the temperature of boiling water when you continue to add energy through heating?

15. **Describing Events** What happens to the temperature of freezing water when you continue to remove energy through cooling?

16. **Analyzing Data** What does the slope of each graph represent?

17. **Analyzing Results** How does the slope of the graph that shows water boiling compare with the slope of the graph before the water starts to boil? Why is the slope different for the two periods?

18. **Analyzing Results** How does the slope of the graph showing water freezing compare with the slope of the graph before the water starts to freeze? Why is the slope different for the two periods?

Draw Conclusions

19. **Drawing Conclusions** Using your answers to the previous two questions, make a general statement that describes what happens to temperature during a change of state.

Big Idea Question

20. **Applying Concepts** The particles that make up solids, liquids, and gases are in constant motion. Adding or removing energy causes changes in the movement of these particles. Using this idea, describe in terms of the motion of the water molecules what is happening at each time represented in your two graphs.

Science Skills Activity

Investigation and Experimentation
8.9.g Distinguish between linear and nonlinear relationships on a graph of data.

Linear and Nonlinear Relationships

▶ Tutorial

1 The graph below represents an example of a linear relationship. You can tell that the relationship is linear because when you graph the two factors, they will form a straight line.

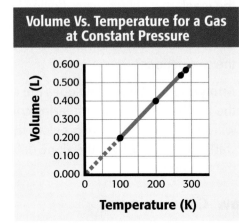

2 You can also tell that a relationship is linear by analyzing the data set that represents the relationship. For a relationship that is linear, as in the above graph, choose any two pairs of data. Then, divide each pair the same way, and you will get the same number, as shown below.

$$\frac{0.200 \text{ L}}{100 \text{ K}} = 0.002 \text{ L/K} \qquad \frac{0.400 \text{ L}}{200 \text{ K}} = 0.002 \text{ L/K}$$

3 A linear relationship is one that involves a constant rate of change. This was shown in the previous step because the two data pairs have the same ratio.

4 The graph below represents an example of a nonlinear relationship. A nonlinear relationship is one in which the rate of change over time between the two factors is not constant.

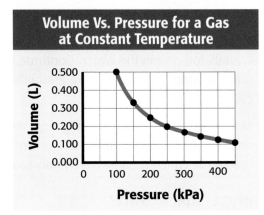

5 You can tell that a relationship between two factors is nonlinear by looking at its graph: it does not form a straight line. You can also tell that a relationship is nonlinear by doing the test described in item 2 at left: two pairs of data will not have the same ratio.

▶ You Try It!

1 **Identifying Relationships** Analyze the data in the table at right as was demonstrated in item 2 above. Is the relationship linear or nonlinear?

2 **Evaluating Conclusions** Make a graph of the data from the table at right. Did your graph confirm your initial conclusions? Explain.

3 **Analyzing Relationships** What does your analysis tell you about how the pressure and temperature of a gas vary together?

Pressure Vs. Temperature for a Gas at Constant Volume	
Pressure (atm)	**Temperature (K)**
1.0	100
2.0	200
3.5	350
4.0	400
5.0	500

Chapter Summary

The Big Idea Matter exists in various physical states, which are determined by the movement of that matter's particles.

Section

Vocabulary

1 Four States of Matter

Key Concept Each state of matter has a characteristic way in which its particles interact.

- All matter is made of particles that are in constant motion.

- Each state of matter depends on the motion of its particles.

- In solids, particles can only vibrate; in liquids, particles can collide with and move past one another; in gases, particles are free to move independently, colliding frequently.

- In plasmas, particles move independently and are broken apart.

The three familiar states of matter are solid, liquid, and gas.

states of matter p. 110
solid p. 111
liquid p. 111
gas p. 112
plasma p. 113

2 Changes of State

Key Concept A change of state, which is a physical change, occurs when matter changes from one physical state to another.

- A change of state is a physical process in which a material changes form with no chemical reaction.

- Changes of state include melting, freezing, evaporation, condensation, and sublimation and involve either gain or loss of energy by a material's particles.

- Every material has a characteristic melting point and freezing point.

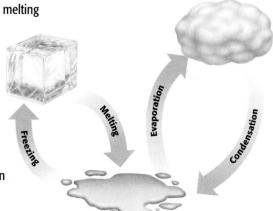

Matter can undergo physical changes between its physical states.

change of state p. 114
melting p. 115
evaporation p. 116
boiling p. 116
condensation p. 117
sublimation p. 118

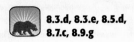

8.3.d, 8.3.e, 8.5.d,
8.7.c, 8.9.g

Organize

Table Fold Review the FoldNote that you created at the beginning of the chapter. Add to or correct the Fold-Note based on what you have learned.

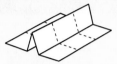

Using Vocabulary

1 **Academic Vocabulary** Which of the following words means "a set of steps or events"?
  a. reaction
  b. process
  c. principle
  d. role

For each pair of terms, explain how the meanings of the terms differ.

2 *solid* and *liquid*

3 *evaporation* and *boiling*

4 *condensation* and *sublimation*

Understanding Concepts

Multiple Choice

5 Which of the following statements best describes the particles of a liquid?
  a. The particles are far apart and moving fast.
  b. The particles are close together but moving past each other.
  c. The particles are far apart and moving slowly.
  d. The particles are closely packed and vibrating in place.

6 Dew collecting on a spider web in the early morning is an example of
  a. condensation.
  b. evaporation.
  c. sublimation.
  d. melting.

7 During which change of state do atoms or molecules become more ordered?
  a. boiling   **c.** melting
  b. condensation   **d.** sublimation

8 As the particles of a solid undergo sublimation, they
  a. lose energy.
  b. move closer to one another.
  c. change temperature.
  d. move farther apart from one another.

Short Answer

9 **Listing** Rank solids, liquids, and gases in order of particle speed from the highest speed to the lowest speed.

10 **Classifying** At atmospheric pressure, what is the characteristic boiling point of water, in degrees Celsius?

11 **Analyzing** Explain why liquid water takes the shape of its container but an ice cube does not.

12 **Concluding** Water's states of matter include steam, liquid water, and ice. What about water is the same in these states? What can you conclude about what changes and what does not change during a change of state?

INTERPRETING GRAPHICS Use the graph below to answer the next two questions.

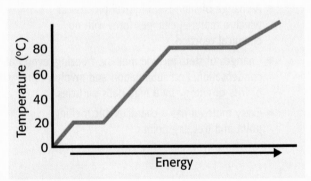

13 **Identifying** What is the boiling point of the substance? What is the melting point?

14 **Concluding** How does the substance change while energy is being added to the liquid at 20°C?

15 Creative Writing Imagine that you are a gas particle and that the material you are in condenses and then freezes. From your point of view as a particle, write a clear step-by-step description of what happens as you go through each change of state.

16 Concept Mapping Use the following terms to create a concept map: *states of matter, solid, liquid, gas, changes of state, freezing, evaporation, condensation,* and *melting.*

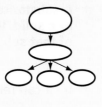

INTERPRETING GRAPHICS Use the picture below to answer the next two questions.

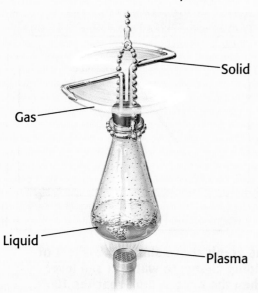

Solid

Gas

Liquid

Plasma

17 Analyzing Processes Explain, based on the motion of the gas particles, how the gas is causing the tubes to spin around as shown.

18 Making Inferences If the liquid shown in the picture above is water and if the air pressure is equal to the normal atmospheric pressure at sea level, what must the temperature of the water be, in degrees Celsius?

19 Applying Concepts After taking a shower, you notice that small droplets of water cover the bathroom mirror. Explain how these drops form. Be sure to describe where the water comes from and the changes it undergoes.

20 Making Inferences At sea level, water boils at 100°C and methane boils at −161°C. Which of these substances has a stronger force of attraction between its particles? Explain your reasoning.

21 Analyzing Ideas By using an electric current, you can split liquid water to form two new substances, hydrogen and oxygen gases. Is this a change of state? Explain your answer.

22 Evaluating Hypotheses Imagine that a gas is bubbling up from a sample of water. Laurel forms the hypothesis that the water is boiling. How could she test that hypothesis?

23 Analyzing Data Kate placed 100 mL of water in five different pans, placed the pans on a windowsill for a week, and measured how much water evaporated from each pan. Draw a graph of her data, which is shown below. Place surface area on the *x*-axis and volume evaporated on the *y*-axis. Is the graph linear or nonlinear? What does this information tell you?

Pan number	1	2	3	4	5
Surface area (cm²)	44	82	20	30	65
Volume evaporated (mL)	42	79	19	29	62

24 Analyzing Methods To protect their crops during freezing temperatures, orange growers spray water onto the trees and allow it to freeze. In terms of energy lost and energy gained, explain why this practice protects the oranges from damage.

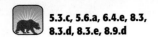

5.3.c, 5.6.a, 6.4.e, 8.3,
8.3.d, 8.3.e, 8.9.d

REVIEWING ACADEMIC VOCABULARY

1 In the sentence "Each element has distinct physical and chemical properties," what does the word *distinct* mean?

A easy to hear, see, or smell

B large enough to be noticed

C clearly different and separate

D very great in degree

2 Which of the following words is the closest in meaning to the word *structure*?

A composition

B stability

C function

D combination

3 Which of the following sets of words best completes the following sentence: "After they conduct their experiment, the students _____ a graph based on their data"?

A have constructed

B will have constructed

C would construct

D will construct

4 Which of the following words means "to figure out the meaning of"?

A interpret

B communicate

C suggest

D describe

REVIEWING CONCEPTS

5 The state of matter of a substance depends upon how the particles in that substance

A freeze.

B move.

C expand.

D shrink.

6 A substance changes state from a liquid to a solid. Which of the following is true of that substance?

A It passes through a plasma state.

B It can return to a liquid state.

C It will soon become a gas.

D It will remain permanently solid.

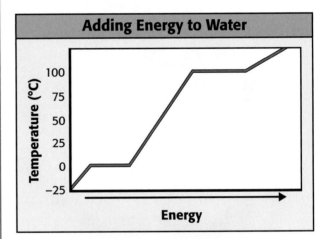

7 The graph above shows the effect of adding energy to water at sea level. When the temperature reaches 100°C, what happens to the water molecules as energy continues to be added?

A The water molecules gain energy as the temperature continues to rise.

B The water molecules gain no energy and the temperature stays the same.

C The water molecules become more ordered as the state changes to a gas.

D The water molecules move farther apart as the state changes to a gas.

8 Which of the following statements best describes the particles contained in a glass of milk?

A They are closely locked into position and can only vibrate.

B They are loosely connected and can slide past each other.

C They have broken apart.

D They move about freely.

9 Which of the following sentences best describes the process that occurs when liquid water becomes ice?

A Energy is added to the water, so its molecules move more slowly.

B Energy is added to the water, so its molecules move more quickly.

C Energy is removed from the water, so its molecules lock into place.

D Energy is removed from the water, so its molecules move apart.

10 A change in the state of matter always includes

A a loss of energy.

B a gain of energy.

C a change in the chemical properties of a substance.

D a change in the physical form of a substance.

11 Plasma is the most common state of matter in the universe. How are plasmas different from gases?

A Plasmas conduct electric currents.

B Plasmas have a definite shape.

C Plasmas have a definite volume.

D Plasmas are unaffected by magnetism.

REVIEWING PRIOR LEARNING

12 Precipitation occurs at the point where

A moist air is cooled below its condensation point.

B dry air picks up water through evaporation.

C warm air rises into the atmosphere and cools.

D cool air sinks because of convection in the atmosphere.

13 The molecules in an unknown substance collide with and slide past each other. They are moving quickly enough that the substance's vapor pressure equals the atmospheric pressure. How would you classify the unknown substance?

A It is a gas at its condensation point.

B It is a liquid at its boiling point.

C It is a solid at its melting point.

D It is a liquid at its freezing point.

Altitude and Atmospheric Pressure

Altitude above sea level (m)	Atmospheric pressure (kPa)
0	101
100	98.2
1000	85.8
10000	20.4

14 According to the table above, what is the relationship between atmospheric pressure and altitude?

A Atmospheric pressure remains constant at any altitude.

B Atmospheric pressure differs at sea level according to location.

C Atmospheric pressure increases as altitude increases.

D Atmospheric pressure decreases as altitude increases.

Standards Assessment

Science in Action

Science, Technology, and Society

Deep-Sea Diving with Helium

Deep-sea divers in the ocean run the risk of getting nitrogen narcosis. Nitrogen narcosis produces an alcohol-like effect, which can cause a diver to become disoriented and to use poor judgment. This effect can be dangerous. To avoid nitrogen narcosis, divers who work at depths of more than 60 m breathe heliox instead of air. *Heliox* is a mixture of helium and oxygen. The main disadvantage of heliox is that helium conducts heat about 6 times as fast as nitrogen does, so a diver using heliox will feel cold sooner than a diver who is breathing air.

Math ACTIVITY

There are 2.54 cm in one inch. Below what depth in feet should heliox be used instead of air? Write your answer in your **Science Journal.**

Scientific Discoveries

The Fourth State of Matter

Plasma is known as "the fourth state of matter." Atoms of plasma are broken apart and have a lot of energy. At the University of Southern California's Plasma Accelerator Lab, Tom Katsouleas and his team of scientists are trying to find a way to use plasma's unique properties to build smaller particle accelerators. Particle accelerators are huge devices that scientists use to smash atoms to break them apart and study the forces that hold them together. Smaller particle accelerators would enable scientists to do so much more easily. The results could lead to the development of new technologies.

Social Studies ACTIVITY

Research plasma. Find out how plasma is used in today's technology, such as plasma TVs. How will this technology affect you and society in general? Describe your findings in a poster.

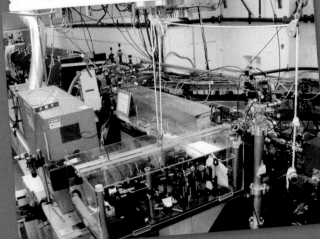

Unpacking the Standards

The information below "unpacks" the standards by breaking them down into basic parts. The higher-level, academic vocabulary is highlighted and defined to help you understand the language of the standards. "What It Means" restates the standards as simply as possible.

California Standard	Academic Vocabulary	What It Means
8.3.b Students know that compounds are formed by combining two or more different elements and that compounds have properties that are different from their **constituent** elements.	**constituent** (kuhn STICH oo uhnt) serving as part of a whole	Compounds form when two or more elements combine. The properties of a compound differ from the properties of the elements that make up the compound.
8.5.a Students know reactant atoms and molecules **interact** to form products with different **chemical** properties.	**interact** (IN tuhr AKT) to act upon one another **chemical** (KEM i kuhl) of or having to do with the properties or actions of substances	When atoms and molecules are put together, they can interact to form new substances whose chemical properties differ from the properties of the original substances.
8.7.c Students know substances can be classified by their properties, including their melting temperature, density, hardness, and thermal and electrical conductivity.		Different kinds of matter can be grouped by their characteristics, including the temperature at which they melt, the amount of mass per unit volume, their hardness, and their ability to transfer thermal energy or electrical energy.

5

Elements, Compounds, and Mixtures

The Big Idea

Matter can be classified into elements, compounds, and mixtures.

California Standards

Focus on Physical Sciences

8.3 Each of the more than 100 elements of matter has distinct properties and a distinct atomic structure. All forms of matter are composed of one or more of the elements. (Section 2)

8.5 Chemical reactions are processes in which atoms are rearranged into different combinations of molecules. (Section 2)

8.7 The organization of the periodic table is based on the properties of the elements and reflects the structure of atoms. (Sections 1, 2, and 3)

Investigation and Experimentation

8.9 Scientific progress is made by asking meaningful questions and conducting careful investigations. (Science Skills Activity)

Math
6.1.4 Number Sense

English–Language Arts
8.2.2 Reading
8.1.1, 8.1.2, 8.1.3 Writing

About the Photo

Within these liquid-filled glass lamps, colored globs slowly rise and fall. But what keeps these liquids from mixing? The liquid inside these lamps is a mixture that is composed of mineral oil, wax, water, and alcohol. The water and alcohol mix with each other but remain separated from the globs of wax and oil.

Organize

Key-Term Fold

Before you read this chapter, create the FoldNote entitled "Key-Term Fold." Write a key term from the chapter on each tab of the key-term fold. As you read the chapter, write the definition of each key term under the appropriate tab.

Instructions for creating FoldNotes are located in the Study Skills section on p. 519 of the Appendix.

Figure 4   The Three Major Categories of Elements

Metals	Nonmetals	Metalloids

Lead
Tin
Copper

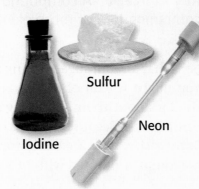

Sulfur
Neon
Iodine

Boron
Silicon
Antimony

Metals are elements that are shiny and are good conductors of heat and electric current. They are *malleable.* (They can be pounded or rolled into shape.) They are also *ductile.* (They can be drawn into thin wires.)

Nonmetals are elements that are dull (not shiny) and that are poor conductors of heat and electric current. Solids tend to be brittle and unmalleable. Few familiar objects are made of only nonmetals.

Metalloids are also called *semimetals.* They have properties of both metals and nonmetals. Some metalloids are shiny. Some are dull. Metalloids are somewhat malleable and ductile. Some metalloids conduct heat and electric current.

SECTION Review

 8.7.c

Summary

- A substance in which all of the particles are alike is a pure substance.

- An element is a pure substance that cannot be broken down into anything simpler by physical or chemical means.

- Each element has a unique set of physical and chemical properties.

- Elements are classified as metals, nonmetals, or metalloids, based on their properties.

Using Vocabulary

1. Use *element* and *pure substance* in the same sentence.

Understanding Concepts

2. **Classifying** Compare the properties of metals and nonmetals.

Critical Thinking

3. **Applying Concepts** From which category of elements would you choose to make a container that would not shatter if dropped? Explain your answer.

4. **Making Inferences** List four possible properties of a substance classified as a metalloid. Can your list be used to classify an unknown substance as a metalloid? Explain your answer.

Math Skills

5. **Making Calculations** There are 8 elements that together make up 98.5% of Earth's crust: oxygen, 46.6%; aluminum, 8.1%; iron, 5.0%; calcium, 3.6%; sodium, 2.8%; potassium, 2.6%; magnesium, 2.1%; and silicon. What percentage of Earth's crust is silicon?

Challenge

6. **Evaluating Assumptions** Your friend tells you that a shiny element has to be a metal. Do you agree? Explain your reasoning.

Internet Resources

For a variety of links related to this chapter, go to www.scilinks.org
Topic: Elements
SciLinks code: HY70496

What You Will Learn

- A compound is made up of two or more elements that are chemically combined to form a new substance with different properties.
- During a chemical reaction, the reactant atoms of two or more elements interact and join to form molecules of one or more compounds.
- Each compound has a unique set of physical and chemical properties that differ from the properties of the elements that make up the compound.

Why It Matters

Understanding how compounds are formed can help you understand the different properties that result when you combine certain substances.

Vocabulary

- compound

READING STRATEGY

Summarizing Read this section silently. In pairs, take turns summarizing the material. Stop to discuss ideas and words that seem confusing.

Figure 1 *As magnesium (a solid) burns, it reacts with oxygen (a gas) and forms the compound magnesium oxide (a solid).*

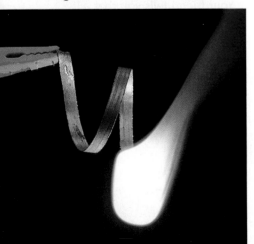

Compounds

Key Concept A compound is formed by chemically combining two or more elements.

▶ What do salt, sugar, baking soda, and water have in common? You might use all of these to bake bread. Is there anything else similar about them? Salt, sugar, baking soda, and water are all compounds. Because most elements take part in chemical changes fairly easily, they are rarely found alone in nature. Instead, they are found combined with other elements as compounds.

Compounds: Made of Elements

A **compound** is a pure substance composed of two or more elements that are chemically combined. Elements combine by reacting, or undergoing a chemical change, with one another. A chemical change, or reaction, happens when one or more substances are changed into one or more new substances that have new and different properties.

Figure 1 shows magnesium reacting with oxygen. A compound called *magnesium oxide* is forming. The compound is a new pure substance. It is different from the elements that make it up. Most of the substances that you see every day are compounds. **Table 1** lists some familiar examples.

Table 1	Familiar Compounds
Compound	**Elements combined**
Table salt	sodium and chlorine
Water	hydrogen and oxygen
Citric acid	hydrogen, carbon, and oxygen
Carbon dioxide	carbon and oxygen
Baking soda	sodium, hydrogen, carbon, and oxygen

Chemical Reactions Form Compounds

A chemical reaction is the process by which substances change into new substances. This process involves rearranging the atoms of a substance into new combinations with atoms of other substances. The atoms join in various patterns to form new substances that have different chemical properties. When two or more elements combine, a new compound is formed. The properties of the new compound are different from the properties of the elements that formed the compound.

Standards Check Explain how a compound is formed. 🐻 **8.3.b**

Identifying Compounds

1. Place **4 g of compound A** in a **clear plastic cup.**
2. Place **4 g of compound B** in a **second clear plastic cup.**
3. Observe the color and texture of each compound. Record your observations.
4. Add **5 mL of vinegar** to each cup. Record your observations.
5. Baking soda reacts with vinegar. Powdered sugar does not react with vinegar. Which compound is baking soda, and which compound is powdered sugar? Explain your answer.

8.5.a
8.7.c

15 min

Properties of Compounds

Like an element, each compound has its own physical properties. Physical properties include melting point, density, and color. Compounds can also be identified by their chemical properties. Some compounds, such as calcium carbonate (found in chalk), react with acid. Other compounds, such as hydrogen peroxide, react when exposed to light.

compound (KAHM POWND) a substance made up of atoms of two or more different elements joined by chemical bonds

Standards Check What are three physical properties used to identify compounds? 8.7.c

Properties: Compounds Versus Elements

A compound has properties that differ from the properties of the elements that make up the compound. **Figure 2** shows that table salt, or sodium chloride, is made of two very dangerous elements—sodium and chlorine. Sodium reacts violently with water. Chlorine is a poisonous gas. But when combined, these elements form a harmless compound that has unique properties. Sodium chloride is safe to eat. It also dissolves (without exploding!) in water.

8.3.b Students know that compounds are formed by combining two or more different elements and that compounds have properties that are different from their constituent elements.
8.5.a Students know reactant atoms and molecules interact to form products with different chemical properties.
8.7.c Students know substances can be classified by their properties, including their melting temperature, density, hardness, and thermal and electrical conductivity.

Figure 2 Forming Sodium Chloride

Sodium is a soft, silvery white metal that reacts violently with water.

Chlorine is a poisonous, greenish yellow gas.

Sodium chloride, or table salt, is a white solid. It dissolves easily in water and is safe to eat.

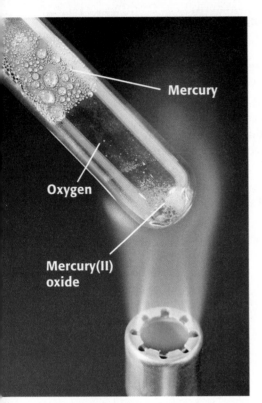

Figure 3 *When mercury(II) oxide is heated, it undergoes a chemical change in which it separates into the elements mercury and oxygen.*

The Ratio of Elements in a Compound

Elements do not randomly join to form compounds. Instead, elements join in a specific ratio according to their masses. For example, for water, the ratio of the mass of hydrogen to the mass of oxygen is 1 to 8. This mass ratio can be written as 1:8. For water, this ratio is always 1:8. That is, every sample of water has a 1:8 mass ratio of hydrogen to oxygen. If a sample of a compound has a mass ratio of hydrogen to oxygen that is not 1:8, the compound cannot be water.

Breaking Down Compounds

Some compounds can be broken down into their elements by chemical changes. Other compounds break down to form simpler compounds instead of elements. These simpler compounds can then be broken down into elements through more chemical changes. For example, carbonic acid is a compound that helps give carbonated beverages their "fizz." When you open a can of soda, carbonic acid breaks down into carbon dioxide and water and makes the soda fizz. This carbon dioxide and water could then be broken down into the elements carbon, oxygen, and hydrogen through chemical changes.

Methods of Breaking Down Compounds

The only way to break down a compound is through a chemical change. Sometimes, energy is needed for a chemical change to happen. Two ways to add energy to break down a compound are to apply heat and to apply an electric current. For example, heating the compound mercury(II) oxide breaks it down into the elements mercury and oxygen, as shown in **Figure 3**.

Standards Check What elements combine to form mercury(II) oxide? 8.3.b

Compounds in Your World

Compounds are all around you. They make up the food you eat, the school supplies you use, and the clothes you wear—even you are made of compounds!

Compounds in Industry

The compounds found in nature are not usually the raw materials needed by industry. Often, these compounds must be broken down to provide elements or other compounds that can be used as raw material. For example, aluminum is used in cans and airplanes. But in nature, aluminum is found in the form of the compound aluminum oxide. Pure aluminum is produced by breaking down aluminum oxide.

Compounds in Nature

Proteins are compounds found in all living things. Nitrogen is one of the elements needed to make proteins. **Figure 4** shows how some plants get their nitrogen from the air. Other plants get nitrogen from nitrogen compounds in the soil. Animals get their nitrogen by eating plants or by eating animals that have eaten plants. The proteins in the food are broken down as an animal digests the food. The simpler compounds that form are used by the animal's cells to make new proteins.

Another compound that plays an important role in life is carbon dioxide. You exhale carbon dioxide that was made in your body. Plants take in carbon dioxide, which is used in photosynthesis. Plants use photosynthesis to make compounds called *carbohydrates*. Plants and plant-eating animals get energy by breaking down these carbohydrates through chemical changes.

Figure 4 *The bumps on the roots of this pea plant are home to bacteria that form compounds from nitrogen in the air. The pea plant makes proteins from these compounds.*

SECTION Review

 8.3.b, 8.5.a, 8.7.c

Summary

- A compound is a pure substance composed of two or more elements.
- During a chemical reaction, the atoms of two or more elements react with each other to form molecules of compounds.
- Each compound has unique physical and chemical properties that differ from those of the elements that make up the compound.
- Compounds can be broken down into simpler substances only by chemical changes.

Understanding Concepts

1. **Identifying** What type of change is needed to break down a compound?

INTERPRETING GRAPHICS The chart below shows the composition of table sugar in percent by mass. Use the chart to answer the next two questions.

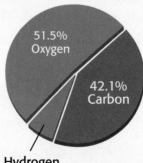

51.5% Oxygen

42.1% Carbon

Hydrogen

2. **Evaluating** List the 3 elements that make up table sugar.

3. **Analyzing** What percentage by mass of table sugar is hydrogen?

Critical Thinking

4. **Applying Concepts** Iron is a solid, gray metal. Oxygen is a colorless gas. When iron and oxygen chemically combine, rust is made. Rust has a reddish brown color. Why does rust differ from iron and oxygen?

Challenge

5. **Analyzing Ideas** A jar contains samples of the elements carbon and oxygen. Does the jar contain a compound? Explain your answer.

Internet Resources

For a variety of links related to this chapter, go to www.scilinks.org

Topic: Compounds
SciLinks code: HY70332

Mixtures

Key Concept A mixture is a combination of two or more substances that are not chemically combined.

mixture (MIKS chuhr) a combination of two or more substances that are not chemically combined

▶ Imagine that you roll out some dough, add tomato sauce, and sprinkle some cheese on top. Then, you add mushrooms, olives, and pepperoni! What have you just made? A pizza, of course! But that's not all. You have also created a mixture!

Properties of Mixtures

All mixtures share certain properties. A **mixture** is a combination of two or more substances that are not chemically combined. When two or more materials are put together, they form a mixture if they do not react to form a compound.

No Chemical Changes in a Mixture

No chemical change happens when a mixture is made. So, each substance in a mixture has the same chemical makeup it had before the mixture formed. That is, each substance in a mixture keeps its identity. In some mixtures, such as the pizza in **Figure 1,** you can see each of the components. In other mixtures, such as salt water, you cannot see all the components.

Standards Check Describe one property of all mixtures. **8.7.c**

Separating Mixtures Through Physical Methods

If you don't like mushrooms on your pizza, you can just pick them off. This change is a physical change of the mixture. The identities of the substances do not change. But not all mixtures are as easy to separate as a pizza. You cannot just pick salt out of salt water. One way to separate the salt from the water is to heat the mixture until the water evaporates. The salt is left behind. Other ways to separate mixtures are shown in **Figure 2.**

Figure 1 *You can see each topping on this mixture, which is better known as a* pizza.

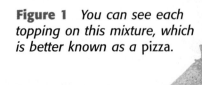

Figure 2 Common Ways to Separate Mixtures

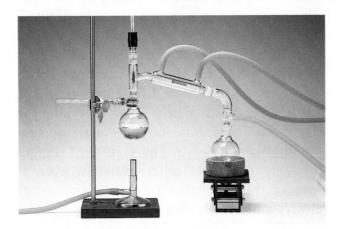

Distillation (DIS tuh LAY shuhn) is a process that separates a mixture based on the boiling points of the mixture's components. Pure water (flask on the right) is being distilled from salt water (flask on the left). Also, distillation is used to separate crude oil into components, such as gasoline.

A **magnet** can be used to separate a mixture of the elements iron and aluminum. Iron is attracted to the magnet, but aluminum is not.

Blood is separated into its parts by a machine called a **centrifuge** (SEN truh FYOOJ). In the test tube of blood at left, a layer of plasma rests atop a layer of red blood cells. A centrifuge separates mixtures by the densities of the components.

Separating a mixture of sodium chloride (table salt) and sulfur takes more than one step.

❶ **Dissolving** In the first step, water is added, and the mixture is stirred. Salt dissolves in water. Sulfur does not.

❷ **Filtering** In the second step, the mixture is poured through a filter. The filter traps the solid sulfur.

❸ **Evaporating** In the third step, the water is evaporated. The sodium chloride is left behind.

Figure 3 *These paperweights are made of granite. Their colors differ because the granite in each paperweight has ratios of minerals that differ from the ratios in the other paperweights.* **Based on this information, how can you tell that granite is not a compound?**

The Ratio of Components in a Mixture

A compound is made of elements that are mixed in a specific mass ratio. However, the components of a mixture do not need to be mixed in a definite ratio. For example, granite is a mixture made of three minerals: feldspar, mica, and quartz. Feldspar is pink. Mica is black. Quartz is colorless. Look at the egg-shaped paperweights in **Figure 3.** The granite of the pink one has more feldspar than it does mica or quartz. So, this paperweight is pink. The granite of the black one has more mica than it does other minerals. The granite of the gray one has more quartz than it does other minerals. Even though the proportions of the minerals change, the combination of minerals is always a mixture called *granite.* **Table 1** summarizes the differences between mixtures and compounds.

Table 1	Mixtures and Compounds
Mixtures	**Compounds**
Made of elements, compounds, or both	Made of elements
No change in original properties of components	Change in original properties of components
Separated by physical means	Separated by chemical means
Formed using any ratio of components	Formed using a set ratio of components

Solutions

A **solution** is a homogeneous mixture that appears to be a single substance. A solution is composed of particles of two or more substances that are distributed evenly among each other. Solutions have the same appearance and properties throughout the mixture.

The process in which particles of substances separate and spread evenly throughout a mixture is known as *dissolving.* In solutions, the **solute** is the substance that is dissolved. The **solvent** is the substance in which the solute is dissolved. A solute must be *soluble,* or able to dissolve, in the solvent. A substance that is *insoluble,* or unable to dissolve, forms a mixture that is not a solution.

Salt water is a solution. Salt is soluble in, or can dissolve in, water. So, salt is the solute, and water is the solvent. When two liquids or two gases form a solution, the substance that is present in the largest amount is the solvent.

solution (suh LOO shuhn) a homogeneous mixture throughout which two or more substances are uniformly dispersed

solute (SAHL yoot) in a solution, the substance that dissolves in the solvent

solvent (SAHL vuhnt) in a solution, the substance in which the solute dissolves

Table 2	Examples of Solutions in Various States
States	**Examples**
Gas in gas	dry air (oxygen in nitrogen)
Gas in liquid	soft drinks (carbon dioxide in water)
Liquid in liquid	antifreeze (alcohol in water)
Solid in liquid	salt water (salt in water)
Solid in solid	brass (zinc in copper)

Examples of Solutions

You may think that all solutions are liquids. Tap water, soft drinks, gasoline, and many cleaners are liquid solutions. But, solutions may also be gases. Air is a solution that is a gas. Solutions may even be solids—steel is a solid solution. *Alloys* are solid solutions in which metals or nonmetals are dissolved in metals. Brass is an alloy of the metal zinc dissolved in copper. Steel is an alloy of the nonmetal carbon and other elements dissolved in iron. **Table 2** lists more examples of solutions.

Particles in Solutions

The particles in solutions are so small that they will not come out of solution. They also cannot be removed by filtering. Solute particles are so small that they do not scatter light. Both jars in **Figure 4** contain mixtures. The mixture in the jar on the left is a solution of salt in water. The jar on the right holds a mixture—but not a solution—of gelatin in water.

Standards Check What property of the mixture of gelatin in water tells you that the mixture is not a solution? 8.7.c

A Physical Science Fairytale

What methods are used to separate mixtures? Write a fairytale about how scientific methods helped separate a mixture when magic failed. Go to **go.hrw.com,** and type in the keyword HY7MIXW.

Figure 4 *Both of these jars contain mixtures. The mixture in the jar on the left, however, is a solution. The particles in solutions are so small that they do not scatter light. Therefore, you can't see the path of light through the solution.*

Figure 5 *The dilute solution (left) contains less solute than the concentrated solution (right).*

Concentration of Solutions

A measure of the amount of solute dissolved in a given amount of solvent is **concentration.** Concentration can be expressed in grams of solute per milliliter of solvent (g/mL). Solutions can be described as being concentrated or dilute. In **Figure 5,** the two solutions have the same amount of solvent, but different amounts of solute. The solution on the left contains less solute than the solution on the right. The solution on the left is dilute. The solution on the right is more concentrated than the solution on the left. The terms *dilute* and *concentrated* do not tell you the concentration of solute.

Solubility

If you add too much sugar to a glass of lemonade, some of the sugar cannot dissolve. Some of it sinks to the bottom. To find the maximum amount of sugar that can dissolve, you must know the solubility of sugar. **Solubility** refers to the ability of a solute to dissolve in a solvent at a certain temperature. **Figure 6** shows how temperature affects the solubility of several solid substances.

concentration (KAHN suhn TRAY shuhn) the amount of a particular substance in a given quantity of a mixture, solution, or ore

solubility (SAHL yoo BIL uh tee) the ability of one substance to dissolve in another at a given temperature and pressure

 Wordwise The root *solute-* means "to free" or "to loosen."

Quick Lab

Identifying Solutes by Solubility

In water, sugar is almost eight times as soluble as table salt is. In this activity, you will use solubility to distinguish sugar from table salt.

1. Label one **50 mL beaker** as A and a second **50 mL beaker** as B. Using a **graduated cylinder,** measure and pour **10 mL of water** into each beaker.

2. Use a **balance** to measure **2 g of compound A** and place it into beaker A. Measure **2 g of compound B** and put it into beaker B. Stir each mixture.

3. If both substances completely dissolve, repeat step 2.

4. When one of the unknown substances no longer dissolves in the solution, record which substance stopped dissolving and how much of each substance was used.

5. Identify which substance is sugar and which is salt.

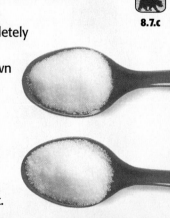

8.7.c

⏱ **20 min**

Figure 6 **Solubility of Different Solids In Water**

For most solids, solubility increases as temperature increases. So, the amount of solute that can dissolve increases as temperature increases. But, some solids, such as cerium sulfate, become less soluble as temperature increases.

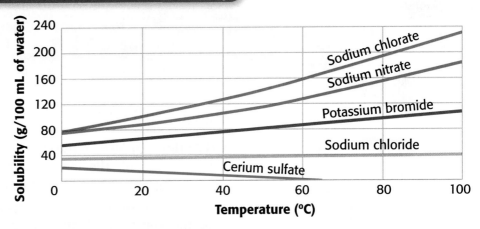

SECTION
Review

8.7.c

Summary

- A mixture is a combination of two or more substances, each of which keeps its own characteristics.
- Mixtures can be separated by physical means, such as filtration and evaporation.
- A solution is a mixture that appears to be a single substance but is composed of a solute dissolved in a solvent.
- Concentration is a measure of the amount of solute dissolved in a given amount of solvent.
- The solubility of a solute is the ability of the solute to dissolve in a solvent at a certain temperature.

Using Vocabulary

Correct each statement by replacing the underlined term.

1 The <u>solvent</u> is the substance that is dissolved.

2 A measure of the amount of solute dissolved in a solvent is <u>solubility</u>.

Understanding Concepts

INTERPRETING GRAPHICS Use the graph below to answer the next two questions.

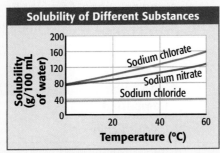

3 **Identifying** At what temperature is 120 g of sodium nitrate soluble in 100 mL of water?

4 **Comparing** At 60°C, how much more sodium chlorate than sodium chloride will dissolve in 100 mL of water?

5 **Analyzing** Identify the solute and solvent in a solution made of 15 mL of oxygen and 5 mL of helium.

Critical Thinking

6 **Applying Concepts** Soft drinks contain sugar and carbon dioxide. An open soda will lose carbonation. But, the soda will not become less sweet. Use the properties of the solutes to explain why.

7 **Making Comparisons** What are three ways that mixtures differ from compounds?

Challenge

8 **Applying Concepts** Suggest a procedure by which to separate iron filings from sawdust. Explain why this procedure works.

Internet Resources

For a variety of links related to this chapter, go to www.scilinks.org
Topic: Mixtures
SciLinks code: HY70974

Skills Practice Lab

Flame Tests

Fireworks produce fantastic combinations of color when they are ignited. The many colors are the results of burning many different compounds. Imagine that you are the head chemist for a fireworks company. The label has fallen off one box, and you must identify the unknown compound inside so that the fireworks may be used in the correct fireworks display. To identify the compound, you will use your knowledge that every compound has a unique set of properties.

Ask a Question

1 How can you identify an unknown compound by heating it in a flame?

Form a Hypothesis

2 Write a hypothesis that is a possible answer to the question above. Explain your reasoning.

Test the Hypothesis

3 Arrange the test tubes in the test-tube rack. Use masking tape to label each tube with one of the following names: calcium chloride, potassium chloride, sodium chloride, and unknown.

4 Copy the table below. Then, ask your teacher for your portions of the solutions. **Caution:** Be very careful in handling all chemicals. Tell your teacher immediately if you spill a chemical.

OBJECTIVES

Observe flame colors emitted by various compounds.

Determine the composition of an unknown compound.

MATERIALS

- Bunsen burner
- chloride test solutions (4)
- hydrochloric acid, dilute, in a small beaker
- spark igniter
- tape, masking
- test tubes, small (4)
- test-tube rack
- water, distilled, in a small beaker
- wire and holder

SAFETY

8.3.b Students know that compounds are formed by combining two or more different elements and that compounds have properties that are different from their constituent elements.
8.5.a Students know reactant atoms and molecules interact to form products with different chemical properties.
8.7.c Students know substances can be classified by their properties, including their melting temperature, density, hardness, and thermal and electrical conductivity.

Investigation and Experimentation
8.9.a Plan and conduct a scientific investigation to test a hypothesis.

Test Results	
Compound	**Color of flame**
Calcium chloride	
Potassium chloride	DO NOT WRITE
Sodium chloride	IN BOOK
Unknown	

5 Light the burner. Clean the wire by dipping it into the dilute hydrochloric acid and then into distilled water. Holding the wooden handle, heat the wire in the blue flame of the burner until the wire is glowing and it no longer colors the flame. **Caution:** Use extreme care around an open flame.

6 Dip the clean wire into the first test solution. Hold the wire at the tip of the inner cone of the burner flame. Record in the table the color that the burning solution gives to the flame.

7 Clean the wire by repeating step 5. Then, repeat steps 5 and 6 for the other solutions.

8 Follow your teacher's instructions for cleanup and disposal.

Analyze the Results

9 **Identifying Patterns** Is the flame color a test for the metal or for the chloride in each compound? Explain your answer.

10 **Analyzing Data** What is the identity of your unknown solution? How do you know?

Draw Conclusions

11 **Evaluating Methods** Why is it necessary to carefully clean the wire before testing each solution?

12 **Making Predictions** Would you expect the compound sodium fluoride to produce the same color as sodium chloride in a flame test? Why or why not?

13 **Interpreting Information** Each of the compounds that you tested is made from chlorine, which is a poisonous gas at room temperature. Why is it safe to use these compounds without a gas mask?

Big Idea Question

14 **Analyzing Methods** You can use the flame test to determine if sodium is one of the elements in a compound. But you would not use the flame test on a pure metal to determine if the metal is sodium. Explain why.

Science Skills Activity

Investigation and Experimentation
8.9.c Distinguish between variable and controlled parameters in a test.

Identifying Types of Parameters

▶ Tutorial

Many factors can affect the results of an experiment. So, when you plan an experiment, you must consider all of these factors or parameters. As part of your test plan, you will need to identify each parameter as controlled or variable.

1 Identify what you want to test. For example, you may want to test how temperature affects the solubility of a substance. The parameters that change during the experiment are the variable parameters. Your goal is to find out the relationship between the variable parameters.

2 List all of the other factors that could affect the results of your experiment. Examples of factors other than temperature that could affect the solubility of a substance are the amount of solute and the amount of solvent. To prevent these factors from affecting your test, you will need to keep their values constant. These factors that are kept constant are your controlled parameters.

3 When designing your experiment, you choose how much the values of a variable parameter will change between each measurement. For example, you might want to record the substance's solubility every 20°C, every 10°C, or even every 1°C.

4 The values of the controlled parameters will not change during your experiment.

5 After your experiment is complete, you could make a table or graph to determine the relationship between your variable parameters.

> Trial 1:
> Amount of water = 100 ml (controlled)
> Temperature = 20° C   (variable)
> Amount of sodium nitrate
> dissolved = 88 g

> Trial 3:
> Amount of water = 100 ml (controlled)
> Temperature = 60° C   (variable)
> Amount of sodium nitrate
> dissolved = 122 g

▶ You Try It!

Plan an experiment to find out the relationship between the solubility of Epsom salt and the volume of water. You will do this by mixing increasing amounts of Epsom salt in water until no more will dissolve. Your parameters will be the amount of Epsom salt (in grams), the amount of water (in milliliters), and the temperature of the water (in degrees Celsius). If your plan is approved by your teacher, conduct the experiment.

1 **Identifying** What are your variable parameters? Why did you choose those parameters?

2 **Designing** What is your controlled parameter? Why is having a controlled parameter during your experiment important?

3 **Concluding** What relationship did you find between your variable parameters?

4 **Concluding** Calculate the solubility of Epsom salt (g of Epsom salt/mL of water).

5 **Designing** If you needed to repeat this experiment, how would you change your design to improve your results? Explain your reasoning.

Chapter Summary

The Big Idea Matter can be classified into elements, compounds, and mixtures.

Section

Vocabulary

1 Elements

Key Concept An element is made up of only one type of atom and can be classified by a unique set of properties.

- An element is a pure substance in which there is only one kind of atom.
- An element cannot be broken down into a simpler substance by physical or chemical means.
- Each element can be classified by a unique set of physical and chemical properties.
- Based on their properties, elements are classified as metals, nonmetals, or metalloids.

Copper

Iodine

Boron

Each element has a unique set of properties that sets it apart from other elements.

element p. 134
pure substance p. 134
metal p. 136
nonmetal p. 136
metalloid p. 136

2 Compounds

Key Concept A compound is formed by chemically combining two or more elements.

- A compound is made up of two or more elements that are chemically combined to form a new substance with different properties.
- During a chemical reaction, the reactant atoms of two or more elements interact and join to form molecules of one or more compounds.
- Each compound has a unique set of physical and chemical properties that differ from the properties of the elements that make up the compound.

The properties of a compound differ from the properties of the elements it is composed of.

compound p. 138

3 Mixtures

Key Concept A mixture is a combination of two or more substances that are not chemically combined.

- Mixtures can be separated by physical means, such as distillation, filtration, and evaporation.
- A solution is a mixture that appears to be a single substance but is composed of a solute dissolved in a solvent.
- Concentration is a measure of the amount of a solute dissolved in a given amount of solvent.

Substances in mixtures can be separated by physical means.

mixture p. 142
solution p. 144
solute p. 144
solvent p. 144
concentration p. 146
solubility p. 146

Chapter Review

 8.3.b, 8.5.a, 8.7.c

Organize

Key-Term Fold Review the FoldNote that you created at the beginning of the chapter. Add to or correct the FoldNote based on what you have learned.

Using Vocabulary

1 **Academic Vocabulary** In the sentence "The constituent elements of water are hydrogen and oxygen, " what does the word *constituent* mean?
a. empowered to elect
b. component
c. two
d. only

Complete each of the following sentences by choosing the correct term from the word bank.

compound	element
solution	solute
nonmetal	metal

2 A(n) ___ has a definite ratio of components.

3 A(n) ___ is a pure substance that cannot be broken down into simpler substances by chemical means.

4 A(n) ___ is an element that is brittle and dull.

5 The ___ is the substance that dissolves to form a solution.

Understanding Concepts

Multiple Choice

6 Which of the following statements describes elements?
a. All of the particles in the same element are different.
b. Elements can be broken down into simpler substances.
c. Elements have unique sets of properties.
d. Elements cannot be joined in chemical reactions.

7 Which of the following best describes chicken noodle soup?
a. element   c. compound
b. mixture   d. solution

8 An element that conducts thermal energy well and is easily shaped is a
a. metal.
b. metalloid.
c. nonmetal.
d. None of the above

9 Which of the following substances can be separated into simpler substances only by chemical means?
a. sodium   c. water
b. salt water d. gold

Short Answer

INTERPRETING GRAPHICS The pie graphs below show the composition of citric acid and table sugar by element (percentage by mass). Use the pie graphs to answer the next three questions.

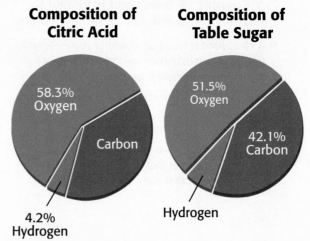

Composition of Citric Acid
58.3% Oxygen
Carbon
4.2% Hydrogen

Composition of Table Sugar
51.5% Oxygen
42.1% Carbon
Hydrogen

10 **Analyzing** What is the percentage by mass of carbon found in citric acid?

11 **Identifying** What is the difference between the percentage of hydrogen in citric acid and the percentage of hydrogen in table sugar?

12 **Comparing** Citric acid and table sugar are compounds. How can you tell from the pie graphs that citric acid and table sugar are not the same compound? Explain your reasoning.

⑬ **Comparing** What is the difference between an element and a compound?

⑭ **Evaluating** When nail polish is dissolved in acetone, which substance is the solute, and which is the solvent?

⑮ **Evaluating** Many gold rings are made out of 14-karat gold, which is an alloy of gold, silver, and copper. Is 14-karat gold a pure substance?

Writing Skills

⑯ **Communicating Concepts** Write an essay that could clearly explain to a third grade student the difference between elements, compounds, and mixtures. Your essay should have a thesis statement and include examples that support your ideas. Finally, make sure that your essay has a conclusion sentence.

Critical Thinking

⑰ **Concept Mapping** Use the following terms to create a concept map: *matter, element, compound, mixture,* and *solution.*

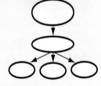

⑱ **Making Inferences** A light green powder is heated in a test tube. A gas is given off, and the powder becomes a black solid. In which classification of matter does the green powder belong? Explain your reasoning.

⑲ **Applying Concepts** Explain two properties of mixtures using a fruit salad as an example of a mixture.

⑳ **Forming Hypotheses** Temperature affects the solubility of substances. Gases become less soluble as temperature increases. To keep the "fizz" in carbonated beverages after they have been opened, should you store them in a refrigerator or in a cabinet? Explain.

㉑ **Analyzing Ideas** Both carbon monoxide and carbon dioxide are made of carbon and oxygen, but they are not the same compound. Explain why these compounds differ from each other.

㉒ **Applying Concepts** When hydrogen and oxygen react to form water, what happens to the atoms of the hydrogen and oxygen?

INTERPRETING GRAPHICS Dr. Sol Vent did an experiment to find the solubility of a compound. The data below were collected using 100 mL samples of water. Use the table below to answer the next two questions.

Temperature (°C)	10	25	40	60	95
Dissolved solute (g)	150	70	34	25	15

㉓ **Forming Hypotheses** Use a computer or graph paper to construct a graph of Dr. Vent's results. Examine the graph. To increase the solubility, would you increase or decrease the temperature? Explain.

㉔ **Predicting Consequences** If 200 mL samples of water were used instead of 100 mL samples, how many grams of the compound would dissolve at 40°C?

Math Skills

㉕ **Making Calculations** What is the concentration of a solution prepared by dissolving 50 g of salt in 200 mL of water?

㉖ **Making Calculations** How many grams of sugar must be dissolved in 150 mL of water to make a solution that has a concentration of 0.6 g/mL?

Challenge

㉗ **Applying Concepts** Describe a procedure that will separate a mixture of salt, finely ground pepper, and pebbles. Carefully consider the order in which you will perform each step. Explain why you chose the steps you did for each substance. How does knowing the properties of matter help you separate the substances in mixtures?

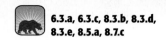

6.3.a, 6.3.c, 8.3.b, 8.3.d,
8.3.e, 8.5.a, 8.7.c

REVIEWING ACADEMIC VOCABULARY

1 Which of the following words means "to act upon one another"?

A interact

B convert

C dissolve

D transform

2 In the sentence "Argon has several properties distinct from other gases," what does *distinct* mean?

A making a clear impression

B notable

C separate

D easily seen

3 Which of the following words means "a substance formed by chemically combining two or more elements"?

A molecule

B compound

C mixture

D solution

4 In the sentence "Atoms of a certain element have a definite structure," which word is the closest in meaning to *structure*?

A arrangement

B size

C property

D density

5 Choose the word that best completes the sentence "Elements sometimes undergo a chemical ___ to form new substances."

A react

B reactor

C reaction

D reactive

REVIEWING CONCEPTS

6 Fundamental substances that cannot be broken down chemically into simpler substances are _____.

A elements

B ions

C bonds

D electrons

7 Imagine that you were asked to classify four samples of equal and known volume, each of which was made up of a single element. Which factor would be most useful for identifying them?

A mass

B shape

C hardness

D original source

Properties of Substances

Substance	Mass (g)	Boiling Point (°C)	Density (kg/m³)
A	20	40	20
B	1,000	100	35
C	1,000	40	100
D	1,000	40	20

8 Which two substances in the table are most likely the same?

A substances A and C

B substances B and D

C substances C and D

D substances A and D

9 If two poisonous gases are combined chemically, which of the following will be true of the resulting compound?

 A The compound will be more poisonous than the gases.

 B The compound will be as poisonous as the gases.

 C The compound may or may not be poisonous.

 D The compound will not be poisonous.

10 Which of the following processes can break down a compound?

 A dissolving and filtering

 B distilling at the boiling points of the compound's components

 C using a magnet to attract the compound's metallic components

 D applying an electric current

The diagrams below represent the distribution of substances in four samples.

Sample 1		Sample 2			
<AB> <AB> <AB>		A	B	A	A
<AB> <AB> <AB>		B	B	A	A
<AB> <AB> <AB>		A	B	A	A

Sample 3				Sample 4			
<AB>	A	B	B	A	B	A	B
A	B	A	A	B	A	B	A
B	<AB>	A	B	A	B	A	B

11 In the illustrations above, A and B are elements, and <AB> is a compound of elements A and B. Which illustration represents a solution of A and B?

 A Sample 1

 B Sample 2

 C Sample 3

 D Sample 4

REVIEWING PRIOR LEARNING

12 When a solid copper block is heated at one end, the entire block is eventually heated. By what process is the heat transferred?

 A conduction

 B convection

 C refraction

 D radiation

13 Which of the following is most likely to occur when warm water is mixed with cold water?

 A The warm and cold water remain at their original temperatures.

 B The mixed water soon reaches the same temperature as the cold water.

 C The mixed water soon reaches the same temperature as the warm water.

 D The mixed water soon reaches a temperature between the temperatures of the warm water and the cold water.

14 If the molecules of a substance are locked in place, the substance is most likely a(n)

 A element.

 B compound.

 C gas.

 D solid.

15 Which of the following occurs when a liquid is boiled?

 A Its molecules break apart from each other.

 B It undergoes a chemical reaction.

 C It breaks down into its elements.

 D Its molecules lock into place.

Science in Action

Weird Science

Dry Cleaning: How Stains Are Dissolved

Sometimes, water and detergent alone won't remove stains. For example, have you gotten ink on your sweater? Or have you spilled something greasy on your shirt? If so, your clothes probably need to be dry-cleaned. Dry cleaning does involve liquids, but it does not involve water. First, the kind of stain must be determined. If the stain will dissolve in water, a stain remover for that particular stain is applied. Then, the stain is removed with a steam gun. But some stains, such as grease or oil, won't dissolve in water. This kind of stain is treated with a nonwater liquid solvent, such as perchloroethylene. The clothing is then cleaned in a dry-cleaning machine.

Language Arts ACTIVITY

Imagine that you are a stained article of clothing. Write a five-paragraph short story describing how you became stained and how the stain was removed by the dry-cleaning process. You may need to research the dry-cleaning process before writing your story.

Science, Technology, and Society

Fireworks Over California

From Chinese New Year celebrations in San Francisco to daily shows in San Diego amusement parks, brilliant fireworks light up the California skies. But have you ever wondered how the explosions of color are created? Firework shells contain a mixture of chemical compounds. The compounds that cause the fireworks to explode are found in gunpowder. Each of the compounds that create the colors give off light of a certain color when they are heated. The mixture is cut into pieces called *stars* that are put into the firework casing. The stars are sent across the sky, creating the dazzling light display.

Social Studies ACTIVITY

Fireworks or pyrotechnics have been used for hundreds of years in China and in Europe. Use the library or the Internet to find information about the types of fireworks used in past centuries and what the fireworks were used for. Make a timeline on a poster that summarizes what you have learned.

Aundra Nix

Metallurgist Aundra Nix is a chief metallurgist for a copper mine in Sahuarita, Arizona, where she runs laboratories and supervises other engineers. "To be able to look at rock in the ground and follow it through a process of drilling, blasting, hauling, crushing, grinding, and finally mineral separation—where you can hold a mineral that is one-third copper in your hand—is exciting."

Although she is a supervisor, Nix enjoys the flexible nature of her job. "My work environment includes office and computer work, plant work, and outdoor work. In this field you can 'get your hands into it,' which I always prefer," says Nix. "I did not want a career where it may be years before you see the results of your work." Nix enjoyed math and science, "so engineering seemed to be a natural area to study," she says. Nix's advice to students planning their own career is that they learn all they can about science and technology, because that is the future.

Math ACTIVITY

A copper-mining company employed a total of about 2,300 people at three locations in New Mexico. Because of an increase in demand for copper, 570 of these workers were hired over a period of a year. Of the 570 new workers, 115 were hired within a three-week period. What percentage of the total work force do the newly hired employees represent? Of the new workers who were hired, what percentage was hired during the three-week hiring period?

Internet Resources

- To learn more about careers in science, visit www.scilinks.org and enter the SciLinks code HY70225.

- To learn more about these Science in Action topics, visit go.hrw.com and type in the keyword HY7MIXF.

- Check out articles related to this chapter by visiting go.hrw.com. Just type in the keyword HY7MIXC.

UNIT 3

TIMELINE

The Atom

Thousands of years ago, people began asking the question, "What is matter made of?" This unit follows the discoveries and ideas that have led to our current theories about what makes up matter. You will learn about the atom—the building block of all matter—and its structure. You will also learn how the periodic table is used to classify and organize elements according to patterns in atomic structure and other properties. This timeline illustrates some of the events that have led to our current understanding of atoms and of the periodic table in which they are organized.

Around 400 BCE
The Greek philosopher Democritus proposes that small particles called *atoms* make up all matter.

1897
British scientist J. J. Thomson identifies electrons as particles that are present in every atom.

1911
Ernest Rutherford, a physicist from New Zealand, discovers the positively charged nucleus of the atom.

1981
Scientists in Switzerland develop a scanning tunneling microscope, which is used to see atoms for the first time.

1803

British scientist and school teacher John Dalton reintroduces the concept of atoms with evidence to support his ideas.

1848

James Marshall finds gold while building Sutter's Mill, starting the California gold rush.

1869

Russian chemist Dmitri Mendeleev develops a periodic table that organizes the elements known at the time.

1932

The neutron, one of the particles in the nucleus of an atom, is discovered by British physicist James Chadwick.

1945

The United Nations is formed. Its purpose is to maintain world peace and develop friendly relations between countries.

1989

Germans celebrate when the Berlin Wall ceases to function as a barrier between East and West Germany.

1996

Another element is added to the periodic table after a team of German scientists synthesize an atom containing 112 protons in its nucleus.

2001

Researchers use electron beam technology to create a tiny silicon transistor that is only 80 atoms wide and that can run at speeds of almost 20 gigahertz.

Improving Comprehension

Graphic Organizers are important visual tools that can help you organize information and improve your reading comprehension. The Graphic Organizer below is called a *concept map*. Instructions for creating other types of Graphic Organizers are located in the **Study Skills** section of the Appendix.

How to Make a Concept Map

1 Identify main ideas from the text, and write the ideas as short phrases or single words.

2 Select a main concept. Place this concept at the top or center of a piece of paper.

3 Place other ideas under or around the main concept based on their relationship to the main concept. Draw a circle around each idea.

4 Draw lines between the concepts, and add linking words to connect the ideas.

When to Use a Concept Map

Concept maps are useful when you are trying to identify how several ideas are connected to a main concept. Concept maps may be based on vocabulary terms or on main topics from the text. The concept map below shows how the important concepts of this chapter are related. As you read about science, look for terms that can be organized in a concept map.

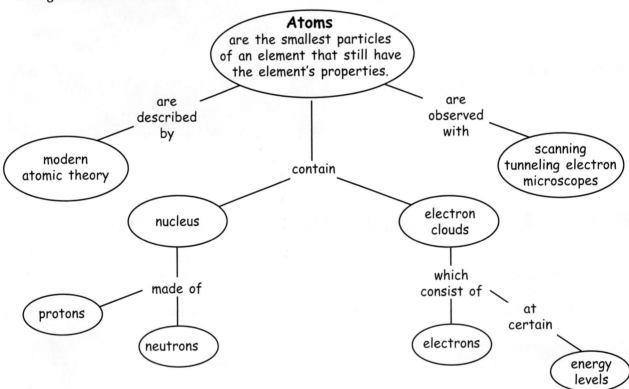

You Try It!

This Reading Strategy can also be used within the chapter that you are about to read. Practice making your own *concept map* as directed in the Reading Strategy for Section **1**. Record your work in your **Science Journal**.

Unpacking the Standards

The information below "unpacks" the standards by breaking them down into basic parts. The higher-level, academic vocabulary is highlighted and defined to help you understand the language of the standards. "What It Means" restates the standards as simply as possible.

California Standard	Academic Vocabulary	What It Means
8.3.a Students know the **structure** of the atom and know it is composed of protons, neutrons, and electrons.	**structure** (STRUHK chuhr) the arrangement of the parts of a whole	An atom is made up of small particles called *protons, neutrons,* and *electrons,* which are arranged in a predictable pattern.
8.7.b Students know each element has a **specific** number of protons in the nucleus (the atomic number) and each isotope of the element has a different but **specific** number of neutrons in the nucleus.	**specific** (spuh SIF ik) unique; peculiar to or characteristic of; exact	The number of protons in the nucleus of an atom of an element differs from the number of protons in the nucleus of an atom of a different element. Isotopes are atoms of an element that have different numbers of neutrons in their nuclei.

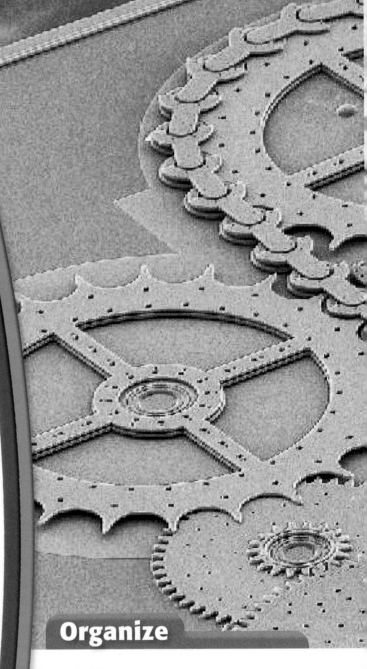

6

Introduction to Atoms

The Big Idea

Atoms are composed of small particles that determine the properties of the atom.

 California Standards

Focus on Physical Sciences
8.3 Each of the more than 100 elements of matter has distinct properties and a distinct atomic structure. All forms of matter are composed of one or more of the elements. (Section 1)
8.7 The organization of the periodic table is based on the properties of the elements and reflects the structure of atoms. (Sections 1 and 2)

Investigation and Experimentation
8.9 Scientific progress is made by asking meaningful questions and conducting careful investigations. (Science Skills Activity)

Math
7.1.2 Number Sense

English–Language Arts
8.2.2 Reading
8.2.3 Writing

About the Photo

Would you believe that the gears and chain shown are so small that the whole thing would fit on a pinhead? Researchers at Sandia National Laboratories made this tiny machine. This image shows the machine at great magnification. But the atoms that the machine is made of are so small that they still cannot be seen in this image.

Organize

Booklet

Before you read the chapter, create the FoldNote entitled "Booklet." On the front cover, title the booklet "Atoms." Label each page of the booklet with a step in the historical development of ideas about atoms beginning with the ideas of Democritus. As you read the chapter, fill in the booklet with details about the historical development of ideas about atoms.

Instructions for creating FoldNotes are located in the Study Skills section on p. 518 of the Appendix.

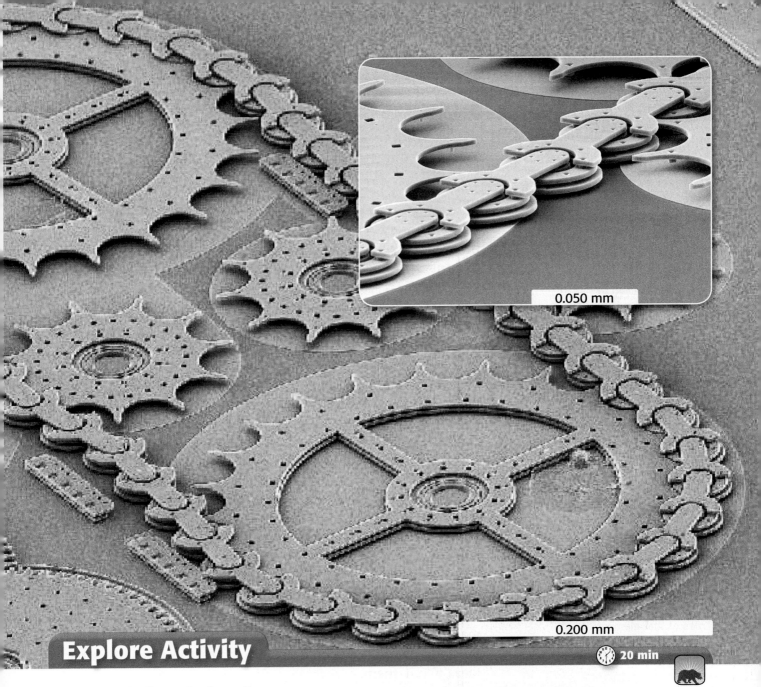

0.050 mm

0.200 mm

Explore Activity

🕐 **20 min**

8.9.a

A Model of Exploring the Atom

Scientists have been able to gather information about atoms without actually seeing them. In this activity, you will do something similar. You will form an idea about the location and size of a hidden object by rolling marbles at it.

Procedure

1. Place a **rectangular piece of cardboard** on **four books or blocks** so that each corner of the cardboard rests on a book or block.

2. Your teacher will place an **unknown object** under the cardboard. Be sure that you cannot see the object.

3. Place a **large piece of paper** on top of the cardboard.

4. Carefully roll a **marble** under the cardboard. Record on the paper the position where the marble enters and exits. Also, record the direction it travels.

5. Keep rolling the marble from different directions to collect data about the shape and location of the object. Write down all of your observations.

Analysis

6. Form a conclusion about the object's shape, size, and location. Record your conclusion.

7. Lift the cardboard, and look at the object. Compare your conclusions with the object's actual size, shape, and location.

Development of the Atomic Theory

Key Concept Scientists have done experiments that have revealed important clues about the structure of atoms.

What You Will Learn

- There have been different models of the atom over time.
- The atomic theory has changed as scientists have experimented and discovered new information about the atom.

Why It Matters

Scientific ideas change as new data are gathered. This is an important characteristic of science.

Vocabulary

- atom
- nucleus
- electron
- electron cloud

READING STRATEGY

Graphic Organizer In your **Science Journal,** create a Concept Map by using the terms *modern atomic theory, Dalton's atomic theory, atom, created, divided, destroyed, element, new substances.*

atom (AT uhm) the smallest unit of an element that maintains the properties of that element
  Wordwise The prefix *a-* means "not." The root *tom-* means "to cut."

▶ Have you ever watched a mystery movie and thought you knew who the criminal was? Have you ever changed your mind because of a new fact or clue? The same thing happens in science! Sometimes, an idea or model must be changed as new information is gathered. In this section, you will see how our ideas about atoms have changed over time.

The Beginning of Atomic Theory

Imagine that you cut something in half. Then, you cut each half in half and continue doing so. Could you keep cutting the pieces in half forever? Around 440 BCE, a Greek philosopher named Democritus (di MAHK ruh tuhs) thought that you would eventually end up with a particle that could not be cut. He called this particle an atom. The word *atom* is from the Greek word *atomos,* which means "not able to be divided."

Although it was a long time before most people agreed that matter was made of atoms, Democritus was right in an important way. We now know that matter is made of particles that we call atoms. An **atom** is the smallest particle into which an element can be divided and still have the properties of that element. Today's technology allows us to produce images of atoms. **Figure 1** shows a picture of aluminum atoms made using a scanning tunneling electron microscope (STM). But long before they could actually scan atoms, scientists had ideas about them.

Figure 1 *Aluminum cans, like all matter, are made of atoms. Aluminum atoms can be seen here as an image from a scanning tunneling electron microscope.*

Dalton's Atomic Theory Based on Experiments

8.3.a Students know the structure of the atom and know it is composed of protons, neutrons, and electrons.

By the late 1700s, scientists had learned that elements combine in certain proportions based on mass to form compounds. For example, hydrogen and oxygen always combine in the same proportion to form water, H_2O. John Dalton, a British chemist and teacher, wanted to know why. He experimented with different substances. His results suggested that elements combine in certain proportions because they are made of atoms. Dalton, shown in **Figure 2,** published his atomic theory in 1803. His theory stated the following ideas:

- All substances are made of atoms. Atoms are small particles that cannot be created, divided, or destroyed.
- Atoms of the same element are exactly alike, and atoms of different elements are different.
- Atoms join with other atoms to make new substances.

Dalton's theory was an important step toward the current understanding of atoms. By the end of the 1800s, scientists agreed that Dalton's theory explained much of what they saw. However, new information was found that did not fit some of Dalton's ideas. The atomic theory was then changed to describe the atom more accurately. As you read on, you will learn how Dalton's theory has changed, step by step, into the modern atomic theory.

Figure 2 *John Dalton developed his atomic theory from observations gathered from many experiments.*

Figure 3 Thomson's Cathode-Ray Tube Experiment

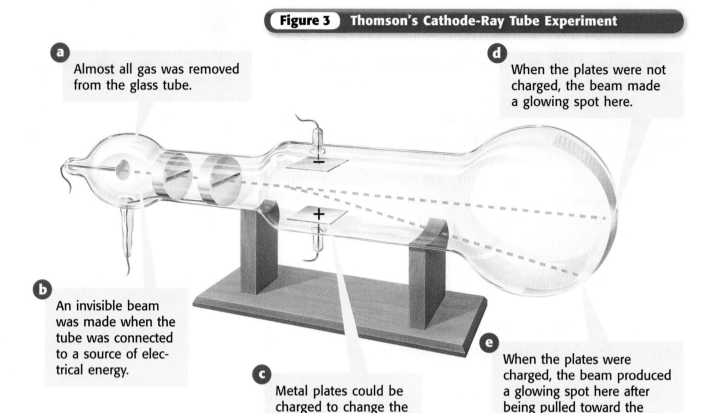

a Almost all gas was removed from the glass tube.

d When the plates were not charged, the beam made a glowing spot here.

b An invisible beam was made when the tube was connected to a source of electrical energy.

c Metal plates could be charged to change the path of the beam.

e When the plates were charged, the beam produced a glowing spot here after being pulled toward the positively charged plate.

Thomson's Discovery of Electrons

In 1897, a British scientist named J. J. Thomson showed that Dalton's theory was not quite right. Thomson discovered that there are small particles *inside* the atom. Thus, atoms can be divided into even smaller parts.

Thomson experimented with a cathode-ray tube like the one shown in **Figure 3.** He discovered that a positively charged plate (marked with a plus sign in the drawing) attracted the beam and made it bend down. Thomson concluded that the beam must be made of particles that have negative electric charges, because opposite charges attract. The negatively charged particles that Thomson discovered are now called **electrons.**

Thomson showed that electrons are a part of atoms, but his experiment did not provide a way of knowing where electrons were located in atoms. So, he made a guess that the electrons were mixed throughout an atom, like plums in a pudding. Thomson's proposed model of the atom is sometimes called the *plum-pudding model,* after a dessert that was popular in Thomson's day. This model is shown in **Figure 4.** Today, you might call Thomson's model the *chocolate chip ice-cream model.* Chocolate chips represent electrons. The ice cream represents the rest of the atom.

electron (ee LEK TRAHN) a subatomic particle that has a negative charge

Figure 4 *Thomson proposed that electrons were located throughout an atom like plums in a pudding, as shown in this model.*

166 Chapter 6 Introduction to Atoms

Rutherford's Atomic "Shooting Gallery"

In 1909, a former student of Thomson's named Ernest Rutherford decided to test Thomson's theory. He designed an experiment to study the parts of the atom. He aimed a beam of small, positively charged particles at a thin sheet of gold foil. Rutherford put a special coating behind the foil. The coating glowed when hit by the positively charged particles. Rutherford could then see where the particles went after hitting the gold. This experiment would show if atoms have different parts or if they are all the same throughout, as the plum-pudding model suggested. **Figure 5** shows how Rutherford's experiment was set up.

Rutherford started with Thomson's idea that atoms are soft "blobs" of matter through which electrons are evenly distributed. Therefore, he expected the particles to pass right through the gold in a straight line. Most of the particles did just that. But to Rutherford's great surprise, a few of the particles were deflected (turned to one side). Some even bounced straight back. Rutherford reportedly said,

"It was quite the most incredible event that has ever happened to me in my life. It was almost as if you fired a fifteen-inch shell into a piece of tissue paper and it came back and hit you."

Quick Lab

Mystery Box   8.9.a

1. Get a small sealed **box** from your teacher. Do not open the box.

2. Write a hypothesis about what you think the box contains.

3. Carefully observe the box and its properties. Record your observations.

4. From your observations, draw the inside of the box. Label as many materials as possible.

5. How is this process similar to the process scientists have used to study the atom?

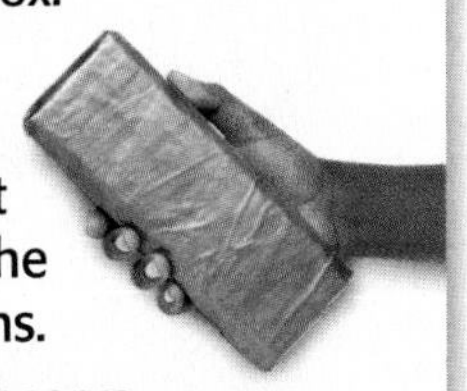

⏱ **20 min**

Figure 5 Rutherford's Gold-Foil Experiment

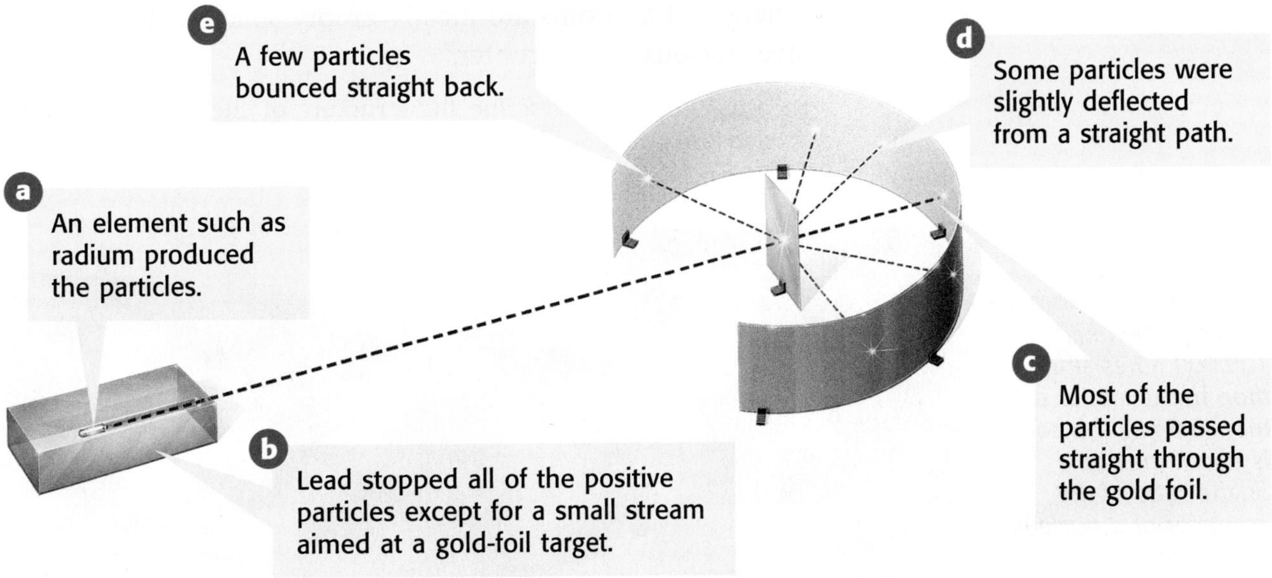

e A few particles bounced straight back.

d Some particles were slightly deflected from a straight path.

a An element such as radium produced the particles.

b Lead stopped all of the positive particles except for a small stream aimed at a gold-foil target.

c Most of the particles passed straight through the gold foil.

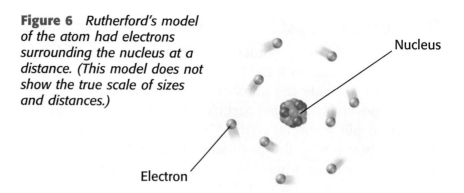

Figure 6 *Rutherford's model of the atom had electrons surrounding the nucleus at a distance. (This model does not show the true scale of sizes and distances.)*

Nucleus

Electron

The Nucleus and the Electrons

The plum-pudding model of the atom did not explain what Rutherford saw. Most of the tiny particles went straight through the gold foil. A small number of them were deflected. He realized that the explanation for this must be that most matter in an atom is found in a very small part of the atom.

Based on his experiment, Rutherford revised the atomic theory in 1911. He made a new model of the atom, as **Figure 6** shows. Rutherford proposed that in the center of the atom is a tiny, extremely dense, positively charged area called the **nucleus.** Because like charges repel, Rutherford reasoned that positively charged particles that passed close by the nucleus were pushed away by the positive charges in the nucleus. A particle that headed straight for a nucleus would be pushed almost straight back in the direction from which it came. From his results, Rutherford calculated that the diameter of the nucleus was 100,000 times smaller than the diameter of the gold atom. To get an idea of this difference in size, look at **Figure 7.** From Rutherford's results, the important idea emerged that atoms are mostly empty space with a tiny, massive nucleus at the center.

Standards Check Describe the structure of the atom according to Rutherford's model. 🐻 **8.3.a**

nucleus (NOO klee uhs) in physical science, an atom's central region, which is made up of protons and neutrons

Figure 7 *The diameter of this pinhead is 100,000 times smaller than the diameter of the stadium. This ratio is about the same as the ratio of the diameter of a nucleus to its atom.*

Bohr's Electron Levels

In 1913, Niels Bohr, a Danish scientist who worked with Rutherford, studied the way that atoms react to light. Bohr's results led him to propose that electrons move around the nucleus in definite paths. In Bohr's model, there are no paths between the levels. But electrons can jump from a path in one level to a path in another level. Think of the levels as rungs on a ladder. You can stand on the rungs of a ladder but not *between* the rungs. Bohr's model was a valuable tool in predicting some atomic behavior. But the atomic theory still had room for improvement.

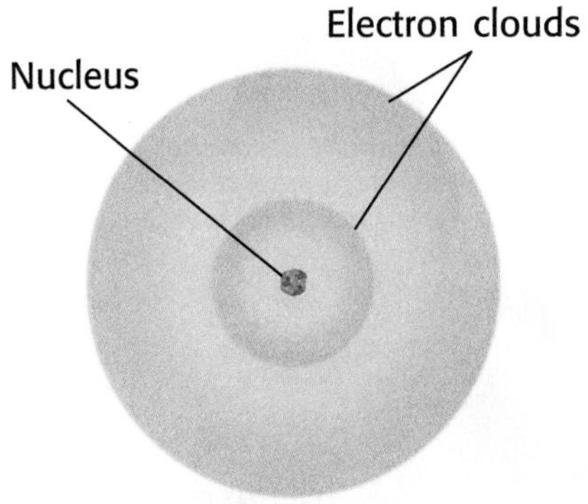

The Modern Atomic Theory

Many 20th-century scientists added to our current understanding of the atom. An Austrian physicist named Erwin Schrödinger (ER veen SHROH ding uhr) and a German physicist named Werner Heisenberg (VER nuhr HIE zuhn berkh) did especially important work. They further explained the nature of electrons in the atom. For example, electrons do not travel in definite paths as Bohr suggested. In fact, the exact path of an electron cannot be predicted. According to the current theory, there are regions inside the atom where electrons are *likely* to be found. These regions are called **electron clouds.** Sometimes the regions are called *orbitals*. The electron-cloud model of the atom is shown in **Figure 8.**

Figure 8 *In the current model of the atom, electrons surround the nucleus in electron clouds or orbitals.*

Nucleus

Electron clouds

electron cloud (ee LEK TRAHN KLOWD) a region around the nucleus of an atom where electrons are likely to be found

Energy Levels

Electron clouds are regions in an atom where electrons are likely to be found. Each electron cloud exists at a certain energy level. Instead of traveling in a definite path, as Bohr suggested, each electron has a definite energy based on its location around the nucleus. The energy of each electron in an atom keeps it in motion around the positive nucleus to which it is attracted.

The bookshelves shown in **Figure 9** can help you understand electrons in atoms. Each shelf represents an energy level. Each book represents an electron. You can move a book to a higher or lower shelf, but the right amount of energy must be used. And the book cannot be between shelves. Likewise, electrons can move by gaining or losing energy, but they are never found between energy levels.

Standards Check What determines the definite energies of electrons? 8.3.a

Figure 9 *Like books on shelves, electrons have definite energies.*

The Size of an Atom

Most of what we know about the atom was discovered without seeing a single atom. But how small is an atom? Think about a penny. A penny contains about 2×10^{22} atoms (which can be written as 20,000,000,000,000,000,000,000 atoms) of copper and zinc. That's 20 thousand billion billion atoms—more than 3,000,000,000,000 times more atoms than people on Earth! If there are that many atoms in a penny, each atom must be very small.

Scientists know that aluminum is made of average-sized atoms. An aluminum atom has a diameter of about 0.00000001 cm. That's one hundred-millionth of a centimeter. Take a look at **Figure 10.** Even things that are very thin, such as aluminum foil, are made up of very large numbers of atoms.

Observing Atoms

In fact, atoms are so small that light waves are too large to be used to observe them. Until recently, there were no tools that could produce images of individual atoms. Even though scientists have figured out a lot about the atom without direct images, theories about the atom can be extended and refined with these images. The tools that scientists now use to observe atoms include the scanning tunneling electron microscope. This tool can provide images like the one shown in **Figure 11.** Still, these images do not show an actual picture of an atom. They show a color-enhanced image of the surface of a material at the atomic level. From Dalton's time to the present day, scientists have done a lot of work showing that the atoms that Democritus suspected to exist really do exist!

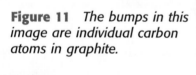

Figure 10 *This aluminum foil might seem thin to you. But it is about 100,000 atoms thick!*

Figure 11 *The bumps in this image are individual carbon atoms in graphite.*

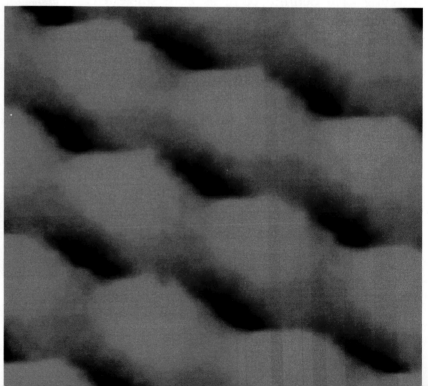

Summary

- Democritus thought that matter is composed of atoms.
- Dalton based his theory on observations of how elements combine.
- Thomson discovered electrons in atoms.
- Rutherford discovered that atoms are mostly empty space with a dense, positive nucleus.
- Bohr proposed that electrons are located in levels at certain distances from the nucleus.
- The electron-cloud model represents the current atomic theory.
- Atoms are extremely tiny, but scanning tunneling electron microscopes can be used to form direct images of them.

Using Vocabulary

1. In your own words, write a definition for the term *atom*.

Correct each statement by replacing the underlined term.

2. The <u>nucleus</u> is a particle that has a negative electric charge.

3. The <u>electron cloud</u> is where most of an atom's mass is located.

Understanding Concepts

4. **Describing** What did Dalton do that Democritus did not do in developing his atomic theory?

5. **Identifying** What discovery demonstrated that atoms are mostly empty space?

6. **Comparing** What refinements did Bohr make to Rutherford's proposed atomic theory?

7. **Evaluating** What about Bohr's atomic theory was partially correct and was also refined by other scientists?

INTERPRETING GRAPHICS Use the diagram below to answer the next question.

8. **Identifying** On a separate piece of paper, make a copy of the diagram above. Label the electrons and nucleus on your diagram. Identify the kind of charge on each.

Critical Thinking

9. **Making Comparisons** Compare the location of electrons in an atom based on Bohr's theory with the location of electrons in an atom based on the current atomic theory.

10. **Analyzing Methods** How does the design of Rutherford's experiment show what he was trying to find out?

11. **Analyzing Ideas** Why are the parts of an atom that electrons occupy called *electron clouds*?

Challenge

12. **Forming Hypotheses** Rutherford performed his gold-foil experiment to test Thomson's plum-pudding model. Describe what the results of Rutherford's experiment would have looked like if it had supported the plum-pudding model instead of contradicted it.

Internet Resources

For a variety of links related to this chapter, go to www.scilinks.org

Topic: Development of the Atomic Theory; Current Atomic Theory

SciLinks code: HY70399; HY70371

The Atom

Key Concept An atom is made of protons, neutrons, and electrons. Its properties are determined by these particles.

Even though atoms are very small, they are made up of even smaller particles. You can learn a lot about the parts that make up an atom and what holds an atom together. In this section, you will learn about how atoms are alike and how they are different.

The Parts of an Atom

Almost all kinds of atoms are made of the same three particles. These particles are protons, neutrons, and electrons, as the model in **Figure 1** shows. The particles in the pictures are not shown in their correct proportions. If the particles were shown correctly, the electrons would be too small to see. Also, the electrons would be spaced much farther apart from one another and from the nucleus. Atoms are mostly empty space.

Subatomic Particles

Protons, neutrons, and electrons are called *subatomic particles* because they are each much smaller than an atom. The number of subatomic particles that are in an atom and the way the particles interact determine the properties of the atom.

| Figure 1 | Parts of an Atom |

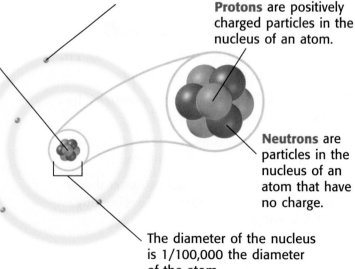

Electrons are negatively charged particles found in electron clouds outside the nucleus. The size of the electron clouds determines the size of the atom.

Protons are positively charged particles in the nucleus of an atom.

The **nucleus** is the small, dense, positively charged center of the atom. It contains most of the atom's mass.

Neutrons are particles in the nucleus of an atom that have no charge.

The diameter of the nucleus is 1/100,000 the diameter of the atom.

Figure 2 *Stars are the birthplace of many atoms.*

The Nucleus

In stars, such as those shown in **Figure 2,** atomic nuclei may collide and join. Thus, a new larger nucleus of a different element forms. But no matter what element you study, only two kinds of particles can make up a nucleus.

Protons are positively charged particles of the nucleus. The mass of a proton is about 1.7×10^{-24} g. This number can also be written as 0.0000000000000000000000017 g. Because the masses of particles in atoms are so small, scientists made a new unit for these particles. The SI unit that describes the mass of a particle in an atom is the **atomic mass unit** (amu). Each proton has a mass of about 1 amu. **Neutrons** are the particles of the nucleus that have no electric charge. Neutrons are a little more massive than protons. But the difference in mass is so small that the mass of a neutron can be thought of as 1 amu.

Protons and neutrons are the most massive particles in an atom. The volume of the nucleus is very small. So, the nucleus is very dense. If it were possible to have a nucleus that has the volume of a grape, that nucleus would have a mass greater than 9 million metric tons!

Standards Check Name the two kinds of particles that make up the nucleus of an atom. 8.3.a

Outside the Nucleus

Electrons are the negatively charged particles in atoms. Electrons are found outside the nucleus in electron clouds. Compared with protons and neutrons, electrons have a very small mass. It takes more than 1,800 electrons to equal the mass of 1 proton. The mass of an electron is so small that the mass is usually thought of as almost zero.

The charges of protons and electrons are opposite but equal, so the charges cancel out. Because an atom has no overall charge, an atom is neutral. If the numbers of electrons and protons become unequal, the atom becomes a charged particle called an *ion* (IE ahn). An atom that loses one or more electrons becomes a positively-charged ion. An atom that gains one or more electrons becomes a negatively-charged ion.

proton (PROH TAHN) a subatomic particle that has a positive charge and that is located in the nucleus of an atom; the number of protons in the nucleus is the atomic number, which determines the identity of an element

atomic mass unit (uh TAHM ik MAS YOON it) a unit of mass that describes the mass of an atom or molecule

neutron (NOO TRAHN) a subatomic particle that has no charge and that is located in the nucleus of an atom

Atoms and Elements

There are more than 110 different elements. The atoms of each of these elements are different from the atoms of all other elements. What makes atoms different from each other? To find out, imagine that you could build an atom by putting together protons, neutrons, and electrons.

The Simplest Atom

To understand atoms, you should start with the simplest atom. Protons and electrons are found in all atoms. The simplest atom is made of just one of each. The atom is so simple that it doesn't even have a neutron. To "build" this atom, put just one proton in the center of the atom for the nucleus. To have a neutral charge, your atom will also need the same number of electrons as protons. So, you put one electron in the electron cloud outside the nucleus. Congratulations! You have just made a hydrogen atom.

The Role of Neutrons

Now, build an atom that has two protons. Both of the protons are positively charged, so they repel one another. You cannot form a nucleus with them unless you add some neutrons. For this atom, two neutrons will do. Then, add two electrons outside the nucleus. You have just made an atom of the element helium. A model of this atom is shown in **Figure 3.**

Building Bigger Atoms

You could build a carbon atom using 6 protons, 6 neutrons, and 6 electrons. You could build a fluorine atom using 9 protons, 10 neutrons, and 9 electrons. You could even build a gold atom using 79 protons, 118 neutrons, and 79 electrons! As you can see, an atom does not have to have equal numbers of protons and neutrons.

Atomic Scientist Biography

What did some of the most famous atomic scientists do? Write a biography about a scientist who studied atoms. Go to **go.hrw.com,** and type in the keyword HY7ATSW.

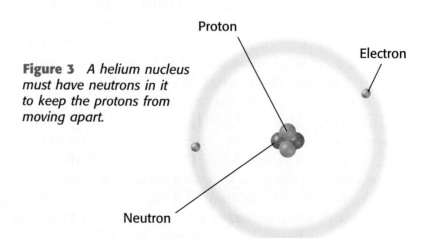

Figure 3 *A helium nucleus must have neutrons in it to keep the protons from moving apart.*

Protons and Atomic Number

How can you tell which elements these atoms represent? The key is the number of protons. The number of protons in the nucleus of an atom is the **atomic number** of that atom. All atoms of an element have the same atomic number. The element hydrogen has an atomic number of 1, which means that every hydrogen atom has only one proton in its nucleus. The element carbon has an atomic number of 6. So, every carbon atom has six protons in its nucleus. Similarly, if an atom has 8 protons, you know that it is an oxygen atom, because the element oxygen has an atomic number of 8. The atomic number of each element is listed on the periodic table.

Isotopes

Models of two kinds of hydrogen atoms are shown in **Figure 4.** They are both hydrogen atoms because they each have one proton. But one of the atoms also has a neutron in its nucleus.

The two hydrogen atoms are isotopes of each other. **Isotopes** are atoms that have the same number of protons but have different numbers of neutrons. Atoms that are isotopes of each other are always the same element, because isotopes of the same element always have the same number of protons. They have different numbers of neutrons, however, which gives them different masses. Isotopes of the same element are similar to one another in many ways. However, some elements have isotopes whose properties differ in important ways.

Standards Check How do isotopes of the same element differ from one another? 8.7.b

atomic number (uh TAHM ik NUHM buhr) the number of protons in the nucleus of an atom; the atomic number is the same for all atoms of an element

isotope (IE suh TOHP) an atom that has the same number of protons (or the same atomic number) as other atoms of the same element do but that has a different number of neutrons (and thus a different atomic mass)

Figure 4 **Isotopes of Hydrogen**

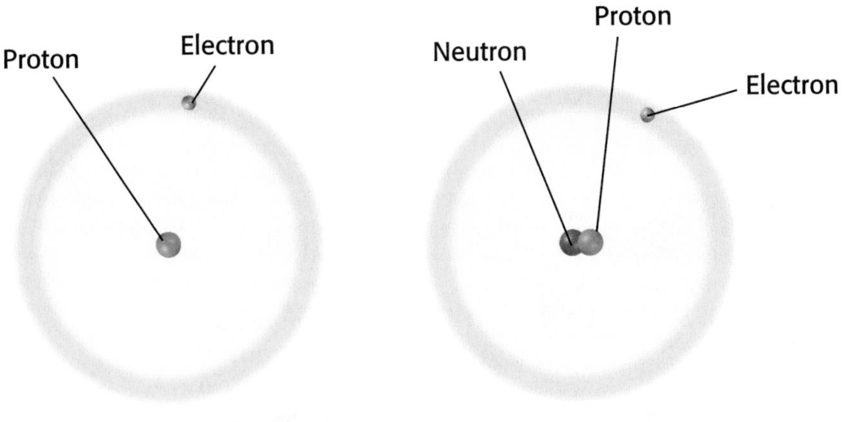

Proton
Electron

Proton
Neutron
Electron

This isotope is a hydrogen atom that has one proton in its nucleus.

This isotope is a hydrogen atom that has one proton and one neutron in its nucleus.

mass number (MAS NUHM buhr) the sum of the numbers of protons and neutrons in the nucleus of an atom

atomic mass (uh TAHM ik MAS) the mass of an atom expressed in atomic mass units

Properties of Isotopes

Each element has a limited number of isotopes that are found in nature. Some isotopes of an element have special properties because they are unstable. An unstable atom is an atom with a nucleus that will change over time. This type of isotope is *radioactive.* Radioactive atoms spontaneously fall apart after a certain amount of time. As they fall apart, they give off smaller particles and energy.

However, isotopes of an element share most of the same chemical and physical properties. For example, the most common oxygen isotope has 8 neutrons in its nucleus. Other isotopes of oxygen have 9 or 10 neutrons. All three kinds of oxygen are colorless, odorless gases at room temperature. Each one has the chemical property of combining with a substance as it burns. Different isotopes of an element even behave similarly in chemical changes in your body.

Standards Check In what cases are differences between isotopes important? **8.7.b**

The Difference Between Isotopes

You can identify each isotope of an element by its mass number. The **mass number** is the sum of the protons and neutrons in an atom. Electrons are not included in an atom's mass number because their mass is so small that they have little effect on the atom's total mass. Look at the two boron isotope models shown in **Figure 5.** The isotope on the left has 5 protons and 5 neutrons. This isotope has a mass number of 10. The isotope on the right has a mass number of 11 because it has one more neutron than the one on the left.

Figure 5 *Because each of these boron isotopes has a different number of neutrons, each isotope has a different mass number.* **How can you tell that these two atoms are of the same element?**

Protons: 5
Neutrons: 5
Electrons: 5
Mass number =
protons + neutrons = 10

Protons: 5
Neutrons: 6
Electrons: 5
Mass number =
protons + neutrons = 11

Naming Isotopes

To identify a specific isotope of an element, write the name of the element followed by a hyphen and the mass number of the isotope. A hydrogen atom that has one proton and no neutrons has a mass number of 1. It is called hydrogen-1. Hydrogen-2 has one proton and one neutron. The carbon isotope that has a mass number of 12 is called carbon-12. If you know that the atomic number for carbon is 6, you can calculate the number of neutrons in carbon-12 by subtracting the atomic number from the mass number. For carbon-12, the number of neutrons is 12 − 6, which is equal to 6.

$$\begin{array}{r} 12 \text{ Mass number} \\ - \ 6 \text{ Number of protons (atomic number)} \\ \hline 6 \text{ Number of neutrons} \end{array}$$

Isotopes and Atomic Mass

Most elements contain a mixture of two or more isotopes. For example, copper is composed of atoms of copper-63 and of copper-65. The **atomic mass** of an element is the weighted average of the masses of all the naturally occurring isotopes of that element. A weighted average accounts for the percentages of each isotope that are present. Copper is 69% copper-63 and 31% copper-65. The atomic mass of copper is 63.6 amu.

Mass Number Calculations

Use the definition of *mass number* to answer the following questions:

1. Uranium's atomic number is 92. Determine the number of neutrons and protons in uranium-235.
2. Identify the isotope of nitrogen that has 7 protons and 8 neutrons.

Quick Lab

Atomic Bead Models

Models are useful tools for understanding things that are too small to see. These models will help you understand the structure of an atom.

8.3.a
8.7.b

▶ Try It!

1. Gather at least **12 beads in each of three different colors** and a **paper plate.**
2. Let each color of bead represent one of the following subatomic particles: protons, neutrons, and electrons. Record your decisions.
3. Use the beads to create a model of an atom of carbon-14 (carbon's atomic number is 6).
4. Repeat step 3 for the following atoms: carbon-12, boron-10 (atomic number = 5), and sodium-21 (atomic number = 11).

▶ Think About It!

5. How do the models of boron and carbon differ from one another? How do the two carbon models differ from one another?
6. What are some limitations of these models?

 15 min

Forces in Atoms

You have seen that atoms are made of smaller particles. But what holds atoms together? What are the *forces* (the pushes or pulls between objects) acting between these particles? There are four basic forces that are at work everywhere in nature, even within the atom. These forces are gravitational force, electromagnetic force, strong force, and weak force. Each particle is acted on in a certain way by these basic forces. These forces work together to give an atom its structure and properties. Look at **Figure 7** to learn about each force.

Figure 7 Forces in the Atom

Gravitational Force Probably the most familiar of the four forces is *gravitational force*. Gravitational force acts between all objects all of the time. The amount of gravitational force between objects depends on their masses and on the distance between them. Gravitational force pulls objects, such as the sun, Earth, cars, and books, toward one another. However, because the masses of particles in atoms are so small, the gravitational force within atoms is very small.

Electromagnetic Force As mentioned earlier, objects that have the same charge repel each other, while objects that have opposite charges attract each other. This is due to the *electromagnetic force*. Protons and electrons are attracted to each other because they have opposite charges. The electromagnetic force holds the electrons around the nucleus.

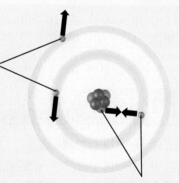

Particles with the same charges repel each other.

Particles with opposite charges attract each other.

Strong Force Protons push away from one another because of the electromagnetic force. A nucleus containing two or more protons would fly apart if the *strong force* did not hold them together. At the close distances between protons and neutrons in the nucleus, the strong force is greater than the electromagnetic force, so the nucleus stays together.

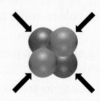

Weak Force The *weak force* is an important force in radioactive atoms. In certain unstable atoms, a neutron can change into a proton and an electron. The weak force plays a key role in this change.

Summary

- Atoms consist of a nucleus, which has protons and usually neutrons, and electrons, which are located in electron clouds around the nucleus.

- The number of protons in the nucleus of an atom is that atom's atomic number. All atoms of an element have the same atomic number.

- Different isotopes of an element have different numbers of neutrons in their nuclei. Isotopes of an element share most chemical and physical properties.

- The mass number of an atom is the sum of the atom's neutrons and protons.

- Atomic mass is a weighted average of the masses of all natural isotopes of an element.

- The forces at work in an atom are gravitational force, electromagnetic force, strong force, and weak force.

Using Vocabulary

1. Use the following terms in the same sentence: *proton, neutron,* and *isotope.*

Complete each of the following sentences by choosing the correct term from the word bank.

    atomic mass unit   atomic number
    mass number   atomic mass

2. An atom's ___ is equal to the number of protons in the atom's nucleus.

3. The ___ of an element is equal to the weighted average of the masses of all the naturally occurring isotopes of that element.

Understanding Concepts

4. **Describing** Name and describe the four forces that are at work within the nucleus of an atom.

5. **Summarizing** Explain what an atom is composed of. Be sure to list specific properties of each of the particles in an atom.

6. **Analyzing** Many elements have two or more isotopes. How do scientists tell the difference between two isotopes of the same element?

Critical Thinking

7. **Applying Concepts** Could a nucleus that has more than one proton but no neutrons exist? Explain.

INTERPRETING GRAPHICS Use the atomic diagrams below to answer the next two questions. Assume all of the particles in the nuclei of the atoms that are represented are visible.

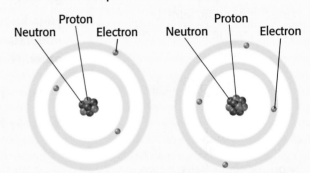

8. **Making Comparisons** Without looking at the nuclei of the atoms represented above, can you determine whether the atoms are of the same element? Explain.

9. **Predicting Consequences** What would happen if one electron were removed from each of the atoms?

Challenge

10. **Analyzing Relationships** When the elements on the periodic table are arranged by increasing atomic number, the atomic mass generally increases as the atomic number increases. For some elements, however, the atomic mass of the element is *lower* than the atomic mass for the element that came before it. Explain how this could be possible.

Model-Making Lab

Building Atomic Nuclei

Imagine that you are an employee at the Elements-4-U Company, which builds custom-made elements. Your job is to construct the atomic nucleus for each element that is ordered by your clients. You were hired for the position because of your knowledge about what a nucleus is made of and your understanding of how isotopes of an element differ from each other. Now, it's time to put that knowledge to work!

Procedure

① Copy the table below onto another sheet of paper. Be sure to leave room to expand the table to include more elements.

② Your first assignment is the nucleus of hydrogen-1. Pick up one proton (a white plastic-foam ball). Congratulations! You have built a hydrogen-1 nucleus, the simplest nucleus.

③ Count the number of protons and neutrons in the nucleus, and fill in rows 1 and 2 for this element in the table.

④ Use the information in rows 1 and 2 to determine the atomic number and mass number of the element. Record this information in the table.

Data Collection Table

	Hydrogen-1	Hydrogen-2	Helium-3	Helium-4	Beryllium-9	Beryllium-10
Number of protons						
Number of neutrons						
Atomic number						
Mass number						

DO NOT WRITE IN BOOK

8.3.a Students know the structure of the atom and know it is composed of protons, neutrons, and electrons.
8.7.b Students know each element has a specific number of protons in the nucleus (the atomic number) and each isotope of the element has a different but specific number of neutrons in the nucleus.

5 Draw a picture of your model.

6 Hydrogen-2 is an isotope of hydrogen that has one proton and one neutron. Using a strong-force connector, add a neutron to your hydrogen-1 nucleus. (Remember that in a nucleus, the protons and neutrons are held together by the strong force, which is represented in this activity by the toothpicks.) Repeat steps 3–5.

7 Helium-3 is an isotope of helium that has two protons and one neutron. Add one proton to your hydrogen-2 nucleus to create a helium-3 nucleus. Each particle should be connected to the other two particles so that they make a triangle, not a line. Protons and neutrons always form the smallest arrangement possible because the strong force pulls them together. Then, repeat steps 3–5.

8 For the next part of the lab, you will need to use information from the periodic table of the elements. Look at the illustration below. It shows the periodic table entry for carbon. You can find the atomic number of any element at the top of its entry on the periodic table. For example, the atomic number of carbon is 6.

Atomic number ——— 6
C
Carbon

9 Use the information in the periodic table to build models of the following isotopes of elements: helium-4, beryllium-9, and beryllium-10. Remember to put the protons and neutrons as close together as possible—each particle should attach to at least two others. Repeat steps 3–5 for each isotope.

Analyze the Results

10 **Examining Data** What is the relationship between the number of protons and the atomic number?

11 **Analyzing Data** If you know the atomic number and the mass number of an isotope, how could you figure out the number of neutrons in its nucleus?

Draw Conclusions

12 **Applying Conclusions** Find uranium on the periodic table. What is the atomic number of uranium? How many neutrons does the isotope uranium-235 have?

13 **Evaluating Models** Compare your model with the models of your classmates. How are the models similar? How are they different?

Big Idea Question

14 **Applying Concepts** How do the properties of the isotopes that you constructed differ from one another, and what do those differences depend on?

181

Science Skills Activity

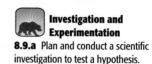

Investigation and Experimentation
8.9.a Plan and conduct a scientific investigation to test a hypothesis.

Testing a Hypothesis

▶ Tutorial

Scientific progress is made by asking meaningful questions and conducting careful investigations. The first step in this process is asking a question. Asking a question leads directly to the next step, which is proposing an answer, or a hypothesis, that you can test. Then, you are ready to plan and conduct a scientific investigation.

1 Ask a question that you would like to answer through scientific investigation.

2 Propose a hypothesis, or an answer to your question, that you will be able to test.

3 Plan an experiment that will test your hypothesis. Include the materials that you will need, the procedure that you will use, and the safety precautions that you should follow. When planning an experiment, it is important to think about factors such as controls and reproducibility. This will allow you to get valid results.

4 If your teacher approves your plan, conduct your experiment. Analyze your data and communicate your findings in writing.

1

Question: What brand of paper towel absorbs the most water?

2

Question: What brand of paper towel absorbs the most water?
Hypothesis: "Sop-It-Up" brand

3

Materials:
Procedure, with controls and number of trials:
Safety:

4

Data:
Conclusion:

▶ You Try It!

Procedure
Plan and conduct a scientific investigation, as directed in the Tutorial.

Analysis

1 Evaluating Hypotheses What was the hypothesis that you planned to test? Give two other possible hypotheses that you could have tested to answer your question.

2 Organizing Data Conduct your experiment, and organize your data in either a table or a graph.

3 Evaluating Data Give reasons, based on your procedure and analysis, that support the accuracy of the data you collected.

4 Evaluating Conclusions How do your data support your conclusion? What are some other experiments that you could do to verify your conclusion?

Chapter Summary

The Big Idea
Atoms are composed of small particles that determine the properties of the atom.

Section	Vocabulary

1 Development of the Atomic Theory

Key Concept Scientists have done experiments that have revealed important clues about the structure of atoms.

- There have been different models of the atom over time.
- The atomic theory has changed as scientists have experimented and discovered new information about the atom.

Ernest Rutherford's experiment with gold foil, which the diagram below represents, was one of many experiments that shaped the modern atomic theory.

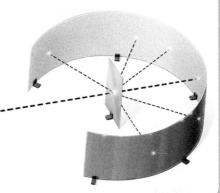

Vocabulary:

atom p. 164
electron p. 166
nucleus p. 168
electron cloud p. 169

2 The Atom

Key Concept An atom is made of protons, neutrons, and electrons. Its properties are determined by these particles.

- Protons, neutrons, and electrons make up atoms.
- All atoms of a given element have the same number of protons in the nucleus.
- Isotopes of an element differ by the number of neutrons in the nucleus.
- Atomic mass is an average of the masses of all of the naturally occurring isotopes of an element.
- Four forces are at work in atoms.

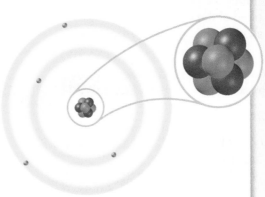

In the model above, electrons are outside of the nucleus, which is composed of protons and neutrons.

Vocabulary:

proton p. 173
atomic mass unit p. 173
neutron p. 173
atomic number p. 175
isotope p. 175
mass number p. 176
atomic mass p. 177

Organize

Booklet Review the FoldNote that you created at the beginning of the chapter. Add to or correct the FoldNote based on what you have learned.

Using Vocabulary

1 **Academic Vocabulary** In the sentence, "Each element of matter has distinct properties and a distinct atomic structure," what does the word *structure* mean?

Correct each statement by replacing the underlined term.

2 Electrons have a positive charge.

3 All atoms of the same element contain the same number of neutrons.

4 Protons have no electric charge.

5 The atomic number of an element is the number of protons and neutrons in the nucleus.

6 The mass number is a weighted average of the masses of all of the naturally occurring isotopes of an element.

Understanding Concepts

Multiple Choice

7 The discovery of which particle proved that the atom is not indivisible?
   a. proton
   b. neutron
   c. electron
   d. nucleus

8 How many protons are in the nucleus of an atom that has an atomic number of 23 and a mass number of 51?
   a. 23
   b. 28
   c. 51
   d. 74

9 Which of the following determines the identity of an element?
   a. atomic number
   b. mass number
   c. atomic mass
   d. overall charge

10 Isotopes exist because atoms of the same element can have different numbers of
   a. protons.
   b. neutrons.
   c. electrons.
   d. None of the above

Short Answer

11 **Describing** In his experiment, what discovery was Rutherford trying to test and learn more about?

12 **Identifying** What keeps an electron in motion around the nucleus to which it is attracted?

INTERPRETING GRAPHICS Use the diagram below to answer the next three questions.

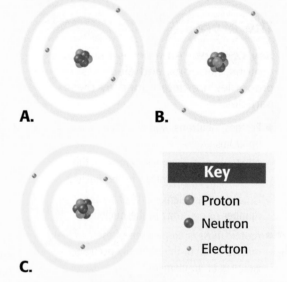

A.

B.

C.

Key

● Proton
● Neutron
• Electron

13 **Identifying** What is the atomic number for the atom represented in diagram A?

14 **Identifying** What is the mass number for the atom represented in diagram B?

15 **Classifying** Which diagrams represent isotopes of the same element?

Writing Skills

16 Writing from Research Choose a scientist who made important contributions to atomic theory, and write a research paper on him or her. Discuss what influenced his or her ideas, and elaborate on the historical significance of his or her research.

Critical Thinking

17 Concept Mapping Use the following terms to create a concept map: *atom, nucleus, protons, neutrons, electrons, isotopes, atomic number,* and *mass number.*

18 Analyzing Ideas John Dalton made a number of statements about atoms that are now known to be incorrect. Why do you think his atomic theory is still mentioned in science textbooks?

19 Applying Concepts If scientists had tried to repeat Thomson's experiment and found that they could not, would Thomson's conclusion have been valid? Explain your answer.

INTERPRETING GRAPHICS Use the diagram below to answer the next two questions.

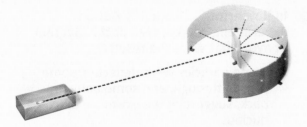

20 Analyzing Methods A diagram of an important atomic experiment is shown above. What do the dotted lines represent, and how do they relate to the conclusion of the experiment?

21 Analyzing Processes How did the experiment represented above demonstrate that atoms are mostly empty space?

22 Evaluating Assumptions What assumptions did Thomson make when, based on his experimental results, he proposed the plum-pudding model? Based on the information he had available at the time, were his assumptions valid?

23 Analyzing Processes Particle accelerators are devices that speed up charged particles to smash the particles together. Scientists use these devices to make atoms. How can scientists determine whether the atoms formed are new elements or new isotopes of known elements?

24 Predicting Consequences What would happen to a stable nucleus in which the number of neutrons suddenly decreased?

25 Applying Concepts Imagine that you have a sample of an unknown element and that you know only the element's mass number. Without directly measuring the number of protons in the nucleus of that element, what other information would you need to know to identify the element?

Math Skills

26 Making Calculations Calculate the number of neutrons in an atom of an element that has a mass number of 98 and an atomic number of 42.

27 Making Calculations Calculate the number of protons, neutrons, and electrons in an atom of zirconium-90 that has no overall charge and an atomic number of 40.

Challenge

28 Expressing Opinions Ernest Rutherford's experimental results greatly surprised him. What had Rutherford been expecting to find? Imagine that you lived in Rutherford's day and had the same information about the atom that he did. Do you think that you would have been surprised at his findings? Explain.

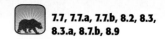
REVIEWING ACADEMIC VOCABULARY

1 **Which of the following words is the closest in meaning to the word *distinct*?**

A separate

B similar

C approximate

D varying

2 **In the sentence "The structure of a substance is determined by its atoms," what does the word *structure* mean?**

A destruction

B resistance

C composition

D elements

3 **Which of the following words best completes the following sentence: "An element has a _____ number of protons in its nucleus"?**

A large

B specific

C differing

D negative

4 **Which of the following words is closest in meaning to the word *investigation*?**

A plan

B inquiry

C gathering

D development

REVIEWING CONCEPTS

5 **All matter is made up of atoms. Which sentence correctly describes atoms?**

A All substances are made of the same atoms.

B Atoms are the smallest particle of a nucleus.

C An atom is the smallest particle of an element.

D An atom is a substance that has been cut in half.

6 **The particles inside an atom that are negatively charged are called**

A protons.

B neutrons.

C nuclei.

D electrons.

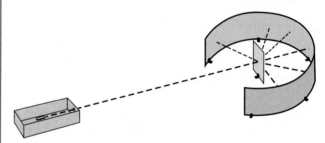

7 **In Rutherford's "Shooting Gallery" experiment, represented in the diagram above, what were the results?**

A Some particles were deflected, some passed through, and some bounced back, suggesting the existence of a nucleus.

B Only one of the particles passed through the foil, suggesting that atoms were denser than previously thought.

C Almost all of the particles hit the foil and bounced back, proving Thomson's hypothesis of atomic structure.

D Many particles were deflected, proving that electrons do not travel in predictable paths.

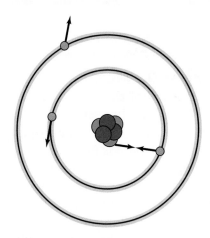

8 What principle of electromagnetic force is shown in the above diagram of an atom?

A Particles with the same charges have no effect on each other.

B Particles with opposite charges attract each other.

C Electromagnetic force repels objects from around the nucleus.

D Protons and neutrons repel each other because they have the same charge.

9 How can you determine the atomic number of an atom?

A by counting its protons and neutrons

B by determining the atomic mass unit of the atom

C by counting the number of protons

D by determining the number of electrons in its outermost energy level

10 When two atoms have the same number of protons but different numbers of neutrons, they are called

A isotopes.

B nuclei.

C ions.

D helium.

11 Careful investigations can answer meaningful questions. Which of the following is an example of an investigation?

A reading about protons in a textbook

B testing the atomic theory with an experiment

C writing an outline of a chapter

D drawing a diagram of an atom

12 Appropriate tools are needed to determine data in an experiment. Which tool would a scientist use to observe atoms?

A an electron-cloud model

B a scientific calculator

C an electron microscope

D a cathode-ray tube

13 Appropriate research materials need to be used to collect evidence. Which source would be best for finding information on naming isotopes?

A a newspaper article about the discovery of atoms

B a science Web site written by a seventh-grade student

C a movie about a fictional scientist who splits atoms

D a book about determining the mass of atoms

14 Elements are

A the substances that make up all matter.

B ions that have been positively charged.

C the combination of particles in a molecule.

D the nuclei in isotopic atoms.

Standards Assessment

Science in Action

Weird Science

Mining on the Moon?

Since the end of the Apollo moon missions in 1972, no one has set foot on the surface of the moon. But today, an isotope of helium known as *helium-3* is fueling new interest in returning to the moon. Some scientists speculate that helium-3 can be used as a safe and nonpolluting fuel for a new kind of power plant. Helium-3 is very rare on Earth, but a huge amount of the isotope exists on the surface of the moon. But how can helium-3 be brought to Earth? Some researchers imagine a robotic lunar mining operation that will harvest the helium-3 and transport it to Earth.

Language Arts ACTIVITY

Write a paragraph in your **Science Journal** in which you rephrase the information above in your own words. Be sure to include what helium-3 is, where it can be found, and how it could be used.

Scientific Discoveries

Californium

Look at the bottom row of the periodic table. There are some elements there that are named after famous scientists such as Mendeleev and Einstein. The state of California also has an element named after it. Californium was artificially created at the University of California, Berkeley in 1950. It is a radioactive element, and made in very small amounts. In the picture above, less than a millionth of a gram of californium is encased in protective stainless steel.

Math ACTIVITY

Find the element californium (Cf) on the periodic table. One isotope of californium is californium-249. How many neutrons does an atom of californium-249 contain? Write your answer in your **Science Journal.**

Explore Activity

 **20 min**

8.3.f

A Tool To Predict Properties

In this activity, you will identify the pattern your teacher used to make a new seating chart and will make a prediction based on the pattern.

Procedure

1. Draw a seating chart for the new classroom arrangement that your teacher gave to you. Write the name of each of your classmates in the place on the chart that corresponds to his or her seat.

2. Write information about yourself, such as your name, date of birth, hair color, and height, in the space that represents you on the chart.

3. Gather the same information about the people near you, and write it in the spaces on the chart.

Analysis

4. From the information you gathered, identify a pattern that could explain the order of people in the chart. Collect more information if needed.

5. Test your pattern by gathering information from a person you did not talk to before. If the new information does not support your pattern, collect more information and identify another pattern.

6. If your teacher left a seat open for a student who will be joining the class, what information could you predict about the student by using your pattern as a tool?

Arranging the Elements

Key Concept Elements are arranged on the periodic table according to their atomic number and their chemical properties.

What You Will Learn

- Elements on the periodic table are arranged in order of increasing atomic number.
- Elements on the periodic table are classified as metals, nonmetals, or metalloids.
- Elements in a horizontal row, or period, are listed in order of increasing atomic number.
- Elements in a vertical column, or group, usually have similar chemical properties.
- The periodic law states that the properties of elements form a pattern according to increasing atomic number.

Why It Matters

If you understand the arrangement of the elements on the periodic table, you can use the table as a tool for predicting the structure of atoms.

Vocabulary
- periodic   • group
- period   • periodic law

READING STRATEGY

Graphic Organizer In your **Science Journal,** make a Spider Map that shows metals, nonmetals, and metalloids as classes of elements in the periodic table.

▶ Suppose that you are at a video store and all the videos are mixed together. How can you quickly find a comedy or an action movie? If the videos are not arranged in a pattern, you won't know where to look!

Scientists in the early 1860s had a similar problem. At that time, scientists knew some of the properties of more than 60 elements. However, no one had organized the elements according to these properties. Finding patterns among the elements would help scientists understand the elements. And organizing the elements according to their properties would help scientists understand how elements interact with each other.

Discovering a Pattern

Dmitri Mendeleev (duh MEE tree MEN duh LAY uhf), who was a Russian chemist, discovered a pattern to the elements in 1869. First, he wrote the names and properties of the elements on cards. Then, he played "chemical solitaire" with the cards. He arranged his cards, as shown in **Figure 1,** by different properties, such as density, appearance, and melting point. After much thought, he arranged the elements in order of increasing atomic mass. When he did so, a pattern appeared.

Figure 1 By playing "chemical solitaire" on long train rides, Mendeleev organized the elements according to their properties.

Periodic Properties of the Elements

Mendeleev saw that when the elements were arranged in order of increasing atomic mass, those that had similar properties fell into a repeating pattern. That is, the pattern was periodic. **Periodic** means "happening at regular intervals." The days of the week are periodic. They repeat in the same order every seven days. Similarly, Mendeleev found that the elements' properties followed a pattern that repeated every seven elements. His table became known as the *periodic table of the elements*.

Predicting Properties of Missing Elements

Figure 2 shows part of Mendeleev's first try at arranging the elements. The question marks show gaps in the pattern. Mendeleev predicted that elements yet to be found would fill these gaps. He used the pattern he found to predict their properties. **Table 1** compares his predictions for one missing element—germanium—with its actual properties. By 1886, all of the gaps that he had noted had been filled. His predictions were right.

periodic (PIR ee AHD ik) describes something that occurs or repeats at regular intervals

Wordwise The suffix *-ic* means "pertaining to."

Figure 2 *Mendeleev used question marks to note elements that he thought would be found later.*

Table 1	Properties of Germanium	
	Mendeleev's predictions (1869)	**Actual properties**
Atomic mass	70	72.6
Density*	5.5 g/cm^3	5.3 g/cm^3
Appearance	dark gray metal	gray metal
Melting point*	high melting point	937°C

*at room temperature and pressure

Changing the Arrangement

A few elements' properties did not fit the pattern in Mendeleev's table. Mendeleev thought that more-accurate atomic masses would fix these flaws in his table. But new measurements showed that the masses he had used were correct. In 1914, Henry Moseley (MOHZ lee), a British scientist, determined the number of protons—the atomic number—in an atom. All elements fit the pattern in Mendeleev's periodic table when they were arranged by atomic number.

Look at the periodic table on the next two pages. The elements are arranged horizontally in order of increasing atomic number. Elements that have similar chemical properties are grouped in vertical columns.

Standards Check How are the elements arranged horizontally and vertically on the periodic table? 8.3.f

8.3.f Students know how to use the periodic table to identify elements in simple compounds.
8.7.a Students know how to identify regions corresponding to metals, nonmetals, and inert gases.
8.7.b Students know each element has a specific number of protons in the nucleus (the atomic number) and each isotope of the element has a different but specific number of neutrons in the nucleus.
8.7.c Students know substances can be classified by their properties, including their melting temperature, density, hardness, and thermal and electrical conductivity.

Periodic Table of the Elements

Each square on the table includes an element's name, chemical symbol, atomic number, and atomic mass.

The color of the chemical symbol indicates the physical state at room temperature. Carbon is a solid.

6	Atomic number
C	Chemical symbol
Carbon	Element name
12.0	Atomic mass

The background color indicates the type of element. Carbon is a nonmetal.

Background
Metals
Metalloids
Nonmetals

Chemical symbol
Solid
Liquid
Gas

Period 1

| 1 |
| **H** |
| Hydrogen |
| 1.0 |

| **Group 1** | **Group 2** |

Period 2

3	4
Li	**Be**
Lithium	Beryllium
6.9	9.0

Period 3

11	12
Na	**Mg**
Sodium	Magnesium
23.0	24.3

| | | **Group 3** | **Group 4** | **Group 5** | **Group 6** | **Group 7** | **Group 8** | **Group 9** |

Period 4

19	20	21	22	23	24	25	26	27
K	**Ca**	**Sc**	**Ti**	**V**	**Cr**	**Mn**	**Fe**	**Co**
Potassium	Calcium	Scandium	Titanium	Vanadium	Chromium	Manganese	Iron	Cobalt
39.1	40.1	45.0	47.9	50.9	52.0	54.9	55.8	58.9

Period 5

37	38	39	40	41	42	43	44	45
Rb	**Sr**	**Y**	**Zr**	**Nb**	**Mo**	**Tc**	**Ru**	**Rh**
Rubidium	Strontium	Yttrium	Zirconium	Niobium	Molybdenum	Technetium	Ruthenium	Rhodium
85.5	87.6	88.9	91.2	92.9	95.9	(98)	101.1	102.9

Period 6

55	56	57	72	73	74	75	76	77
Cs	**Ba**	**La**	**Hf**	**Ta**	**W**	**Re**	**Os**	**Ir**
Cesium	Barium	Lanthanum	Hafnium	Tantalum	Tungsten	Rhenium	Osmium	Iridium
132.9	137.3	138.9	178.5	180.9	183.8	186.2	190.2	192.2

Period 7

87	88	89	104	105	106	107	108	109
Fr	**Ra**	**Ac**	**Rf**	**Db**	**Sg**	**Bh**	**Hs**	**Mt**
Francium	Radium	Actinium	Rutherfordium	Dubnium	Seaborgium	Bohrium	Hassium	Meitnerium
(223)	(226)	(227)	(261)	(262)	(266)	(264)	(277)	(268)

A row of elements is called a *period*.

A column of elements is called a *group* or *family*.

Values in parentheses are the mass numbers of those radioactive elements' most stable or most common isotopes.

These elements are placed below the table to allow the table to be narrower.

Lanthanides

58	59	60	61	62
Ce	**Pr**	**Nd**	**Pm**	**Sm**
Cerium	Praseodymium	Neodymium	Promethium	Samarium
140.1	140.9	144.2	(145)	150.4

Actinides

90	91	92	93	94
Th	**Pa**	**U**	**Np**	**Pu**
Thorium	Protactinium	Uranium	Neptunium	Plutonium
232.0	231.0	238.0	(237)	(244)

Topic: **Periodic Table**
Go to: **go.hrw.com**
Keyword: **HN0 PERIODIC**
Visit the HRW Web site for updates on the periodic table.

This zigzag line reminds you where the metals, nonmetals, and metalloids are.

			Group 13	Group 14	Group 15	Group 16	Group 17	Group 18
								2 **He** Helium 4.0
			5 **B** Boron 10.8	6 **C** Carbon 12.0	7 **N** Nitrogen 14.0	8 **O** Oxygen 16.0	9 **F** Fluorine 19.0	10 **Ne** Neon 20.2
Group 10	Group 11	Group 12	13 **Al** Aluminum 27.0	14 **Si** Silicon 28.1	15 **P** Phosphorus 31.0	16 **S** Sulfur 32.1	17 **Cl** Chlorine 35.5	18 **Ar** Argon 39.9
28 **Ni** Nickel 58.7	29 **Cu** Copper 63.5	30 **Zn** Zinc 65.4	31 **Ga** Gallium 69.7	32 **Ge** Germanium 72.6	33 **As** Arsenic 74.9	34 **Se** Selenium 79.0	35 **Br** Bromine 79.9	36 **Kr** Krypton 83.8
46 **Pd** Palladium 106.4	47 **Ag** Silver 107.9	48 **Cd** Cadmium 112.4	49 **In** Indium 114.8	50 **Sn** Tin 118.7	51 **Sb** Antimony 121.8	52 **Te** Tellurium 127.6	53 **I** Iodine 126.9	54 **Xe** Xenon 131.3
78 **Pt** Platinum 195.1	79 **Au** Gold 197.0	80 **Hg** Mercury 200.6	81 **Tl** Thallium 204.4	82 **Pb** Lead 207.2	83 **Bi** Bismuth 209.0	84 **Po** Polonium (209)	85 **At** Astatine (210)	86 **Rn** Radon (222)
110 **Ds** Darmstadtium (281)	111 **Uuu** Unununium (272)	112 **Uub** Ununbium (285)	113 **Uut** Ununtrium (284)	114 **Uuq** Ununquadium (289)	115 **Uup** Ununpentium (288)			

The discovery of elements 113, 114, and 115 has been reported but not confirmed.

The names and three-letter symbols of elements are temporary. They are based on the atomic numbers of the elements. Official names and symbols will be approved by an international committee of scientists.

63 **Eu** Europium 152.0	64 **Gd** Gadolinium 157.2	65 **Tb** Terbium 158.9	66 **Dy** Dysprosium 162.5	67 **Ho** Holmium 164.9	68 **Er** Erbium 167.3	69 **Tm** Thulium 168.9	70 **Yb** Ytterbium 173.0	71 **Lu** Lutetium 175.0
95 **Am** Americium (243)	96 **Cm** Curium (247)	97 **Bk** Berkelium (247)	98 **Cf** Californium (251)	99 **Es** Einsteinium (252)	100 **Fm** Fermium (257)	101 **Md** Mendelevium (258)	102 **No** Nobelium (259)	103 **Lr** Lawrencium (262)

The Periodic Table and Classes of Elements

At first glance, you may think that studying the periodic table is like trying to explore a thick jungle without a guide—you can easily get lost! However, the table itself contains a lot of information that will help you along the way.

Elements are classified according to their properties as metals, nonmetals, and metalloids. Regions of the periodic table correspond to classes of elements. The number of electrons in the outer energy level of an atom helps determine the category in which an element belongs. The zigzag line on the periodic table can help you recognize which elements are metals, which are nonmetals, and which are metalloids.

Metals

Most elements are metals. Metals are found to the left of the zigzag line on the periodic table. Atoms of most metals have few electrons in their outer energy level. Most metals are solid at room temperature. Mercury, however, is a liquid at room temperature. Some more information on metallic properties is shown in **Figure 3.**

Standards Check Identify where metals are found on the periodic table. 🐻 **8.7.a**

Figure 3 **Properties of Metals**

Metals tend to be **shiny.** You can see a reflection in a mirror because light reflects off the shiny surface of a thin layer of silver behind the glass.

Most metals are **ductile,** which means that they can be drawn into thin wires. All metals are **good conductors of electric current.** The wires in the electrical devices in your home are made of copper.

Most metals are **malleable,** which means that they can be rolled or pounded into shape and will not shatter. Aluminum is flattened into sheets to make cans and foil.

Most metals are **good conductors of thermal energy.** An iron griddle can conduct thermal energy from a stove top to cook foods.

Figure 4 Properties of Nonmetals and Metalloids

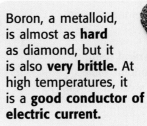

Nonmetals are **not malleable or ductile.** Solid nonmetals, such as carbon in the graphite of pencil lead, are **brittle** and will break or shatter when hit with a hammer.

Boron, a metalloid, is almost as **hard** as diamond, but it is also **very brittle.** At high temperatures, it is a **good conductor of electric current.**

Nonmetals

Nonmetals are found to the right of the zigzag line on the periodic table. Atoms of most nonmetals have an almost complete set of electrons in their outer level. More than half of the nonmetals are gases at room temperature. Many properties of nonmetals are the opposite of the properties of metals.

Metalloids

Metalloids, also called *semimetals,* are the elements that border the zigzag line on the periodic table. Atoms of metalloids have about half of a complete set of electrons in their outer energy level. Metalloids have some properties of metals and some properties of nonmetals. **Figure 4** compares some of the properties of nonmetals and metalloids.

Standards Check Name two properties that metals have and that nonmetals do not have. 🐾 8.7.c

Decoding the Periodic Table

The periodic table may seem to be in code. In a way, it is. But learning what the symbols and numbers mean can help you find your way around the table.

Chemical Symbols

Each square on the periodic table includes an element's name, chemical symbol, atomic number, and atomic mass. A scientist who discovers an element can suggest a name for it. Some elements, such as curium, einsteinium, seaborgium, and mendelevium, are named after scientists. Others, such as californium, are named after places. Some element names vary by country. But the chemical symbols are the same worldwide.

For most elements, the chemical symbol has one or two letters. The first letter is always capitalized. Any other letter is always lowercase. When you see a chemical formula, you can use the periodic table as a tool to quickly identify the elements that make up the compound.

SCHOOL to HOME

Patterns of Symbols

Divide a sheet of paper in your **Science Journal** into four columns. Look at the elements whose atomic numbers are 1 to 20 on the periodic table. With an adult, find patterns that describe the relationship between the chemical symbols and names of elements. In each column, write all of the chemical symbols and names that follow a single pattern. At the top of each column, write a sentence describing the pattern.

ACTIVITY

period (PIR ee uhd) in chemistry, a horizontal row of elements in the periodic table

group (GROOP) a vertical column of elements in the periodic table; elements in a group share chemical properties

periodic law (PIR ee AHD ik LAW) the law that states that the repeating chemical and physical properties of elements change periodically with the atomic numbers of the elements

Periods

Each horizontal row of elements (from left to right) on the periodic table is called a **period.** The physical and chemical properties of elements in a row follow a repeating, or periodic, pattern as you move across the period.

Groups

Each vertical column of elements (from top to bottom) on the periodic table is called a **group.** Elements in the same group often have similar chemical and physical properties. For this reason, a group is also called a *family.*

Atomic Number

All of the elements follow the periodic law. The **periodic law** states that the repeating chemical and physical properties of elements change periodically with the elements' atomic numbers. The atomic number of an element is the number of protons in the nucleus of an atom of that element. All atoms of a given element have the same number of protons in the nucleus. Atoms with different atomic numbers are atoms of different elements. Look at **Figure 5.** The atomic number is above the chemical symbol of each element on the periodic table.

Although each element has a specific number of protons, the number of neutrons for an element can vary. Atoms that have the same number of protons but different numbers of neutrons are *isotopes* of each other. Each isotope of an element has a specific number of neutrons in the nucleus.

Standards Check **What does an element's atomic number equal?** **8.7.b**

MATH PRACTICE

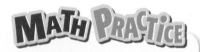

Percentages

Elements are classified as metals, nonmetals, and metalloids. Use the periodic table to determine the percentage of elements in each of the three categories. Record your work in your **Science Journal.**

Figure 5 **Finding the Atomic Number**

14
Si
Silicon
28.1

Atomic Number: 14
Number of protons: 14

86
Rn
Radon
(222)

Atomic Number: 86
Number of protons: 86

92
U
Uranium
238.0

Atomic Number: 92
Number of protons: 92

Summary

- Mendeleev developed the first periodic table by listing the elements in order of increasing atomic mass. He used his table to predict that elements with certain properties would be discovered later.

- Properties of elements repeat in a regular, or periodic, pattern.

- Moseley rearranged the elements in order of increasing atomic number.

- Elements in the periodic table are classified as metals, nonmetals, and metalloids.

- Each element has a chemical symbol that identifies elements that make up compounds.

- A horizontal row of elements is called a *period*. Physical and chemical properties of elements change across each period.

- A vertical column of elements is called a *group* or *family*. Elements in a group usually have similar properties.

- The periodic law states that the repeating chemical and physical properties of elements relate to and depend on elements' atomic numbers.

Using Vocabulary

1. Write an original definition for *periodic*.

Understanding Concepts

2. **Comparing** What is the difference between a period and a group on the periodic table?

3. **Identifying** Identify the elements in the compound NaCl.

4. **Describing** What is atomic number, and what relationship does it have to the periodic table?

5. **Classifying** What class of elements makes up the groups on the right side of the periodic table?

6. **Describing** On the basis of what property did Mendeleev position the elements on the periodic table?

Critical Thinking

7. **Identifying Relationships** An atom that has 117 protons in its nucleus has not yet been made. Once this atom is made, to which period and group will element 117 belong? Explain your answer.

INTERPRETING GRAPHICS Use the image below of part of a periodic table to answer the next three questions.

1	1 H 1.0079 水素				
2	3 Li 6.941 リチウム	4 Be 9.01218 ベリリウム			
3	11 Na 22.98977 ナトリウム	12 Mg 24.305 マグネシウム			
4	19 K	20 Ca	21 Sc	22 Ti	23 V

8. **Making Comparisons** To which region of the periodic table does this image correspond?

9. **Making Comparisons** How does the information shown compare with the information shown in the periodic table in your book?

10. **Applying Concepts** Can you determine the number of protons in an atom of sodium from this image? Explain your reasoning.

Challenge

11. **Applying Concepts** Locate sodium, lithium, and magnesium on the periodic table. Identify the group and period for each. Are the properties of sodium more like the properties of lithium or of magnesium? Explain your answer.

Grouping the Elements

Key Concept Elements within each group, or column, on the periodic table have similar properties.

Although the element hydrogen appears above the alkali metals on the periodic table, it is not considered a member of Group 1. It will be described separately at the end of this section.

▶ You probably know a family with several members who look a lot alike. The elements in a family or group in the periodic table often—but not always—have similar properties. The properties are similar because the atoms of the elements in a group have the same number of electrons in their outer energy level. Atoms will often take, give, or share electrons with other atoms in order to have a complete set of electrons in their outer energy level. Elements whose atoms undergo such processes are called *reactive.* They can combine to form compounds.

Group 1: Alkali Metals

3 Li Lithium
11 Na Sodium
19 K Potassium
37 Rb Rubidium
55 Cs Cesium
87 Fr Francium

Group contains: metals
Electrons in the outer level: 1
Reactivity: very reactive
Other shared properties: softness; color of silver; shininess; low density

Alkali metals are elements in Group 1 of the periodic table. **Figure 1** shows some of the properties they share. Alkali metals are the most reactive metals. Their atoms can easily give away their one outer-level electron. Pure alkali metals are often stored in oil. The oil keeps them from reacting with water and oxygen in the air. Alkali metals are so reactive that in nature they are found only combined with other elements. Compounds formed from alkali metals have many uses. Sodium chloride (table salt) flavors food.

Figure 1 **Properties of Alkali Metals**

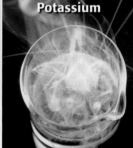

Alkali metals are soft enough to be cut with a knife.

Alkali metals react with water to form hydrogen gas.

Group 2: Alkaline-Earth Metals

| 4
Be
Beryllium |
| 12
Mg
Magnesium |
| 20
Ca
Calcium |
| 38
Sr
Strontium |
| 56
Ba
Barium |
| 88
Ra
Radium |

Group contains: metals
Electrons in the outer level: 2
Reactivity: very reactive but less reactive than alkali metals
Other shared properties: color of silver; density higher than density of alkali metals

Alkaline-earth metals are less reactive than alkali metals are. Atoms of alkaline-earth metals have two outer-level electrons. It is more difficult for atoms to give away two electrons than to give away one when joining with other atoms. Group 2 elements and their compounds have many uses. For example, magnesium can be mixed with other metals to make low-density materials used in airplanes. And compounds of calcium are found in cement, chalk, and even you, as shown in **Figure 2.**

Figure 2 *Calcium, an alkaline-earth metal, is an important part of a compound that keeps your bones and teeth healthy.*

alkali metal (AL kuh LIE MET uhl) one of the elements of Group 1 of the periodic table (lithium, sodium, potassium, rubidium, cesium, and francium)

alkaline-earth metal (AL kuh LIEN UHRTH MET uhl) one of the elements of Group 2 of the periodic table (beryllium, magnesium, calcium, strontium, barium, and radium)

Groups 3–12: Transition Metals

21 **Sc**	22 **Ti**	23 **V**	24 **Cr**	25 **Mn**	26 **Fe**	27 **Co**	28 **Ni**	29 **Cu**	30 **Zn**
39 **Y**	40 **Zr**	41 **Nb**	42 **Mo**	43 **Tc**	44 **Ru**	45 **Rh**	46 **Pd**	47 **Ag**	48 **Cd**
57 **La**	72 **Hf**	73 **Ta**	74 **W**	75 **Re**	76 **Os**	77 **Ir**	78 **Pt**	79 **Au**	80 **Hg**
89 **Ac**	104 **Rf**	105 **Db**	106 **Sg**	107 **Bh**	108 **Hs**	109 **Mt**	110 **Ds**	111 **Uuu**	112 **Uub**

Group contains: metals
Electrons in the outer level: 1 or 2
Reactivity: less reactive than alkaline-earth metals
Other shared properties: shininess; good conductivity of thermal energy and electric current; density and melting points higher than those of elements in Groups 1 and 2 (except for mercury)

Elements of Groups 3–12 are all called *transition metals.* The atoms of transition metals do not give away their electrons as easily as atoms of the Group 1 and Group 2 metals do. So, transition metals are less reactive than alkali metals and alkaline-earth metals are.

The lanthanides and the actinides make up two rows of transition metals that are placed at the bottom of the table to save space. However, you should still read them as you read the rest of the table, from left to right and then down. The elements in each of these two rows tend to have similar properties.

8.7.a Students know how to identify regions corresponding to metals, nonmetals, and inert gases.
8.7.c Students know substances can be classified by their properties, including their melting temperature, density, hardness, and thermal and electrical conductivity.

Figure 3 Properties of Transition Metals

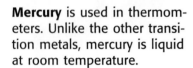

Mercury is used in thermometers. Unlike the other transition metals, mercury is liquid at room temperature.

Many transition metals are silver colored. The **gold** that this ring is made out of is an exception.

Some transition metals, such as **titanium** in the artificial hip at right, are not very reactive. But others, such as **iron,** are reactive. The iron in the steel trowel on the left has reacted to form rust.

Properties of Transition Metals

The number of outer-level electrons in atoms of transition metals can vary. So, the properties of the transition metals vary widely, as shown in **Figure 3.** But because these elements are metals, they share the properties of metals. Transition metals tend to be shiny and to conduct thermal energy and electric current well.

Standards Check Why are transition metals not as reactive as alkali metals and alkaline-earth metals? 🐻 **8.7.c**

Group 13: Boron Group

5 **B** Boron
13 **Al** Aluminum
31 **Ga** Gallium
49 **In** Indium
81 **Tl** Thallium
113 **Uut** Ununtrium

Group contains: one metalloid and five metals
Electrons in the outer level: 3
Reactivity: reactive
Other shared properties: solids at room temperature

The most common element from Group 13 is aluminum. In fact, aluminum is the most abundant metal in Earth's crust. Until the 1880s, however, aluminum was considered a precious metal. Pure aluminum was very expensive to make. Today, making pure aluminum is easier and cheaper than it was in the 1800s. Aluminum is useful because it is such a lightweight metal. It is now an important metal used in making aircraft parts, lightweight automobile parts, foil, cans, and siding.

Like the other elements in the boron group, aluminum is reactive. However, when aluminum reacts with oxygen in the air, a thin layer of aluminum oxide quickly forms on aluminum's surface. This layer prevents further reaction of the aluminum.

Group 14: Carbon Group

6
C
Carbon

14
Si
Silicon

32
Ge
Germanium

50
Sn
Tin

82
Pb
Lead

114
Uuq
Ununquadium

Group contains: one nonmetal, two metalloids, and three metals
Electrons in the outer level: 4
Reactivity: varies among the elements
Other shared properties: solids at room temperature

The nonmetal carbon can be found uncombined in nature, as shown in **Figure 4.** Carbon also forms a wide variety of compounds. Some of these compounds, such as proteins, fats, and carbohydrates, are necessary for living things on Earth.

The metalloids silicon and germanium are used in semiconductors, which are needed to make computer chips. The metal tin is useful because it is not very reactive. A layer of tin helps prevent iron in steel cans from rusting.

Standards Check What three types of elements are found in Group 14 of the periodic table? **8.7.a**

Figure 4 *Diamond and soot have very different properties, yet both are natural forms of carbon.*

Diamond is the hardest material known. It is used as a jewel and on cutting tools, such as saws, drills, and files.

Soot is formed from burning oil, coal, and wood and is used as a pigment in paints and crayons.

Group 15: Nitrogen Group

7
N
Nitrogen

15
P
Phosphorus

33
As
Arsenic

51
Sb
Antimony

83
Bi
Bismuth

115
Uup
Ununpentium

Group contains: two nonmetals, two metalloids, and two metals
Electrons in the outer level: 5
Reactivity: varies among the elements
Other shared properties: solids at room temperature (except nitrogen)

Nitrogen, which is a gas at room temperature, makes up about 80% of the air that you breathe. Nitrogen removed from air can be reacted with hydrogen to make ammonia for fertilizers.

Although nitrogen is not very reactive, phosphorus is extremely reactive, as shown in **Figure 5.** In fact, in nature, phosphorus is found only combined with other elements.

Figure 5 *Simply striking a match on the side of this box causes chemicals on the match to react with phosphorus on the box and begin to burn.*

Figure 6 *This diver is breathing a mixture that contains oxygen gas.*

Group 16: Oxygen Group

| 8
O
Oxygen |
| 16
S
Sulfur |
| 34
Se
Selenium |
| 52
Te
Tellurium |
| 84
Po
Polonium |

Group contains: three nonmetals, one metalloid, and one metal
Electrons in the outer level: 6
Reactivity: reactive
Other shared properties: solids at room temperature (except oxygen)

Oxygen makes up about 20% of air. Oxygen is necessary for substances to burn. Oxygen is also important to most living things, such as the diver shown in **Figure 6.** It is even found dissolved in ocean water, which is where fish get the oxygen they need.

Sulfur is another commonly found member of Group 16. Sulfur can be found as a yellow solid in nature. It is used to make sulfuric acid, the most widely used compound in the chemical industry.

Group 17: Halogens

| 9
F
Fluorine |
| 17
Cl
Chlorine |
| 35
Br
Bromine |
| 53
I
Iodine |
| 85
At
Astatine |

Group contains: nonmetals
Electrons in the outer level: 7
Reactivity: very reactive
Other shared properties: poor conductors of electric current; violent reactions with alkali metals to form salts; never in uncombined form in nature

Halogens are very reactive because their atoms need to gain only one electron to have a complete outer level. The atoms of halogens combine readily with other atoms, especially metals, to gain that extra electron. The reaction of a halogen with a metal makes a salt, such as sodium chloride. Both chlorine and iodine are used as disinfectants. Chlorine is used to treat water. Iodine mixed with alcohol is used in hospitals.

Although the chemical properties of the halogens are similar, the physical properties are quite different, as shown in **Figure 7.**

Chlorine is a yellowish green gas.

Bromine is a dark red liquid.

Iodine is a dark gray solid.

Figure 7 *The physical properties of some halogens are shown above.* **How does the state of matter change as you move from top to bottom in Group 17?**

Group 18: Noble Gases

2 **He** Helium
10 **Ne** Neon
18 **Ar** Argon
36 **Kr** Krypton
54 **Xe** Xenon
86 **Rn** Radon

Group contains: nonmetals
Electrons in the outer level: 8 (except helium, which has 2)
Reactivity: unreactive
Other shared properties: colorless, odorless gases at room temperature

Noble gases are unreactive nonmetals and are in Group 18 of the periodic table. The atoms of these elements have a full set of electrons in their outer level. So, they do not need to lose or gain any electrons. Under normal conditions, they do not react with other elements. In fact, these elements were first called *inert gases* because scientists thought that these elements would not react at all! However, scientists have made compounds from some elements in Group 18. So, the name *noble gases* is more correct. Earth's atmosphere is almost 1% argon. But all the noble gases are found in small amounts.

The unreactivity of the noble gases makes them useful. For example, ordinary light bulbs last longer when they are filled with argon. Because argon is unreactive, it does not react with the hot metal filament in the light bulb. A more reactive gas might react with the filament, causing the light to burn out. The low density of helium makes blimps and weather balloons float. Another popular use of noble gases is shown in **Figure 8.**

Standards Check Where are the noble gases located on the periodic table? 🐻 **8.7.a**

halogen (HAL oh juhn) one of the elements of Group 17 of the periodic table (fluorine, chlorine, bromine, iodine, and astatine); halogens combine with most metals to form salts

noble gas (NOH buhl GAS) one of the elements of Group 18 of the periodic table (helium, neon, argon, krypton, xenon, and radon); noble gases are unreactive

INTERNET ACTIVITY

The Right Element for You
Which types of elements are the most useful? Create an advertisement that promotes these types of elements. Go to **go.hrw.com,** and type in the keyword HY7PRTW.

Figure 8 *In addition to neon, other noble gases can be used to make "neon" lights.*

Hydrogen

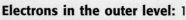
1
H
Hydrogen

Electrons in the outer level: 1
Reactivity: reactive
Other properties: colorless, odorless gas at room temperature; low density; explosive reactions with oxygen

Figure 9 *Hydrogen reacts violently with oxygen. The hot water vapor that forms as a result of this reaction helps guide the space shuttle into orbit.*

Hydrogen is the most abundant element in the universe. It is found in large amounts in stars. Atoms of hydrogen can give away one electron when they join with other atoms. Hydrogen reacts with many elements, and is found in many compounds. Hydrogen's reactive nature makes it useful as a fuel in rockets, as shown in **Figure 9.**

The Uniqueness of Hydrogen

Most atoms of hydrogen have just one proton and one electron. The properties of hydrogen do not match the properties of any single group, so hydrogen is set apart in the table. Hydrogen is above Group 1 because atoms of the alkali metals also have only one electron in their outer level. However, the physical properties of hydrogen are more like those of nonmetals than those of metals. So, hydrogen really is in a group of its own.

Standards Check Why is hydrogen classified apart from the other elements in the periodic table? **8.7.c**

Quick Lab

Locating Elements on the Table

In this activity, you will make and trade "element cards" to better understand the organization of the periodic table.

8.3.f
8.7.a

▶ Try It!

1. Choose four elements from the **periodic table.**

2. For each element, create an "element card." On an **index card,** write a set of directions that will lead someone to your element. For example, "Begin at nickel, and add 3 protons" could be written on a card as "Ni + 3 protons." Another direction could be "2nd alkali metal from the bottom."

3. Exchange cards with a classmate. Identify the element described on each card.

▶ Think About It!

4. How do the cards show the way in which atomic number relates to the periodic table?

5. Can you use the information on the cards to identify regions, periods, and groups of elements on the periodic table? Explain.

 20 min

Summary

- Elements that are classified as alkali metals (Group 1) are the most reactive metals. Atoms of the alkali metals have one electron in their outer level.

- Elements that are classified as alkaline-earth metals (Group 2) are less reactive than the alkali metals are. Atoms of the alkaline-earth metals have two electrons in their outer level.

- Elements that are classified as transition metals (Groups 3–12) include most of the well-known metals and the lanthanides and actinides.

- Groups 13–16 contain the metalloids and some metals and nonmetals.

- Halogens (Group 17) are very reactive non-metals. Atoms of the halogens have seven electrons in their outer level.

- Noble gases (Group 18) are unreactive non-metals. Atoms of the noble gases have a full set of electrons in their outer level.

- Hydrogen is set off by itself in the periodic table. Its properties do not match the properties of any one group.

Using Vocabulary

Complete each of the following sentences by choosing the correct term from the word bank.

noble gases   alkaline-earth metals
halogens   alkali metals

1. Elements in the leftmost column of the periodic table are ___. Elements in the right-most column of the periodic table are ___.

2. Elements that are very reactive nonmetals are ___.

Understanding Concepts

3. **Listing**   List two properties of the alkali metals.

4. **Describing**   Explain why the properties of the elements in a group are usually similar.

INTERPRETING GRAPHICS   Use the image below from the periodic table to answer the next two questions.

43
Tc
Technetium
(98)

5. **Classifying**   Could this element be classified as a noble gas? Explain your answer.

6. **Analyzing**   What can you tell about the properties of this element?

Critical Thinking

7. **Applying Concepts**   Why would you not be able to make jewelry out of sodium?

8. **Identifying Relationships**   Identify the region on the periodic table where nonmetals are found. Does this region contain the noble gases?

INTERPRETING GRAPHICS   Use the model of the atom below to answer the next question.

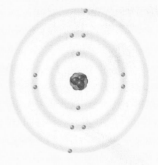

9. **Applying Concepts**   Does the model represent a metal atom or a nonmetal atom? Explain your answer.

Challenge

10. **Making Inferences**   In general, the noble gases were discovered later than many of the other elements. Suggest a reason for this fact.

Model-Making Lab

OBJECTIVES

Classify objects based on their properties.

Identify patterns and trends in data.

MATERIALS

- bag of objects
- balance, metric
- meterstick
- paper, graphing (2 sheets)
- paper, 3 × 3 cm squares (20)

SAFETY

8.3.f Students know how to use the periodic table to identify elements in simple compounds.

Investigation and Experimentation
8.9.a Plan and conduct a scientific investigation to test a hypothesis.
8.9.e Construct appropriate graphs from data and develop quantitative statements about the relationships between variables.
8.9.g Distinguish between linear and nonlinear relationships on a graph of data.

Create a Periodic Table

You probably have classification systems for many things in your life, such as your clothes, your books, and your CDs. One of the most important classification systems in science is the periodic table of the elements. In this lab, you will develop your own classification system for a collection of ordinary objects. You will also use your system as a tool to make predictions about the properties of a missing object.

Ask a Question

1 Your teacher will give you a bag of objects. Your bag is missing one item. Examine the items carefully. Describe the missing object in as many ways as you can. Be sure to include the reasons why you think the missing object has the characteristics you describe.

2 Can a classification system be developed to use as a tool to make better predictions about the characteristics of a missing object?

Form a Hypothesis

3 Write a few sentences that answer the question in step 2.

Test the Hypothesis

4 Lay the paper squares out on your desk or table so that you have a grid of five rows of four squares each.

5 Arrange your objects on the grid in a logical order. (You must decide what order is logical!) You should end up with one blank square for the missing object. Record a description of the basis for your arrangement.

6 Measure the mass (g) and diameter (mm) of each object, and record your results in the appropriate square. Each square (except the empty one) should have one object and two written measurements on it.

7 Examine your pattern again. Does the order in which your objects are arranged still make sense? Explain. Rearrange the squares and their objects if necessary to improve your arrangement. Record a description of the basis for the new arrangement.

8 Working across the rows, number the squares "1" to "20." When you get to the end of a row, continue numbering in the first square of the next row.

9 Copy your grid onto a sheet of paper. In each square, be sure to list the type of object and label all measurements with appropriate units.

Analyze the Results

10 Constructing Graphs Make a graph of mass (*y*-axis) versus object number (*x*-axis). Label each axis, and title the graph.

11 Constructing Graphs Now, make a graph of diameter (*y*-axis) versus object number (*x*-axis). Label each axis, and title the graph.

Draw Conclusions

12 Analyzing Graphs Discuss each graph with your classmates. Try to identify any important features of the graph. For example, does the graph form a line or a curve? Is there anything unusual about the graph? What do these features tell you? Record your answers.

13 Making Predictions Look again at your prediction about the missing object. Use your classification system as a tool to improve your predictions about the characteristics of the missing object. Record your results.

14 Evaluating Models How is your arrangement of objects similar to the arrangement of elements on the periodic table found in this textbook? How is your arrangement different?

Big Idea Question

15 Evaluating Methods How do your results show the value of organizing items according to their properties?

Science Skills Activity

Investigation and Experimentation
8.9.e Construct appropriate graphs from data and develop quantitative statements about the relationships between variables.

Constructing a Line Graph

▶ Tutorial

1 Follow these steps to build your graph.
- Draw the axes for your graph on a sheet of graph paper.
- Write the numbers of the scale next to the tick marks of the axis.
- Label the *x*-axis in terms that describe the types of data. Usually, the independent variable is placed on the *x*-axis.
- Write the numbers of the scale next to the tick marks of the axis.
- Title the *x*-axis.
- Determine a scale for the *y*-axis that includes the range of your data. Write the numbers of the scale next to the tick marks of the axis.
- Title the *y*-axis.
- Write the title of your graph on the top of the graph.

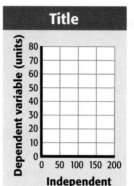

2 Follow these steps to plot your data.
- Plot a series of points by using your data. Each point indicates an (*x*, *y*) coordinate on the graph.
- On the graph, draw a line through all of the points that you have plotted.

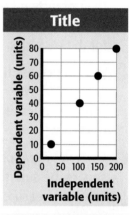

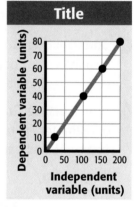

▶ You Try It!

Procedure

Electronegativity is a measure of the strength with which atoms in compounds attract electrons. Each element has a certain electronegativity. The table at right shows electronegativity values for the first six elements of Period 2 of the periodic table.

Analysis

1 Identifying Relationships Make a graph of electronegativity versus atomic number for the elements shown in the table at right. Describe the relationship between atomic number and electronegativity for those elements.

2 Applying Concepts What would you expect the electronegativity for the element with atomic number 9, fluorine, to be? Explain.

3 Analyzing Relationships According to the periodic law, what would you expect to be the relationship between atomic number and electronegativity for Period 3 elements?

Electronegativity of Period 2 Elements

Element	Atomic Number	Electronegativity
Lithium	3	1.0
Beryllium	4	1.5
Boron	5	2.0
Carbon	6	2.5
Nitrogen	7	3.0
Oxygen	8	3.5

Chapter Summary

The Big Idea   Elements are organized on the periodic table according to their properties.

Section

Vocabulary

1 Arranging the Elements

Key Concept   Elements are arranged on the periodic table according to their atomic number and their chemical properties.

- Elements on the periodic table are arranged in order of increasing atomic number.

- Elements on the periodic table are classified as metals, nonmetals, or metalloids.

- Elements in a horizontal row, or period, are listed in order of increasing atomic number.

- Elements in a vertical column, or group, usually have similar chemical properties.

- The periodic law states that the properties of elements form a pattern according to increasing atomic number.

Mendeleev first arranged elements based on the property of atomic mass.

periodic p. 195
period p. 200
group p. 200
periodic law p. 200

2 Grouping the Elements

Key Concept   Elements within each group, or column, on the periodic table have similar properties.

- Elements in a group often have similar properties because their atoms have the same number of electrons in their outer energy level.

- Hydrogen is set off by itself in the periodic table because its properties do not match the properties of any one group.

- Metals are in Groups 1–16. Metalloids are in Groups 13–16. Nonmetals are in Groups 14–18. Noble gases are in Group 18.

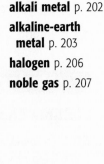

Solid iodine and liquid bromine are in Group 17 of the periodic table and are reactive nonmetals.

alkali metal p. 202
alkaline-earth metal p. 203
halogen p. 206
noble gas p. 207

Chapter Review

 8.3.f, 8.7.a, 8.7.b, 8.7.c

Organize

Three-Panel Flip Chart   Review the FoldNote that you created at the beginning of the chapter. Add to or correct the FoldNote based on what you have learned.

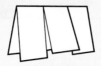

Using Vocabulary

1 **Academic Vocabulary**   Which of the following words means "an area"?
a. region
b. type
c. structure
d. property

Complete each of the following sentences by choosing the correct term from the word bank.

group	period
alkali metals	halogens
alkaline-earth metals	noble gases

2 Elements in the same vertical column on the periodic table belong to the same ___.

3 Elements in the same horizontal row on the periodic table belong to the same ___.

4 Elements that are unreactive are called ___.

Understanding Concepts

Multiple Choice

5 Mendeleev's periodic table was useful because it
a. had elements arranged by atomic number.
b. had no empty spaces.
c. showed the atomic number of the elements.
d. allowed for the prediction of the properties of missing elements.

6 An element that is very reactive is most likely a member of the
a. noble gases.
b. alkali metals.
c. transition metals.
d. actinides.

7 Which of the following items is NOT found on the periodic table?
a. the atomic number of each element
b. the name of each element
c. the date that each element was discovered
d. the atomic mass of each element

8 Which of the following statements about elements is true?
a. Every element occurs naturally.
b. All elements are found in their uncombined form in nature.
c. Each element has a unique atomic number.
d. All of the elements exist in approximately equal quantities.

9 Which of the following statements about the periodic table is false?
a. There are more metals than nonmetals on the periodic table.
b. Atoms of elements in the same group have the same number of electrons in their outer level.
c. The elements at the far left of the periodic table are nonmetals.
d. Elements are arranged by increasing atomic number.

Short Answer

10 **Comparing**   How was Moseley's basis for arranging the elements different from Mendeleev's?

11 **Describing**   What is the periodic law?

INTERPRETING GRAPHICS   Use the images below from the periodic table to answer the next three questions.

19	36
K	**Kr**
Potassium	Krypton
39.1	83.8

12 **Identifying**   What is the atomic number of each of these elements?

13 **Comparing**   An atom of which element has the most protons in its nucleus?

14 **Classifying**   To which region and which group does each of these elements belong?

Writing Skills

15 Communicating Concepts Write an essay that clearly explains how elements are organized on the periodic table. Your essay should have a thesis statement and include examples that support your ideas. Finally, make sure that your essay has a conclusion sentence.

Critical Thinking

16 Concept Mapping Use the following terms to create a concept map: *periodic table, elements, groups, periods, metals, nonmetals,* and *metalloids.*

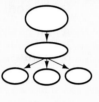

17 Analyzing Methods Why was Mendeleev unable to make any predictions about the noble-gas elements?

18 Analyzing Relationships Suppose that a certain unidentified element is a metal. Based on that information alone, to which two groups of the periodic table could it NOT belong? To which period of the periodic table could it NOT belong?

19 Making Inferences Could a new element be discovered that would be placed in between two consecutive known elements on the periodic table? Explain.

20 Applying Concepts Identify each element described below.
  a. This metal is very reactive, has properties similar to those of magnesium, and is in the same period as bromine.
  b. This nonmetal is in the same group as lead.
  c. This metal is the most reactive metal in its period. It cannot be found uncombined in nature. Each atom of the element contains 19 protons.

21 Making Comparisons Identify something from everyday life that is periodic, and explain the way in which it is periodic. How is the way in which it is periodic similar to the periodic table, and how is it different?

INTERPRETING GRAPHICS Use the diagram below to answer the next question.

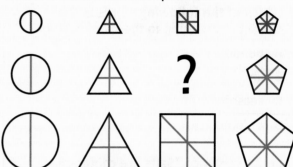

22 Identifying Relationships Predict the missing image, and draw it. Identify which properties are periodic and which properties are shared within a group.

Math Skills

INTERPRETING GRAPHICS Use the chart below of the percentages of elements in Earth's crust to answer the next two questions.

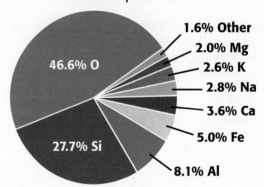

46.6% O
27.7% Si
1.6% Other
2.0% Mg
2.6% K
2.8% Na
3.6% Ca
5.0% Fe
8.1% Al

23 Analyzing Data Excluding the "Other" category, what percentage of elements in Earth's crust can be classified as metals?

24 Analyzing Data Excluding the "Other" category, what percentage of elements in Earth's crust are alkaline-earth metals?

Challenge

25 Analyzing Relationships Halogens tend to form compounds with alkali metals. Using what you have learned about the reactivities of halogens and alkali metals, suggest a reason for this fact.

Standards Assessment

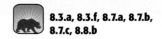

8.3.a, 8.3.f, 8.7.a, 8.7.b, 8.7.c, 8.8.b

REVIEWING ACADEMIC VOCABULARY

1 Which of the following words is the closest in meaning to the word *regular*?

A periodic

B limited

C seasonal

D ordered

2 In the sentence "Salts are compounds made of a metal and a nonmetal," what does the word *compounds* mean?

A substances that cannot be broken down into simpler ones

B substances made of two or more substances without chemical bonding

C the materials or elements that make up a substance

D substances made by the combination of two or more different things

3 Which of the following sets of words best completes the following sentence: "A certain region of the periodic table _____ metals."?

A corresponds to

B correspond by

C corresponding of

D corresponded in

4 Choose the appropriate form of the word *specific* in the following sentence: "Elements have a _____ number of protons."

A specify

B specific

C specification

D specifically

REVIEWING CONCEPTS

5 According to the periodic table, which elements form the compound CO_2?

A cobalt and osmium

B carbon and oxygen

C copper and osmium

D calcium and oxygen

6 According to its location on the periodic table, sodium can be described as

A an alkaline-earth metal.

B a transition metal.

C an alkali metal.

D a metalloid.

7 What is the purpose of the zigzag line on the right side of the periodic table?

A It marks the border between the alkali metals and the transition metals.

B It indicates a family of elements that have the same chemical properties.

C It connects the elements in the table that have the same atomic number.

D It divides the metals and nonmetals, and shows where the metalloids are.

6

C

Carbon

12.0

8 What does the number at the top of the square above tell you about carbon?

A Carbon has 6 protons in its nucleus.

B Carbon has an average atomic mass of 12.0.

C Carbon has 12 isotopes.

D Carbon has 6 electrons in its outer level.

9 Elements that have the same number of protons but a different number of neutrons in the nucleus are called

   A periods.

   B metalloids.

   C groups.

   D isotopes.

10 Which of the following best describes the properties of metals?

   A hard, brittle, and unconductive

   B liquid, dark, and conductive

   C shiny, malleable, and conductive

   D soft, oily, and very reactive

11 In what order are the regions arranged on the periodic table, reading left to right?

   A inert gases, metals, nonmetals, metalloids

   B metalloids, metals, nonmetals, inert gases

   C metals, metalloids, nonmetals, inert gases

   D nonmetals, inert gases, metals, metalloids

12 Fluorine, chlorine, bromine, iodine, and astatine make up group 17, the halogens. Why are these elements grouped together?

   A They are all very reactive nonmetals with similar chemical properties.

   B They are all nonreactive gases with similar physical properties.

   C Their atoms all have 8 electrons in their outer energy levels.

   D They all have the same atomic number.

REVIEWING PRIOR LEARNING

13 Which of the following would be the best way to compare the densities of two rock samples?

   A Divide each rock's mass by its volume. The rock with the higher number is denser.

   B Measure the rocks in a graduated cylinder. The one that displaces more water is denser.

   C Use a balance to measure the samples. The higher number is the denser rock.

   D Hold the samples in your hands. The rock that feels heavier is denser.

14 Which of the following describes a chemical property of rubbing alcohol?

   A It is colorless.

   B It has a strong odor.

   C It evaporates quickly.

   D It burns easily.

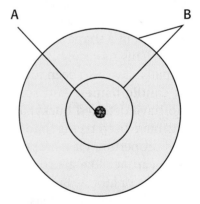

15 Which of the following can be found at point A?

   A electrons

   B protons

   C ions

   D electron clouds

Science in Action

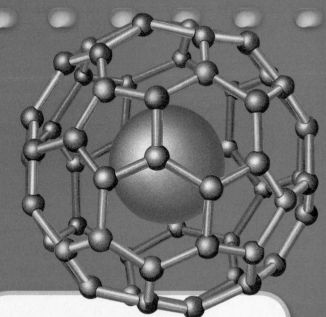

Scientific Discoveries

Modern Alchemy

Hundreds of years ago, many people thought that if you treated lead with certain chemicals, it would turn into gold. People called *alchemists* often spent their whole lives trying to find a way to make gold from other metals, such as lead. We now know that the methods alchemists used to try to change one element to another could not work. But in the 20th century, scientists learned to change one element to another! In a nuclear reaction, small particles collide with atomic nuclei and can change the nuclei into nuclei of different elements. Using this method, researchers have actually been able to add new elements to the periodic table.

Weird Science

Buckyballs

In 1985, scientists found a completely new kind of molecule! This carbon molecule has 60 carbon atoms linked in a shape similar to that of a soccer ball. This molecule is called a *buckyball*. Buckyballs have also been found in the soot from candle flames. And some scientists claim to have detected buckyballs in space. Chemists have been trying to identify the molecule's properties. One property is that a buckyball can act like a cage and hold smaller molecules or atoms. Buckyballs are both slippery and strong. Scientists are exploring their use in tough plastics and cutting tools.

Math ACTIVITY

If you split an atom of lead (atomic number = 82) and one of the atoms that results is gold (atomic number = 79), what element will the other atom that results from this change be? Write your answer in your **Science Journal.**

Language Arts ACTIVITY

Imagine that you are trapped within a buckyball. Write a one-page short story in your **Science Journal** describing your experience. Describe the windows in your molecular prison.

Glenn T. Seaborg

Making Elements When you look at the periodic table, you can thank Dr. Glenn Theodore Seaborg and his colleagues for many of the actinide elements. While working at the University of California at Berkeley, Seaborg and his team added a number of elements to the periodic table. His work in identifying properties of plutonium led to his working on the top-secret Manhattan Project at the University of Chicago. He was outspoken about the beneficial uses of atomic energy and, at the same time, opposed the production and use of nuclear weapons.

Seaborg's revision of the layout of the periodic table—the introduction of the actinide concept—is the most significant since Mendeleev's original design. For his scientific achievements, in 1951 Seaborg was awarded the Nobel Prize in chemistry jointly with his colleague, Edwin M. McMillan. Element 106, which Seaborg neither discovered nor created, was named *seaborgium* in his honor. For the first time, an element had been named after a living person.

Social Studies ACTiViTY

Write a newspaper editorial in your **Science Journal** expressing an opinion for or against the Manhattan Project. Be sure to include information to support your view.

Internet Resources

- To learn more about careers in science, visit **www.scilinks.org** and enter the SciLinks code HY70225.

- To learn more about these Science in Action topics, visit **go.hrw.com** and type in the keyword HY7PRTF.

- Check out articles related to this chapter by visiting **go.hrw.com**. Just type in the keyword HY7PRTC.

Interactions of Matter

In this unit you will study the interactions through which matter can change its identity. You will learn how atoms bond with one another to form compounds and how atoms join in different combinations to form new substances through chemical reactions. You will also learn about the properties of several categories of compounds. This timeline includes some of the events leading to the current understanding of these interactions of matter.

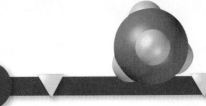

1828

Urea, a compound found in urine, is produced in a laboratory. Until this time, chemists had believed that compounds created by living organisms could not be produced in the laboratory.

1858

German chemist Friedrich August Kekulé suggests that carbon forms four chemical bonds and can form long chains.

1942

The first nuclear chain reaction is carried out in a squash court under the football stadium at the University of Chicago.

1979

Public fear about nuclear power grows after an accident occurs at the Three Mile Island nuclear power station located in Pennsylvania.

1867
Swedish chemist Alfred Nobel develops dynamite. Dynamite's explosive power is a result of the decomposition reaction of nitroglycerin.

1898
The United States defeats Spain in the Spanish-American War.

1903
Marie Curie, Pierre Curie, and Henri Becquerel are awarded the Nobel Prize in physics for the discovery of radioactivity.

1964
Dr. Martin Luther King, Jr., American civil rights leader, is awarded the Nobel Peace Prize.

1969
The *Nimbus III* weather satellite is launched by the United States, representing the first civilian use of nuclear batteries.

1996
Evidence of organic compounds in a meteorite leads scientists to speculate that life may have existed on Mars more than 3.6 billion years ago.

2001
The first total solar eclipse of the millenium occurs on June 21.

2002
Hy-wire, the world's first drivable vehicle to combine a hydrogen fuel cell with by-wire technology, is introduced.

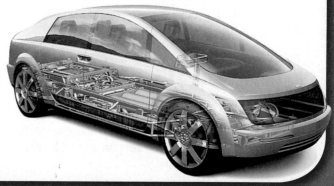

Improving Comprehension

Graphic Organizers are important visual tools that can help you organize information and improve your reading comprehension. The Graphic Organizer below is called a *comparison table*. Instructions for creating other types of Graphic Organizers are located in the **Study Skills** section of the Appendix.

How to Make a Comparison Table

1 Draw a table like the one shown below. Draw as many columns and rows as you want to draw.

2 In the top row, write the topics that you want to compare.

3 In the left column, write the general characteristics that you want to compare. As you read the chapter, fill in the characteristics for each topic in the appropriate boxes.

When to Use a Comparison Table

A comparison table is useful when you want to compare the characteristics of two or more topics in science. Organizing information in a table helps you compare several topics at one time. In a table, all topics are described in terms of the same list of characteristics, which helps you make a thorough comparison. As you read, look for topics whose characteristics you may want to compare in a table.

	Ionic bonds	Covalent bonds	Metallic bonds
How the bond forms	• valence electrons are transferred from one atom to another	• valence electrons are shared between two atoms	• positively charged metal ions are attracted to the electrons around them
Types of atoms usually bonded	• metal and nonmetal	• nonmetal and nonmetal	• metal and metal
Properties of compounds	• brittle at room temperature • high melting and boiling points • highly soluble in water	• brittle solids • high melting and boiling points	• conductivity • ductility • malleability

You Try It!

This Reading Strategy can also be used within the chapter that you are about to read. Practice making your own *comparison table* as directed in the Reading Strategies for Section **2** and Section **3**. Record your work in your **Science Journal**.

Unpacking the Standards

The information below "unpacks" the standards by breaking them down into basic parts. The higher-level, academic vocabulary is highlighted and defined to help you understand the language of the standards. "What It Means" restates the standards as simply as possible.

California Standard	Academic Vocabulary	What It Means
8.3.a Students know the **structure** of the atom and know it is composed of protons, neutrons, and electrons.	**structure** (STRUHK chuhr) the arrangement of the parts of a whole	An atom is made up of small particles called *protons, neutrons,* and *electrons,* which are arranged in a predictable pattern.
8.3.b Students know that compounds are formed by combining two or more different elements and that compounds have properties that are different from their **constituent** elements.	**constituent** (kuhn STICH oo uhnt) serving as part of a whole	Compounds form when two or more elements combine. The properties of a compound differ from the properties of the elements that make up the compound.
8.3.c Students know atoms and molecules form solids by building up repeating patterns, such as the crystal **structure** of NaCl or long-chain polymers.	**structure** (STRUHK chuhr) a whole that is built or put together from parts	Solids are made up of atoms and molecules arranged in organized, repeating patterns. For example, table salt is made up of crystals, and plastics are made up of polymer chains.
8.3.f Students know how to use the periodic table to **identify** elements in simple compounds.	**identify** (ie DEN tuh FIE) to point out or pick out	You must know how to use the table that arranges elements by atomic number to find which elements are in simple compounds.
8.5.a Students know reactant atoms and molecules **interact** to form products with different **chemical** properties.	**interact** (IN tuhr AKT) to act upon one another **chemical** (KEM i kuhl) of or having to do with the properties or actions of substances	When atoms and molecules are put together, they can interact to form new substances whose chemical properties differ from the properties of the original substances.

Chemical Bonding

The Big Idea

Atoms combine by forming ionic, covalent, and metallic bonds.

 California Standards

Focus on Physical Sciences

8.3 Each of the more than 100 elements of matter has distinct properties and a distinct atomic structure. All forms of matter are composed of one or more of the elements. (Sections 1, 2, and 3)

8.5 Chemical reactions are processes in which atoms are rearranged into different combinations of molecules. (Section 2)

Investigation and Experimentation

8.9 Scientific progress is made by asking meaningful questions and conducting careful investigations. (Science Skills Activity)

Math
6.2.3 Number Sense

English–Language Arts
8.2.2 Reading
8.1.3 Writing

About the Photo

What looks like a fantastic "sculpture" is really a model of deoxyribonucleic acid (DNA). DNA is one of the most complex molecules in living things. In DNA, atoms are joined by chemical bonds in two very long spiral strands. These strands join to form a double spiral. The DNA in living cells has all the coding for passing on the traits of that cell and that organism.

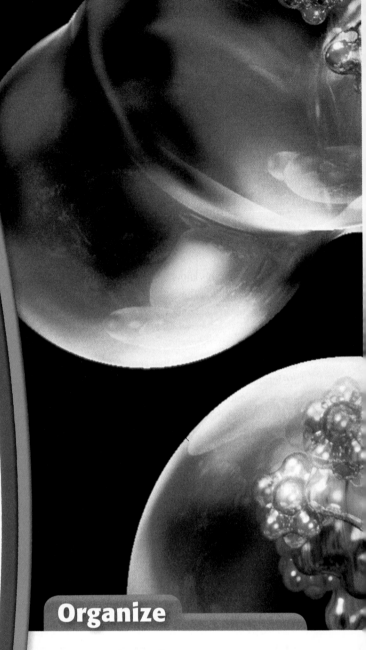

Organize

Layered Book

Before you read this chapter, create the FoldNote entitled "Layered Book." Label the tabs of the layered book with "Chemical bond," "Ionic bond," "Covalent bond," and "Metallic bond." As you read the chapter, write information that you learn about each category on the appropriate tab.

Instructions for creating FoldNotes are located in the Study Skills section on p. 518 of the Appendix.

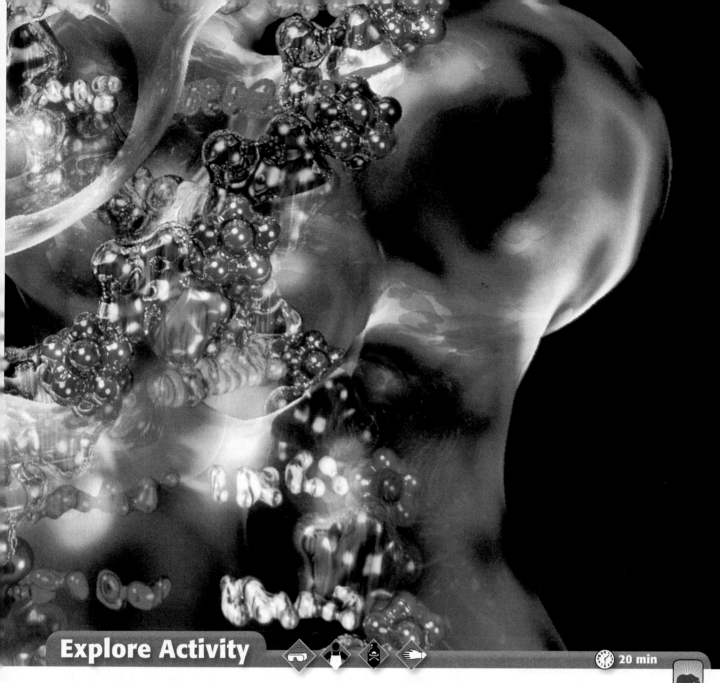

Explore Activity

 20 min

8.5.a

Bonding and Properties

Particles of glue bond to other particles and hold objects together. Different types of bonds create differences in the properties of substances. In this activity, you will see how the formation of bonds causes a change in the properties of white glue.

Procedure

1. Fill a **small paper cup** one-fourth full of **white glue.** Record the physical properties of the glue.

2. Fill a **second small paper cup** one-fourth full of **borax solution.** Describe the appearance of the borax.

3. Pour the borax solution into the cup of white glue, and stir well using a **plastic spoon** or a **wooden craft stick.**

4. When the material becomes too thick to stir, remove it from the cup and knead it with your fingers. Describe the physical properties of this substance.

Analysis

5. Compare the physical properties of the glue with those of the product formed.

6. The properties of the product resulted from bonds between the borax and the glue. Predict the properties of the material if less borax is used.

Electrons and Chemical Bonding

Key Concept Atoms share, gain, or lose electrons when chemical bonds form.

What You Will Learn

● Chemical bonding is the joining of atoms to form new substances.

● Valence electrons are used to form chemical bonds.

● The number of valence electrons in an atom determines whether the atom will form bonds.

Why It Matters

Understanding chemical bonding helps explain why some elements combine and some do not.

Vocabulary

• chemical bonding
• chemical bond
• valence electron

READING STRATEGY

Clarifying Concepts Take turns reading this section out loud with a partner. Stop to discuss ideas that seem confusing.

8.3.a Students know the structure of the atom and know it is composed of protons, neutrons, and electrons.

8.3.b Students know that compounds are formed by combining two or more different elements and that compounds have properties that are different from their constituent elements.

8.3.f Students know how to use the periodic table to identify elements in simple compounds.

Have you ever stopped and thought that by using only the 26 letters of the alphabet, you make all of the words you use every day? Even though the number of letters is limited, joining the letters in different ways allows you to make a huge number of words. In the same way that words can be formed by joining letters, substances can be formed by combining atoms.

Combining Atoms Through Chemical Bonding

Look at **Figure 1.** Now, look around the room. Everything you see is made of atoms of elements. All substances are made of atoms of one or more of the more than 100 elements. For example, the atoms of carbon, hydrogen, and oxygen combine in different patterns to form sugar, alcohol, and citric acid. **Chemical bonding** is the joining of atoms to form new substances. The properties of these new substances are different from the properties of the original elements. An interaction that holds two atoms together is called a **chemical bond.** When chemical bonds form, electrons are shared, gained, or lost.

Standards Check What is chemical bonding? 8.3.b

Discussing Bonding Using Models

We cannot see atoms and chemical bonds with the eye alone. Because atoms are complex, models are used to discuss how and why atoms form bonds. But the simple models that are used to discuss the electrons in an atom do not show all of the details of the structure of the atom or chemical bond.

Figure 1 *Everything you see in this photo is formed by combining atoms.*

Figure 2 Electron Arrangement in an Atom

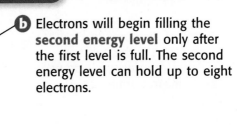

a The **first energy level** is closest to the nucleus. It can hold up to two electrons.

b Electrons will begin filling the **second energy level** only after the first level is full. The second energy level can hold up to eight electrons.

c The **third energy level** fills with electrons after the second level is full. This model of a chlorine atom has a total of 17 electrons. The outer level of this atom has seven electrons and is not full.

Electron Number and Organization

To understand how atoms form chemical bonds, you need to know about the electrons in an atom. The number of electrons in an atom is the same as the atomic number of the element. The *atomic number* is the number of protons in an atom. But atoms have no charge. So, the atomic number also tells you the number of electrons in the atom.

Electrons in an atom are organized in energy levels. **Figure 2** shows a model of how the 17 electrons in a chlorine atom fill up the energy levels. This model and models like it are useful for counting electrons in energy levels of atoms. But these models do not show the true structure of atoms.

Outer-Level Electrons and Bonding

Not all of the electrons in an atom make chemical bonds. Most atoms form bonds using only the electrons in the outermost energy level. An electron in the outermost energy level of an atom is a **valence electron.** The models in **Figure 3** show the valence electrons for two atoms.

Standards Check Where in the atom are the electrons that are used to form bonds located? 🐾 **8.3.a**

chemical bonding (KEM i kuhl BAHN ding) the combining of atoms to form molecules or ionic compounds

chemical bond (KEM i kuhl BAHND) an interaction that holds atoms or ions together

valence electron (VAY luhns ee LEK TRAHN) an electron that is found in the outermost shell of an atom and that determines the atom's chemical properties

---

Figure 3 Counting Valence Electrons

Oxygen
Atomic number: 8
Electron total: 8
First level: 2 electrons
Second level: 6 electrons

An oxygen atom has six valence electrons.

Sodium
Atomic number: 11
Electron total: 11
First level: 2 electrons
Second level: 8 electrons
Third level: 1 electron

A sodium atom has one valence electron.

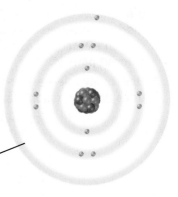

Figure 4 Determining the Number of Valence Electrons

Atoms of elements in **Groups 1 and 2** have the same number of valence electrons as their group number.

Atoms of elements in **Groups 13–18** have 10 fewer valence electrons than their group number. However, helium atoms have only 2 valence electrons.

Atoms of elements in **Groups 3–12** do not have a rule relating their valence electrons to their group number.

H																		18
1	**2**											**13**	**14**	**15**	**16**	**17**	He	
Li	Be											B	C	N	O	F	Ne	
Na	Mg	**3**	**4**	**5**	**6**	**7**	**8**	**9**	**10**	**11**	**12**	Al	Si	P	S	Cl	Ar	
K	Ca	Sc	Ti	V	Cr	Mn	Fe	Co	Ni	Cu	Zn	Ga	Ge	As	Se	Br	Kr	
Rb	Sr	Y	Zr	Nb	Mo	Tc	Ru	Rh	Pd	Ag	Cd	In	Sn	Sb	Te	I	Xe	
Cs	Ba	La	Hf	Ta	W	Re	Os	Ir	Pt	Au	Hg	Tl	Pb	Bi	Po	At	Rn	
Fr	Ra	Ac	Rf	Db	Sg	Bh	Hs	Mt	Ds	Uuu	Uub	Uut	Uuq	Uup				

Valence Electrons and the Periodic Table

You can use a model to find the number of valence electrons of an atom. But what if you don't have a model? For some elements, you could use the periodic table!

Elements are grouped based on similar properties. Within a group, or family, the atoms of each element have the same number of valence electrons. So, the group numbers can help you determine the number of valence electrons. **Figure 4** shows how to use the periodic table to find the number of valence electrons for some atoms.

To Bond or Not to Bond

Not all atoms bond in the same way. In fact, some atoms hardly ever bond at all! The number of valence electrons in the outermost energy level of an atom determines if an atom will form bonds.

Atoms of the noble gases (Group 18) do not usually form bonds. Atoms of Group 18 elements (except helium) have eight valence electrons. Atoms that have eight electrons in their outermost energy level are nonreactive. So, they do not tend to form bonds. The outermost energy level of an atom is full if the level contains eight electrons.

Standards Check The atoms of which group in the periodic table rarely form chemical bonds? **8.3.f**

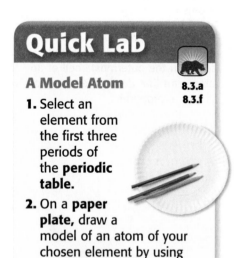

Quick Lab

A Model Atom

8.3.a
8.3.f

1. Select an element from the first three periods of the **periodic table.**

2. On a **paper plate,** draw a model of an atom of your chosen element by using **colored pencils.**

3. How many valence electrons does your atom have?

⏱ **20 min**

Filling The Outermost Level

Atoms that have fewer than eight valence electrons usually form bonds. In order to fill the outermost energy level, atoms bond by gaining, losing, or sharing electrons. **Figure 5** shows how two kinds of atoms can have a full outermost energy level with eight electrons.

Are Two Electrons a Full Set?

Not all atoms need eight valence electrons to have a filled outermost energy level. Helium atoms need only two. The first energy level in a helium atom is also the outermost one. This level can hold only two electrons. So, the outermost energy level of a helium atom is full with only two electrons. Atoms of hydrogen and lithium also form bonds by gaining, losing, or sharing electrons so that there are two electrons in the first energy level.

Figure 5 **Filling Outermost Energy Levels**

Sulfur
An atom of sulfur has six valence electrons. It can have eight valence electrons by sharing two electrons with or gaining two electrons from other atoms.

Magnesium
An atom of magnesium has two valence electrons. It can have a full outer level by losing two electrons. The second energy level becomes the outermost energy level and has eight electrons.

SECTION Review

8.3.a, 8.3.b, 8.3.f

Summary

- Chemical bonds form when atoms join to form new substances. A chemical bond is an interaction that holds two atoms together.

- A valence electron is an electron in the outermost energy level of an atom.

- Most atoms form bonds by gaining, losing, or sharing electrons until they have eight valence electrons. Atoms of some elements need only two electrons to fill their outermost level.

Understanding Concepts

1. **Comparing** How are valence electrons different from other electrons in an atom?

2. **Identifying** Use the periodic table to identify three elements whose atoms are not likely to form bonds.

3. **Describing** Describe chemical bonding.

4. **Applying** Explain how to use valence electrons to predict if an atom will form bonds.

Critical Thinking

5. **Making Inferences** How can an atom that has five valence electrons achieve a full set of valence electrons?

6. **Applying Concepts** Identify the number of valence electrons in a barium atom.

Challenge

INTERPRETING GRAPHICS Use the image below to answer the next question.

Fluorine

7. **Applying Concepts** How many valence electrons are in a fluorine atom? Will fluorine atoms form bonds? Explain.

Internet Resources

For a variety of links related to this chapter, go to www.scilinks.org
Topic: The Electron; Periodic Table
SciLinks code: HY70489; HY71125

Ionic Bonds

Key Concept Ionic bonds form when electrons are transferred from one atom to another atom.

What You Will Learn

- Ions of different elements can combine by forming ionic bonds.
- Positive ions and negative ions form when atoms lose or gain electrons.
- Ionic compounds form solids by building up a repeating pattern called a *crystal lattice*.

Why It Matters

Learning about ionic bonds can help you understand the properties of ionic compounds, such as table salt.

Vocabulary

- ionic bond
- ion
- crystal lattice

READING STRATEGY

Graphic Organizer In your **Science Journal,** make a Comparison Table that compares the outermost energy level and the ions that tend to form between metallic and nonmetallic atoms.

ionic bond (ie AHN ik BAHND) the attractive force between oppositely charged ions, which form when electrons are transferred from one atom to another

ion (IE ahn) a charged particle that forms when an atom or group of atoms gains or loses one or more electrons

▶ Have you ever tasted sea water? If so, you most likely didn't enjoy it. Sea water tastes different from tap water because salt is dissolved in sea water. One of the salts in sea water is the same as the table salt that you eat. The chemical bonds in salt are ionic bonds.

Forming Ionic Bonds

Figure 1 shows another substance that contains ionic bonds. An **ionic bond** forms when valence electrons are transferred from one atom to another atom. Like all chemical bonds, ionic bonds form so that the outermost energy levels of the atoms in the bonds are filled. In an ionic bond, one atom has lost electrons. And the other atom has gained electrons.

Standards Check What happens during ionic bonding? 🐻 **8.3.b**

Charged Particles

An atom is neutral because the number of electrons in an atom equals the number of protons. So, the electric charges of the electrons and protons cancel each other. A transfer of electrons between atoms changes the number of electrons in each atom. But the number of protons stays the same in each atom. The negative charges and positive charges no longer cancel out, and the atoms become ions. **Ions** are charged particles that form when atoms gain or lose electrons. If an ion has more protons than electrons, it is a positive ion. If it has more electrons than protons, it is a negative ion.

Figure 1 *Calcium carbonate in this snail's shell contains ionic bonds.*

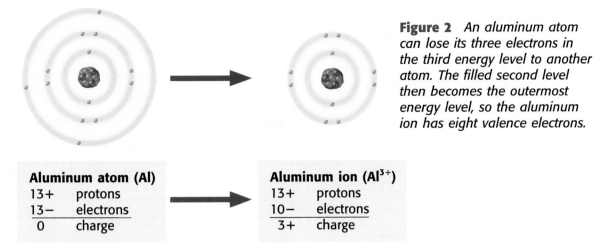

Figure 2 *An aluminum atom can lose its three electrons in the third energy level to another atom. The filled second level then becomes the outermost energy level, so the aluminum ion has eight valence electrons.*

Aluminum atom (Al)
13+ protons
13− electrons
0 charge

Aluminum ion (Al³⁺)
13+ protons
10− electrons
3+ charge

Forming Positive Ions

During chemical changes, ionic bonds form when atoms pull electrons away from other atoms. The atoms that lose electrons form positive ions because these atoms have more protons than electrons. There are more positive charges than negative charges. So, the net charge on these ions is positive.

Metal Atoms and the Loss of Electrons

Atoms of most metals have few electrons in their outermost energy level. When metal atoms bond with other atoms, the metal atoms tend to lose these valence electrons and form positive ions. The aluminum atom shown in **Figure 2** has three valence electrons. When it loses these electrons to another atom, the aluminum atom becomes an ion. So, an aluminum ion has three more protons than it has electrons. The ion has a 3+ charge. The chemical symbol for this ion is written as Al^{3+}. Notice that the charge is written to the upper right of the chemical symbol.

The Energy Needed to Remove Electrons

When an atom loses electrons, energy is needed to overcome the attraction of the electrons to the protons in the nucleus. Much less energy is needed to take electrons from metal atoms than from nonmetal atoms. The elements in Groups 1 and 2 react very easily because the energy needed to remove electrons from their atoms is so small. So, only the ions, and not the atoms, of these elements are found in nature. In ionic bonding, the energy needed to remove electrons from metal atoms comes from the formation of negative ions.

Standards Check Explain why energy is needed to form positive ions. **8.3.a**

Studying Salt
Spread several grains of salt on a dark sheet of construction paper. Use a magnifying lens to examine the salt. Ask an adult at home to examine the salt. Discuss what you saw. Then, gently tap the salt with a small hammer. Examine the salt again. Describe your observations in your **Science Journal.**

8.3.a Students know the structure of the atom and know it is composed of protons, neutrons, and electrons.
8.3.b Students know that compounds are formed by combining two or more different elements and that compounds have properties that are different from their constituent elements.
8.3.c Students know atoms and molecules form solids by building up repeating patterns, such as the crystal structure of NaCl or long-chain polymers.
8.5.a Students know reactant atoms and molecules interact to form products with different chemical properties.

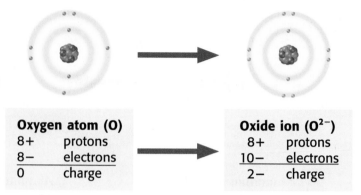

Figure 3 *An oxygen atom can gain two electrons in the second energy level from another atom. An oxide ion that has eight valence electrons is formed. Thus, its outermost energy level is filled.*

Oxygen atom (O)
8+ protons
8− electrons
0 charge

Oxide ion (O²⁻)
8+ protons
10− electrons
2− charge

Forming Negative Ions

During chemical changes, some atoms gain electrons from other atoms. The ions that form have more electrons than protons. These ions have an overall negative charge because there are more negative charges than positive charges.

How Nonmetal Atoms Become Negative Ions

The outermost energy level of nonmetal atoms is almost full. Only a few electrons are needed to fill it. So, atoms of nonmetals tend to gain electrons from other atoms.

Figure 3 shows how an atom can become a negative ion. An atom of oxygen has six valence electrons. So, an oxygen atom needs only two electrons to have a full set of valence electrons. When an oxygen atom gains two electrons, it becomes an oxide ion that has a 2− charge. The symbol for the oxide ion is O^{2-}.

Notice that the name of the negative ion formed from oxygen ends with *-ide*. This ending is used for the names of the negative ions formed when atoms gain electrons.

The Energy of Gaining Electrons

Atoms of most nonmetals fill their outermost energy level by gaining electrons. Energy is given off by most nonmetal atoms when they gain electrons. The more easily an atom gains an electron, the more energy the atom releases. Atoms of Group 17 elements (the halogens) give off the most energy when they gain an electron. The halogens, such as fluorine and chlorine, are very reactive because they release a large amount of energy. An ionic bond forms because of the strong forces of attraction between the positive metal ions and the negative nonmetal ions.

Standards Check Atoms of which group in the periodic table give off the most energy when forming negative ions? **8.3.a**

Calculating Charge

Calculating the charge of an ion is the same as adding integers (positive or negative whole numbers and 0) that have opposite signs. You write the number of protons as a positive integer and the number of electrons as a negative integer. Then, you add the integers. For example, the sodium ion has 11 protons and 10 electrons, so you would add (11+) and (10−) to get a charge of 1+. Calculate the charge of an ion that contains 16 protons and 18 electrons. Write the ion's symbol and name. Record your work in your **Science Journal.**

Forming Ionic Compounds

When ionic bonds form, the number of electrons lost by the metal atoms equals the number gained by the nonmetal atoms, as shown in **Figure 4.** The ions that bond are charged. But the compound formed is neutral because the charges cancel each other. An ionic bond forms because the opposite charges of the ions cause the ions to stick together.

When a metal and a nonmetal combine by ionic bonding, the resulting compound has different properties than the metal and nonmetal did. In **Figure 4,** you can see how the properties of sodium and chlorine differ from the properties of the ionic compound sodium chloride.

Standards Check Compare the properties of sodium chloride with the properties of the elements sodium and chlorine. 🐻 8.5.a

---

Figure 4 **Forming Sodium Chloride**

How It Works: A sodium atom loses its one electron in the third energy level to a chlorine atom. The filled second level becomes the outermost level.

How It Works: A chlorine atom gains one electron in the third energy level from a sodium atom.

How It Works: After the transfer of an electron, the resulting sodium ion and chloride ion form an ionic bond. Together, the ions have no overall charge.

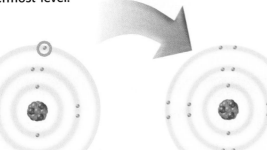

Sodium atom (Na)
11+	protons
11−	electrons
0	charge

Chlorine atom (Cl)
17+	protons
17−	electrons
0	charge

Sodium ion (Na⁺)
11+	protons
10−	electrons
1+	charge

Chloride ion (Cl⁻)
17+	protons
18−	electrons
1−	charge

Sodium is a soft, silvery white metal that reacts violently with water.

Chlorine is a poisonous, greenish yellow gas.

Sodium chloride, or table salt, is a white solid. It dissolves easily in water and is safe to eat.

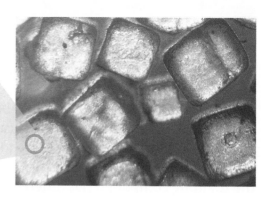

Figure 5 *This model of the crystal lattice of sodium chloride, or table salt, shows a three-dimensional view of the bonded ions. In the model, the sodium ions are pink and the chloride ions are green.* **What pattern do you see in the order of the ions?**

Ionic Compounds

crystal lattice (KRIS tuhl LAT is) the regular pattern in which a crystal is arranged

The ions that make up an ionic compound are bonded in a repeating three-dimensional pattern called a **crystal lattice.** In ionic compounds such as table salt, the crystal lattice is built up so that the positive ions are nearest to the negative ions, forming a solid. The model in **Figure 5** shows a small part of a crystal lattice. The shape of the crystals of an ionic compound depends on the pattern of ions in its crystal lattice.

Standards Check What is a crystal lattice? 8.3.c

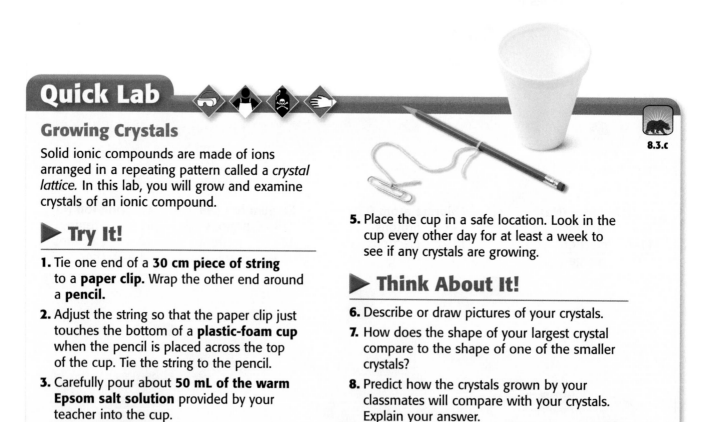

Quick Lab

Growing Crystals

Solid ionic compounds are made of ions arranged in a repeating pattern called a *crystal lattice.* In this lab, you will grow and examine crystals of an ionic compound.

8.3.c

▶ Try It!

1. Tie one end of a **30 cm piece of string** to a **paper clip.** Wrap the other end around a **pencil.**

2. Adjust the string so that the paper clip just touches the bottom of a **plastic-foam cup** when the pencil is placed across the top of the cup. Tie the string to the pencil.

3. Carefully pour about **50 mL of the warm Epsom salt solution** provided by your teacher into the cup.

4. Lower the paper clip into the cup, and lay the pencil across the top of the cup.

5. Place the cup in a safe location. Look in the cup every other day for at least a week to see if any crystals are growing.

▶ Think About It!

6. Describe or draw pictures of your crystals.

7. How does the shape of your largest crystal compare to the shape of one of the smaller crystals?

8. Predict how the crystals grown by your classmates will compare with your crystals. Explain your answer.

9. Compare your crystals to a classmate's crystals. Describe the similarities and differences.

20 min plus follow-up

Properties of Ionic Compounds

The strong attraction between ions in a crystal lattice gives ionic compounds certain physical properties. Ionic compounds tend to be brittle solids at room temperature. So, these solids will break apart when they are hit with a hammer. Ionic compounds have high melting points. For example, magnesium oxide has to be heated to 2,800°C before it will melt. Because most substances have to melt before they boil, ionic compounds also have very high boiling points.

Another property of many ionic compounds is high solubility in water. High solubility means that compounds dissolve easily in water. Sea water tastes salty because it has sodium chloride and many other ionic compounds dissolved in it.

SECTION Review

8.3.a, 8.3.b, 8.3.c, 8.5.a

Summary

- An ionic bond forms when electrons are transferred from one atom to another. During ionic bonding, the atoms become oppositely charged ions.

- Ionic bonding usually occurs between atoms of metals and atoms of nonmetals.

- Energy is needed to remove electrons from metal atoms. Energy is released when most nonmetal atoms gain electrons.

- Ionic compounds form solids by building up a three-dimensional repeating pattern called a crystal lattice.

- Ionic compounds are brittle and highly soluble, with high melting and boiling points.

Using Vocabulary

1. Use *ion*, *ionic bond*, and *crystal lattice* in separate sentences.

Understanding Concepts

2. **Justifying** Why do pieces of table salt have cubic shapes?

3. **Describing** How does an atom become a positive ion? a negative ion?

4. **Listing** What are four physical properties of ionic compounds?

Critical Thinking

5. **Applying Concepts** Explain why you will not become sick if you eat sodium chloride, even though chlorine is poisonous.

6. **Identifying Relationships** Explain why ionic compounds are neutral even though they are made up of charged particles.

7. **Making Comparisons** Compare the formation of positive ions with the formation of negative ions in terms of energy changes.

INTERPRETING GRAPHICS Use the images of atoms below to answer the next question.

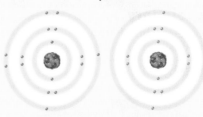

Sulfur   **Magnesium**

8. **Predicting Consequences** Which atom will form a positive ion during ionic bonding? Which atom will form a negative ion?

Math Skills

9. **Making Calculations** What is the charge of an ion that has 12 protons and 10 electrons? Write the ion's symbol.

Internet Resources

For a variety of links related to this chapter, go to www.scilinks.org

Topic: Types of Chemical Bonds
SciLinks code: HY71565

Covalent and Metallic Bonds

Key Concept   Covalent bonds form when atoms share electrons. Metallic bonds form by the attraction of metal ions and the electrons around them.

What You Will Learn

- Covalent compounds form when atoms of elements share electrons.
- Molecules are particles of covalent compounds and can be simple or complex.
- Atoms of metals are held together by metallic bonds.
- Metallic bonding gives metals certain properties.

Why It Matters

Learning about covalent and metallic bonds can help you understand the properties of covalent compounds, such as water and sugar, and metals, such as copper and aluminum.

Vocabulary

- covalent bond
- molecule
- metallic bond

READING STRATEGY

Graphic Organizer   In your **Science Journal,** make a Comparison Table that compares various characteristics of covalent and metallic bonds.

▶ Imagine bending a wooden coat hanger and a wire coat hanger. The wire one will bend easily. But the wooden one will break. Why do these objects behave differently?

One reason is that the bonds between the atoms of each object are different. The atoms of the wood are held together by covalent bonds. But the atoms of the wire are held together by metallic bonds. Read on to learn about the difference between these kinds of chemical bonds.

Covalent Bonds

Most things around you, such as water, sugar, oxygen, and the cellulose in wood, are held together by covalent bonds. Substances that have covalent bonds tend to have low melting and boiling points and are brittle in the solid state. For example, oxygen has a low boiling point, so oxygen is a gas at room temperature. And cellulose is brittle, so wood breaks when bent.

A **covalent bond** forms when atoms share one or more pairs of electrons. When two atoms of nonmetals bond, a large amount of energy is needed for either atom to lose an electron. So, two nonmetal atoms don't transfer electrons to fill their outermost energy levels. Instead, the atoms bond by sharing electrons with one another, as shown in the model in **Figure 1.**

Standards Check   What is a covalent bond?   🐻 **8.3.b**

Figure 1   *By sharing electrons in a covalent bond, each hydrogen atom (the smallest atom) has a full outermost energy level containing two electrons.*

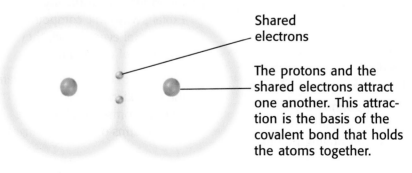

Shared electrons

The protons and the shared electrons attract one another. This attraction is the basis of the covalent bond that holds the atoms together.

8.3.a Students know the structure of the atom and know it is composed of protons, neutrons, and electrons.
8.3.b Students know that compounds are formed by combining two or more different elements and that compounds have properties that are different from their constituent elements.

Figure 2   Covalent Bonds in a Water Molecule

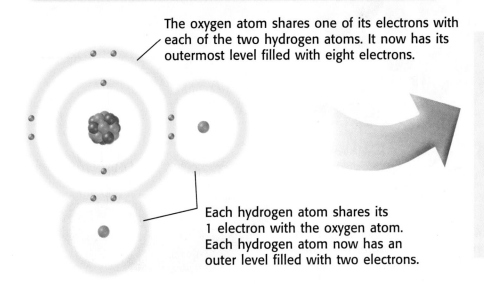

The oxygen atom shares one of its electrons with each of the two hydrogen atoms. It now has its outermost level filled with eight electrons.

Each hydrogen atom shares its 1 electron with the oxygen atom. Each hydrogen atom now has an outer level filled with two electrons.

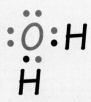

This electron-dot diagram for water shows only the outermost level of electrons for each atom to show how these atoms share electrons.

Covalent Bonds and Molecules

Substances that have covalent bonds consist of particles called molecules. A **molecule** is usually made of two or more atoms joined in a definite ratio. A hydrogen molecule is made of two covalently bonded hydrogen atoms. However, most molecules are composed of atoms of two or more elements. The models in **Figure 2** show two ways to represent the covalent bonds in a water molecule.

One way to represent atoms and molecules is to use electron-dot diagrams. An electron-dot diagram is a model that shows only the valence electrons in an atom. Electron-dot diagrams can help you predict how atoms might bond. To draw an electron-dot diagram, write the symbol of the element and place one dot around the symbol for every valence electron in the atom, as shown in **Figure 3.** Place the first four dots alone on each side, and then pair up any remaining dots.

covalent bond (KOH vay luhnt BAHND) a bond formed when atoms share one or more pairs of electrons

molecule (MAHL i kyool) a group of atoms that are held together by chemical forces; a molecule is the smallest unit of matter that can exist by itself and retain all of a substance's chemical properties

Figure 3   Using Electron–Dot Diagrams

Carbon atoms have four valence electrons. A carbon atom needs four more electrons to have a filled outermost energy level.

Oxygen atoms have six valence electrons. An oxygen atom needs two more electrons to have a filled outermost energy level.

Krypton atoms have eight valence electrons. Krypton is nonreactive. Krypton atoms do not need any more electrons.

This diagram represents a hydrogen molecule. The dots between the letters represent a pair of shared electrons.

Figure 4 *The water in this fishbowl is made up of many tiny water molecules. Each molecule is the smallest particle that has the chemical properties of water.*

Quick Lab

Studying Sugar

8.3.b

1. Spread a small amount of **table sugar** on a **sheet of dark construction paper.**

2. Use a **magnifying lens** to examine the sugar crystals. Write a description of what you see.

3. Molecules of table sugar are made up of atoms of carbon, oxygen, and hydrogen. How do the properties of the compound table sugar compare with the properties of the elements that compose it?

20 min

Covalent Compounds and Molecules

An atom is the smallest particle into which an element can be divided and still be the same element. Likewise, a molecule is the smallest particle into which a covalently bonded compound can be divided and still be the same compound. The models in **Figure 4** show how a sample of water is made up of many individual molecules of water. Imagine dividing water again and again. You would finally end up with a single molecule of water. What would happen if you separated the hydrogen and oxygen atoms that make up a water molecule? Then, you would no longer have water.

Standards Check How do the properties of oxygen and hydrogen compare with the properties of water? 8.3.b

The Simplest Molecules

Molecules are composed of at least two covalently bonded atoms. The simplest molecules are made up of two bonded atoms. Molecules made up of two atoms are called *diatomic molecules*. Elements that are found in nature as diatomic molecules are called *diatomic elements*. Hydrogen is a diatomic element and is written as H_2. Oxygen, nitrogen, and the halogens fluorine, chlorine, bromine, and iodine are also diatomic elements. In a molecule of any of these elements, the shared electrons are counted as valence electrons for each atom. So, both atoms of the molecule have filled outermost energy levels.

Figure 5 *A granola bar contains sucrose, or table sugar. A molecule of sucrose is composed of carbon atoms, hydrogen atoms, and oxygen atoms joined by covalent bonds.*

Hydrogen

Carbon

Oxygen

More-Complex Molecules

Diatomic molecules are the simplest molecules. They are also some of the most important molecules. You could not live without diatomic oxygen molecules. But other important molecules are much more complex. Soap, plastic bottles, and even proteins in your body are examples of complex molecules. Carbon atoms are the basis of many of these complex molecules. Each carbon atom needs to make four covalent bonds to have eight valence electrons. These bonds can be with atoms of other elements or with other carbon atoms, as shown in the model in **Figure 5.**

Metallic Bonds

Look at the unusual metal sculptures shown in **Figure 6.** Some metal pieces have been flattened, and others have been shaped into wires. How could the artist change the shape of the metal into all of these different forms without breaking the metal into pieces? Metal can be shaped because of the presence of metallic bonds, a special kind of chemical bond. A **metallic bond** is a bond formed by the attraction between positively charged metal ions and the electrons around the ions. Positively charged metal ions form when metal atoms lose electrons.

metallic bond (muh TAL ik BAHND) a bond formed by the attraction between positively charged metal ions and the electrons around them

Wordwise The suffix *-ic* means "pertaining to."

Figure 6 *The different shapes of metal in these sculptures are possible because of the bonds that hold the metal together.*

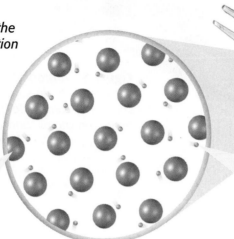

Figure 7 *Free-moving electrons are attracted to the metal ions, and the attraction forms metallic bonds.*

The positive metal ions are in fixed positions in the metal.

Negative electrons are free to move.

Movement of Electrons Throughout a Metal

Bonding in metals is a result of many metal atoms being so close to one another that their outermost energy levels overlap. Because of this overlapping, metallic bonds extend throughout the metal in all directions. So, valence electrons can move throughout the metal. You can think of a metal as being made up of positive metal ions that have valence electrons "swimming" around, as shown in **Figure 7.** The electrons keep the ions together and cancel the positive charge of the ions.

Properties of Metals

Metallic bonding gives metals their particular properties. These properties include electrical conductivity, malleability, and ductility.

Conducting Electric Current

Metallic bonding allows metals to conduct electric current. For example, when you turn on a lamp, electrons move within the copper wire that connects the lamp to the outlet. The electrons that move are the valence electrons in the copper atoms. These electrons are free to move because the electrons are not connected to any one atom.

Reshaping Metals

Because the electrons move freely around the metal ions, the atoms in metals can be rearranged. As a result, metals can be reshaped. The properties of *ductility* (the ability to be drawn into wires) and *malleability* (the ability to be rolled or pounded) describe a metal's ability to be reshaped. For example, copper is made into wires for use in electrical cords. Aluminum can be pounded into thin sheets and made into aluminum foil.

Standards Check What allows metals to be reshaped? 🐻 **8.3.a**

Atomic Attraction

Which is it: a love story or a tale of trickery and deception? You decide! Go to **go.hrw.com,** and type in the keyword HY7BNDW.

Bending Without Breaking

When a piece of metal is bent, some of the metal ions are forced closer together. You may expect the metal to break because all of the metal ions are positively charged. Positively charged ions repel one another. However, positive ions in a metal are always surrounded by and attracted to the electrons in the metal—even if the metal ions move. The electrons constantly move around and between the metal ions. The moving electrons maintain the metallic bonds no matter how the shape of the metal changes. So, metal objects can be bent without being broken, as shown in **Figure 8.**

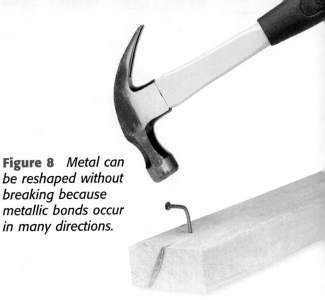

Figure 8 *Metal can be reshaped without breaking because metallic bonds occur in many directions.*

SECTION Review

 8.3.a, 8.3.b

Summary

- In covalent bonding, two atoms share electrons. A covalent bond forms when atoms share one or more pairs of electrons.

- Covalently bonded atoms form a particle called a *molecule*. A molecule is the smallest particle of a compound that has the chemical properties of the compound.

- In metallic bonding, the valence electrons move throughout the metal. A metallic bond is formed by the attraction between positive metal ions and the electrons in the metal.

- Properties of metals include electrical conductivity, ductility, and malleability.

Using Vocabulary

1 Use *covalent bond* and *metallic bond* in separate sentences.

Understanding Concepts

2 **Describing** What happens to the electrons in covalent bonding?

3 **Applying** How many dots does an electron-dot diagram of a sulfur atom have?

4 **Listing** List three properties of metals that are a result of metallic bonds.

5 **Summarizing** Describe how the valence electrons in a metal move.

6 **Comparing** Explain the difference between ductility and malleability. Give an example of when each property is useful.

Critical Thinking

7 **Making Inferences** You need to breathe oxygen to stay alive. Water is composed of oxygen. Why can't you breathe water to stay alive?

8 **Applying Concepts** Draw an electron-dot diagram for ammonia (a nitrogen atom covalently bonded to three hydrogen atoms).

9 **Identifying Relationships** How do the metallic bonds in a staple allow it to function properly?

INTERPRETING GRAPHICS Use the image below to answer the next question.

$$H$$
$$H : \overset{..}{\underset{..}{C}} : H$$

10 **Applying Concepts** This electron-dot diagram is not complete. Which atom needs to form another bond? Explain.

Internet Resources

For a variety of links related to this chapter, go to www.scilinks.org

Topic: Types of Chemical Bonds; Properties of Metals

SciLinks code: HY71565; HY71231

Model-Making Lab

Covalent Marshmallows

OBJECTIVES

Build a three-dimensional model of a water molecule.

Draw an electron-dot diagram of a water molecule.

MATERIALS

- marshmallows (two of one color, one of another color)
- toothpicks

SAFETY

A hydrogen atom has one electron in its outermost energy level, but two electrons are required to fill its outermost level. An oxygen atom has six electrons in its outermost level, but eight electrons are required to fill its outermost level. To fill their outermost energy levels, two atoms of hydrogen and one atom of oxygen can share electrons, as shown below. Such a sharing of electrons to fill the outermost level of atoms is called *covalent bonding*. When hydrogen and oxygen bond in this manner, a molecule of water is formed. In this lab, you will build a three-dimensional model of water to better understand the covalent bonds formed in a water molecule.

Model of a Water Molecule

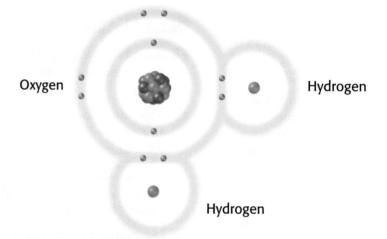

Oxygen

Hydrogen

Hydrogen

Procedure

1. Using the marshmallows and toothpicks, create a model of a water molecule. Use the diagram above for guidance in building your model.

2. Draw a sketch of your model. Be sure to label the hydrogen and oxygen atoms on your sketch.

3. Draw an electron-dot diagram of the water molecule.

8.3.a Students know the structure of the atom and know it is composed of protons, neutrons, and electrons.

8.3.b Students know that compounds are formed by combining two or more different elements and that compounds have properties that are different from their constituent elements.

Analyze the Results

4 Analyzing Methods What do the marshmallows represent? What do the toothpicks represent?

5 Analyzing Methods Why are the marshmallows different colors?

6 Analyzing Results Compare your model with the diagram on the previous page. How can your model be improved to more accurately represent a water molecule?

Draw Conclusions

7 Making Predictions Hydrogen in nature can covalently bond to form hydrogen molecules, H_2. How could you use the marshmallows and toothpicks to model this bond?

8 Applying Conclusions Draw an electron-dot diagram of a hydrogen molecule.

9 Making Predictions Hydrogen and oxygen also combine to form another compound called *hydrogen peroxide* (H_2O_2). Would you expect the properties of hydrogen peroxide to be the same as the properties of water? Explain your answer.

Big Idea Question

10 Drawing Conclusions Which do you think would be more difficult to create—a model of an ionic bond or a model of a covalent bond? Explain your answer.

Applying Your Data

Create a model of a carbon dioxide molecule, which consists of two oxygen atoms and one carbon atom. The structure is similar to the structure of water, although the three atoms bond in a straight line instead of at angles. The bond between each oxygen atom and the carbon atom in a carbon dioxide molecule is a *double bond,* so use two connections. A double bond forms when two atoms share four electrons. Do the double bonds in carbon dioxide appear stronger or weaker than the single bonds in water? Explain your answer.

Science Skills Activity

Investigation and Experimentation

8.9.a Plan and conduct a scientific investigation to test a hypothesis.

Planning an Investigation

▶ Tutorial

Use the following steps to plan and conduct an investigation to test a hypothesis.

① Make observations, and ask a question: "This material is shiny. Does this material contain metallic bonds?"

② Form a hypothesis that is a possible answer to your question, and make a prediction to test your hypothesis: "This material contains metallic bonds. If this material contains metallic bonds, then the material will flatten and not break when hit with a hammer."

③ Plan your investigation. Consider the materials and safety equipment that you will need, and review all safety procedures: "I will need a piece of the material, a hammer, and safety goggles. I must be sure to keep my hands away from the hammer in motion."

④ Conduct your investigation and gather data: "A piece of the material broke off when struck."

⑤ Analyze your results and draw conclusions. You may need to repeat or revise your investigation to verify your results: "Each time I struck the material with a hammer, a piece broke off. The material does not contain metallic bonds."

▶ You Try It!

Substances that contain ionic bonds tend to be very soluble in water. When an ionic compound, such as table salt, is dissolved in water, the solution made often looks similar to plain water. Your teacher will give you a sample of water. You need to plan and conduct an investigation to find out if the water is salt water or plain water. Write your hypothesis and plan on a sheet of paper. Remember that tasting an unknown substance is not an acceptable way to find out what it is. Be sure that your teacher approves your plan before you conduct your investigation.

① **Applying Concepts** What safety equipment do you need for your investigation? What safety precautions do you need to follow?

② **Making Inferences** What other ways could you test your hypothesis?

③ **Evaluating Data** Was your hypothesis supported by your investigation? Explain your answer.

Chapter Summary

The Big Idea
Atoms combine by forming ionic, covalent, and metallic bonds.

Section	Vocabulary

1 Electrons and Chemical Bonding

Key Concept Atoms share, gain, or lose electrons when chemical bonds form.

- Chemical bonding is the joining of atoms to form new substances.
- Valence electrons are used to form chemical bonds.
- The number of valence electrons in an atom determines whether the atom will form bonds.

This model shows how a chlorine atom's 17 electrons are arranged in energy levels.

chemical bonding p. 226
chemical bond p. 226
valence electron p. 227

2 Ionic Bonds

Key Concept Ionic bonds form when electrons are transferred from one atom to another atom.

- Ions of different elements can combine by forming ionic bonds.
- Positive ions and negative ions form when atoms lose or gain electrons.
- Ionic compounds form solids by building up a repeating pattern called a *crystal lattice*.

The ions in sodium chloride are arranged in a crystal lattice.

ionic bond p. 230
ion p. 230
crystal lattice p. 234

3 Covalent and Metallic Bonds

Key Concept Covalent bonds form when atoms share electrons. Metallic bonds form by the attraction of metal ions and the electrons around them.

- Covalent compounds form when atoms of elements share electrons.
- Molecules are particles of covalent compounds and can be simple or complex.
- Atoms of metals are held together by metallic bonds.
- Metallic bonding give metals certain properties.

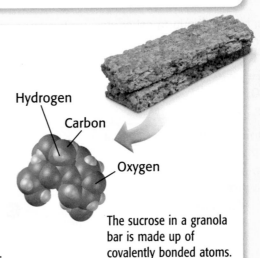

Hydrogen

Carbon

Oxygen

The sucrose in a granola bar is made up of covalently bonded atoms.

covalent bond p. 236
molecule p. 237
metallic bond p. 239

Chapter Review

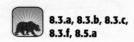
Organize

Layered Book Review the FoldNote that you created at the beginning of the chapter. Add to or correct the FoldNote based on what you have learned.

Using Vocabulary

1 Academic Vocabulary In the sentence "The crystal structure of a salt influences the shape of the salt's particles," what does the word *structure* mean?

Complete each of the following sentences by choosing the correct term from the word bank.

crystal lattice	ionic bond
molecule	chemical bond
ion	covalent bond

2 A charged particle that forms when an atom transfers electrons is a(n) ___.

3 A bond formed when atoms share electrons is a(n) ___.

4 Ionic compounds are bonded in a three-dimensional pattern called a(n) ___.

Understanding Concepts

Multiple Choice

5 Which atom has a full outermost energy level containing only two electrons?
a. fluorine, F
b. helium, He
c. oxygen, O
d. hydrogen, H

6 When an atom becomes an ion with a 2– charge, the atom
a. gains two protons.
b. loses two protons.
c. gains two electrons.
d. loses two electrons.

7 The properties of ductility and malleability are associated with which kind of bond?
a. ionic   c. metallic
b. covalent   d. All of the above

8 Atoms of which type of element tend to lose electrons when they form bonds?
a. metal   c. nonmetal
b. metalloid   d. noble gas

9 Which pair of atoms can form an ionic bond?
a. sodium, Na, and potassium, K
b. potassium, K, and fluorine, F
c. fluorine, F, and chlorine, Cl
d. sodium, Na, and neon, Ne

Short Answer

10 Listing List two properties of covalent compounds.

11 Applying Explain why an iron ion is attracted to a sulfide ion but not to a zinc ion.

12 Comparing Compare the three types of bonds based on what happens to the valence electrons of the atoms.

13 Evaluating Use the periodic table to draw a model of a calcium atom. Study your model, and predict whether calcium will form ionic or covalent bonds.

14 Summarizing What is the relationship between the properties of a compound and the properties of the elements that make up the compound?

INTERPRETING GRAPHICS Use the image below to answer the next question.

15 Justifying What kind of bonds does this material contain? Explain your answer.

N:H:H:H

16 Analyzing   Explain what is wrong with this electron-dot diagram of ammonia (NH_3).

Writing Skills

17 Communicating Concepts   Analyze the information in the chapter. Identify the main concepts, and summarize them in your own words.

Critical Thinking

18 Concept Mapping   Use the following terms to create a concept map: *chemical bonds, ionic bonds, covalent bonds, metallic bonds, molecule,* and *ions.*

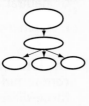

19 Identifying Relationships   Use the periodic table to predict the type of bond that each of the following pairs of atoms would form.
a. zinc, Zn, and zinc, Zn
b. oxygen, O, and nitrogen, N
c. phosphorus, P, and oxygen, O
d. magnesium, Mg, and chlorine, Cl

20 Applying Concepts   Draw electron-dot diagrams for each of the following atoms, and state how many covalent bonds the atom will have to make to fill its outer energy level.
a. sulfur, S
b. nitrogen, N
c. neon, Ne
d. iodine, I

21 Analyzing Ideas   Explain why different samples of a solid ionic compound are made up of crystals that have approximately the same shape.

22 Making Inferences   Does the substance being hit contain ionic bonds or does it contain metallic bonds? Explain your answer.

23 Making Comparisons   Identify two differences between the properties of the material in the pencil that has metallic bonds and the materials that have covalent bonds.

Math Skills

24 Making Calculations   For each atom below, write the number of electrons it must gain or lose to have eight valence electrons. Then, calculate the charge of the ion that would form.
a. calcium, Ca   **c.** bromine, Br
b. phosphorus, P   **d.** sulfur, S

Challenge

25 Predicting Consequences   What shape do you think smaller pieces chipped from a large crystal of sodium chloride will have? Explain.

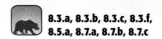
REVIEWING ACADEMIC VOCABULARY

1 Choose the appropriate form of the word *constituent* for the following sentence: "The compound has properties that differ from the properties of the elements that ___ it."

A constituent

B constituting

C constitute

D constitutes

2 Which of the following words means "the make up of parts of a whole"?

A structure

B ion

C bond

D constituent

3 Which of the following words is the closest in meaning to the word *chemical*?

A poison

B artificial

C property

D substance

4 Which of the following words means "to pick out"?

A discuss

B identify

C review

D analyze

5 Which of the following is closest in meaning to the word *compound*?

A partner

B fabrication

C combination

D recipe

REVIEWING CONCEPTS

6 A ___ forms when atoms share one or more pairs of electrons.

A covalent bond

B ionic bond

C valence electron

D nonmetal ion

7 Ionic bonds form when atoms pull electrons away from other atoms. If an atom loses electrons, what is the charge of the resulting ion?

A negative

B positive

C neutral

D unchanged

8 The ions that make up an ionic compound are bonded in a repeating three-dimensional pattern. What is this pattern called?

A chloride lattice

B covalent bond

C crystal lattice

D crystal pattern

9 The above diagram represents an oxygen atom. How many more valence electrons does the oxygen atom need to fill its outermost energy level?

A 2

B 4

C 6

D 11

10 **What is a molecule?**

A the smallest particle of a substance that cannot be broken down any further by chemical reaction

B a particle that forms when atoms gain or lose electrons

C matter of particular or definite chemical composition

D the smallest unit of a substance that keeps the physical and chemical properties of the substance

11 **Atoms of elements in ___ of the periodic table rarely form chemical bonds.**

A Group 1

B Group 9

C Group 17

D Group 18

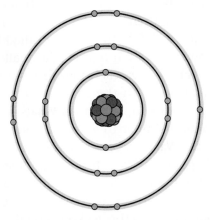

12 **How many electrons are in the second energy level of the atom represented in the above diagram?**

A 2

B 7

C 8

D 10

13 **Which of the following sentences best describes electrons in relation to energy levels?**

A Electrons can be found in and between energy levels.

B Electrons have definite energies, and they do not exist between energy levels.

C Electrons exist inside the nucleus at definite energy levels.

D Electrons can have an exact path within an energy level.

14 **Protons are always found in the nucleus of an atom. What is the number of protons in the nucleus of an atom called?**

A atomic number

B atomic mass

C mass number

D atomic mass unit

15 **In the periodic table, elements that have similar properties are organized into vertical groups. The element argon is located in the group of elements known as the**

A alkali metals.

B halogens.

C noble gases.

D transition metals.

16 **Which of the following is generally true of an element?**

A It cannot be melted into a liquid.

B It has a characteristic density.

C It conducts electric current.

D It can be broken down into a simpler substance.

Science in Action

Science, Technology, and Society

Superglue Bandages and Stitches

If you aren't careful when using superglue, you may accidentally learn that superglue quickly bonds one piece of skin to another! This property of superglue led to the development of new kinds of superglue that can be used as alternatives for bandages and stitches. Using superglue to close wounds has several advantages over using bandages and stitches. For example, superglue bandages can cover cuts on parts of the body that are difficult to cover with regular bandages. And superglue stitches are less painful than regular stitches. Wounds closed with superglue are easier to care for than wounds covered by bandages or closed with stitches.

Math ACTIVITY

A wound can be closed with glue 3 times as fast as it can be closed with stitches. If a doctor can close a wound in 27 min by using stitches, how long would closing the same wound by using glue take?

Weird Science

How Geckos Stick to Walls

Geckos are known for their ability to climb up smooth surfaces. Scientists have found the secret to the gecko's sticky talent. Geckos have millions of microscopic hairs on the bottom of their feet. Each hair splits into as many as 1,000 tinier hairs called *hairlets*. At the end of each hairlet is a small pad. As the gecko walks, each pad forms a van der Waals force with the surface on which the gecko is walking. A van der Waals force is an attraction similar to an ionic bond, but the van der Waals force is much weaker than an ionic bond and lasts for only an instant. But because there are so many pads on a gecko's foot, the van der Waals forces are strong enough to keep the gecko from falling.

Language Arts ACTIVITY

Imagine that you could stick to walls as well as a gecko can. Write a five-paragraph short story describing what you would do with your wall-climbing ability.

Michael Fan

Wastewater Manager If you are concerned about clean water and you like to work both in a laboratory and outdoors, you might like a career in wastewater management. The water cycle helps keep water in nature pure enough for most organisms. But when humans use water in houses, factories, and farms, we create *wastewater*, often faster than natural processes can clean it up. To make the water safe again, we can imitate the ways that water gets cleaned up in nature—and speed up the process.

Michael M. Fan is the assistant superintendent of wastewater operations at the wastewater treatment plant at the University of California in Davis, California. This plant has one of the most advanced wastewater management systems in the country. Fan finds his job exciting. The plant operates 24 hours a day, and there are many tasks to manage. Running the plant requires skills in chemistry, physics, microbiology, and engineering. Many organisms in the Davis area are counting on Fan to make sure that the water used by the university campus is safely returned to nature.

Social Studies Activity

Research the ways that the ancient Romans managed their wastewater. Make a poster that illustrates some of their methods and technologies.

Internet Resources

- To learn more about careers in science, visit www.scilinks.org and enter the SciLinks code HY70225.

- To learn more about these Science in Action topics, visit go.hrw.com and type in the keyword HY7BNDF.

- Check out articles related to this chapter by visiting go.hrw.com. Just type in the keyword HY7BNDC.

Improving Comprehension

Graphic Organizers are important visual tools that can help you organize information and improve your reading comprehension. The Graphic Organizer below is called a *cause-and-effect map*. Instructions for creating other types of Graphic Organizers are located in the **Study Skills** section of the Appendix.

How to Make a Cause-and-Effect Map

1. Draw a box, and write a cause in the box. You can have as many cause boxes as you want. The diagram shown here is one example of a cause-and-effect map.

2. Draw another box to the right of the cause box to represent an effect. You can have as many effect boxes as you want. Draw arrows from each cause box to the appropriate effect boxes.

3. In the cause boxes, explain the process that makes up the cause. In the effect boxes, write a description of the effect or details about the effect.

When to Use a Cause-and-Effect Map

A cause-and-effect map is a useful tool for illustrating a specific type of scientific process. Use a cause-and-effect map when you want to describe how, when, or why one event causes another event. As you read, look for events that are either causes or results of other events, and draw a cause-and-effect map that shows the relationships between the events.

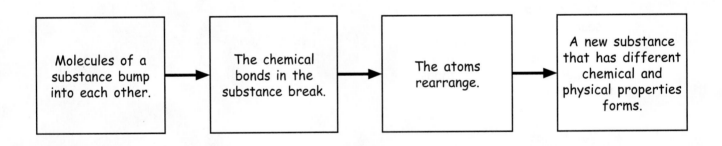

Molecules of a substance bump into each other. → The chemical bonds in the substance break. → The atoms rearrange. → A new substance that has different chemical and physical properties forms.

You Try It!

This Reading Strategy can also be used within the chapter that you are about to read. Practice making your own *cause-and-effect map* as directed in the Reading Strategy for Section **1**. Record your work in your **Science Journal**.

Unpacking the Standards

The information below "unpacks" the standards by breaking them down into basic parts. The higher-level, academic vocabulary is highlighted and defined to help you understand the language of the standards. "What It Means" restates the standards as simply as possible.

California Standard	Academic Vocabulary	What It Means
8.3.b Students know that compounds are formed by combining two or more different elements and that compounds have properties that are different from their **constituent** elements.	**constituent** (kuhn STICH oo uhnt) serving as part of a whole	Compounds form when two or more elements combine. The properties of a compound differ from the properties of the elements that make up the compound.
8.3.f Students know how to use the periodic table to **identify** elements in simple compounds.	**identify** (ie DEN tuh FIE) to point out or pick out	You must know how to use the table that arranges elements by atomic number to find which elements are in simple compounds.
8.5.a Students know reactant atoms and molecules **interact** to form products with different **chemical** properties.	**interact** (IN tuhr AKT) to act upon one another **chemical** (KEM i kuhl) of or having to do with the properties or actions of substances	When atoms and molecules are put together, they can interact to form new substances whose chemical properties differ from the properties of the original substances.
8.5.b Students know the idea of atoms explains the conservation of matter: In **chemical reactions** the number of atoms stays the same no matter how they are arranged, so their total mass stays the same.	**reaction** (ree AK shuhn) a response or change	The idea of atoms explains why matter is not created or destroyed: In chemical reactions, the total number of atoms stays the same. The atoms are simply rearranged. So, the total mass of the atoms stays the same.
8.5.c Students know **chemical reactions** usually **liberate** heat or absorb heat.	**liberate** (LIB uhr AYT) to release; to set free	When new substances are formed, thermal energy is usually either given off or absorbed.

Chemical Reactions

The Big Idea

Substances undergo chemical reactions, which form new substances whose properties differ from the properties of the original substances.

California Standards

Focus on Physical Sciences
8.3 Each of the more than 100 elements of matter has distinct properties and a distinct atomic structure. All forms of matter are composed of one or more of the elements. (Sections 1 and 2)
8.5 Chemical reactions are processes in which atoms are rearranged into different combinations of molecules. (Sections 1 and 2)

Investigation and Experimentation
8.9 Scientific progress is made by asking meaningful questions and conducting careful investigations. (Science Skills Activity)

Math
6.1.2, 6.2.3, 6.2.4 Number Sense

English–Language Arts
8.2.2 Reading
8.2.6 Writing

About the Photo

These dazzling fireworks over the Golden Gate Bridge in San Francisco are great examples of chemical reactions. Chemical reactions cause fireworks to soar, explode, and light up the sky. The bright lights from the fireworks are one of the signs that energy is released.

Organize

Four-Corner Fold

Before you read the chapter, create the FoldNote entitled "Four-Corner Fold." Label each flap of the four-corner fold with "Signs of chemical reactions," "Reactions and energy," "Chemical formulas," and "Chemical equations." As you read the chapter, add details about each topic under the appropriate flap.

Instructions for creating FoldNotes are located in the Study Skills section on p. 519 of the Appendix.

Explore Activity

A Model Chemical Formula

Chemicals react in very precise ways. In this activity, you will model a chemical reaction and will predict how chemicals react.

Procedure

1. You will receive **several clay models.** The models are balls of clay attached by **toothpicks.** Each of these models is a Model A.

2. Your teacher will show you an example of Model B and Model C. Take apart one or more Model As to make copies of Model B and Model C.

3. If you have balls of clay left over, use them to make more Model Bs and Model Cs. If you need more parts to complete a Model B or Model C, take apart another Model A.

4. Repeat step 3 until you have no balls of clay left over.

8.3.b
8.5.a

Analysis

5. How many Model As did you use to make copies of Model B and Model C?

6. How many Model Bs did you make? How many Model Cs did you make?

7. Suppose that you needed to make six Model Bs. How many Model As would you need? How many Model Cs could you make with the leftover balls of clay?

255

Forming New Substances

Key Concept During chemical reactions, atoms rearrange to form new substances that have different properties than the original substances had.

Do you know why tree leaves change color in the fall? Leaves are green because they contain a colored substance, or *pigment*. This green pigment is called *chlorophyll* (KLAWR uh FIL). During the spring and summer, the leaves have a large amount of chlorophyll in them. But in the fall, when temperatures drop and there are fewer hours of sunlight, trees stop making chlorophyll molecules. The chlorophyll in the leaves breaks down to form new substances. The green chlorophyll is no longer present to hide the other pigments. So, you can see the orange and yellow colors of the other pigments.

Chemical Reactions

A chemical change takes place when chlorophyll breaks down into new substances. This change is an example of a chemical reaction. A **chemical reaction** is a process in which one or more substances change to make one or more new substances. The chemical and physical properties of the new substances differ from those of the original substances. Some results of chemical reactions are shown in **Figure 1.**

Figure 1 Results of Chemical Reactions

When you mix water with baking powder, substances in the baking powder react to form bubbles of carbon dioxide gas. These bubbles give the muffin its spongelike texture.

Leaves change color in the fall as a result of chemical changes in the leaves.

Signs of Chemical Reactions

How can you tell when a chemical reaction is taking place? **Figure 2** shows some signs that tell you that a reaction may be taking place. Some reactions form solid precipitates. A **precipitate** is a solid substance that forms in a solution. In other chemical reactions, gas bubbles form. Some reactions make new substances that have different colors than the starting substances did. During other chemical reactions, energy is given off. This energy may be in the form of light, heat, or electrical energy. Reactions often have more than one of these signs. The more signs that you see, the more likely it is that a chemical reaction is taking place.

chemical reaction (KEM i kuhl ree AK shuhn) the process by which one or more substances change to produce one or more different substances

precipitate (pree SIP uh tit) a solid that is produced as a result of a chemical reaction in solution

Standards Check What is a precipitate? 🐻 **8.5.a**

Figure 2 Some Signs of Chemical Reactions

Gas Formation
The chemical reaction in the beaker has formed a brown gas, nitrogen dioxide. This gas forms when a strip of copper is placed into nitric acid.

Solid Formation
Here you see potassium chromate solution being added to a silver nitrate solution. The dark red solid is a precipitate of silver chromate.

Energy Change
Energy is released during some chemical reactions. The fire in this photo gives off energy in the form of light and heat. During other chemical reactions, energy is taken in.

Color Change
Don't spill chlorine bleach on your jeans! The bleach reacts with the blue dye on the fabric and causes the color of the material to change.

A Change of Properties

Even though the signs we look for to see if a reaction is taking place are good signals of chemical reactions, they do not guarantee that a reaction is happening. For example, gas can be given off when a liquid boils. But boiling is a physical change, not a chemical reaction.

So, how can you be sure that a chemical reaction is happening? The most important sign is the formation of new substances that have new properties. In **Figure 3,** the starting materials in the reaction are sugar and sulfuric acid. Several signs tell you that a chemical reaction is taking place. Bubbles form, which tells you that a gas is given off. The beaker becomes very hot. But most important, new substances form. And the properties of these substances are very different from those of the starting substances.

Bonds: Holding Molecules Together

A *chemical bond* is a force that holds two atoms together in a molecule. For a chemical reaction to take place, the original bonds must break and new bonds must form.

Breaking and Making Bonds

How do new substances form in a chemical reaction? First, chemical bonds in the starting substances must break. Molecules are always moving. If the molecules bump into each other with enough energy, the chemical bonds in the molecules can break. The atoms then rearrange, and new bonds form to make the new substances. **Figure 4** shows how atoms rearrange when hydrogen and chlorine react with each other.

Standards Check What happens to the bonds of substances during a chemical reaction? 8.5.a

Figure 3 *The top photo shows table sugar, a white solid, being mixed with sulfuric acid, a clear liquid. These two starting substances react to form new substances that are very different from the sulfuric acid or sugar.* **What are some of the properties of the new substances?**

Figure 4 **Reaction of Hydrogen and Chlorine**

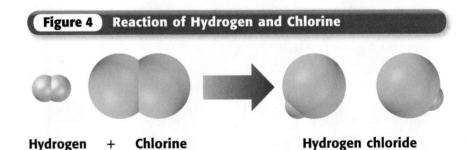

Hydrogen + Chlorine → Hydrogen chloride

Breaking Bonds Hydrogen and chlorine are diatomic. Diatomic molecules are two atoms bonded together. The bonds joining these atoms must break before the atoms can react with each other.

Making Bonds A new substance, hydrogen chloride, forms as new bonds are made between hydrogen atoms and chlorine atoms. Hydrogen chloride is also a diatomic molecule.

New Bonds, New Substances

What happens when hydrogen and chlorine react? A chlorine gas molecule is a diatomic (DIE uh TAHM ik) molecule. That is, the molecule is made of two atoms of chlorine. Chlorine gas has a greenish yellow color. Hydrogen gas is also a diatomic molecule. Hydrogen gas is a flammable, colorless gas. When chlorine gas and hydrogen gas react, the bond between the hydrogen atoms breaks. The bond between the chlorine atoms also breaks. A new bond forms between each hydrogen atom and each chlorine atom. A new substance, hydrogen chloride, forms. Hydrogen chloride is a nonflammable, colorless gas. Its properties differ from the properties of both of the starting substances.

Reactions and Energy

Chemical energy is part of all chemical reactions. Energy is needed to break chemical bonds in the starting substances. As new bonds form in the final substances, energy is released. By comparing the chemical energy of the original substances with the chemical energy of the final substances, you can decide if energy is released or absorbed in the overall reaction.

Exothermic Reactions

A chemical reaction in which energy is released is called an **exothermic reaction.** *Exo* means "go out" or "exit." *Thermic* means "heat" or "energy." Exothermic reactions can give off energy in several forms, as **Figure 5** shows. If heat is released in an exothermic reaction, the nearby matter will become warmer. The nearby matter absorbs the heat released by the reaction. The reaction between gasoline and oxygen in a car's engine is an exothermic reaction.

exothermic reaction
(EK soh THUHR mik ree AK shuhn) a chemical reaction in which heat is released to the surroundings

---

Figure 5 Types of Energy Released in Exothermic Reactions

Light energy is released in the exothermic reaction that is taking place in these light sticks.

Electrical energy is released in the exothermic reaction that will take place in this battery.

Light and heat are released in the exothermic reaction taking place in this campfire.

Figure 6 *The reaction in the flask absorbs energy and causes water between the bottom of the flask and the wood to freeze.*

Endothermic Reactions

A chemical reaction in which energy is taken in is called an **endothermic reaction.** *Endo* means "go in." The energy taken in during an endothermic reaction is absorbed from the surroundings. An example of an endothermic process is photosynthesis. In photosynthesis, plants use light energy from the sun to produce glucose molecules. Glucose is a simple sugar that is used as a source of energy for living things.

An endothermic reaction is happening in the flask in **Figure 6.** During the reaction, energy from nearby materials is absorbed. As a result, the flask, the wood block, and the nearby air become cooler. A few drops of water placed between the wood block and the flask become cool enough to freeze. The ice that forms between the flask and the block of wood causes the two objects to stick together.

Standards Check What is the difference between an endothermic reaction and an exothermic reaction? **8.5.c**

Quick Lab

Endothermic and Exothermic Processes

Exothermic processes release heat to the surroundings and warm the nearby matter. Endothermic processes absorb heat from the surroundings and cool the nearby matter.

8.5.c

▶ Try It!

1. Fill **three large plastic-foam cups** halfway with **water.**

2. Using a **thermometer,** measure the temperature of the water in each cup. Record your results.

3. Following the instructions on the package, activate an **instant hot pack** and an **instant cold pack.**

4. Hold each pack in your hands. Record your observations.

5. Place the hot pack into the water in one of the cups and the cold pack into the water in another cup. The packs do not need to be completely covered with water.

6. Wait 5 min. Then, measure the water temperature in each of the three cups. Record your results.

▶ Think About It!

7. Based on your observations in step 4, which pack involves an exothermic process?

8. Calculate the change in the temperature of the water in each cup. Based on the temperature change, which pack involved an endothermic process? Which pack involved an exothermic process?

9. Explain why the temperature of the water in each cup changed after the packs were added.

10. Explain why measuring the temperature change is more reliable than simply feeling the packs to identify the kind of process.

 20 min

The Law of Conservation of Energy

Neither mass nor energy can be created or destroyed in chemical reactions. The **law of conservation of energy** states that energy cannot be created or destroyed. However, energy can change forms. And energy can be transferred from one object to another in the same way that a baton is passed from one runner to another runner.

The energy released in exothermic reactions was first stored in the chemical bonds in the reactants. The energy taken in during endothermic reactions is stored in the products. If you could measure all of the energy in a reaction, you would find that the total amount of energy (of all types) is the same before and after the reaction.

endothermic reaction
(EN doh THUHR mik ree AK shuhn) a chemical reaction that requires heat

law of conservation of energy
(LAW UHV KAHN suhr VAY shuhn UHV EN uhr jee) the law that states that energy cannot be created or destroyed but can be changed from one form to another

---

SECTION Review

 8.3.b, 8.5.a, 8.5.c

Summary

- A chemical reaction is a process by which substances change to form new substances with new chemical and physical properties.

- Signs that indicate a chemical reaction has taken place are a color change, formation of a gas or a solid, and the release or absorption of energy.

- During a reaction, bonds are broken, atoms are rearranged, and new bonds are formed.

- Exothermic reactions give off energy, and endothermic reactions absorb energy.

- The law of conservation of energy states that energy is neither created nor destroyed.

Using Vocabulary

1. Use the following terms in the same sentence: *chemical reaction* and *precipitate*.

Correct the statement below by replacing the underlined term.

2. An <u>exothermic reaction</u> absorbs energy.

Understanding Concepts

3. **Describing** What happens to the atoms of the starting substances during a chemical reaction?

4. **Analyzing** If the chemical properties of a substance have not changed, has a chemical reaction occurred? Explain your reasoning.

Critical Thinking

5. **Making Comparisons** Compare exothermic and endothermic reactions.

6. **Analyzing Processes** Steam escapes from a teapot. Is a chemical reaction occurring? Explain.

INTERPRETING GRAPHICS

Use the photo below to answer the next two questions.

7. **Making Inferences** What evidence of a chemical reaction is shown in the photo?

8. **Applying Concepts** What is happening to the bonds of the starting substances?

Challenge

9. **Applying Concepts** Explain why the burning of charcoal in a grill is a chemical change.

Internet Resources

For a variety of links related to this chapter, go to www.scilinks.org

Topic: Chemical Reactions; Wildfires in California
SciLinks code: HY70274; HY7C12

261

SECTION 2

Chemical Formulas and Equations

Key Concept Chemical formulas and chemical equations are used to show how atoms are rearranged to form new substances in a chemical reaction.

What You Will Learn
- Chemical formulas are a simple way to describe which elements are in a chemical substance.
- Chemical equations are a concise way to write how atoms are rearranged in a chemical reaction.
- A balanced chemical equation shows the law of conservation of mass.

Why It Matters
Chemical equations provide a great deal of information about chemical reactions.

Vocabulary
- chemical formula
- chemical equation
- reactant
- product
- law of conservation of mass

READING STRATEGY

Outlining In your **Science Journal,** create an outline of the section. Use the headings from the section in your outline.

8.3.f Students know how to use the periodic table to identify elements in simple compounds.
8.5.b Students know the idea of atoms explains the conservation of matter: In chemical reactions the number of atoms stays the same no matter how they are arranged, so their total mass stays the same.

Letters are used to form words. In the same way, chemical symbols are put together to make chemical formulas that describe substances. Chemical formulas are added together to describe a chemical reaction just as words make a sentence.

Chemical Formulas

All substances are formed from about 100 elements. Each element has its own chemical symbol, which is found in the periodic table. A **chemical formula** is a shorthand way to use chemical symbols and numbers to represent a substance. A chemical formula shows how many atoms of each kind of element are present in a molecule.

The chemical formula for water, shown in **Figure 1,** is H_2O. This formula tells you that one water molecule is made of two hydrogen atoms and one oxygen atom. The small 2 in the formula is a subscript. A *subscript* is a number written below and to the right of a chemical symbol in a formula. Sometimes, a symbol—such as O for oxygen in the formula for water—has no subscript. If there is no subscript, only one atom of that element is present. **Figure 1** has more examples of chemical formulas.

Figure 1 **Chemical Formulas of Different Substances**

Water

H_2O

Water molecules are made up of 2 atoms of hydrogen bonded to 1 atom of oxygen.

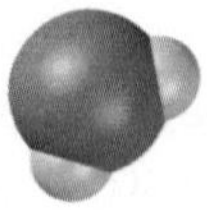

Oxygen

O_2

Oxygen is a diatomic molecule. Each molecule has 2 atoms of oxygen bonded together.

Glucose

$C_6H_{12}O_6$

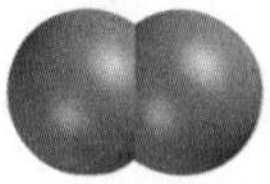

Glucose molecules have 6 atoms of carbon, 12 atoms of hydrogen, and 6 atoms of oxygen.

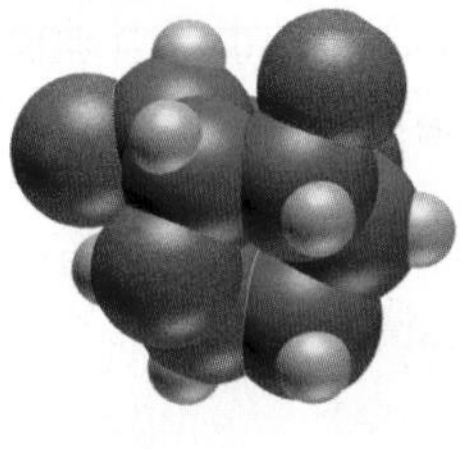

Carbon dioxide

$$CO_2$$

The **absence of a prefix** indicates one carbon atom.

The prefix **di-** indicates two oxygen atoms.

Dinitrogen monoxide

$$N_2O$$

The prefix **di-** indicates two nitrogen atoms.

The prefix **mono-** indicates one oxygen atom.

Figure 2 *The formulas of these covalent compounds can be written by using the prefixes in the names of the compounds.*

Writing Formulas for Covalent Compounds

If you know the name of a covalent compound, you can often write the chemical formula for that compound. Simple covalent compounds are usually composed of two nonmetals. The names of many covalent compounds use prefixes. Each prefix represents a number, as shown in **Table 1**. The prefixes tell you how many atoms of each element are in a formula. **Figure 2** shows you how to write a chemical formula from the name of a covalent compound.

Writing Formulas for Ionic Compounds

If the name of a compound contains the name of a metal and the name of a nonmetal, the compound is ionic. To write the formula for an ionic compound, make sure that the compound's charge is 0. In other words, the formula must have subscripts that cause the charges of the ions to cancel out. **Figure 3** shows you how to write a chemical formula from the name of an ionic compound.

Standards Check Use the periodic table in the Appendix to write the formula for the covalent compound silicon tetrachloride. 🐻 **8.3.f**

chemical formula (KEM i kuhl FAWR myoo luh) a combination of chemical symbols and numbers to represent a substance

Table 1	Prefixes Used in Chemical Names		
mono-	1	hexa-	6
di-	2	hepta-	7
tri-	3	octa-	8
tetra-	4	nona-	9
penta-	5	deca-	10

Sodium chloride

$$NaCl$$

A sodium ion has a **1+ charge.**

A chloride ion has a **1− charge.**

One sodium ion and one chloride ion have an overall **charge of (1+) + (1−) = 0.**

Magnesium chloride

$$MgCl_2$$

A magnesium ion has a **2+ charge.**

A chloride ion has a **1− charge.**

One magnesium ion and two chloride ions have an overall **charge of (2+) + 2(1−) = 0.**

Figure 3 *The formula of an ionic compound is written by using enough of each ion so that the overall charge is 0.* **What is the group number from the periodic table for each of these elements?**

Chemical Equations

Think about a piece of music, such as the one in **Figure 4.** The person writing the music must tell the musician what notes to play, how long to play each note, and how each note should be played. Words aren't used to describe the musical piece. Instead, musical symbols are used. The symbols can be understood by anyone who can read music.

Figure 4 *Like chemical symbols, the symbols on this musical score are understood around the world!*

Describing Reactions by Using Equations

In the same way that composers use musical symbols, chemists around the world use chemical symbols and chemical formulas. Chemists use chemical equations to describe reactions. A **chemical equation** uses chemical symbols and formulas as a short way to describe a chemical reaction. Anyone around the world who understands chemical formulas can understand chemical equations.

From Reactants to Products

When carbon burns, it reacts with oxygen to form carbon dioxide. **Figure 5** shows how to write an equation to describe this reaction. The starting materials in a chemical reaction are **reactants.** The substances formed from a reaction are **products.** In this example, carbon and oxygen are reactants. Carbon dioxide is the product. The plus sign is used to show that the reactants are added together. The arrow points to the products.

chemical equation (KEM i kuhl ee KWAY zhuhn) a representation of a chemical reaction that uses symbols to show the relationship between the reactants and the products
 Wordwise The root *equ-* means "even" or "equal."

reactant (ree AK tuhnt) a substance or molecule that participates in a chemical reaction

product (PRAHD uhkt) a substance that forms in a chemical reaction

---

Figure 5 **The Parts of a Chemical Equation**

Charcoal is used to cook food on a barbecue grill. When carbon in charcoal reacts with oxygen in the air, the primary product is carbon dioxide, as the chemical equation shows.

The formulas of the reactants are written before the arrow.

The formulas of the products are written after the arrow.

$$C + O_2 \longrightarrow CO_2$$

A **plus sign** separates the formulas of two or more reactants or the formulas of two or more products.

The **arrow,** also called the *yields sign,* separates the formulas of the reactants from the formulas of the products.

Figure 6 Examples of Similar Symbols and Formulas

Co

CO

CO_2

Cobalt The chemical symbol for the element cobalt is Co. Cobalt is a hard, bluish gray metal.

Carbon Monoxide The chemical formula for the compound carbon monoxide is CO. Carbon monoxide is a colorless, odorless, and poisonous gas.

Carbon Dioxide The chemical formula for the compound carbon dioxide is CO_2. Carbon dioxide is a colorless, odorless gas that you exhale.

The Importance of Accuracy

The symbol or formula for each substance in an equation must be written correctly. For an element, use the proper chemical symbol. For a compound, use the correct chemical formula. An equation that has a wrong chemical symbol or formula will not describe the reaction correctly. Even a simple mistake can make a huge difference, as **Figure 6** shows.

Why Equations Must Be Balanced

Atoms are never lost or gained in a chemical reaction. They are just rearranged. Every atom in the reactants becomes part of the products. When writing a chemical equation, make sure that the total number of atoms of each element in the reactants equals the total number of atoms of that element in the products. This process is called *balancing* the equation.

Balancing equations comes from the work of a French chemist, Antoine Lavoisier (lah vwah ZYAY). In the 1700s, Lavoisier found that the total mass of the reactants was always the same as the total mass of the products. Lavoisier's work led to the **law of conservation of mass.** This law states that mass is neither created nor destroyed in chemical and physical changes. This law means that the total mass of the reactants is the same as the total mass of the products. So, a chemical equation must show the same numbers and kinds of atoms on both sides of the arrow even though the atoms are rearranged.

Standards Check Why must the number of atoms of each element remain the same in a chemical equation? 8.5.b

Counting Atoms

Some chemical formulas contain parentheses. When counting atoms, multiply everything inside the parentheses by the subscript. For example, $Ca(NO_3)_2$ has one calcium atom, two (2×1) nitrogen atoms, and six (2×3) oxygen atoms. Find the number of atoms of each element in the formulas $Mg(OH)_2$ and $Al_2(SO_4)_3$. Record your work in your **Science Journal.**

law of conservation of mass (LAW UHV KAHN suhr VAY shuhn UHV MAS) the law that states that mass cannot be created or destroyed in ordinary chemical and physical changes

How to Balance an Equation

INTERNET ACTIVITY

Middle Ages Chemistry

You have traveled back in time to the Middle Ages, and people believe in magic. Create a brochure that tells them how to identify chemical reactions. Go to **go.hrw.com,** and type in the keyword HY7REAW.

You must use coefficients (KOH uh FISH uhnts) to balance an equation. A *coefficient* is a number that is placed in front of a chemical symbol or formula. For example, 2CO represents two carbon monoxide molecules. The number 2 is the coefficient.

For an equation to be balanced, all atoms must be counted. So, you must multiply the subscript of each element in a formula by the formula's coefficient. For example, $2H_2O$ contains a total of four hydrogen atoms and two oxygen atoms. Only coefficients—not subscripts—are changed when balancing equations. Changing the subscripts in the formula of a compound would change the compound. **Figure 7** shows you how to use coefficients to balance an equation.

Standards Check If you see $4O_2$ in an equation, what is the coefficient? 🐻 **8.5.b**

Figure 7 Balancing a Chemical Equation

Follow these steps to write a balanced equation for $H_2 + O_2 \longrightarrow H_2O$.

① **Count the atoms** of each element in the reactants and in the products. You can see that there are fewer oxygen atoms in the product than in the reactants.

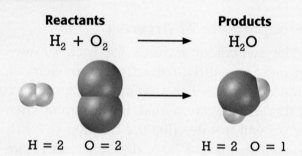

Reactants $\quad$ Products
$H_2 + O_2 \longrightarrow H_2O$

$H = 2 \quad O = 2 \qquad H = 2 \quad O = 1$

② **To balance the oxygen atoms,** place the coefficient 2 in front of H_2O. Doing so gives you two oxygen atoms both in the reactants and in the products. But now there are too few hydrogen atoms in the reactants.

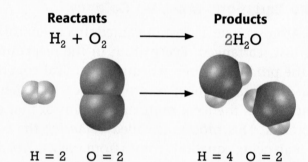

Reactants $\quad$ Products
$H_2 + O_2 \longrightarrow 2H_2O$

$H = 2 \quad O = 2 \qquad H = 4 \quad O = 2$

③ **To balance the hydrogen atoms,** place the coefficient 2 in front of H_2. But to be sure that your answer is correct, always double-check your work!

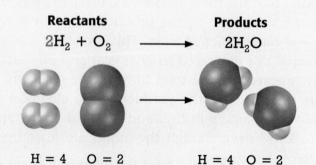

Reactants $\quad$ Products
$2H_2 + O_2 \longrightarrow 2H_2O$

$H = 4 \quad O = 2 \qquad H = 4 \quad O = 2$

Quick Lab

Conservation of Mass

1. Place **5 g of baking soda** into a **sealable plastic bag.**
2. Place **5 mL of vinegar** into a **plastic film canister.** Put the lid on the canister.
3. Place the canister into the bag. Squeeze the air out of the bag. Seal the bag tightly.
4. Use a **balance** to measure the mass of the bag and its contents. Record the mass.
5. Keeping the bag closed, open the canister in the bag. Mix the vinegar with the baking soda. Record your observations.
6. When the reaction has stopped, measure the mass of the bag and its contents. Record the mass.
7. Compare the mass of the materials before the reaction with the mass of the materials after the reaction. Explain your observations.

8.5.b

🕐 **20 min**

SECTION Review

8.3.f, 8.5.b

Summary

- A chemical formula uses symbols and subscripts to describe the makeup of a compound.
- Chemical formulas can often be written from the names of covalent and ionic compounds.
- A chemical equation uses chemical formulas, chemical symbols, and coefficients to describe a reaction.
- A balanced equation has the same numbers and kinds of atoms on each side of the equation.
- A balanced equation shows the law of conservation of mass: mass is neither created nor destroyed during ordinary physical and chemical changes.

Using Vocabulary

Correct each statement by replacing the underlined term.

1. A <u>chemical formula</u> describes a chemical reaction.
2. The substances formed from a chemical reaction are <u>reactants</u>.

Understanding Concepts

3. **Applying** How does a balanced chemical equation show that mass is never lost or gained in a chemical reaction?

INTERPRETING GRAPHICS Use the image below to answer the next two questions.

$$Sb + I_2 \longrightarrow SbI_3$$

Sb   I₂   SbI₃

4. **Identifying** Use the periodic table to name the reactants.

5. **Modeling** Balance the equation. Draw a molecular model of your balanced equation.

6. **Comparing** Compare a subscript with a coefficient.

Critical Thinking

7. **Analyzing Methods** Using silicon dioxide as an example and the periodic table as a reference, describe how to write the formula of a covalent compound.

Math Skills

8. **Using Formulas** Calculate the number of atoms of each element represented in each of the following formulas: $2Na_3PO_4$, $4Al_2(SO_4)_3$, and $6PCl_5$.

Challenge

9. **Applying Concepts** When balancing an equation, can you change the subscript in a formula? Why or why not?

Internet Resources

For a variety of links related to this chapter, go to www.scilinks.org

Topic: Chemical Formulas; Chemical Equations

SciLinks code: HY70271; HY70269

Skills Practice Lab

Putting Elements Together

A synthesis reaction is a reaction in which two or more substances combine to form a single compound. The chemical and physical properties of the resulting compound differ from those of the substances from which the compound is made. In this activity, you will synthesize, or create, copper(II) oxide, CuO, from the elements copper, Cu, and oxygen, O_2.

Procedure

1. Copy the table below.

Data Collection Table	
Object	**Mass (g)**
Evaporating dish	
Copper powder	
Copper + evaporating dish after heating	
Copper(II) oxide	

2. Use the metric balance to measure the mass of the empty evaporating dish. Record this mass (to the nearest 0.1 g) in your table.

3. Place a piece of weighing paper on the metric balance, and measure approximately 10 g of copper powder. Record the mass (to the nearest 0.1 g) in the table. **Caution:** Wear protective gloves when working with copper powder.

4. Use the weighing paper to place the copper powder in the evaporating dish. Spread the powder over the bottom and up the sides as much as possible. Discard the weighing paper.

5. Set up the ring stand and ring. Place the wire gauze on top of the ring. Carefully place the evaporating dish on the wire gauze.

6. Place the Bunsen burner under the ring and wire gauze. Use the igniter to light the Bunsen burner. **Caution:** Use extreme care when working near an open flame.

7. Heat the evaporating dish for 10 min.

8.3.b Students know that compounds are formed by combining two or more different elements and that compounds have properties that are different from their constituent elements.

8.5.a Students know reactant atoms and molecules interact to form products with different chemical properties.

8.5.b Students know the idea of atoms explains the conservation of matter: In chemical reactions the number of atoms stays the same no matter how they are arranged, so their total mass stays the same.

8 Turn off the burner, and allow the evaporating dish to cool for 10 min. While the dish is cooling, record your observations of the product. Use tongs to remove the evaporating dish and to place it on the balance to determine its mass. Record the mass in the table.

9 Determine the mass of the reaction product—copper(II) oxide—by subtracting the mass of the evaporating dish from the mass of the evaporating dish and copper powder after heating. Record this mass in the table.

Analyze the Results

10 **Describing Events**   What evidence of a chemical reaction did you observe after the copper was heated?

11 **Describing Events**   Write the balanced chemical equation for the reaction between the copper and oxygen.

12 **Analyzing Results**   Using the balanced equation for the chemical reaction, explain why there was a change in mass. (Hint: Think about the states of the substances in the reaction.)

Draw Conclusions

13 **Defending Conclusions**   Does the change in mass that you observed conflict with the law of conservation of mass?

14 **Applying Conclusions**   The copper bottoms of some cooking pots can turn black when the pots are used. How is that fact related to the results obtained in this lab?

Big Idea Question

15 **Evaluating Results**   Compare the properties of the reactants with those of the product.

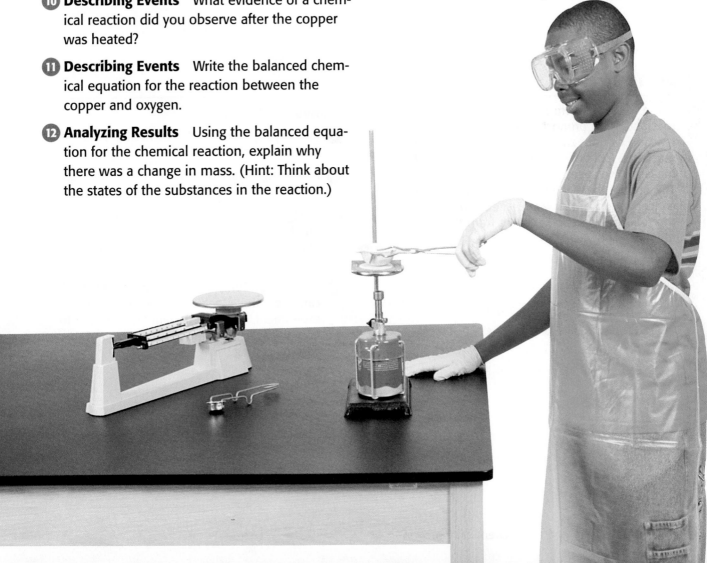

Science Skills Activity

Identifying Types of Parameters

Investigation and Experimentation
8.9.c Distinguish between variable and controlled parameters in a test.

▶ Tutorial

When you design an experiment, you have controlled parameters, which stay constant during the experiment. You also have variable parameters, whose values change during the experiment.

1 List the possible variables in the experiment.

2 Identify the variable and controlled parameters. The variable parameters are the parameters that you will allow to change in the experiment. They may cause your results to change. The controlled parameters do not change.

3 When designing an experiment, you should record data in regular increments.

4 You will record the values for your variable parameters during your experiment. The values of the controlled parameters will not change during your experiment.

5 After your experiment is complete, you could make a table or graph to help determine the relationship between your variable parameters.

▶ You Try It!

Some reactants form products quickly, but other reactants form products slowly. The speed of a reaction can depend on the concentration of reactants. A chemist designs an experiment to measure the speed of the reaction A + 2B → C. The goal of this experiment is to find out if the concentration of reactant B affects the speed of the reaction. Notebook entries from the experiment are shown below.

Trial 1:
Concentration of A (M) 0.10 M
Concentration of B (M) 0.10 M
Speed of reaction = 0.0015 M/s

Trial 4:
Concentration of A (M) 0.10 M
Concentration of B (M) 0.40 M
Speed of reaction = 0.0058 M/s

Analysis

1 **Identifying** Identify the controlled parameters and the variable parameters in this experiment.

2 **Analyzing** How does the speed of the reaction vary with the concentration of reactant B?

3 **Designing** How would you design an experiment to find out how the speed of the reaction depends on the concentration of reactant A?

4 **Designing** Temperature is another factor that can affect the speed of a reaction. In this experiment, would you want temperature to be a variable or controlled parameter? Explain your reasoning.

Chapter Summary

The Big Idea
Substances undergo chemical reactions, which form new substances whose properties differ from the properties of the original substances.

Section

Vocabulary

① Forming New Substances

Key Concept During chemical reactions, atoms rearrange to form new substances that have different properties than the original substances had.

- Four signs that indicate that a chemical reaction may be taking place are a change in color, the formation of a gas, the formation of a precipitate, and a change in energy.

- Chemical reactions produce new substances whose chemical and physical properties differ from the properties of the original substances.

- In a chemical reaction, chemical bonds break and atoms rearrange.

- Chemical reactions absorb or release energy.

The properties of the substances made by a chemical reaction differ from the properties of the starting substances.

chemical reaction
p. 256

precipitate p. 257

exothermic reaction
p. 259

endothermic reaction
p. 260

law of conservation of energy p. 261

② Chemical Formulas and Equations

Key Concept Chemical formulas and chemical equations are used to show how atoms are rearranged to form new substances in a chemical reaction.

- Chemical formulas are a simple way to describe which elements are in a chemical substance.

- Chemical equations are a concise way to write how atoms are rearranged in a chemical reaction.

- A balanced chemical equation shows the law of conservation of mass.

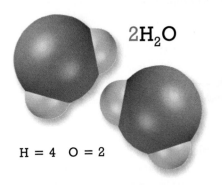

$2H_2O$

$H = 4 \quad O = 2$

The subscripts in a chemical formula tell you how many atoms of each element are in the substance. A coefficient is used before a formula to balance a chemical equation.

chemical formula
p. 262

chemical equation
p. 264

reactant p. 264

product p. 264

law of conservation of mass p. 265

Chapter Review

Organize

Four-Corner Fold   Review the FoldNote that you created at the beginning of the chapter. Add to or correct the FoldNote based on what you have learned.

Using Vocabulary

1 Academic Vocabulary   Which of the following words means "to act on each other"?
a. relate   **c.** mix
b. observe   **d.** interact

Complete each of the following sentences by choosing the correct term from the word bank.

subscript	exothermic reaction
reactant	endothermic reaction
product	coefficient

2 A(n) ___ is a starting substance in a chemical reaction.

3 A chemical reaction that gives off heat is called a(n) ___.

4 The 2 in the formula Ag_2S is a(n) ___.

Understanding Concepts

Multiple Choice

5 Balancing a chemical equation so that the same number of atoms of each element is found in both the reactants and the products is an example of
a. an endothermic reaction.
b. the law of conservation of energy.
c. the law of conservation of mass.
d. a chemical formula.

6 Which of the following is the correct chemical formula for dinitrogen tetroxide?
a. N_4O_2
b. NO_2
c. N_2O_5
d. N_2O_4

7 Which of the following is a formula for an ionic compound?
a. N_2O **c.** $MgBr_2$
b. CH_4 **d.** $SiCl_4$

8 Which of the following chemical equations is balanced?
a. $Ba(CN)_2 + 2H_2SO_4 \longrightarrow BaSO_4 + 2HCN$
b. $2Na + MgSO_4 \longrightarrow Na_2SO_4 + Mg$
c. $Cu + O_2 \longrightarrow 2CuO$
d. $3H_2 + N_2 \longrightarrow NH_3$

Short Answer

INTERPRETING GRAPHICS   Use the model of a chemical equation below to answer the next three questions.

$$H_2 + N_2 \longrightarrow NH_3$$

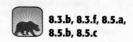

| H_2 | N_2 | NH_3 |

9 Identifying   Identify the reactants and the products in the chemical reaction.

10 Modeling   Balance the chemical equation for the reaction. Draw molecular diagrams of your balanced chemical equation.

11 Analyzing   Which bonds are broken and which bonds are formed in the reaction?

INTERPRETING GRAPHICS   Use the table below to answer the next two questions.

	Reactants	Products
Trial equation	$4NH_3 + 2O_2$	$4NO + 6H_2O$
Number of nitrogen atoms		
Number of oxygen atoms		
Number of hydrogen atoms		

DO NOT WRITE IN BOOK

12 Evaluating   Complete the table to determine if the chemical equation shown is balanced.

13 Applying   If the equation is not balanced, use the information that you put into the table to write the balanced equation.

14 Describing Describe what happens to chemical bonds during a chemical reaction.

15 Listing Name four clues that signal that a chemical reaction may be taking place.

Writing Skills

16 Technical Writing Write a procedure that your classmates can use to balance equations. Your procedure should include clear steps that take into account all of the factors that must be considered when balancing an equation.

Critical Thinking

17 Concept Mapping Use the following terms to create a concept map: *products, chemical reaction, chemical equation, chemical formulas, reactants, coefficients,* and *subscripts*.

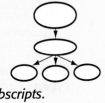

18 Evaluating Assumptions Your friend is very worried by rumors that he has heard about a substance called *dihydrogen monoxide* in the city's water system. What could you say to your friend to calm his fears? (Hint: Write the formula for the substance.)

19 Applying Concepts Before leaving a steel pipe outdoors, you measured its mass. One month later, the pipe had rusted, and its mass had increased. Does this change violate the law of conservation of mass? Explain your answer.

20 Applying Concepts Acetic acid, a compound found in vinegar, reacts with baking soda to produce carbon dioxide, water, and sodium acetate. Without writing an equation, identify the reactants and the products of this reaction.

21 Applying Concepts During the process of photosynthesis, carbon dioxide and water react to produce glucose, $C_6H_{12}O_6$, and oxygen, O_2. Write the balanced equation that describes the overall chemical reaction that occurs during photosynthesis.

INTERPRETING GRAPHICS Use the photo below to answer the next two questions.

22 Applying Concepts What evidence in the photo supports the claim that a chemical reaction is taking place?

23 Identifying Relationships Is this reaction an exothermic or endothermic reaction? Explain your answer.

Math Skills

24 Using Formulas Calculate the number of atoms of each element shown in the following formulas:
a. $CaSO_4$
b. $4NaOCl$
c. $Fe(NO_3)_2$
d. $2Al_2(CO_3)_3$

25 Balancing Equations Write balanced equations for the following:
a. $Fe + O_2 \longrightarrow Fe_2O_3$
b. $Al + CuSO_4 \longrightarrow Al_2(SO_4)_3 + Cu$
c. $Mg(OH)_2 + HCl \longrightarrow MgCl_2 + H_2O$

Challenge

26 Applying Concepts In a car engine, oxygen reacts with gasoline to produce carbon dioxide and water. This reaction is exothermic. Is more energy or less energy needed to break the bonds in the oxygen and gasoline than is released when the bonds in the carbon dioxide and water are made? Explain your reasoning.

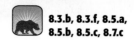
REVIEWING ACADEMIC VOCABULARY

1 In the sentence "She wrote a chemical formula that showed the parts of the compound," what does the word *compound* mean?

A a group of buildings set off and enclosed by a barrier

B a word that consists of two or more elements or parts

C a substance made up of two or more elements that are joined by chemical bonds

D a leaf whose blade is divided into at least two leaflets

2 Choose the appropriate form of the word *react* for the following sentence: "When an atom has one electron in its outer energy level, it ___ easily with other atoms."

A reacting

B reactive

C reaction

D reacts

3 Which of the following phrases means "a process that changes a substance into another substance"?

A chemical reaction

B physical process

C atomic structure

D buoyant force

4 Which of the following words or phrases is the closest in meaning to the word *identify*?

A observe

B pick out

C acquire

D ask

REVIEWING CONCEPTS

5 The model above shows the reaction of hydrogen and chlorine. Which of the following best describes the result of the reaction shown in the model?

A Four new diatomic molecules form.

B Bonds are formed between two hydrogen atoms.

C The properties of the new molecules are the same as those of the original molecules.

D Two molecules of a new compound are formed.

6 Which of the following contains one oxygen atom?

A H_2O

B CO_2

C $2N_2O$

D Co

7 Atoms are never lost or gained during a chemical reaction. They are just

A rearranged.

B changed into other atoms.

C corrected.

D converted.

8 Which chemical equation correctly shows the formation of water from hydrogen and oxygen?

A $H_2 + O_2 \longrightarrow H_2O$

B $2H_2 + O_2 \longrightarrow 2H_2O$

C $H_2 + 2O \longrightarrow H_2O$

D $H + O_2 \longrightarrow H_2O$

9 According to the periodic table, what is the chemical makeup of the compound $MgCl_2$?

A the elements manganese and chromium

B the elements mendelevium and chlorine

C the elements magnesium and chlorine

D the elements molybdenum and carbon

10 Use the periodic table to locate the elements Na and Cl. What type of compound is created when these two elements react?

A isotopic

B covalent

C ionic

D metallic

11 Ammonium sulfate has the chemical formula $(NH_4)_2SO_4$. How many atoms does one unit of ammonium sulfate contain?

A 4

B 7

C 9

D 15

12 Chemical reactions are endothermic or exothermic. Which of the following is an example of an endothermic reaction?

A Ice absorbs energy and melts to form liquid water.

B Wood burns and releases light and heat.

C Fireworks explode and release light.

D Water absorbs energy and decomposes to form hydrogen and oxygen.

REVIEWING PRIOR LEARNING

13 According to the periodic table, what is the atomic number of zinc, Zn?

A 2.018

B 30

C 65.4

D 19,620

14 A cake is an example of a

A solution.

B compound.

C mixture.

D nonmetal.

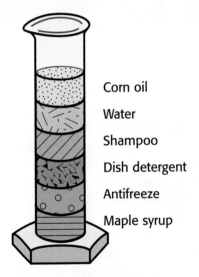

Corn oil

Water

Shampoo

Dish detergent

Antifreeze

Maple syrup

15 Which of the following best describes the liquids in the graduated cylinder?

A Of the six liquids, corn oil is the least dense.

B The density of the liquids increases from maple syrup to corn oil.

C The density of the top layers holds down less-dense liquids.

D Of the six liquids, maple syrup is the least dense.

Science in Action

Science, Technology, and Society

Western Wildfires

Wildfires burn thousands of acres of land in California every year. They cause millions of dollars of damage. If we were not able to put out wildfires, their effects would be even more devastating. One of the steps in putting out wildfires is the use of fire retardants. Some fire retardants are mixtures of chemicals that include some of the same chemicals used in fertilizers. The mixture is dropped by airplanes on the trees and land in front of the raging fire. The fire retardants slow the fire and give firefighters time to clear potential fuel from the fire's path. Without fuel, the fire cannot burn.

Weird Science

Light Sticks

Have you ever seen light sticks at a concert? Your family may even keep them in the car for emergencies. But how do light sticks work? To activate the light stick, you have to bend it. Most light sticks are made of a plastic tube that contains a mixture of two chemicals. Also inside the tube is a thin glass vial, which contains hydrogen peroxide. As long as the glass vial is unbroken, the two chemicals are kept separate. But bending the ends of the tube breaks the glass vial. This action releases the hydrogen peroxide into the other chemicals, and a chemical reaction occurs, which makes the light stick glow.

Social Studies ACTiViTY

Who invented light sticks? What was their original purpose? Research the answers to these questions. Make a poster that shows what you have learned.

Math ACTiViTY

In the United States, 4.5 million acres of land were burned by wildfires in a year. Of this land, 3.8% was in California. A single fire burned 23% of the land in California. How many acres were burned in this fire?

Larry McKee

Arson Investigator   Once a fire dies down, you might see an arson investigator such as Lt. Larry McKee on the scene. "After the fire is out, I can investigate the fire scene to determine where the fire started and how it started," says McKee, who questions witnesses and firefighters about what they have seen. He knows that the color of the smoke can indicate certain chemicals. He also gets help in detecting chemicals from an accelerant-sniffing dog, Nikki. Nikki has been trained to detect about 11 chemicals.

If Nikki finds one of these chemicals, she begins to dig. McKee takes a sample of the suspicious material to the laboratory. He treats the sample so that any chemicals present will dissolve in a liquid. A sample of this liquid is placed into an instrument called a *gas chromatograph* and is tested. The results of this test are printed out in a graph, from which the suspicious chemical is identified. Next, McKee begins to search for suspects. By combining detective work with scientific evidence, fire investigators can help find clues that can lead to the conviction of an arsonist.

Language Arts ACTIVITY

Write a one-page story about an arson investigator. Begin the story at the scene of a fire. Take the story through the steps that you think an investigator would follow to solve the crime.

Internet Resources

- To learn more about careers in science, visit www.scilinks.org and enter the SciLinks code HY70225.

- To learn more about these Science in Action topics, visit go.hrw.com and type in the keyword HY7REAF.

- Check out articles related to this chapter by visiting go.hrw.com. Just type in the keyword HY7REAC.

Improving Comprehension

Graphic Organizers are important visual tools that can help you organize information and improve your reading comprehension. The Graphic Organizer below is called an *idea wheel*. Instructions for creating other types of Graphic Organizers are located in the **Study Skills** section of the Appendix.

How to Make an Idea Wheel

1 Draw a circle. Draw a larger circle around the first circle. Divide the ring between the circles into sections by drawing lines from one circle to the other across the ring. Divide the ring into as many sections as you want.

2 Write a main idea or topic in the smaller circle. Label each section in the ring with a category or characteristic of the main idea.

3 In each section of the ring, include details that are unique to the topic.

When to Use an Idea Wheel

An idea wheel is an effective type of visual organization in which ideas in science can be divided into categories or parts. It is also a useful way to illustrate characteristics of a main idea or topic. As you read, look for topics that are divided into ideas or categories, that can be organized around an idea wheel.

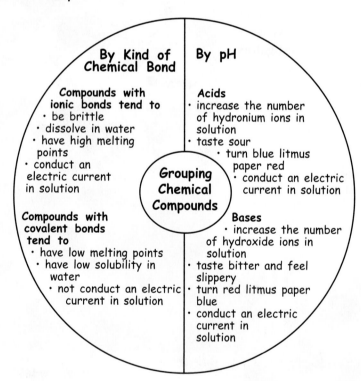

By Kind of Chemical Bond

Compounds with ionic bonds tend to
· be brittle
· dissolve in water
· have high melting points
· conduct an electric current in solution

Compounds with covalent bonds tend to
· have low melting points
· have low solubility in water
· not conduct an electric current in solution

Grouping Chemical Compounds

By pH

Acids
· increase the number of hydronium ions in solution
· taste sour
· turn blue litmus paper red
· conduct an electric current in solution

Bases
· increase the number of hydroxide ions in solution
· taste bitter and feel slippery
· turn red litmus paper blue
· conduct an electric current in solution

You Try It!

This Reading Strategy can also be used within the chapter that you are about to read. Practice making your own *idea wheel* as directed in the Reading Strategies for Section **1** and Section **2**. Record your work in your **Science Journal.**

Unpacking the Standards

The information below "unpacks" the standards by breaking them down into basic parts. The higher-level, academic vocabulary is highlighted and defined to help you understand the language of the standards. "What It Means" restates the standards as simply as possible.

California Standard	Academic Vocabulary	What It Means
8.3.b Students know that compounds are formed by combining two or more different elements and that compounds have properties that are different from their **constituent** elements.	**constituent** (kuhn STICH oo uhnt) serving as part of a whole	Compounds form when two or more elements combine. The properties of a compound differ from the properties of the elements that make up the compound.
8.3.c Students know atoms and molecules form solids by building up repeating patterns, such as the crystal **structure** of NaCl or long-chain polymers.	**structure** (STRUHK chuhr) a whole that is built or put together from parts	Solids are made up of atoms and molecules arranged in organized, repeating patterns. For example, table salt is made up of crystals, and plastics are made up of polymer chains.
8.5.e Students know how to determine whether a solution is acidic, basic, or **neutral.**	**neutral** (NOO truhl) being neither acidic nor basic	You must know how to figure out if a substance is an acid or a base, or is neutral.
8.7.c Students know substances can be classified by their properties, including their melting temperature, density, hardness, and thermal and electrical conductivity.		Different kinds of matter can be grouped by their characteristics, including the temperature at which they melt, the amount of mass per unit volume, their hardness, and their ability to transfer thermal energy or electrical energy.

10

Chemical Compounds

The Big Idea

Chemical compounds are classified into groups based on their bonds and on their properties.

 California Standards

Focus on Physical Sciences

8.3 Each of the more than 100 elements of matter has distinct properties and a distinct atomic structure. All forms of matter are composed of one or more of the elements. (Section 1)
8.5 Chemical reactions are processes in which atoms are rearranged into different combinations of molecules. (Sections 2 and 3)
8.7 The organization of the periodic table is based on the properties of the elements and reflects the structure of atoms. (Section 1)

Investigation and Experimentation

8.9 Scientific progress is made by asking meaningful questions and conducting careful investigations. (Science Skills Activity)

Math

7.1.1 Mathematical Reasoning

English–Language Arts

8.2.2 Reading
8.2.6 Writing

About the Photo

Mono Lake in the eastern Sierra Nevada is saltier than the ocean because it has a high concentration of dissolved ionic compounds. One ionic compound, calcium carbonate, precipitates and forms interesting rock towers like the ones in this photo. Mono Lake is also so basic that no native fish live in the lake.

 **Organize**

Layered Book

Before you read this chapter, create the FoldNote entitled "Layered Book." Label the tabs of the layered book with "Properties of ionic and covalent compounds," "Acids," "Bases," and "pH." As you read the chapter, write information that you learn about each category on the appropriate tab.

Instructions for creating FoldNotes are located in the Study Skills section on p. 518 of the Appendix.

Explore Activity

⚪ 20 min

A Model of Salt

In this activity, you will build a model of the structure of sodium chloride, commonly known as table salt.

Procedure

1. Choose **one color of clay** to use for the sodium ions and a **second color of clay** to use for the chloride ions. Make a square by using **toothpicks** to join two sodium ions with two chloride ions. Each sodium ion should be connected to two chloride ions.

2. Make a second square, and use more toothpicks to connect your squares to make a cube. Make sure that sodium ions are connected only to chloride ions.

3. Continue to build up your model by adding more sodium ions and chloride ions.　8.3.c

4. Make a big crystal by connecting all of the models made in the class.

Analysis

5. Why was it important not to connect two sodium ions or two chloride ions together?

6. Describe the repeating pattern of ions in the model that you built.

7. How did the shape of the individual models affect the shape of the final class model?

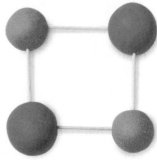

Ionic and Covalent Compounds

Key Concept The properties of ionic compounds are different from the properties of covalent compounds.

What You Will Learn

- The physical properties of a compound are determined by the type of bonding in the compound.
- Ionic compounds tend to be brittle, have high melting points, dissolve in water, and often conduct electric current in solution.
- Many covalent compounds tend to be insoluble in water, have low melting points, are not water soluble, and often do not conduct electric current in solution.

Why It Matters

The properties of a compound determine how the compound can be used.

Vocabulary

- chemical bond
- ionic compound
- covalent compound

READING STRATEGY

Graphic Organizer In your **Science Journal,** create an Idea Wheel about the properties of ionic compounds.

Compounds can be grouped by the kind of chemical bond they have. A **chemical bond** is an interaction that holds atoms and ions together. Bonding happens between valence electrons of different atoms. *Valence electrons* are electrons in the outermost energy level of an atom. The type of compound that forms depends on what happens to the valence electrons.

Ionic Compounds and Their Properties

An *ionic bond* is an attraction between oppositely charged ions. Compounds that have ionic bonds are called **ionic compounds.** The properties of ionic compounds are a result of strong attractive forces. Ionic compounds can be formed by the reaction of a metal with a nonmetal. Metal atoms become positively charged ions when electrons are transferred from the metal atoms to the nonmetal atoms. This transfer of electrons also causes the nonmetal atom to become a negatively charged ion. Sodium chloride, or *table salt,* is an ionic compound.

Standards Check Name the ions in sodium chloride. **8.3.b**

Brittleness

Ionic compounds tend to be brittle solids at room temperature. So, they often break apart when hit. They break because their ions are arranged in a repeating three-dimensional pattern called a *crystal lattice,* shown in **Figure 1.** Each ion in a lattice is bonded to the surrounding ions of the opposite charge. When an ionic compound is hit, the ions move and the pattern changes. Ions that have the same charge line up and repel one another, which causes the crystal to break.

Figure 1 *Sodium chloride crystals have a regular cubic shape because of the way sodium and chloride ions are arranged in the crystal lattice.*

High Melting Points

Because of the strong bonds that hold ions together, ionic compounds have high melting points. These high melting points are the reason that most ionic compounds are solids at room temperature. For example, solid sodium chloride must be heated to 801°C before it will melt. The melting points of two other ionic compounds are given in **Figure 2.**

Solubility and Electrical Conductivity

Many ionic compounds are highly soluble in water. So, they dissolve easily in water. Water molecules attract each of the ions of an ionic compound and pull the ions away from one another. The solution that forms when an ionic compound dissolves in water can conduct an electric current, as shown in **Figure 3.** The solution can conduct an electric current because the ions are charged and are able to move freely past one another. However, an undissolved crystal of an ionic compound does not conduct an electric current.

Standards Check Why do solutions of ionic compounds dissolved in water conduct an electric current? 🐻 **8.7.c**

chemical bond (KEM i kuhl BAHND) an interaction that holds atoms or ions together

ionic compound (ie AHN ic KAHM pownd) a compound made of oppositely charged ions

Figure 2 *Ionic compounds have high melting points.*

Potassium dichromate
Melting point: 398°C

Nickel(II) oxide
Melting point: 1,984°C

Pure water

Salt water

Figure 3 *The pure water does not conduct an electric current. However, the solution of salt water conducts an electric current, so the bulb lights up.*

8.3.b Students know that compounds are formed by combining two or more different elements and that compounds have properties that are different from their constituent elements.
8.3.c Students know atoms and molecules form solids by building up repeating patterns, such as the crystal structure of NaCl or long-chain polymers.
8.7.c Students know substances can be classified by their properties, including their melting temperature, density, hardness, and thermal and electrical conductivity.

Covalent Compounds and Their Properties

Like most compounds, many of the compounds in your body are covalent compounds. **Covalent** **compounds** are compounds that form when atoms share electrons. A *covalent bond* forms as a result of this sharing of electrons. By sharing valence electrons, atoms fill their outermost energy level. The group of atoms that make up a covalent compound is called a molecule. A *molecule* is the smallest particle into which a covalently bonded compound can be divided and still be the same compound. Properties of covalent compounds are very different from the properties of ionic compounds.

Solubility

Some covalent compounds are not soluble in water. So, they do not dissolve well in water. Before you use a bottle of oil-based salad dressing, you shake the bottle to mix the oil and water. The oil separates from the water because it contains covalent compounds that are not soluble in water. When the attraction between water molecules is stronger than their attraction to the molecules of the other covalent compound, the water molecules tend to stay together. So, the molecules of water and the covalent compound do not mix.

Standards Check Explain why some covalent compounds won't dissolve in water. ■ 8.7.c

Quick Lab

8.7.c

Ionic or Covalent?

The properties of compounds can be used to classify the compounds as ionic or covalent.

▶ Try It!

1. Examine the table below.
2. Use the information in the table to classify each compound as ionic or covalent.

Melting Points of Compounds	
Compound	**Melting point**
A	−78°C
B	772°C
C	20°C
D	2,800°C

▶ Think About It!

3. What did you use to classify the substances as ionic or covalent?
4. What other properties could you add to the table to help you be sure of your classification?
5. Would adding information about the color of the compound help you classify the compound? Explain your answer.
6. You need to classify two unknown substances as ionic and covalent. Design an experiment to gather information that you can use to classify the compounds.

 30 min

Low Melting Points

The forces of attraction between the molecules in solids of covalent compounds are much weaker than the bonds holding ionic solids together. Less heat is needed to separate the molecules of covalent compounds, so these compounds have much lower melting and boiling points than ionic compounds do.

Electrical Conductivity

Although many covalent compounds don't dissolve in water, some do. Most of the covalent compounds that dissolve in water form solutions that have uncharged molecules. Sugar is a covalent compound that dissolves in water. But, it does not form ions. So, a solution of sugar and water does not conduct an electric current, as shown in **Figure 4.** However, some covalent compounds do form ions when they dissolve in water. Many acids, for example, form ions in water. Acidic solutions, like ionic solutions, conduct an electric current.

Standards Check Why do the melting points of covalent compounds tend to be lower than those of ionic compounds? 🐻 **8.7.c**

Sugar water

Figure 4 *This solution of sugar, a covalent compound, and water does not conduct an electric current because the molecules of sugar are not charged.* **How is this different from solutions of ionic compounds?**

SECTION Review

8.3.b, 8.3.c, 8.7.c

Summary

- Ionic compounds have ionic bonds between ions of opposite charges.

- Ionic compounds are usually brittle, have high melting points, dissolve in water, and often conduct an electric current in solution.

- Covalent compounds have covalent bonds and consist of particles called *molecules*.

- Many covalent compounds have low melting points, do not dissolve in water, and do not conduct an electric current in solution.

Using Vocabulary

1 Use *ionic compound, covalent compound,* and *chemical bond* in separate sentences.

Understanding Concepts

2 **Describing** Why do ionic compounds tend to be brittle?

3 **Listing** List two properties of covalent compounds.

Critical Thinking

4 **Making Inferences** Solid crystals of ionic compounds do not conduct an electric current. But when the crystals dissolve in water, the solution conducts an electric current. Explain.

Math Skills

5 **Making Calculations** A compound is composed of 39.37% chromium, 38.10% oxygen, and potassium. What percentage of the compound is potassium?

Challenge

6 **Applying Concepts** Solid crystals are dissolved in water. If the solution does not conduct an electric current, is the solid an ionic compound or a covalent compound? Explain.

Internet Resources

For a variety of links related to this chapter, go to www.scilinks.org
Topic: Ionic Compounds;
    Covalent Compounds
SciLinks code: HY70817; HY70365

Acids and Bases

Key Concept You can use the characteristics of a solution to determine if it is acidic or basic.

acid (AS id) any compound that increases the number of hydronium ions when dissolved in water

▶ Lemons contain a substance called an *acid*. One property of acids is a sour taste. In this section, you will learn about the properties of acids and bases.

Acids and Their Properties

A sour taste is not the only property of an acid. Have you noticed that when you squeeze lemon juice into tea, the color of the tea becomes lighter? This change happens because acids cause some substances to change color. An **acid** is any compound that increases the number of hydronium ions, H_3O^+, when dissolved in water. Hydronium ions form when a hydrogen ion, H^+, separates from the acid and bonds with a water molecule, H_2O, to form a hydronium ion, H_3O^+.

Standards Check How is a hydronium ion formed? 🐻 **8.5.e**

Acids Have a Sour Flavor

The boy in **Figure 1** has discovered that acids taste sour. The taste of lemons, limes, and other citrus fruits is a result of citric acid. However, taste, touch, or smell should NEVER be used to identify an unknown chemical. Many acids are *corrosive*, which means that they destroy body tissue, clothing, and many other things. Most acids are also poisonous.

NEVER touch or taste a concentrated solution of a strong acid.

Figure 1 *Foods that have a sour taste usually contain acids.*

8.5.e Students know how to determine whether a solution is acidic, basic, or neutral.

Figure 2 Detecting Acids with Indicators

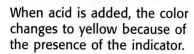

The indicator, bromthymol blue, is pale blue in water.

When acid is added, the color changes to yellow because of the presence of the indicator.

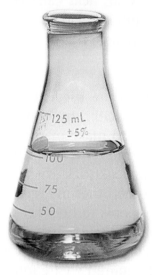

Acids Change Colors of Indicators

A substance that changes color in the presence of an acid or base is an **indicator.** Both flasks shown in **Figure 2** have an indicator called *bromthymol blue* (BROHM THIE MAWL BLOO) in them. The flask on the left contains water and the indicator. Acid has been added to the flask on the right. The color changes from pale blue to yellow because the indicator detects the presence of an acid.

Another indicator commonly used in the lab is litmus. Paper strips containing litmus are available in both blue and red. When an acid is added to blue litmus paper, the color of the litmus changes to red.

Acids React with Metals

Acids react with some metals to make hydrogen gas. For example, hydrogen gas is made when hydrochloric acid reacts with zinc metal, as shown in **Figure 3.** The equation for the reaction is shown below:

$$2HCl + Zn \longrightarrow H_2 + ZnCl_2$$

In this reaction, zinc takes the place of hydrogen in hydrochloric acid. This reaction happens because zinc is an active metal. But if the element silver were put into hydrochloric acid, nothing would happen. Silver is not an active metal, which means it is less reactive. So, it will not take the place of the hydrogen, and no reaction will take place.

indicator (IN di KAYT uhr) a compound that can reversibly change color depending on conditions such as pH

Figure 3 *Bubbles of hydrogen gas form when zinc metal reacts with hydrochloric acid.* **What other substance is produced by this reaction?**

Acids Conduct Electric Current

When acids dissolve in water, they break apart and form ions in the solution. The ions make it possible for the solution to conduct an electric current. A car battery is one example of how an acid can be used to produce an electric current. The sulfuric acid in the battery conducts an electric current to help start the car's engine.

Uses of Acids

Acids are used in many fields of industry and in homes. Sulfuric acid is the most widely made chemical in the world. It is used to make many products, including paper, paint, detergents, and fertilizers. Nitric acid is used to make fertilizers, rubber, and plastics. Hydrochloric acid is used to separate metals from the other materials in their ores. It is also used in swimming pools to help keep them free of algae. Hydrochloric acid even aids in digestion in your stomach. Hydrofluoric acid is used to etch glass, as shown in **Figure 4.** Citric acid and ascorbic acid (vitamin C) are found in orange juice. Acetic (uh SEET ik) acid is the main ingredient in vinegar. And carbonic acid and phosphoric acid help give a sharp taste to soft drinks.

Standards Check What are three uses of acids? 8.5.e

Acids and Bases at Home

Ask an adult to join in a contest with you. The object is to read the labels of products at home to find out if they contain an acid or a base. Each person will write the name of the product and the name of the acid or base that it contains. The person who finds the most products containing an acid or base is the winner.

Figure 4 *Hydrofluoric acid was used to etch the image of a swan into this glass.*

Figure 5 Examples of Bases

Soaps are made by using sodium hydroxide, which is a base. Soaps remove dirt and oils from skin and feel slippery when you touch them.

Baking soda is a very mild base. It is used in toothpastes and mouthwashes to neutralize acids, which can produce unpleasant odors.

Bleach and detergents contain bases and are used for removing stains from clothing. Detergents feel slippery like soap.

Bases and Their Properties

A **base** is any compound that increases the number of hydroxide ions, OH⁻, when dissolved in water. For example, sodium hydroxide breaks apart to form sodium ions and hydroxide ions, as shown below.

$$NaOH \longrightarrow Na^+ + OH^-$$

So, a sodium hydroxide solution will have more hydroxide ions than hydronium ions.

Hydroxide ions give bases their properties. **Figure 5** shows examples of how bases are used in everyday life.

Bases Have a Bitter Flavor and a Slippery Feel

The properties of a base solution include a bitter taste and a slippery feel. If you have ever accidentally tasted soap, you know the bitter taste of a base. Soap will also have the slippery feel of a base. However, taste, touch, or smell should NEVER be used to identify an unknown chemical. Like acids, many bases are corrosive. If your fingers feel slippery when you are using a base in an experiment, you may have gotten the base on your hands. You should quickly rinse your hands with large amounts of water and tell your teacher.

base (BAYS) any compound that increases the number of hydroxide ions when dissolved in water

NEVER touch or taste a concentrated solution of a strong base.

Standards Check What gives bases their properties? 🐻 8.5.e

Figure 6   Detecting Bases with Indicators

The indicator, bromthymol blue, is pale blue in water.

When a base is added to the indicator, the indicator turns dark blue.

Bases Change Colors of Indicators

Like acids, bases change the color of an indicator. Bases turn most indicators a different color than acids do. For example, bases change the color of red litmus paper to blue. And the indicator, bromthymol blue, turns a darker blue when a base is added to it, as shown in **Figure 6.**

Bases Conduct Electric Current

Solutions of bases conduct an electric current because bases increase the number of hydroxide ions, OH⁻, in a solution. A hydroxide ion is actually a hydrogen atom and an oxygen atom bonded together. An extra electron gives the hydroxide ion a negative charge.

Quick Lab

Blue to Red—Acid!

1. Pour about 5 mL of a **test solution** into a **spot plate.** Test the solution using **red litmus paper** and **blue litmus paper** by dipping a **stirring rod** into the solution and touching the rod to a piece of litmus paper.

2. Record any color changes. Clean the stirring rod.

3. Repeat the above steps with each solution. Use new pieces of litmus paper as needed.

4. Identify each solution as acidic or basic.

8.5.e

🕐 10 min

Uses of Bases

Like acids, bases have many uses. Sodium hydroxide is a base used to make soap and paper. It is also used in oven cleaners and in products that unclog drains. Calcium hydroxide, $Ca(OH)_2$, is used to make cement and plaster. Ammonia is found in many household cleaners and is used to make fertilizers. And magnesium hydroxide and aluminum hydroxide are used in antacids to treat heartburn. **Figure 7** shows some of the many products that contain bases. Carefully follow the safety instructions when using these products. Remember that bases can harm your skin.

Standards Check What happens to bromthymol blue when an antacid is added? 📖 8.5.e

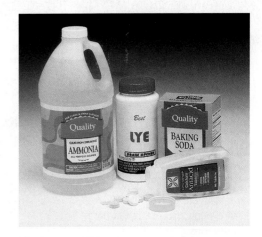

Figure 7 *Bases are common around the house. They are useful as cleaning agents, cooking aids, and medicines.*

SECTION Review

 8.5.e

Summary

- An acid is a compound that increases the number of hydronium ions in solution.

- Acids taste sour, turn blue litmus paper red, react with metals to produce hydrogen gas, and may conduct an electric current when in solution.

- Acids are used for industrial purposes and in household products.

- A base is a compound that increases the number of hydroxide ions in solution.

- Bases taste bitter, feel slippery, and turn red litmus paper blue. Most solutions of bases conduct an electric current.

- Bases are used in cleaning products and antacids.

Using Vocabulary

1. Write an original definition for *acid, base,* and *indicator.*

Understanding Concepts

2. **Describing** What happens to red litmus paper when it touches a base?

3. **Comparing** Compare the properties of acids with the properties of bases.

INTERPRETING GRAPHICS Use the table below to answer the next question.

Indicator Color

Substance	Color of bromthymol blue
water	*DO NOT WRITE IN BOOK*
lemon juice	
soap	

4. **Identifying** Complete the table with the color change that will happen when the substance is added to the indicator.

Critical Thinking

5. **Applying Concepts** What ions are present in a solution of hydrochloric acid (HCl)?

6. **Evaluating Data** A solution conducts electric current. Can you use this property of the solution to determine if it is acidic or basic? Explain.

Challenge

7. **Analyzing Processes** Your teacher gives you a solution of an unknown chemical. The chemical is either an acid or a base. You know that touching or tasting acids and bases is not safe. What two tests could you perform on the chemical to determine whether it is an acid or a base? What results would help you decide if the chemical is an acid or a base?

Internet Resources

For a variety of links related to this chapter, go to www.scilinks.org

Topic: Acids and Bases
SciLinks code: HY70013

Solutions of Acids and Bases

Key Concept The pH of a solution is a measurement of the hydronium concentration and is used to tell how acidic or basic a solution is.

▶ If you have ever had an upset stomach, you may have felt very much like the boy in **Figure 1.** And you may have taken an antacid. But do you know how antacids work? An antacid is a weak base that neutralizes a strong acid in your stomach. In this section, you will learn about the strengths of acids and bases. You will also learn about reactions between acids and bases.

Strengths of Acids and Bases

Acids and bases can be strong or weak. The strength of an acid or a base is not the same as the concentration of an acid or a base. The concentration of an acid or a base is the amount of acid or base dissolved in water. But the strength of an acid or a base depends on the number of molecules that break apart when the acid or the base is dissolved in water.

Strong Versus Weak Acids

As an acid dissolves in water, the acid's molecules break apart and form hydrogen ions, H^+. In water, all of the molecules of a *strong acid* break apart. Sulfuric acid, nitric acid, and hydrochloric acid are all strong acids. In water, only a few molecules of a weak acid break apart. There are only a few hydronium ions in a solution of a weak acid. Acetic acid, citric acid, and carbonic acid are all weak acids.

Standards Check What is the difference between a strong acid and a weak acid? 8.5.e

Figure 1 *Antacids may help relieve your stomachache by reacting with the acid in your stomach.*

8.5.e Students know how to determine whether a solution is acidic, basic, or neutral.

Strong Versus Weak Bases

When all molecules of a base break apart in water to form hydroxide ions, OH⁻, the base is a strong base. Sodium hydroxide, calcium hydroxide, and potassium hydroxide are strong bases. When only a few molecules of a base break apart, the base is a weak base. Two weak bases are ammonium hydroxide and aluminum hydroxide.

Acids, Bases, and Neutralization

The base in an antacid reacts with stomach acid. The reaction between acids and bases is a **neutralization reaction.** Water, H_2O, is formed when the hydrogen ions (H^+) from the acid react with the hydroxide ions (OH^-) from the base. Because water is neutral, acids and bases neutralize one another. The other ions from the acid and the base dissolve in the water. If the water evaporates, these ions join to form a compound called a *salt*.

The pH Scale

An indicator, such as litmus, can identify whether a solution contains an acid or a base. To describe how acidic or basic a solution is, scientists use the pH scale. The **pH** of a solution is a measure of the hydronium ion concentration in the solution. A solution that has a pH of 7 is neutral. A neutral solution is neither acidic nor basic. Pure water has a pH of 7. Basic solutions have a pH greater than 7. Acidic solutions have a pH less than 7. **Figure 2** shows the pH values for many common materials. Notice that the pH values decrease as the acidity increases. But the pH values increase as the basicity increases.

neutralization reaction (NOO truhl i ZAY shuhn ree AK shuhn) the reaction of an acid and a base to form a neutral solution of water and a salt

pH (PEE AYCH) a value that is used to express the acidity or basicity (alkalinity) of a system

Quick Lab

Neutralization

1. Pour **vinegar** into a **small plastic cup** until the cup is half full. Test the vinegar with **red and blue litmus paper.** Record your results.

2. Crush one **antacid tablet,** and mix it with the vinegar. Test the mixture with litmus paper. Record your results.

3. Compare the acidity of the solution before the antacid was added with the acidity of the solution after it was added.

🕐 15 min

Figure 2 pH Values of Common Materials

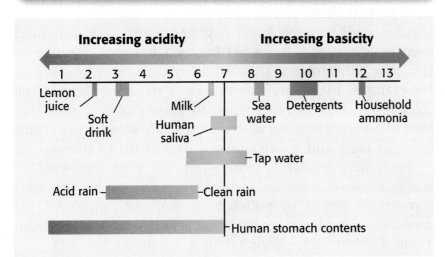

Increasing acidity   Increasing basicity

1 2 3 4 5 6 7 8 9 10 11 12 13

Lemon juice
Soft drink
Milk
Human saliva
Sea water
Detergents
Household ammonia
Tap water
Acid rain — Clean rain
Human stomach contents

Figure 3 Using Indicators to Find pH

pH indicator scale

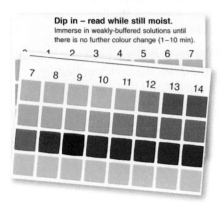

pH 4

pH 10

Using Indicators to Determine pH

A combination of indicators can be used to find out how basic or how acidic a solution is. This can be done if the colors of the indicators are known at different pH values. **Figure 3** shows strips of pH paper, which contains several different indicators. These strips were dipped into two different solutions. The pH of each solution is found by comparing the colors on each strip with the colors on the indicator scale provided. This kind of indicator is often used to test the pH of water in pools. Another way to find the pH of a solution is to use an electronic instrument known as a pH meter. These meters can detect and measure hydronium ion concentration directly in solution.

Standards Check How can indicators determine pH? **8.5.e**

pH and the Environment

Living things depend on having a steady pH in their environment. Some plants, such as pine trees, prefer acidic soil that has a pH between 4 and 6. Other plants, such as lettuce, need basic soil that has a pH between 8 and 9. Plants may also have different traits under different growing conditions. For example, hydrangea flowers have a natural indicator. The color of the flowers varies when they are grown in soils that have different pH values, as shown in **Figure 4.** Many organisms living in lakes and streams need a neutral pH to survive.

Most rain is slightly acidic and has a pH between 5.5 and 6. However, acids are formed when rainwater reacts with compounds found in polluted air. So, the rainwater's pH decreases. In the United States, most acid rain has a pH between 4 and 4.5, but some precipitation has a pH as low as 3.

Figure 4 *To grow blue flowers, plant hydrangeas in soil that has a low pH. To grow pink flowers, use soil that has a high pH.*

Salts

When an acid neutralizes a base, a salt and water are produced. A **salt** is an ionic compound formed from the positive ion of a base and the negative ion of an acid. When you hear the word *salt,* you probably think of the table salt you use to season your food. But the sodium chloride found in your salt shaker is only one example of a large group of compounds called *salts.*

Uses of Salts

Salts have many uses in industry and in homes. You already know that sodium chloride is used to season foods. It is also used to make other compounds, including lye (sodium hydroxide) and baking soda. Sodium nitrate is a salt that is used to preserve food. And calcium sulfate is used to make wallboard, which is used in construction. Another use of salt is shown in **Figure 5.**

salt (SAWLT) an ionic compound that forms when a metal atom replaces the hydrogen of an acid

Figure 5 *Salts help keep roads free of ice by decreasing the freezing point of water.*

SECTION Review

 8.5.e

Summary

- Every molecule of a strong acid or base breaks apart to form ions. Few molecules of weak acids and bases break apart to form ions.
- An acid and a base can neutralize one another to make salt and water.
- pH is a measure of hydronium ion concentration in a solution.
- A salt is an ionic compound formed when an acid reacts with a base.

Using Vocabulary

1 Use *neutralization reaction* and *salt* in the same sentence.

Understanding Concepts

2 **Identifying** What are two ways to measure the pH of a solution?

3 **Comparing** Explain the difference between a strong acid and a weak acid.

Critical Thinking

4 **Analyzing Processes** Predict what will happen to the hydronium ion concentration and the pH of water if hydrochloric acid is added to the water.

5 **Analyzing Relationships** A lake has a low pH. Is it acidic or basic? Would fish be healthy in this lake? Explain.

Math Skills

6 **Solving Problems** For each point lower on the pH scale, the hydrogen ions in solution increase 10-fold. For example, a solution of pH 3 is not twice as acidic as a solution of pH 6 but is 1,000 times as acidic. How many times more acidic is a solution of pH 2 than a solution of pH 4?

Challenge

7 **Applying Concepts** Soap is made from a strong base and oil. Would you expect the pH of soap to be 4 or 9? Explain.

Internet Resources

For a variety of links related to this chapter, go to www.scilinks.org
Topic: pH Scale; Salts
SciLinks code: HY71130; HY71347

Skills Practice Lab

Cabbage Patch Indicators

OBJECTIVES

Make a natural acid-base indicator solution.

Determine the pH of various common substances.

MATERIALS

- beaker, 250 mL
- beaker tongs
- eyedropper
- hot plate
- litmus paper
- potholder
- red cabbage leaf
- sample liquids provided by teacher
- tape, masking
- test tubes
- test-tube rack
- water, distilled

SAFETY

Indicators are weak acids or bases that change color due to the pH of the substance to which they are added. Red cabbage contains a natural indicator. It turns specific colors at specific pHs. In this lab, you will extract the indicator from red cabbage. Then, you will use it to determine the pH of several liquids.

Procedure

1 Copy the table below. Be sure to include one line for each sample liquid.

Data Collection Table			
Liquid	Color with indicator	pH	Effect on litmus paper
Control			

2 Put on protective gloves. Place 100 mL of distilled water in the beaker. Tear the cabbage leaf into small pieces. Place the pieces in the beaker.

3 Use the hot plate to heat the cabbage and water to boiling. Continue boiling until the water is deep blue. **Caution:** Use extreme care when working near a hot plate.

4 Use tongs to remove the beaker from the hot plate. Turn the hot plate off. Allow the solution to cool on a potholder for 5 to 10 minutes.

5 While the solution is cooling, use masking tape and a pen to label the test tubes for each sample liquid. Label one test tube "Control." Place the test tubes in the rack.

6 Use the eyedropper to place a small amount (about 5 mL) of the indicator (cabbage juice) in the test tube labeled "Control." You will use this test tube as a color reference.

7 Pour a small amount (about 5 mL) of each sample liquid into the appropriate test tube.

8 Using the eyedropper, place several drops of the indicator into each test tube. Swirl gently. Record the color of each liquid in the table.

9 Use the chart below to find the pH of each sample. Record the pH values in the table.

10 Litmus paper has an indicator that turns red in an acid and blue in a base. Test each liquid with a strip of litmus paper. Record the results.

Analyze the Results

11 Analyzing Data What purpose does the control serve? What is the pH of the control?

12 Examining Data What colors in your samples indicate the presence of an acid? What colors indicate the presence of a base?

13 Classifying Which solutions are basic and which are acidic?

14 Analyzing Results Why is red cabbage juice considered a good indicator?

Draw Conclusions

15 Interpreting Information Which do you think would be more useful to help identify an unknown liquid—litmus paper or red cabbage juice? Why?

Big Idea Question

16 Evaluating Methods What property did you use to classify the solutions? What other methods could you use to measure this property?

Applying Your Data

Rainwater has carbon dioxide dissolved in it. To find out if rainwater is acidic, basic, or neutral, place about 5 mL of the water-based cabbage juice indicator in a clean test tube. Use a straw to gently blow bubbles in the indicator until you see a color change. What is the pH of your "rainwater"?

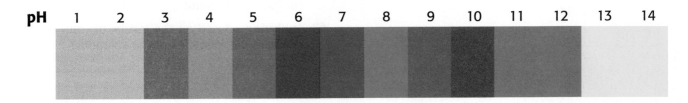

pH 1 2 3 4 5 6 7 8 9 10 11 12 13 14

Science Skills Activity

Planning an Investigation

Investigation and Experimentation
8.9.a Plan and conduct a scientific investigation to test a hypothesis.

▶ Tutorial

Examine the steps below to see how you could plan and conduct an investigation to test a hypothesis about the classification of a substance.

1 Make observations, and ask a question. "This liquid conducts an electric current. Is it acidic, basic, or neutral?"

2 Form a hypothesis that is a possible answer to your question, and make a prediction to test your hypothesis. "This liquid is acidic. If the liquid is acidic, it will turn blue litmus paper red."

3 Plan your investigation. Consider the materials and safety equipment that you will need, and review all safety procedures. "I will need a sample of the liquid, litmus paper, safety goggles, apron, and gloves. I must wash my hands after I complete my experiment."

4 Conduct your investigation, and gather data. "The solution did not change the color of blue litmus paper."

5 Analyze your results, and draw conclusions. You may need to repeat or revise your investigation to verify your results. "The solution is not acidic because it did not change the color of blue litmus paper. So, the solution must be basic or neutral. I should use red litmus paper to find out if the solution is basic."

▶ You Try It!

Procedure

The table below contains information about three solutions. One solution contains sugar, one contains table salt, and one contains baking soda. Using what you know about ionic and covalent compounds and about acids and bases, plan an investigation to find out the identity of each solution. Remember that tasting a solution is not an acceptable way to test an unknown solution.

Electrical Conductivity of Solutions		
Solution	**Electrical conductivity**	**Identity**
A	Yes	
B	No	
C	Yes	

Analysis

1 **Classifying** Table salt and baking soda are ionic compounds. What type of compound is sugar?

2 **Classifying** Classify sugar, salt, and baking soda as acidic or basic.

3 **Applying** Make a hypothesis about which substances should conduct an electric current.

4 **Concluding** Without collecting more data, can you identify the solution that does not conduct an electric current? If so, what is solution B?

5 **Designing** Based on your hypothesis, choose another test to identify the solutions.

6 **Analyzing** Based on the results of your test, what are the identities of the solutions?

Chapter Summary

The Big Idea Chemical compounds are classified into groups based on their bonds and on their properties.

Section		Vocabulary

1 Ionic and Covalent Compounds

Key Concept The properties of ionic compounds are different from the properties of covalent compounds.

- The physical properties of a compound are determined by the type of bonding in the compound.
- Ionic compounds tend to be brittle, have high melting points, dissolve in water, and often conduct electric current in solution.
- Many covalent compounds tend to be insoluble in water, have low melting points, are not water soluble, and often do not conduct electric current in solution.

The shape of a crystal is determined by the specific pattern in which the ions combine.

chemical bond p. 282
ionic compound p. 282
covalent compound p. 284

2 Acids and Bases

Key Concept You can use the characteristics of a solution to determine if it is acidic or basic.

- An acidic solution has an increased number of hydronium ions. A basic solution has an increased number of hydroxide ions.
- Acids are sour, react with many metals, conduct electric current, and change the color of indicators.
- Bases are bitter, feel slippery, conduct electric current, and change the color of indicators.

Indicators change color in an acidic solution or in a basic solution.

acid p. 286
indicator p. 287
base p. 289

3 Solutions of Acids and Bases

Key Concept The pH of a solution is a measurement of the hydronium concentration and is used to tell how acidic or basic a solution is.

- Every molecule of a strong acid or a strong base produces ions in solution. Only a few molecules of a weak acid or a weak base form ions.
- When an acid reacts with a base, a salt forms.
- The pH scale is used to determine if a solution is acidic, basic, or neutral.
- Indicators and pH meters can measure pH.

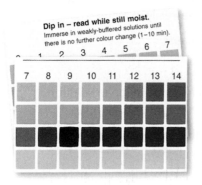

A pH indicator scale can be used to find the pH of a solution.

neutralization reaction p. 293
pH p. 293
salt p. 295

Chapter Review

 8.3.b, 8.3.c, 8.5.e, 8.7.c

Organize

Layered Book Review the FoldNote that you created at the beginning of the chapter. Add to or correct the FoldNote based on what you have learned.

Using Vocabulary

1 **Academic Vocabulary** Choose the appropriate form of the word *neutral* for the following sentence: "An acid can be used to ___ a base, forming water and a salt."
a. neutral
b. neutrally
c. neutralize
d. neutralization

For each pair of terms, explain how the meanings of the terms differ.

2 *ionic compound* and *covalent compound*

3 *acid* and *base*

4 *pH* and *indicator*

Understanding Concepts

Multiple Choice

5 Ionic compounds
a. have a low melting point.
b. are often brittle.
c. do not conduct electric current in water.
d. do not dissolve easily in water.

6 Both acids and bases
a. taste sour.
b. react with metals.
c. produce the hydronium ion in solution.
d. conduct electric current in solution.

7 An increase in the concentration of hydronium ions in solution
a. raises the pH.
b. lowers the pH.
c. does not affect the pH.
d. doubles the pH.

8 The pH of a solution that is neither acidic nor basic is
a. 5.
b. 7.
c. 9.
d. 14.

Short Answer

9 **Analyzing** What type of compound would you use to neutralize a solution of potassium hydroxide?

10 **Identifying** List three properties that you can use to classify a compound as ionic or covalent.

11 **Identifying** What kind of ions are produced when an acid is dissolved in water and when a base is dissolved in water?

12 **Describing** Explain why the reaction of an acid with a base is called *neutralization.*

13 **Listing** List two uses of an acid and two uses of a base.

14 **Concluding** Why do covalent compounds have lower melting points than ionic compounds have?

INTERPRETING GRAPHICS Use the diagram of a model below to answer the next two questions.

15 **Identifying** What type of compound is represented by the model?

16 **Describing** What would happen to the pattern of the ions if you hit a solid crystal of the compound represented by the model?

Writing Skills

17 **Technical Writing** You find an unknown white powder in the lab. Outline an experimental procedure that you can use to determine whether the compound is ionic or covalent and whether it is acidic or basic.

Critical Thinking

18 Concept Mapping Use the following terms to create a concept map: *acid, base, salt, neutral,* and *pH*.

19 Analyzing Ideas Explain why solutions of most covalent compounds do not conduct electric currents.

20 Applying Concepts Fish give off a base, ammonia (NH_3), as waste. How does the release of ammonia affect the pH of the water in an aquarium? What can be done to correct the pH of the water?

21 Analyzing Methods Many insects, such as fire ants, inject a weak acid called formic acid when they bite or sting. What type of compound should be used to treat the bite?

22 Applying Concepts Salt melts at 801°C, but water melts at 0°C. Explain why salt melts at a much higher temperature than water.

23 Applying Concepts Explain why many covalent compounds are not soluble in water, whereas ionic compounds are soluble in water.

INTERPRETING GRAPHICS Use the table below to answer the next question.

pH and Indicator Color

pH	Color of bromthymol blue	Acidic, basic, or neutral
3		
8		
7		
10		

DO NOT WRITE IN BOOK

24 Identifying Relationships Based on the pH, determine what color the indicator bromthymol blue will be in the presence of each substance. Identify each substance as acidic, basic, or neutral.

INTERPRETING GRAPHICS Use the diagram below to answer the next three questions.

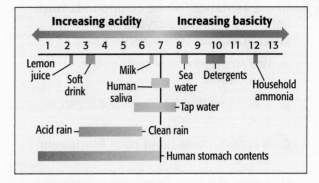

25 Applying Concepts What is the pH range of detergents? Are detergents more or less basic than sea water?

26 Applying Concepts Which materials in the diagram can be neutral?

27 Making Comparisons You drink a glass of milk. Your friend drinks a soft drink. Which of you is drinking the more acidic beverage?

Math Skills

28 Making Calculations Most of the vinegar used to make pickles is 5% acetic acid. So, in 100 mL of vinegar, 5 mL is acid diluted with 95 mL of water. If you bought a 473 mL bottle of 5% vinegar, how many milliliters of acetic acid would be in the bottle? How many milliliters of water were used to dilute the acetic acid?

29 Making Calculations If you dilute a 75 mL can of orange juice with enough water to make a mixture with a total volume of 300 mL, what is the percentage of juice in the mixture?

Challenge

30 Applying Concepts You are given a compound that has a melting point of 560°C. You dissolve some of the compound in water and measure the pH of the resulting solution to be 11. You are told that the compound is either KCl, $Ca(OH)_2$, $C_6H_{12}O_6$, or H_2SO_4. Which of these compounds were you given? Explain.

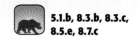
REVIEWING ACADEMIC VOCABULARY

1 In the sentence "Some compounds form solids by creating a crystal structure," what does the word *structure* mean?

- **A** the arrangement of parts of the compound
- **B** a building that has been put together from many parts
- **C** a system made up of parts functioning as a whole
- **D** a part of a body or organism, such as a tissue or an organ

2 Identify the correct meaning of the word *elements* in the following sentence: "Water is made up of the gaseous elements hydrogen and oxygen."

- **A** natural habitats or environments
- **B** parts of appliances that conduct heat
- **C** causes or factors leading to a result
- **D** substances that cannot be broken down into simpler substances

3 In the sentence "Compounds have properties that are different from their constituent elements," what does the word *constituent* mean?

- **A** a person who lives in a certain area and votes there
- **B** one of the words or phrases used in a sentence
- **C** one of the parts that make up a material
- **D** a person who appoints another person to act for him

4 Which of the following words is the noun form of the word *neutral*?

- **A** neutrality
- **B** neuter
- **C** neutron
- **D** neutralize

REVIEWING CONCEPTS

5 What type of compound increases the number of hydronium ions when dissolved in water?

- **A** an acid
- **B** a base
- **C** an indicator
- **D** hydrogen gas

6 A compound dissolved in water turns red litmus paper blue and changes the indicator bromthymol blue to dark blue. What kind of compound is it?

- **A** an acid
- **B** water
- **C** table salt
- **D** a base

7 The ions in an ionic compound are arranged in a repeating three-dimensional pattern called a(n)

- **A** ionic solution.
- **B** chemical bond.
- **C** valence electron.
- **D** crystal lattice.

8 What factor does the pH scale measure?

- **A** the degree of neutralization between acids and bases
- **B** the concentration of hydroxide ions in a solution
- **C** the number of salt molecules present in a solution
- **D** the concentration of hydronium ions in a solution

Properties of Some Compounds

Compound	Melting point	Solubility	Electrical conductivity in solution
A	801°C	high	yes
B	398°C	low	yes
C	20°C	low	no
D	1,200°C	high	yes

9 Which of the compounds in the table above is most likely a covalent compound?

A compound A

B compound B

C compound C

D compound D

pH of Some Solutions

Solution	pH
A	12.89
B	2.33
C	12.1
D	3.50

10 Which solution listed in the table above is the most acidic?

A solution A

B solution B

C solution C

D solution D

11 Under what conditions are particles of covalent compounds formed?

A oppositely-charged ions transfer electrons and form a bond

B two or more atoms share electrons

C an atom of a noble gas bonds with an atom of a transition metal

D two metal atoms form a bond

12 Atoms may combine in chemical reactions to form

A elements.

B electrons.

C neutrons.

D compounds.

13 Two atoms of hydrogen have different masses. Which of the following best explains this phenomenon?

A The atoms are ionic compounds of hydrogen.

B One atom has more protons than the other.

C The two atoms are different isotopes of hydrogen.

D The atoms have different atomic numbers.

14 According to the periodic table, which of the following elements is a transition metal?

A titanium

B magnesium

C aluminum

D tin

15 The chemical formula for two molecules of glucose is shown above. Which part of the formula is the coefficient?

A A

B B

C C

D D

Science in Action

Science, Technology, and Society

In Hot Water

Bubbling hot springs, hot mud pots, and the smell of rotten eggs are signs that the Cascade Range in northern California is still volcanically active. The hydrothermal (hot water) features are the result of water being heated underground by hot magma. Hydrogen sulfide and other gases dissolve in the hot water. When the hot water reaches the surface, steam and the dissolved gases are released in the air. The hydrogen sulfide gas is responsible for the rotten egg smell.

Social Studies ACTIVITY

Mount Lassen, a volcano at the southern end of the Cascade Range, last exploded in 1915. Research how this explosion affected the surrounding communities. Write a newspaper story about the explosion from the perspective of a reporter at the time.

Weird Science

Silly Putty™

During World War II, the supply of natural rubber was very low. So, James Wright, at General Electric, tried to make a synthetic rubber. The putty he made could be molded, stretched, and bounced. But it did not work as a rubber substitute and was ignored. Then, Peter Hodgson, a consultant for a toy company, had a brilliant idea. He marketed the putty as a toy in 1949. It was an immediate success. Hodgson created the name Silly Putty™. Although the Silly Putty toy was invented more than 50 years ago, it has not changed much. More than 300 million eggs of Silly Putty have been sold since 1950.

Math ACTIVITY

In 1949, Hodgson bought 9.5 kg of putty for $147. The putty was divided into balls, each having a mass of 14 g. In your **Science Journal,** calculate his cost for one 14 g ball of putty.

Jeannie Eberhardt

Forensic Scientist Jeannie Eberhardt says that her job as a forensic scientist is not really as glamorous as it may seem on popular TV shows. "If they bring me a garbage bag from the crime scene, then my job is to dig through the trash and look for evidence," she laughs. Eberhardt explains that her job is to "search for, collect, and analyze evidence from crime scenes." Eberhardt says that one of the most important qualities a forensic scientist can have is the ability to be unbiased. She says that she focuses on the evidence and not on any information she may have about the alleged crime or the suspect.

Eberhardt advises students who think they might be interested in a career as a forensic scientist to talk to someone who works in the field. She also recommends that students develop a broad science background. And she advises students that most of these jobs require extensive background checks. "Your actions now could affect your ability to get a job later on," she points out.

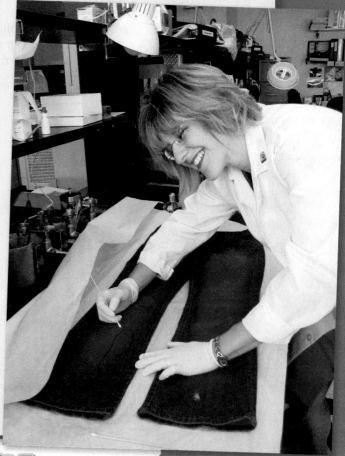

Language Arts ACTIVITY

Eberhardt says that it is very important to be unbiased when analyzing a crime scene. Write a one-page essay explaining why it is necessary to focus on the evidence in a crime and not on personal feelings or news reports.

Internet Resources

- To learn more about careers in science, visit **www.scilinks.org** and enter the SciLinks code HY70225.

- To learn more about these Science in Action topics, visit **go.hrw.com** and type in the keyword HY7CMPF.

- Check out articles related to this chapter by visiting **go.hrw.com**. Just type in the keyword HY7CMPC.

Improving Comprehension

Graphic Organizers are important visual tools that can help you organize information and improve your reading comprehension. The Graphic Organizer below is called a *spider map*. Instructions for creating other types of Graphic Organizers are located in the **Study Skills** section of the Appendix.

How to Make a Spider Map

1 Draw a diagram like the one shown below. In the circle, write the main topic.

2 From the circle, draw legs to represent the main ideas or characteristics of the topic. Draw as many legs as you want to draw. Write an idea or characteristic along each leg.

3 From each leg, draw horizontal lines. As you read the chapter, write details about each idea on the idea's horizontal lines. To add more details, make the legs longer and add more horizontal lines.

When to Use a Spider Map

A spider map is an effective tool for classifying the details of a specific topic in science. A spider map divides a topic into ideas and details. As you read about a topic, look for the main ideas or characteristics of the topic. Within each idea, look for details. Use a spider map to organize the ideas and details of each topic.

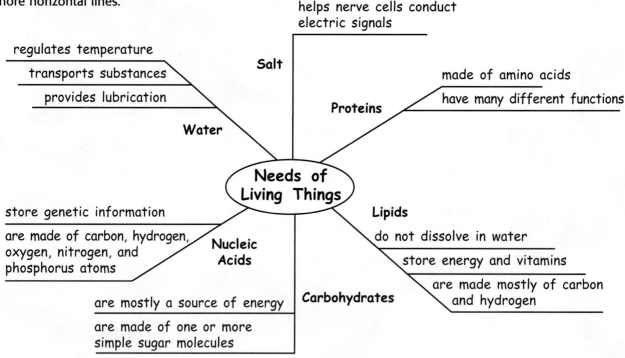

You Try It!

This Reading Strategy can also be used within the chapter that you are about to read. Practice making your own *spider map* as directed in the Reading Strategy for Section **2**. Record your work in your **Science Journal.**

Unpacking the Standards

The information below "unpacks" the standards by breaking them down into basic parts. The higher-level, academic vocabulary is highlighted and defined to help you understand the language of the standards. "What It Means" restates the standards as simply as possible.

California Standard	Academic Vocabulary	What It Means
8.3.c Students know atoms and molecules form solids by building up repeating patterns, such as the crystal **structure** of NaCl or long-chain polymers.	**structure** (STRUHK chuhr) a whole that is built or put together from parts	Solids are made up of atoms and molecules arranged in organized, repeating patterns. For example, table salt is made up of crystals, and plastics are made up of polymer chains.
8.6.a Students know that carbon, because of its ability to combine in many ways with itself and other elements, has a central **role** in the chemistry of living organisms.	**role** (ROHL) a part or function; purpose	Carbon has a main role in the chemistry of living things because carbon atoms can combine with each other and with atoms of other elements in many ways.
8.6.b Students know that living organisms are made of molecules **consisting** largely of carbon, hydrogen, nitrogen, oxygen, phosphorus, and sulfur.	**consist** (kuhn SIST) to be made up of	Living things are made of molecules that are made mostly of carbon, hydrogen, nitrogen, oxygen, phosphorus, and sulfur.
8.6.c Students know that living organisms have many different kinds of molecules, including small ones, such as water and salt, and very large ones, such as carbohydrates, fats, proteins, and DNA.		Knowing about the chemicals that your body uses and makes helps you understand how your body works.

The Chemistry of Living Things

The Big Idea

All living things depend on chemical compounds, especially those that are based on the element carbon.

 California Standards

Focus on Physical Sciences

8.3 Each of the more than 100 elements of matter has distinct properties and a distinct atomic structure. All forms of matter are composed of one or more of the elements. (Section 2)

8.6 Principles of chemistry underlie the functioning of biological systems. (Sections 1 and 2)

Investigation and Experimentation

8.9 Scientific progress is made by asking meaningful questions and conducting careful investigations. (Science Skills Activity)

Math

7.1.1, 7.2.2 Algebra and Functions
7.1.3 Mathematical Reasoning

English–Language Arts

8.2.2 Reading
8.1.1 Writing

About the Photo ↗

These California Sea Lions are fast swimmers. They dart through the water with great speed as they look for food. They eat a wide variety of fish, squid, and shellfish, which give the sea lions the protein they need. Protein is one important chemical compound that all living organisms need.

Organize

Key-Term Fold

Before you read the chapter, create the FoldNote entitled "Key-Term Fold." Write a key term from the chapter on each tab of the key-term fold. As you read the chapter, write the definition of each key term under the appropriate tab.

Instructions for creating FoldNotes are located in the Study Skills section on p. 519 of the Appendix.

Explore Activity

🤿 ⏱ 20 min

Building an Organic Molecule

In this activity, you will build models of carbon-based molecules using clay and toothpicks. Each toothpick represents a chemical bond.

Procedure

1. Choose one color of **modeling clay** to use for carbon atoms, a second color to use for hydrogen atoms, and a third color to use for oxygen atoms.

2. Make a carbon atom. Insert four **toothpicks** into the clay so that each toothpick is at a maximum distance from each of the other toothpicks. (Hint: The result will be three-dimensional.)

3. Place a hydrogen atom at the end of each toothpick to complete a model of a methane molecule.

4. Use two toothpicks to connect two carbon atoms.

5. On each carbon atom, place two more toothpicks to form a Y with the pair of toothpicks. Place a hydrogen atom onto each toothpick to complete a model of an ethene molecule.

8.6.a

6. Make a carbon atom. Attach two pairs of toothpicks in opposite sides of the clay. Attach an oxygen atom to each pair of toothpicks to complete a model of a carbon dioxide molecule.

Analysis

7. Identify the number and type of atoms found in each molecule.

8. How many bonds does each carbon atom make in each of these molecules?

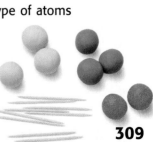

309

Elements in Living Things

Key Concept Carbon atoms combine in many ways with each other and atoms of other elements and form the backbone of many molecules needed by living things.

Would you believe that more than 90% of all compounds belong to a single group of compounds? This group is made up of covalent compounds that are based on the element carbon. All living organisms need these compounds. For example, the carbon compound glucose, a kind of sugar, is an energy source for many living things.

The Bonding of Carbon Atoms

Carbon has a central role in the chemistry of living organisms. You can understand why when you look at the way carbon makes chemical bonds. Carbon atoms can form long chains with other carbon atoms. Some compounds have hundreds or thousands of carbon atoms! Carbon atoms can also bond with atoms of other elements.

Standards Check   Which element has a central role in the chemistry of living organisms? 🐾 8.6.a

Carbon Backbones

Each carbon atom has four valence electrons. So, each carbon atom can make a total of four bonds. Carbon-based molecules can come in many different shapes. Many organic compounds are based on the kinds of carbon backbones shown in **Figure 1.** These models show how atoms are connected. Each line represents a covalent bond.

Figure 1	**Three Kinds of Carbon Backbones**

Straight chain
Carbon atoms are connected one after another.

Branched chain
The chain of carbon atoms branches when a carbon atom bonds to more than two other carbon atoms.

Ring
The chain of carbon atoms forms a ring.

Figure 2 Three Types of Bonds Between Carbon Atoms

Single Bond

H H H
H–C–C–C–H
H H H

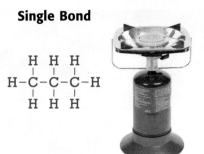

The **propane** in this camping stove contains only single bonds.

Double Bond

H   H
  \C=C/
H   H

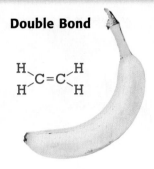

Fruits make **ethene,** which is a compound that helps ripen the fruit.

Triple Bond

H–C≡C–H

Ethyne is better known as *acetylene.* It is burned in this miner's lamp and in welding torches.

Single Bonds

Compounds that contain carbon are called **organic compounds.** All of the compounds shown in **Figure 1** and **Figure 2** are organic compounds.

Atoms of carbon most often form four separate single bonds with other atoms. A *single bond* is a covalent bond made up of one pair of shared electrons. Propane, shown in **Figure 2,** has only single bonds. Gasoline is a mixture of carbon compounds in which the carbon atoms are joined by single bonds. These compounds are similar to propane. But their carbon chains are longer than propane's.

Gasoline is made from *petroleum,* which is a mixture of organic compounds that comes from organic material deep in Earth's crust. Carbon atoms in petroleum come from the remains of organisms that lived long ago. Various fuels, as well as plastics, waxes, and lubricants, are made from petroleum.

Double Bonds

Carbon atoms can also form two covalent bonds between them. This is called a *double bond.* Ethene, shown in **Figure 2,** is the simplest example of an organic compound with a double bond. Many fats and oils are examples of larger organic compounds that have double bonds.

Triple Bonds

Triple bonds, three bonds between carbon atoms, are also possible. One example is in ethyne, shown in **Figure 2.** As you can tell, atoms of carbon can form bonds in many different ways. And so far, we have considered compounds made of only carbon and hydrogen!

Standards Check What are the three kinds of bonds that carbon atoms can form? **8.6.a**

organic compound (awr GAN ik KAHM POWND) a covalently bonded compound that contains carbon

Wordwise petroleum
The root *petr-* means "rock." Another example is *petrify.*

8.6.a Students know that carbon, because of its ability to combine in many ways with itself and other elements, has a central role in the chemistry of living organisms.
8.6.b Students know that living organisms are made of molecules consisting largely of carbon, hydrogen, nitrogen, oxygen, phosphorus, and sulfur.

Figure 3   Elements in Living Organisms

Nitrogen is an important part of all proteins.

Oxygen makes up a large part of carbohydrates.

Phosphorus is an important part of how your cells get energy.

Other Elements in Living Organisms

All living things depend on organic compounds. A single cell in your body contains a very large number of organic compounds. Other elements combine with carbon to make the large variety of compounds on which living things depend. **Figure 3** shows examples of where different elements can be found in living things. Although billions of compounds make up your body, just a few elements make up most of those compounds.

Elements in Organic Compounds

Carbon can combine with elements other than itself and hydrogen. These include oxygen, nitrogen, sulfur, and phosphorus. The pie graph in **Figure 4** shows the elements that make up most of your body. As you can see, your body is made up of a lot of oxygen. Water has atoms of oxygen, and there is a lot of water in your body. Oxygen is found in many organic molecules.

You probably don't think much about elements such as sulfur and phosphorus in your body. But they're there! Atoms of nitrogen and sulfur are important parts of proteins. And without phosphorus, your cells could not get the energy that they need. All of these other elements in your body come from the food you eat.

Standards Check Name the six elements that molecules in living things are mostly made up of. **8.6.b**

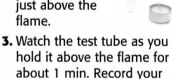

Quick Lab

What's in the Wax?

8.6.a

1. Have your teacher light a **tealight candle.**

2. Using a **test-tube holder,** hold a **cold test tube** upside-down just above the flame.

3. Watch the test tube as you hold it above the flame for about 1 min. Record your observations.

4. What substances appear to have collected on the test tube?

5. What elements make up the wax? Explain your answer.

 10 min

Organic Compounds—Not Just from Living Things!

You have learned that all organic compounds contain the element carbon. The special bonding abilities of carbon allow it to form many different compounds. Organic compounds are also distinctive because they make up living organisms.

For a long time, people thought that organic compounds could be made only by living organisms. It was thought that organic compounds could not be made by chemical reactions in a laboratory. But this thinking began to change in the 1800s, after chemists learned more about the chemistry of carbon.

Today, many kinds of organic compounds are manufactured. Most medicines and drugs are organic compounds. Vitamins, hormones, and other supplements are often manufactured. These compounds are the same ones that you find naturally in food or that are made in your own body. Although living organisms are different from nonliving things, a chemical is a chemical, no matter where it comes from!

Elements in the Human Body

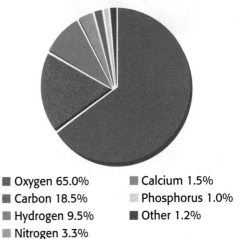

- ■ Oxygen 65.0%
- ■ Carbon 18.5%
- ■ Hydrogen 9.5%
- ■ Nitrogen 3.3%
- ■ Calcium 1.5%
- ■ Phosphorus 1.0%
- ■ Other 1.2%

Figure 4 *After oxygen (which is found in water), carbon is the element found in the greatest percentage by weight in the body.* **After carbon, what is the next most common element in the body?**

SECTION Review

8.6.a, 8.6.b

Summary

- Organic compounds are compounds that contain the element carbon.
- Organic compounds play a central role in the chemistry of living organisms because of carbon's ability to bond with other elements and to form long chains with other carbon atoms.
- Living organisms are made of compounds that are composed mostly of the elements carbon, hydrogen, nitrogen, oxygen, phosphorus, and sulfur.

Using Vocabulary

1. In your own words, write a definition for the term *organic compound.*

Understanding Concepts

2. **Describing** What makes carbon so important to the chemistry of living organisms?

INTERPRETING GRAPHICS Use the diagram below to answer the next two questions.

```
    H   H   H
    |   |   |
H – C – C – C – H
    |   |   |
    H   H   H
```

3. **Identifying** What elements are found in the compound represented in the diagram?

4. **Applying** Is this an organic compound? Explain your answer.

Critical Thinking

5. **Identifying Relationships** On a periodic table, find the six elements that make up most organic compounds in an organism. What do you notice about the location on the periodic table of most of those elements?

6. **Making Inferences** Petroleum products such as gasoline are mostly made of carbon-based compounds. In what way is this an important clue about where petroleum products come from?

Internet Resources

For a variety of links related to this chapter, go to www.scilinks.org

Topic: Carbon Compounds; Organic Compounds
SciLinks code: HY70215; HY71078

Compounds of Living Things

Key Concept Living things depend on very large carbon-based molecules and on smaller compounds, including water and salt.

▶ Imagine you are eating your favorite meal. What kinds of foods are included? Did you ever stop to think about what it's all made of? You have probably heard of carbohydrates, proteins, and fats. Carbohydrates are found in breads, grains, and sugars. Protein is found in meat, beans, eggs, and dairy products. Fats are found in meat, vegetable oils, and dairy products. All of these compounds are *biochemicals:* large organic compounds that living things make and use. You need all of these kinds of compounds, because most of your body is made of them. That's why a balanced diet is important for good health.

Carbohydrates

Biochemicals that are composed of sugar molecules bonded together are called **carbohydrates.** Simple sugars, such as glucose, are simple carbohydrates. But simple sugars can join to form complex carbohydrates, as shown in **Figure 1.** A complex carbohydrate can be a long-chain polymer. A *polymer* is a chain of repeating units. Complex carbohydrates may be made up of a chain of thousands of simple sugars.

Living things use carbohydrates mostly as a source of energy. For example, glycogen supplies energy to muscle cells in animals. But carbohydrates also have other uses in living things. Cellulose gives cell walls in plants their rigid structure.

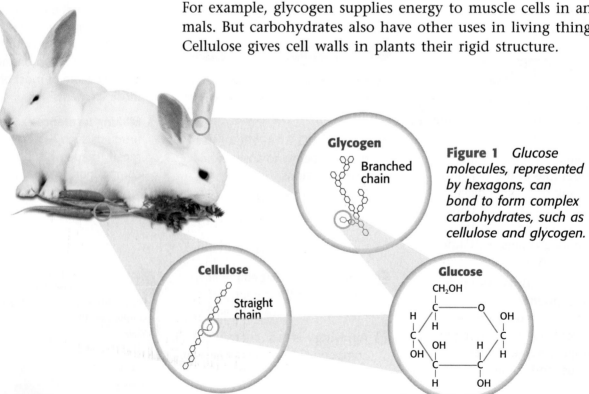

Figure 1 *Glucose molecules, represented by hexagons, can bond to form complex carbohydrates, such as cellulose and glycogen.*

Glycogen
Branched chain

Cellulose
Straight chain

Glucose

Figure 2 *Like most whales, these humpback whales store large amounts of lipids in their bodies. This insulates their bodies from the cold ocean water.*

Lipids

Lipids are biochemicals that do not dissolve in water. Fats, oils, and waxes are lipids. Lipids have many functions in living things. Lipids store energy. They also make up cell membranes. Although too much fat in your diet can be unhealthy, some fat is important to good health.

Lipids are made of mostly carbon and hydrogen. Lipids usually have very long chains of carbon atoms. So, lipids are very large molecules. Saturated fats are lipids that have only single bonds between their carbon atoms. Unsaturated fats are lipids in which the carbon atoms have double bonds and single bonds.

Plants store lipids as oils. Olive oil is an example of a lipid from a plant. Animals tend to store lipids as fats. Some animals, such as the whales shown in **Figure 2,** have many more lipids in their bodies than humans do. When an organism has used up most of its carbohydrates, it can get energy by breaking down lipids. Lipids are also used to store some vitamins.

Proteins

Proteins are biochemicals that are made of much smaller molecules called *amino acids*. Most proteins are made of very long chains of amino acids. So, most proteins are very large molecules and are long-chain polymers.

There are 20 different amino acids that can combine in any order to form proteins in living things. So, proteins are more complex than carbohydrates and lipids. The amino acids that make up proteins give each protein its special function in your body.

Standards Check What do the structures of carbohydrates and proteins have in common? **8.3.c**

carbohydrate (KAHR boh HIE drayt) a class of energy-giving nutrients that includes sugars, starches, and fiber; contains carbon, hydrogen, and oxygen

lipid (LIP id) a fat molecule or a molecule that has similar properties; examples include oils, waxes, and steroids
Wordwise The root *lip-* means "fat."

protein (PROH TEEN) a molecule that is made up of amino acids and that is needed to build and repair body structures and to regulate processes

8.3.c Students know atoms and molecules form solids by building up repeating patterns, such as the crystal structure of NaCl or long-chain polymers.
8.6.c Students know that living organisms have many different kinds of molecules, including small ones, such as water and salt, and very large ones, such as carbohydrates, fats, proteins, and DNA.

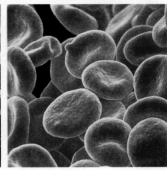

Figure 3 *Proteins play a variety of important roles in living organisms.*

Examples of Proteins

In living things, proteins play important roles and have many different functions. **Figure 3** shows some examples. The structural proteins of silk fibers make the spider web strong and lightweight. Hair is also made of protein. Nuts and beans are foods that have large amounts of proteins.

An especially important protein, called *hemoglobin,* is found in red blood cells. It helps carry oxygen to all of the cells of the body. Some hormones are proteins. For example, insulin is a protein hormone that helps control your blood-sugar level.

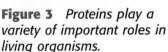

My New Sandwich

Can you think of a new sandwich that is healthy and tasty? Create such a sandwich for your favorite restaurant. Then, explain the nutritional value of each ingredient. Go to **go.hrw.com,** and type in the keyword HY7BD7W.

Quick Lab

Modeling Proteins

8.3.c
8.6.c

Proteins are long chains of amino acids. In this activity, you will make a model of a protein by using balloons.

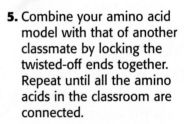

1. Out of **thin balloons of various colors,** take two balloons of the same color.

2. Fill both of the balloons with air, and tie them shut. Twist off each balloon in the middle.

3. Put the twisted-off parts of the two balloons together. Bend each balloon back so that the balloons lock together. You have made a model of an amino acid.

4. Twist off a portion of your amino acid model at one of its four ends.

5. Combine your amino acid model with that of another classmate by locking the twisted-off ends together. Repeat until all the amino acids in the classroom are connected.

6. Describe why proteins can be very large molecules.

7. How is the number of different balloon colors related to the number of different protein models your class could make?

 15 min

Figure 4 The Four Nucleotides of DNA

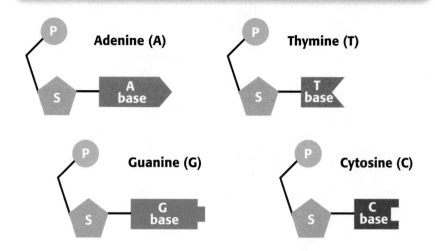

Nucleic Acids

The largest molecules made by living organisms are nucleic acids. **Nucleic acids** are biochemicals made up of *nucleotides* (NOO klee oh TIEDZ). The four kinds of nucleotides in DNA are shown in **Figure 4.** The S represents a sugar, and the P represents a phosphate. Nucleotides are molecules made of carbon, hydrogen, oxygen, nitrogen, and phosphorus atoms.

Nucleic acids store genetic information. Nucleic acids are sometimes called *the blueprints of life,* because they carry all of the information needed for a cell to make all of its proteins. Nucleic acids may have millions of nucleotides bonded together. The reason that living things differ from each other is that each living thing has a different order of nucleotides in its DNA.

nucleic acid (noo KLEE ik AS id) molecule made up of subunits called *nucleotides*

DNA and RNA

There are two kinds of nucleic acids: DNA and RNA. A model of DNA (**d**eoxyribo**n**ucleic **a**cid) is shown in **Figure 5.** DNA is the genetic material of the cell. DNA molecules are long-chain polymers. They can store a huge amount of information because of their length. The DNA molecules in a single human cell have a length of about 2 m—which is more than 6 ft long! When a cell needs to make a certain protein, the cell copies a certain part of the DNA onto another type of nucleic acid, RNA (**r**ibo**n**ucleic **a**cid). The information copied from the DNA onto the RNA directs the order in which amino acids are bonded to make that protein.

Figure 5 *Two strands of DNA are twisted in a spiral shape. Four different nucleotides make up the rungs of the DNA ladder.*

Standards Check What are four types of very large organic molecules that living organisms have? 8.6.c

Figure 6 From Light Energy to Chemical Energy

Light Energy

Carbon dioxide in the air

Chlorophyll in green leaves

carbon dioxide + water

Photosynthesis

$$\text{carbon dioxide} + \text{water} \xrightarrow[\text{chlorophyll}]{\text{light energy}} \text{sugar} + \text{oxygen}$$

Sugar in food

Water in the soil

Other Important Compounds

As you have learned, biochemicals are very important for the functions of living organisms. In addition to very large molecules, such as carbohydrates, fats, proteins, and DNA, organisms also need a variety of much smaller compounds that are not organic compounds. The most important of these is one that you are very familiar with—water!

Water

No living thing on Earth can survive without water. In fact, about 70% of your body is made up of water! Water is in every cell of your body. Water regulates temperature, helps transport substances, and provides lubrication.

An example of the importance of water is shown in **Figure 6.** Without water, a plant will dry up and die. The soil collects water from rain and other sources. Plants, such as trees, get their water from the soil. Plants use light energy from the sun to join water with carbon dioxide to form carbohydrates. Plants use these carbohydrates to get the energy they need to live. Water also moves up the trunks or stems of plants and carries nutrients to all of a plant's cells.

Standards Check **What are three functions of water in living things?**

8.6.c

Water in Fruits

With an adult, put some raisins into a glass of water. Observe the raisins several times over the next two days. Record your observations in your **Science Journal.** Explain how the change in the appearance of the raisins demonstrates that water is in fruits.

Salt

Why is the deer shown in **Figure 7** licking salt? Well, think about your own body. If you have ever tasted a drop of sweat, then you know that salt is present in your body. And if you lose salt through sweating, you need to replace it. But why is salt so important?

Salt plays an important role in nerve cells. Salt helps nerve cells conduct electrical signals throughout your body. Ordinary table salt is the kind of salt that your body uses the most. Other salts may also be found in food.

Figure 7 *Animals have salt in their bodies. Therefore, they need to have a certain amount of salt in their diets.*

SECTION Review

8.3.c, 8.6.c

Summary

- Carbohydrates provide energy for living organisms. Many complex carbohydrates are made of long chains of simple sugars.

- Lipids have long carbon chains, store energy, and make up cell membranes.

- Proteins are composed of amino acids and perform special functions within cells.

- Nucleic acids store the genetic information that cells use to make proteins.

- In addition to large biochemical compounds, much smaller compounds, such as water and salt, are also important to organisms.

Using Vocabulary

Correct each statement by replacing the underlined term.

1. <u>Carbohydrates</u> do not dissolve in water and are used by organisms to store energy.

2. <u>Proteins</u> contain all of the information a cell needs to make its <u>lipids</u>.

Understanding Concepts

3. **Identifying** What smaller molecules make up proteins?

4. **Classifying** What role in organisms do carbohydrates and lipids share?

5. **Analyzing** What feature of protein structure makes proteins especially complex biochemicals?

Critical Thinking

6. **Making Comparisons** Compare the roles of large organic compounds in living organisms with the roles of smaller, nonorganic compounds in living organisms.

7. **Identifying Relationships** Hemoglobin is a protein that is in blood and that transports oxygen to the tissues of the body. What would happen if there was a change in the nucleic acids that carry the information to make hemoglobin?

Challenge

8. **Interpreting Statistics** Suppose a certain organism's DNA has 6.0×10^7 nucleotides that carry information to make proteins. For every three of these nucleotides, one amino acid is made. If this organism's DNA has information to make 4.0×10^4 proteins, what is the average number of amino acids in the organism's proteins? (Hint: First find the number of amino acids coded for by the DNA.)

Internet Resources

For a variety of links related to this chapter, go to www.scilinks.org

Topic: Carbohydrates; Lipids
SciLinks code: HY70213; HY70881

Skills Practice Lab

Enzymes in Action

Enzymes are proteins that are an important part of digestion. This lab will help you see enzymes at work. Hydrogen peroxide is continuously produced by your cells. If it is not quickly broken down, hydrogen peroxide will kill your cells. However, your cells contain an enzyme that converts hydrogen peroxide into nonpoisonous substances. This enzyme is also present in the cells of beef liver. In this lab, you will observe the action of this enzyme on hydrogen peroxide.

Data Table		
Size and condition of liver	Experimental liquid	Observations
1 cm cube beef liver	2 mL water	
1 cm cube beef liver	2 mL hydrogen peroxide	
1 cm cube beef liver (mashed)	2 mL hydrogen peroxide	

OBJECTIVES

Demonstrate that living organisms have protein molecules.

MATERIALS

- beef liver, raw, 1 cm cubes (3)
- gloves, protective
- graduated cylinder, 10 mL
- hydrogen peroxide, 3% solution, fresh (4 mL)
- mortar and pestle (or fork and watch glass)
- plate, small
- spatula
- test tubes (3)
- test-tube rack
- tweezers
- water

SAFETY

8.6.c Students know that living organisms have many different kinds of molecules, including small ones, such as water and salt, and very large ones, such as carbohydrates, fats, proteins, and DNA.

Procedure

1 Draw a data table similar to the one on the previous page. Be sure to leave enough space to write your observations.

2 Get three equal-sized pieces of beef liver from your teacher, and use your forceps to place them on your plate.

3 Pour 2 mL of water into a test tube labeled "Water and liver."

4 Using the tweezers, carefully place one piece of liver in the test tube. Record your observations in your data table.

5 Pour 2 mL of hydrogen peroxide into a second test tube labeled "Liver and hydrogen peroxide." **Caution:** Do not splash hydrogen peroxide on your skin. If you do get hydrogen peroxide on your skin, rinse the affected area with running water immediately, and tell your teacher.

6 Using the tweezers, carefully place one piece of liver in the test tube. Record your observations of the second test tube in your data table.

7 Pour 2 mL of hydrogen peroxide into a third test tube labeled "Ground liver and hydrogen peroxide."

8 Using a mortar and pestle (or fork and watch glass), carefully grind the third piece of liver.

9 Using the spatula, scrape the ground liver into the third test tube. Record your observations of the third test tube in your data table.

Analyze the Results

10 **Analyzing Methods** What was the purpose of putting the first piece of liver in water? Why was this a necessary step?

Draw Conclusions

11 **Making Comparisons** Describe the difference you observed between the liver and the ground liver when each was placed in the hydrogen peroxide. How can you account for this difference?

Big Idea Question

12 **Making Inferences** How do the results of your experiment show that proteins are compounds found in the cells of organisms?

Science Skills Activity

Investigation and Experimentation

8.9.d Recognize the slope of the linear graph as the constant in the relationship $y = kx$ and apply this principle in interpreting graphs constructed from data.

Finding the Slope of a Graph

▶ Tutorial

A linear graph is a graph whose data points form a straight line. A linear graph shows that the quantities used to make the graph are connected by the relationship $y = kx$. The k in this equation is a constant. It is also the slope of the line.

Procedure

Examine the graph below. It shows the relationship between the amount of heat added to 100 g of water (y) and the resulting temperature of that water (x). (The kilojoule, which is represented by the symbol kJ, is a unit of heat or energy.)

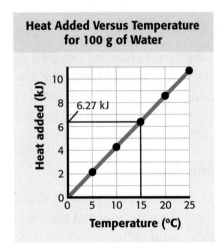

Heat Added Versus Temperature for 100 g of Water

1. The data points form a straight line, so the graph is a linear graph. Pick any two points on the line. For this line, we'll use the point (0°C, 0 kJ) and the point (15°C, 6.27 kJ).

2. To calculate slope (k), remember the phrase "rise over run." The rise is the difference between the y values of the two points. The run is the difference between the x values of the two points. The slope of the line, the constant k, is always the difference in y ("rise") divided by the difference in x ("run").

$$y = 6.27 \text{ kJ} - 0 \text{ kJ} = 6.27 \text{ kJ}$$

$$x = 15°C - 0°C = 15°C$$

$$y = kx$$

$$k = y \div x = 6.27 \text{ kJ} \div 15°C = 0.418 \text{ kJ/°C}$$

3. You can replace k in the equation $y = kx$ with the value of the slope. Then, you can use the equation to find out one value if given the other. For example, you can figure out how much heat is needed to raise the temperature of the water sample to 40°C.

$$y = (0.418 \text{ kJ/°C})x$$

$$y = 0.418 \text{ kJ/°C} \times 40°C = 16.7 \text{ kJ}.$$

▶ You Try It!

Procedure

Find a container that has volume markings on it, such as a graduated cylinder or a measuring cup. Find a stopwatch or a watch that has a second hand. Turn on a water faucet so that a steady stream of water flows. Using the container and the watch, record several data points of volume and time. Make a graph of your data.

Analysis

1. **Analyzing Ideas** How does the graph of your data show that the flow rate of the water faucet was constant throughout the experiment?

2. **Analyzing Data** What is the slope of your graph, k? What does k represent?

3. **Applying Concepts** How much water would have come out of the faucet if you had left the faucet on for twice as long as you measured?

Chapter Summary

The Big Idea All living things depend on chemical compounds, especially those that are based on the element carbon.

Section	**Vocabulary**

① Elements in Living Things

Key Concept Carbon atoms combine in many ways with each other and atoms of other elements and form the backbone of many molecules needed by living things.

- Carbon is a unique element because it can form long chains as well as bond with other elements.

- Living organisms are made of molecules that consist largely of carbon, hydrogen, nitrogen, oxygen, phosphorus, and sulfur.

organic compound p. 311

Bananas are made of carbon-based compounds. The compound ethene, shown here, helps bananas ripen.

② Compounds of Living Things

Key Concept Living things depend on very large carbon-based molecules and on smaller compounds, including water and salt.

- Living organisms depend on large compounds such as carbohydrates, lipids, proteins, and nucleic acids.

- Living organisms depend on many smaller compounds such as water and salt.

carbohydrate p. 314
lipid p. 315
protein p. 315
nucleic acid p. 317

Animals need salt in their diets because their bodies use salt.

Organize

Key-Term Fold Review the
FoldNote that you created at the
beginning of the chapter. Add to
or correct the FoldNote based on
what you have learned.

Using Vocabulary

1 **Academic Vocabulary** Which of the
following words is the closest in meaning
to the word *role*?
a. process
b. function
c. amount
d. piece

For each pair of terms, explain how the meanings
of the terms differ.

2 *carbohydrate* and *lipid*

3 *protein* and *nucleic acid*

Understanding Concepts

Multiple Choice

4 Why does carbon have a central role in the
chemistry of living organisms?
a. Carbon helps organisms to regulate
temperature.
b. Carbon atoms allow organisms to transmit
nerve impulses.
c. Carbon is the most abundant element in
organisms.
d. Carbon atoms combine in many ways with
atoms of carbon and other elements.

5 Which of the following statements describes
lipids?
a. Lipids are used to store energy.
b. Lipids dissolve in water.
c. Lipids are not found in food.
d. Lipids are small molecules.

6 All organic compounds
a. are composed of oxygen.
b. are composed of carbon.
c. can only be made by living organisms.
d. have the same number of atoms.

Short Answer

7 **Listing** Living organisms are made up of molecules consisting largely of which six elements?

8 **Listing** List two functions of proteins.

9 **Describing** Describe the role that lipids play
in the chemistry of living organisms.

10 **Analyzing** Complex carbohydrates, proteins,
and nucleic acids are biochemicals that are
long-chain polymers. What kinds of smaller
molecules make up these polymers?

INTERPRETING GRAPHICS Use the models
below to answer the next three questions.

a.

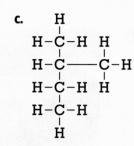

b.

c.

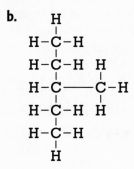

d.

11 **Classifying** Which model(s) represent
organic compounds?

12 **Identifying** A double bond is shown in
which model(s)?

13 **Analyzing** Which model(s) show one or
more carbon atoms bonded to only other
carbon atoms?

INTERPRETING GRAPHICS Use the molecular diagrams below to answer the next three questions.

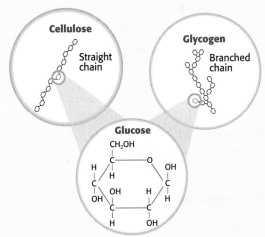

Cellulose — Straight chain

Glycogen — Branched chain

Glucose

14 Comparing Name two ways that cellulose and glycogen are similar.

15 Comparing In what way are cellulose and glycogen different?

16 Classifying What kind of biochemical are both cellulose and glycogen?

Writing Skills

17 Writing from Research Do some research on important organic compounds. Pick one such compound, and write a research paper on it. Include the history of its discovery, its function in living organisms, and current use and manufacture, if applicable. Be sure to include diagrams and to comment in your paper on the meaning of each.

Critical Thinking

18 Concept Mapping Use the following terms to create a concept map: *organic compounds, carbohydrates, lipids, proteins,* and *nucleic acids.*

19 Analyzing Ideas One example of each type of carbon backbone can be formed using four carbon atoms with only single bonds. Draw a model of each one. (Hint: Make sure that all of your models are different. In other words, one model should not be the same as another model turned a different direction.)

20 Applying Concepts The compounds that make up hair, skin, fingernails, and muscle are all composed of the same six elements. Why are hair, skin, fingernails, and muscle so different from each other?

21 Identifying Relationships What might be the health consequences of a diet that is very low in protein? Use what you know about the role of proteins in living organisms to support your answer.

22 Predicting Consequences Imagine a world without water. Give three reasons why it would not be possible for living organisms as we know them to exist without water.

Math Skills

23 Making Calculations A 61 g sample of an organic compound was analyzed and found to consist of 18 g carbon, 16 g oxygen, 16 g sulfur, 7 g nitrogen, and 4 g hydrogen. What is the percentage by mass of the elements that compose this compound?

24 Using Formulas You can use the formula 20^x to calculate the number of possible different proteins that can be made from the 20 different amino acids used by the body. In this formula, *x* is the number of amino acids in the protein. How many different proteins that are five amino acids long could be made?

Challenge

25 Analyzing Relationships Suppose that a certain molecule composed of only carbon and hydrogen has a straight-chain backbone five carbons long and contains double or triple bonds. What is the minimum number of hydrogen atoms that the molecule must have?

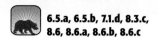
REVIEWING ACADEMIC VOCABULARY

1 In the sentence "We will be studying the principles of chemistry," what does the word *principles* mean?

A basic laws

B ideas

C secondary sources

D assumptions

2 Which of the following sets of words best completes the sentence "Living organisms are made of molecules that _____ carbon, hydrogen, nitrogen, oxygen, phosphorus, and sulfur"?

A consist from

B consisted to

C consist of

D consistent with

3 In the sentence "Principles of chemistry underlie the functioning of living organisms," what does the word *underlie* mean?

A be the basis of

B deny the reasons for

C explain causes of

D have little to do with

4 Which of the following words means "normal actions"?

A negotiating

B functioning

C breaking

D challenging

REVIEWING CONCEPTS

```
        H
        |
    H — C — H
        |
    H — C — H   H
        |       |
    H — C ——— C — H
        |       |
    H — C — H   H
        |
    H — C — H
        |
        H
```

5 What kind of carbon backbone does the figure above represent?

A a pair chain

B a ring chain

C a branched chain

D a straight chain

6 Carbon atoms most often form four separate covalent bonds with other atoms. Carbon atoms can also form two covalent bonds between them. What are these bonds called?

A double bonds

B single bonds

C triple bonds

D pair bonds

7 Molecules of simple sugars can join to form long strings. What are these long strings of sugars called?

A triple bonds

B carbon backbones

C nucleic acids

D complex carbohydrates

8 What element is found in the highest percentage by weight in the human body?

A hydrogen

B oxygen

C carbon

D phosphorus

9 When molecules join to form long chains of repeating units, the chains are called

A phosphorus.

B carbon.

C polymers.

D branches.

10 Which of the following is a kind of biochemical that does not dissolve in water and that makes up cell walls, fats, oils, and waxes?

A glycogen

B carbohydrate

C lipid

D cellulose

11 In what way is the structure of a protein more complex than the structure of a carbohydrate or a lipid?

A Proteins are made up of different combinations of amino acids.

B Proteins are very large molecules.

C Proteins are made up of long-chain polymers.

D Proteins come in two forms: simple proteins and complex proteins.

12 What is the term for the genetic material of a cell?

A hormones

B hemoglobin

C DNA

D protein

REVIEWING PRIOR LEARNING

13 Which of the following is an example of a tertiary consumer?

A an alga

B a wolf

C a duck

D an iguana

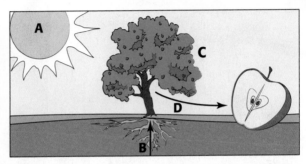

14 According to the diagram above, at what point does light energy become chemical energy?

A at point A

B at point B

C at point C

D at point D

15 The sun is a major source of energy. What is the name for the chemical reaction in plants that is caused by the sun?

A evaporation

B radiation

C photosynthesis

D process

16 In animals, what cell structures are responsible for releasing energy that can be used by the cells?

A vacuoles

B mitochondria

C chloroplasts

D proteins

Science in Action

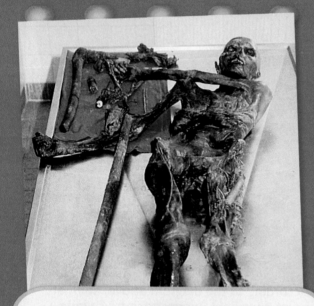

Science, Technology, and Society

Molecular Photocopying

To learn about our human ancestors, scientists can use DNA from mummies. Well-preserved DNA can be copied using a technique called *polymerase chain reaction* (PCR). PCR uses enzymes called *polymerases,* which make new strands of DNA by using old strands as templates. Thus, PCR is called *molecular photocopying.* However, scientists have to be very careful when using this process. If just one of their own skin cells falls into the PCR mixture, it will contaminate the ancient DNA with their own DNA.

Social Studies ACTiViTY

DNA analysis of mummies is helping archeologists study human history. Write a research paper about what scientists have learned about human history through DNA analysis.

Scientific Discoveries

Skunk-Spray Remedy

So, that pretty black cat with the white stripe down its back wasn't a cat after all? Well, hold off on dumping Fido into a tomato-juice bath. Chemistry has a much better way of conquering skunk spray.

Paul Krebaum has invented a new deskunking formula. The key ingredient in the formula is hydrogen peroxide, which reacts with the sulfur in a skunk's spray. The reaction rearranges the atoms in the skunk spray so that the spray no longer has a strong odor. The formula was tested on a skunk-sprayed dog. The result was a wet and unhappy but much less smelly pet!

Language Arts ACTiViTY

Write a humorous story in your **Science Journal** about a family pet that has a run-in with a skunk and then gets treated with the deskunking formula.

Flossie Wong-Staal

Molecular Biologist   Flossie Wong-Staal is a scientist at the University of California at San Diego. She is a molecular biologist, a person who studies the structures of various chemicals in living things. Wong-Staal has dedicated her career to fighting HIV, the virus that causes AIDS. AIDS is a disease that causes the human immune system to fall apart. HIV enters a body's healthy cells and uses the cells' DNA to multiply itself and spread through the body.

In 1983, Wong-Staal and scientist Robert Gallo were the first researchers in the United States to discover HIV. Two years later, Wong-Staal successfully cloned the virus. Cloning is the process of making a genetic copy of an organism or virus in a laboratory. Cloning HIV gives researchers more opportunities to study the virus. With more copies of the virus, scientists can do different experiments, which will help in creating a vaccine or a cure for AIDS.

Today, Wong-Staal continues to try to find ways to treat patients who have HIV and AIDS and ways to prevent other people from becoming infected with HIV.

Math ACTIVITY

A study estimated that 940,000 North Americans have HIV or AIDS. If the population of North America at the time of the study was 316 million, what percentage of the population was infected?

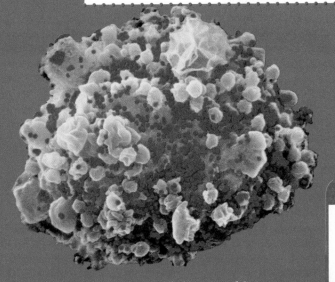

The white blobs are white blood cells. The red dots on the cells are HIV particles.

Internet Resources

- To learn more about careers in science, visit www.scilinks.org and enter the SciLinks code HY70225.

- To learn more about these Science in Action topics, visit go.hrw.com and type in the keyword HY7CLTF.

- Check out articles related to this chapter by visiting go.hrw.com. Just type in the keyword HY7CLTC.

UNIT 5

TIMELINE

Motion and Forces

It's hard to imagine a world where nothing ever moves. Without motion or forces to cause motion, life would be very dull! The relationship between force and motion is the subject of this unit. You will learn how to describe the motion of objects, how forces affect motion, and how fluids exert force. This timeline shows some events and discoveries that have occurred as scientists have worked to understand the motion of objects here on Earth and in space.

Around 250 BCE

Archimedes, a Greek mathematician, develops the principle that bears his name. The principle relates the buoyant force on an object in a fluid to the amount of fluid displaced by the object.

1764

In London, Wolfgang Amadeus Mozart composes his first symphony—at the age of 8.

1846

After determining that the orbit of Uranus is different from what is predicted from the law of universal gravitation, scientists discover Neptune whose gravitational force is causing Uranus's unusual orbit.

1947

While flying a Bell X-1 rocket-powered airplane, American pilot Chuck Yeager becomes the first human to travel faster than the speed of sound.

Around 240 BCE

Chinese astronomers are the first to record a sighting of Halley's Comet.

1519

Portuguese explorer Ferdinand Magellan begins the first voyage around the world.

1687

Sir Isaac Newton, a British mathematician and scientist, publishes *Principia*, a book describing his laws of motion and the law of universal gravitation.

PHILOSOPHIÆ
NATURALIS
PRINCIPIA
MATHEMATICA.

Autore JS. NEWTON, Trin. Coll. Cantab. Soc. Matheseos
Professore Lucasiano, & Societatis Regalis Sodali.

1905

While employed as a patent clerk, German physicist Albert Einstein publishes his special theory of relativity. The theory states that the speed of light is constant no matter what the reference frame is.

1921

Bessie Coleman becomes the first African American woman licensed to fly an airplane.

1971

American astronaut Alan Shepard takes a break from gathering lunar data to play golf on the moon during the *Apollo 14* mission.

1990

The *Magellan* spacecraft begins orbiting Venus for a four-year mission to map the planet. By using the sun's gravitational force, it propels itself to Venus without burning much fuel.

2003

NASA launches *Spirit* and *Opportunity,* two Mars Exploration Rovers, to study Mars.

Improving Comprehension

Graphic Organizers are important visual tools that can help you organize information and improve your reading comprehension. The Graphic Organizer below is called a *cause-and-effect map*. Instructions for creating other types of Graphic Organizers are located in the **Study Skills** section of the Appendix.

How to Make a Cause-and-Effect Map

1. Draw a box, and write a cause in the box. You can have as many cause boxes as you want. The diagram shown here is one example of a cause-and-effect map.

2. Draw another box to the right of the cause box to represent an effect. You can have as many effect boxes as you want. Draw arrows from each cause box to the appropriate effect boxes.

3. In the cause boxes, explain the process that makes up the cause. In the effect boxes, write a description of the effect or details about the effect.

When to Use a Cause-and-Effect Map

A cause-and-effect map is a useful tool for illustrating a specific type of scientific process. Use a cause-and-effect map when you want to describe how, when, or why one event causes another event. As you read, look for events that are either causes or results of other events, and draw a cause-and-effect map that shows the relationships between the events.

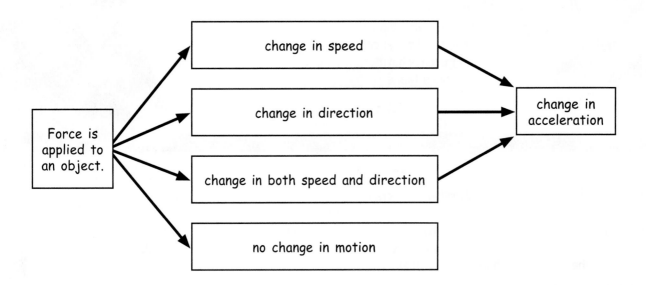

You Try It!

This Reading Strategy can also be used within the chapter that you are about to read. Practice making your own *cause-and-effect map* as directed in the Reading Strategies for Section 2 and Section 3. Record your work in your **Science Journal.**

Unpacking the Standards

The information below "unpacks" the standards by breaking them down into basic parts. The higher-level, academic vocabulary is highlighted and defined to help you understand the language of the standards. "What It Means" restates the standards as simply as possible.

California Standard	Academic Vocabulary	What It Means
8.1.a Students know position is **defined** in relation to some choice of a standard reference point and a set of reference directions.	**define** (dee FIEN) to state or explain the meaning or properties of	The location of an object is described in terms of where the object is relative to another object or to a starting point and by using directions such as left, right, above, behind, north, and south.
8.1.b Students know that average speed is the total distance traveled divided by the total time elapsed and that the speed of an object along the path traveled can **vary.**	**vary** (VER ee) to differ; to have more than one possible state	Average speed is calculated by dividing how far an object moves by how long the object took to move the distance. The speed of an object can change as the object moves along a path.
8.1.c Students know how to solve problems **involving** distance, time, and average speed.	**involve** (in VAHLV) to have as a part of	You must know how to solve problems about how far an object moves, how long an object moves, and how fast an object moves.
8.1.d Students know the velocity of an object must be described by **specifying** both the direction and the speed of the object.	**specify** (SPES uh FIE) to state or tell clearly	Velocity is a measure of how fast an object moves in a particular direction.
8.1.e Students know changes in velocity may be due to changes in speed, direction, or both.		Changing the speed of an object, the direction in which the object is moving, or both will change the object's velocity.
8.1.f Students know how to **interpret** graphs of position versus time and graphs of speed versus time for motion in a single direction.	**interpret** (in TUHR pruht) to figure out the meaning of	You must know how to read graphs that show how an object's position changes over time and how an object's speed changes over time.
8.2.a Students know a force has both direction and magnitude.		A force acts in a particular direction and has a certain size.

The following identifies other standards that are covered in this chapter and indicates where you can go to see them unpacked: **8.2.b** (Chapter 13), **8.2.c** (Chapter 13), **8.2.d** (Chapter 13), and **8.2.e** (Chapter 13).

Matter in Motion

The Big Idea

Forces act on objects and can produce motion.

California Standards

Focus on Physical Sciences

8.1 The velocity of an object is the rate of change of its position. (Sections 1, 2, and 3)

8.2 Unbalanced forces cause changes in velocity. (Sections 2 and 3)

Investigation and Experimentation

8.9 Scientific progress is made by asking meaningful questions and conducting careful investigations. (Section 1; Science Skills Activity)

Math

6.2.3 Algebra and Functions

English–Language Arts

8.2.2 Reading

8.2.1 Writing

About the Photo

Speed skaters are fast. In fact, some skaters can skate 12 m/s! That rate is equal to a speed of 27 mi/h. To reach such a speed, skaters must exert large forces. They also must use the force of friction to turn corners on the slippery surface of the ice.

Organize

Tri-Fold

Before you read this chapter, create the FoldNote entitled "Tri-Fold." Write what you know about motion and forces in the column labeled "Know." Then, write what you want to know about motion and forces in the column labeled "Want." As you read the chapter, write what you learn about motion and forces in the column labeled "Learn."

Instructions for creating FoldNotes are located in the Study Skills section on p. 520 of the Appendix.

Explore Activity

🕐 20 min

The Domino Derby—Measuring Speed

Speed is the distance traveled in a certain amount of time. In this activity, you will observe one factor that affects the speed of falling dominoes.

Procedure

1. Set up **25 dominoes** in a straight line. Try to keep equal spacing between the dominoes.

2. Use a **meterstick** to measure the total length of your row of dominoes. Record this length.

3. Use a **stopwatch** to time how long the dominoes take to fall. Record this measurement.

4. Predict how the amount of time will change if you change the distance between the dominoes. Write your predictions.

5. Using distances between the dominoes that are smaller and larger than the distance used in your first setup, repeat steps 2 and 3 several times. Use the same number of dominoes in each trial.

8.1.b
8.1.c
8.9.f

Analysis

6. Calculate the average speed for each trial by dividing the total distance (the length of the row of dominoes) by the time that the dominoes take to fall.

7. How did the spacing between dominoes affect the average speed? Is this result what you expected? If not, explain.

Measuring Motion

Key Concept Motion can be measured and described in many ways.

What You Will Learn

- Properties used to describe the motion of an object include a reference point, direction, speed, velocity, and acceleration.
- Average speed can be calculated by dividing total distance by total time.
- A change in velocity is due to a change in speed, direction, or both.
- Speed and acceleration can be represented on graphs.

Why It Matters

Learning about motion will help you give directions, plan trips, and predict the future locations of objects.

Vocabulary

- motion
- average speed
- velocity
- acceleration

READING STRATEGY

Prediction Guide Before reading this section, write each heading from this section in your **Science Journal.** Below each heading, write what you think you will learn.

If you look around, you will likely see something in motion. Your teacher may be walking across the room. Perhaps your friend is writing with a pencil. Even if you do not see anything moving, things are in motion all around you. Air particles are moving. Earth is circling the sun. And blood is flowing through your blood vessels!

Motion and Reference Points

You may think that you only have to watch an object to tell that it is moving. But often, you are watching the object in relation to another object that appears to stay in place. The object that appears to stay in place is a *reference point*. When an object changes position over time relative to a reference point, the object is in **motion.** You can use a reference direction—such as north, south, east, west, up, or down—to describe the direction of an object's motion.

Standard Reference Points

As **Figure 1** shows, features on Earth's surface are often used as standard reference points for determining motion. Nonmoving objects, such as trees and buildings, are also useful reference points. A moving object can be used as a reference point, too. For example, suppose that a bird flies by the hot-air balloon shown in **Figure 1.** Anyone in the balloon will see that the bird is changing position in relation to the moving balloon.

Figure 1 *During the interval between the times that these pictures were taken, the hot-air balloon changed position relative to a reference point—the mountain.*

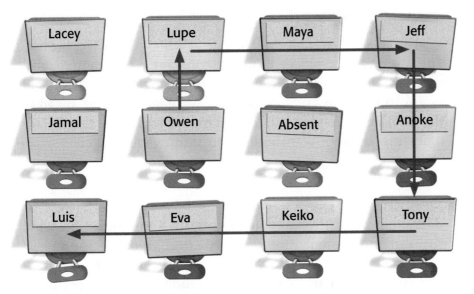

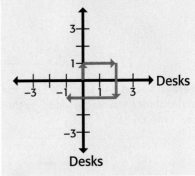

Figure 2 *Owen started passing around a sign-up sheet for choir auditions. The sheet ended up one desk to the left of and one desk behind the origin of the paper's movement.*

Motion in a Two-Dimensional System

Figure 2 shows a two-dimensional system in which a sheet of paper is passed around a room. A grid can be used to describe motion in such a system. The reference point—Owen's desk—is at the origin, where the *x*-axis meets the *y*-axis. Four reference directions are represented by the positive and negative directions on the axes. As the paper in **Figure 2** moves toward the front of the room, the paper moves in the positive direction on the *y*-axis. As the paper moves to the right side of the room, it moves in the positive direction on the *x*-axis. As it moves toward the back of the room, the paper moves in the negative direction on the *y*-axis. Finally, as the paper moves to the left side of the room, it moves in the negative direction on the *x*-axis.

motion (MOH shuhn) an object's change in position relative to a reference point

Standards Check If an object moves to the right, in which direction and along which axis of a grid does the object move? 🐻 **8.1.a**

Quick Lab

Reference Points and Positions

8.1.a

1. Put your finger on the 15 cm mark of a **metric ruler.** This mark is the reference point.

2. Move your finger +5 cm, or 5 cm to the right. From this new position, move your finger −7 cm. Then, move your finger −3 cm, +6 cm, and −4 cm.

3. Describe your finger's new position in relation to the reference point (the 15 cm mark).

4. On a **sheet of paper,** write a series of steps describing five changes of position on a ruler. Begin at 15 cm, and end at 25 cm.

5. Compare your steps with a partner's steps.

6. Why are positive and negative signs needed?

 10 min

Average Speed

The speed of an object is the rate at which the object moves. The speed of an object is rarely constant. For example, the speed of each racer in **Figure 3** varies during the race. So, it is useful to find the average speed of an object. **Average speed** is the total distance traveled divided by the total time taken. The following equation can be used to find average speed:

average speed (AV uhr ij SPEED) the total distance traveled divided by the total time taken

$$average\ speed = \frac{total\ distance}{total\ time}$$

Suppose that it takes you 2 s to walk 4 m down a hallway. You can use the equation above to find your average speed: (4 m)/(2 s), or 2 m/s. The SI unit for speed is meters per second (m/s). Other units for speed include kilometers per hour (km/h), feet per second (ft/s), and miles per hour (mi/h).

Standards Check What is average speed? What is the equation for average speed? 8.1.b, 8.1.c

Figure 3 *A racer's average speed can be determined by timing the racer on a set course.* **What is a racer's average speed if the racer finishes a 200 m race in 25 s?**

Making a Graph Showing Speed

Speed can be shown on a graph of position versus time. On this kind of graph, position is a measure of the distance of an object from a reference point. The object's distance from the reference point in either the positive or negative direction is plotted on the *y*-axis. So, the *y*-axis expresses distance in units such as meters, centimeters, or kilometers. Time is plotted on the *x*-axis. Thus, the *x*-axis displays units such as seconds, minutes, or hours. On a graph of position versus time, the slope of the line is equal to the speed of the object.

MATH FOCUS

Calculating Average Speed

An athlete swims a distance of 50 m from one end of a pool to the other end in 25 s. What is the athlete's average speed?

Step 1: Write the equation for average speed.

$$average\ speed = \frac{total\ distance}{total\ time}$$

Step 2: Replace the total distance and total time with the values given, and solve.

$$average\ speed = \frac{50\ m}{25\ s} = 2\ m/s$$

Now It's Your Turn

1. It takes Kira 36 s to jog to a store that is 72 m away. What is her average speed?
2. What is your average speed if you walk 7.5 km in 1.5 h?
3. An airplane traveling from San Francisco to Chicago flies 1,260 km in 3.5 h. What is the airplane's average speed?

Quick Lab

Changing Average Speed

1. Use a **book** and a **piece of cardboard** to build a ramp. Mark a spot about 75 cm in front of the ramp.

2. Place a **toy car** at the top of the ramp, and let the car roll down the ramp. Use a **stopwatch** to time how long the car takes to travel to the marked spot. Record the time.

3. Measure the distance the car rolls from the top of the ramp to the marked spot. Record this distance.

4. Calculate the car's average speed.

5. Change the height of the ramp, and repeat steps 2–4. How did the change affect the car's average speed?

6. Describe how the car's speed varies along the path traveled.

20 min

Recognizing Speed on a Graph

Suppose that you watched a dog walk beside a fence. The orange line in the graph in **Figure 4** shows the total distance that the dog walked in 10 s. Notice that the dog did not walk the same distance each second. The distance varies because the speed is not constant. The dog walked slowly at first. Then, it moved quickly for 1 s. The dog did not move for the next 3 s. During the last 4 s, the dog walked with a moderate speed.

The dog's average speed can be calculated as follows:

$$average\ speed = \frac{7\ m}{10\ s} = 0.7\ m/s$$

Suppose that the dog walked at a constant speed. The red line on the graph shows how far the dog must walk each second at that speed to cover the same distance covered earlier. The slope of this line is the average speed.

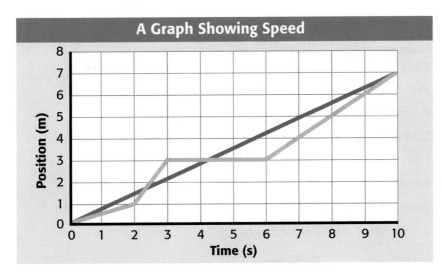

A Graph Showing Speed

Figure 4 *A graph of position versus time can show an object's speed and average speed.*

Velocity: Direction Matters

Suppose that two birds leave the same tree at the same time. They both fly at 10 km/h for 5 min, 12 km/h for 8 min, and 5 km/h for 10 min. Why don't they end up at the same place?

Have you figured out the answer? The birds went in different directions. Their speeds were the same, but they had different velocities. **Velocity** is the speed of an object as well as the direction in which the object is moving.

Speed Versus Velocity

The terms *speed* and *velocity* do not have the same meaning. Velocity must include a direction. If you say that an airplane's velocity is 600 km/h, you are not correct. But you can say that the airplane's velocity is 600 km/h south. **Figure 5** shows an example of the difference between speed and velocity.

Changing Velocity

The velocity of an object is constant only if the speed and direction of the object do not change. So, constant velocity is always motion along a straight line. The velocity of an object changes if the object's speed, direction, or both change.

For example, as a bus driving at 15 m/s south speeds up to 20 m/s south, its velocity changes. If the bus keeps moving at the same speed but changes direction to travel east, its velocity changes again. And if the bus slows down at the same time that it swerves north to avoid a cat, the velocity of the bus changes yet again. **Table 1** shows other examples of velocity changes.

Standards Check How does velocity differ from speed? What changes in motion can result in a change in velocity? 8.1.d, 8.1.e

Figure 5 *The speeds of these cars may be similar, but the velocities of the cars differ because the cars are going in different directions.*

velocity (vuh LAHS uh tee) the speed of an object in a particular direction

Table 1	Examples of Velocity Changes
Situation	**What changes**
Raindrop falling faster and faster	speed
Runner going around a turn on a track	direction
Taking an exit off a highway	speed and direction
Train arriving at a station	speed
Baseball caught by a catcher	speed
Baseball hit by a batter	speed and direction
Cyclist riding a bike around a corner	speed and direction

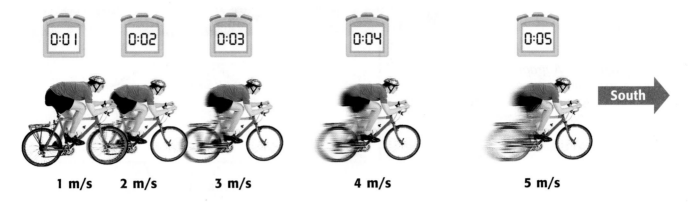

1 m/s 2 m/s 3 m/s 4 m/s 5 m/s

Figure 6 *This cyclist is accelerating at 1 m/s² south.*

Acceleration

The word *accelerate* is often used to mean "speed up," but the word means something else in science. **Acceleration** is the rate at which velocity changes over time. The units for acceleration are the units for velocity divided by a unit for time. A common unit for acceleration is meters per second per second, or (m/s)/s, which is also written as m/s².

Velocity changes if speed, direction, or both change. So, an object accelerates if its speed, direction, or both change. **Figure 6** shows the acceleration of a person on a bicycle. The person is accelerating because his speed is increasing. An increase in speed is sometimes called *positive acceleration*. A decrease in speed is sometimes called *negative acceleration,* or *deceleration.*

acceleration (ak SEL uhr AY shuhn) the rate at which velocity changes over time; an object accelerates if its speed, direction, or both change

<u>Wordwise</u> **centripetal**
The root *centr-* means "center."

Circular Motion: Continuous Acceleration

You may be surprised to know that even when you are sitting still, you are accelerating. You may not seem to be changing speed or direction, but you are! You are moving in a circle as Earth rotates. An object moving in a circular motion is always changing direction. Therefore, the object's velocity is always changing. So, the object is accelerating.

The acceleration that happens when an object moves at a constant speed in circular motion is known as <u>*centripetal acceleration*</u> (sen TRIP uht uhl ak SEL uhr AY shuhn). Centripetal acceleration happens as a Ferris wheel turns at an amusement park and as the moon orbits Earth. **Figure 7** shows another example of centripetal acceleration.

Figure 7 *As the blades of these windmills turn, the blades are constantly changing direction. Thus, the blades are undergoing centripetal acceleration.*

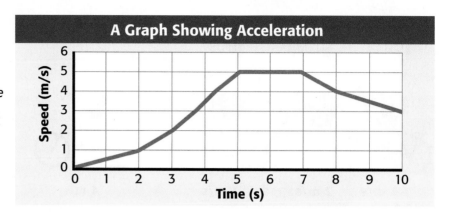

Figure 8 *A graph of speed versus time can show positive acceleration, no acceleration, and negative acceleration.*

Recognizing Acceleration on a Graph

Acceleration can be shown on a graph of speed versus time. Suppose you are playing with a remote-control car. You push the lever on the remote to drive the car forward. The graph in **Figure 8** shows the car's acceleration as the car moves east. For the first 5 s, the car moves faster and faster. You know that the car's acceleration is positive because the car's speed increases as time passes. You also know that the acceleration is changing because the line between 0 s and 5 s is not straight.

For the next 2 s, the speed of the car is constant. So, the slope of the graph is 0, which means that the car is not accelerating (0 m/s²). During the last 3 s, you let go of the lever, and the car slows down. The car's acceleration is negative because the speed of the car decreases as time passes.

Standards Check What does negative acceleration look like on a graph of speed versus time? 🐻 **8.1.f**

Quick Lab

Graphing Acceleration

1. Use a **pencil** to draw an *x*-axis and a *y*-axis on a **sheet of graph paper.**

2. Use the data in the table at right to construct a graph of acceleration.

3. Be sure to label each axis with the proper units. Give your graph a title.

4. During what time period is the cheetah's positive acceleration the greatest? Use the graph to explain your answer.

5. Describe the cheetah's motion between 3 s and 5 s.

6. During what time period is the cheetah's acceleration negative?

8.1.f
8.9.e

Acceleration of a Cheetah	
Time (s)	**Speed (m/s)**
0.0	0.0
1.0	6.0
2.0	12.0
3.0	16.0
4.0	16.0
5.0	16.0
6.0	10.0
7.0	5.0

🕐 **20 min**

SECTION
Review 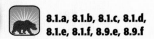 8.1.a, 8.1.b, 8.1.c, 8.1.d,
8.1.e, 8.1.f, 8.9.e, 8.9.f

Summary

- An object is in motion if it changes position over time in relation to a reference point.
- Average speed is the total distance that an object travels divided by the total time that the object takes to travel that distance.
- Speed can be shown on a graph of position versus time.
- Velocity is speed as well as the direction of motion. The velocity of an object changes if the object's speed, direction, or both change.
- Acceleration is the rate at which velocity changes.
- An object can accelerate by changing speed, direction, or both.
- Acceleration can be shown on a graph of speed versus time.

Using Vocabulary

1 Write an original definition for *motion* and *acceleration.*

Understanding Concepts

2 **Listing** Give three examples of acceleration. Be sure that each example describes a different kind of change in velocity.

3 **Demonstrating** Describe the position of an object in the room by using a standard reference point and a set of reference directions.

4 **Describing** What two things must you specify when describing the velocity of an object?

5 **Identifying** What two things must you know to determine average speed?

6 **Justifying** Explain how the average speed of an object moving along a path can differ from the speed of the object at a certain point on that path.

7 **Comparing** How does a graph showing speed differ from a graph showing acceleration?

Critical Thinking

8 **Analyzing Ideas** Suppose that you rode a bicycle to your friend's house. You used the bicycle's odometer to find the distance between your house and your friend's house. You used your watch to time how long you took to reach your friend's house. Can you use this data to figure out what your fastest speed was during your bike ride? Explain your answer.

INTERPRETING GRAPHICS Use the figure below to answer the next question.

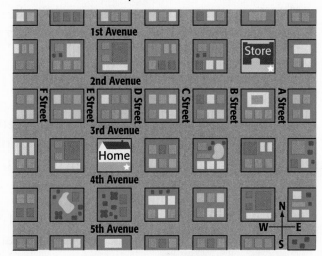

9 **Applying Concepts** A person walked from her home to the store. Use a reference point and reference directions to describe how the person moved.

Math Skills

10 **Using Equations** Find the average speed of a person who swims 105 m in 70 s.

Challenge

11 **Evaluating Data** A wolf is chasing a rabbit. Use the following data to graph the wolf's motion: 15 m/s at 0 s, 10 m/s at 1 s, 5 m/s at 2 s, 2.5 m/s at 3 s, 1 m/s at 4 s, and 0 m/s at 5 s. Interpret the graph to describe the wolf's motion.

Internet Resources

For a variety of links related to this chapter, go to www.scilinks.org

Topic: Measuring Motion
SciLinks code: HY70927

What Is a Force?

Key Concept Forces acting on an object can be combined and may cause changes in motion.

▶ You probably hear the word *force* used often. People say things such as "That storm had a lot of force" or "Our football team is a force to be reckoned with." But what exactly is a force? In science, a **force** is a push or a pull. All forces have two properties: direction and magnitude. A **newton** (N) is the unit used to describe the magnitude, or size, of a force.

Standards Check What two properties do all forces have? 🐾 **8.2.a**

Forces Acting on Objects

All forces act on objects. For any push to occur, something has to receive the push. The same is true for any pull. Your fingers exert forces to pull open books or to push the keys on a computer. So, the forces act on the books and keys.

A force can change the velocity of an object. This change in velocity can be a change in speed, direction, or both. In other words, forces can cause acceleration. Anytime you see a change in an object's motion, you can be sure that the change was caused by a force. **Figure 1** shows an example of a force causing a change in motion.

However, a force can act on an object without causing the object to move. For example, the force that you exert when you sit on a chair does not cause the chair to move. The chair does not move because the floor exerts a balancing force on the chair.

Figure 1 *The soil starts to move because the bulldozer is exerting a force on the soil.*

25 N

Net force
25 N + 20 N = 45 N
to the right

20 N

Figure 2 *When forces act in the same direction, you add the forces to determine the net force. The net force will be in the same direction as the individual forces.*

Combined Effect of Forces

When two or more forces act on an object, the result is the combined, or cumulative, effect of the forces. So, the object's motion changes as if only one force acted on the object. That one force is the net force. The **net force** is the combination of the forces acting on an object. How do you find the net force? The answer depends on the directions of the forces.

Forces in the Same Direction

Suppose that the music teacher asks you and a friend to move a piano. You pull on one end, and your friend pushes on the other end, as **Figure 2** shows. The forces that you and your friend exert on the piano act in the same direction. So, the two forces can be added to find the net force. In this case, the net force is 45 N. This net force is large enough to move the piano—that is, if the piano is on wheels!

Notice that the lengths of the arrows in **Figure 2** represent the magnitudes of the forces. The longer the arrow, the larger the force. Also notice that the combined length of the force arrows equals the length of the net-force arrow.

Standards Check How do you calculate the net force when two or more forces act in the same direction? **8.2.a, 8.2.b**

net force (NET FAWRS) the combination of all of the forces acting on an object

8.2.a Students know a force has both direction and magnitude.
8.2.b Students know when an object is subject to two or more forces at once, the result is the cumulative effect of all the forces.
8.2.c Students know when the forces on an object are balanced, the motion of the object does not change.
8.2.d Students know how to identify separately the two or more forces that are acting on a single static object, including gravity, elastic forces due to tension or compression in matter, and friction.
8.2.e Students know that when the forces on an object are unbalanced, the object will change its velocity (that is, it will speed up, slow down, or change direction).

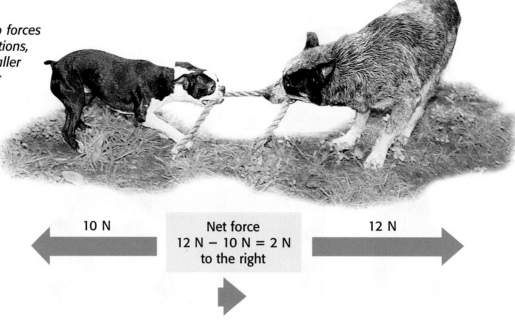

Figure 3 *When two forces act in opposite directions, you subtract the smaller force from the larger force to determine the net force.*

10 N

Net force
12 N − 10 N = 2 N
to the right

12 N

Forces in Opposite Directions

Look at the two dogs playing tug of war in **Figure 3.** Each dog is exerting a force on the rope. But the forces are in opposite directions. Which dog will win the tug of war?

Because the forces are in opposite directions, the net force on the rope is found by subtracting the smaller force from the larger one. The net force is in the same direction as the larger force. In this case, the net force is 2 N in the direction of the dog on the right.

What will happen if each dog pulls with a force of 10 N? The effect of the two forces will be canceled, and the net force on the rope will be 0 N.

Standards Check What is the net force on an object if a force of 7 N north and a force of 5 N south act on the object? **8.2.a, 8.2.b**

Quick Lab

Finding Net Force

1. Tie a **50 cm piece of string** to a **1,000 g mass.** The knot holding the mass should be located near the middle of the string.

2. Attach a **spring scale** to one end of the string. Attach a **second spring scale** to the other end of the string.

3. Lay the mass sideways on a table, and hold the spring scales parallel to the tabletop.

4. Pull both spring scales in one direction. Record the force on each spring scale, and find the net force on the mass.

5. Pull the spring scales in opposite directions. Record the forces, and find the net force.

6. For each trial, compare the direction and magnitude of the net force with the direction and magnitude of each force measured on each spring scale.

7. For each trial, describe the combined effect of the forces on the mass.

8.2.a
8.2.b

🕐 **20 min**

Balanced Forces: No Change in Motion

When the forces on an object produce a net force of 0 N, the forces are *balanced*. Balanced forces will not cause a change in the motion of an object.

Many objects that have balanced forces acting on them are not moving, or are *static*. Often, tension or compression is acting on these static objects. *Tension* is a force that is exerted when matter is pulled or stretched. *Compression* is a force that is exerted when matter is pushed or squeezed. Static objects will not start moving when balanced forces are acting on them. So, a light hanging from the ceiling does not move because the force of gravity pulling down on the light is balanced by the force of tension in the cord pulling upward. **Figure 4** shows other examples of balanced forces.

An object may also be moving when balanced forces are acting on it. Neither the speed nor the direction of the object will change. A car driven in a straight line at a constant speed is an example of balanced forces acting on a moving object.

Standards Check How do you know that the forces on a hanging light are balanced? What forces act on the light? 8.2.c, 8.2.d

Wordwise **compression**
The prefix *com-* means "with" or "together." The root *press-* means "to press." The suffix *-ion* means "the act of." Other examples are *pressure* and *compose*.

Figure 4 Examples of Balanced Forces

The kittens rest comfortably without moving. The downward force of their weight is balanced by the force of compression in the cushion pushing upward.

The bird feeder does not fall down because the weight of the bird and the bird feeder is balanced by the force of tension in the wire.

The dog cannot walk into the surf because the force that the dog is exerting is balanced by the tension in the leash held by the dog's owner.

Unbalanced Forces: Velocity Changes

When the net force on an object is not 0 N, the forces on the object are *unbalanced*. When unbalanced forces are acting on an object, they cause a change in the velocity of the object. The change in velocity may be a change in speed, a change in direction, or both. Unbalanced forces will also cause a static object to start moving or cause a moving object to slow down and stop moving.

Unbalanced Forces and Moving Objects

Unbalanced forces are needed to change the velocity of moving objects. For example, think about a soccer game, such as the one shown in **Figure 5.** The soccer ball is already moving when one player passes it to a second player. When the ball reaches the second player, that player exerts an unbalanced force—a kick—on the ball. After the kick, the ball moves in a new direction and at a new speed.

Unbalanced Forces and Static Objects

Unbalanced forces are needed to cause static objects to start moving. Every moving object started moving because an unbalanced force acted on it. But a moving object can keep moving without an unbalanced force acting on it. For example, when it is kicked, a soccer ball receives an unbalanced force. The ball keeps rolling after the force of the kick has ended.

Standards Check What can happen to the velocity of an object when unbalanced forces act on it? 🐻 **8.2.e**

Figure 5 *The soccer ball moves because the players exert an unbalanced force on the ball each time they kick it.*

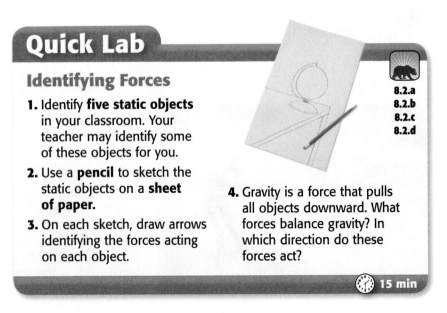

Quick Lab

Identifying Forces

8.2.a
8.2.b
8.2.c
8.2.d

1. Identify **five static objects** in your classroom. Your teacher may identify some of these objects for you.

2. Use a **pencil** to sketch the static objects on a **sheet of paper.**

3. On each sketch, draw arrows identifying the forces acting on each object.

4. Gravity is a force that pulls all objects downward. What forces balance gravity? In which direction do these forces act?

🕐 15 min

Unbalanced Forces and Direction of Motion

You have learned that forces have direction. You have also learned that unbalanced forces can cause a change in the direction of motion. So, you may think that objects always move in the direction of the unbalanced force. But objects do not always move in this direction. Imagine twirling a ball on a string. The string exerts an unbalanced force on the ball. The direction of that force is toward your hand. Yet the ball travels in a circle and does not move toward your hand. **Figure 6** shows another object moving in a direction that differs from the direction of the unbalanced force acting on the object.

Figure 6 *The shuttle is moving forward even though an unbalanced force is acting on it in the opposite direction.*

SECTION Review

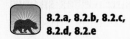

8.2.a, 8.2.b, 8.2.c, 8.2.d, 8.2.e

Summary

- A force is a push or a pull. Forces have magnitude and direction and are expressed in newtons.

- Forces always act on objects.

- The combined effect of the forces acting on an object is the net force.

- Forces acting in the same direction are added. Forces acting in opposite directions are subtracted.

- Balanced forces cause no change in motion. The forces on a static object are balanced and can be identified.

- Unbalanced forces cause a change in velocity.

Using Vocabulary

1. Write an original definition for *force* and *net force.*

Understanding Concepts

2. **Comparing** Explain the difference between balanced and unbalanced forces.

3. **Applying** Give an example of an unbalanced force causing a change in velocity.

4. **Describing** Give an example of balanced forces acting on a static object.

5. **Summarizing** Explain the meaning of the statement "Forces act on objects."

Critical Thinking

6. **Forming Hypotheses** Suppose a person coasting on a skateboard does not speed up, slow down, or change directions. Form a hypothesis about the net force on the person. Explain.

7. **Applying Concepts** List three forces that you exert when riding a bicycle.

8. **Making Inferences** When finding net force, why must you know the directions of the forces acting on an object?

INTERPRETING GRAPHICS Use the images below to answer the next question.

a.

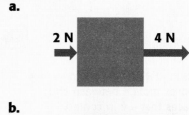

2 N   4 N

b.

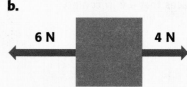

6 N   4 N

9. **Applying Concepts** Identify the magnitude and direction of the net force on each block.

Internet Resources

For a variety of links related to this chapter, go to www.scilinks.org

Topic: Forces

SciLinks code: HY70604

Friction: A Force That Opposes Motion

Key Concept Friction is a force that can balance other forces to prevent motion. Friction is also a force that, when unbalanced, can change the velocity of an object.

What You Will Learn

- The magnitude of the force of friction can vary.
- Kinetic friction is a force that, when unbalanced, can change the velocity of a moving object.
- Static friction balances an applied force and can prevent motion.
- Friction can be both harmful and helpful.

Why It Matters

By controlling friction, you can make tasks easier.

Vocabulary

- friction

READING STRATEGY

Graphic Organizer In your **Science Journal,** create a Cause-and-Effect Map about friction.

friction (FRIK shuhn) a force that opposes motion between two surfaces that are in contact

▶ While playing ball, your friend throws the ball out of your reach. Rather than running after the ball, you walk after it. You know that the ball will slow down and stop. An unbalanced force is needed to change the velocity of objects. So, what force is stopping the ball? The ball is stopped by friction. **Friction** is a force that opposes motion between two surfaces that are touching. Friction can cause a moving object to slow down and stop.

The Source of Friction

The surface of any object is rough. Even surfaces that feel smooth are covered with microscopic hills and valleys. When two surfaces are touching, the hills and valleys of one surface stick to the hills and valleys of the other surface, as shown in **Figure 1.** This contact causes friction. The magnitude of friction between two surfaces depends on many factors. One factor is the force pushing the surfaces together. Another factor is the materials that make up the surfaces.

The Effect of Force on Friction

If the force pushing surfaces together increases, the hills and valleys of the surfaces come into closer contact. This close contact increases the friction between the surfaces. Objects that weigh less exert less downward force than objects that weigh more do, as **Figure 2** shows. But the amount of surface touching another surface does not affect the amount of friction.

8.2.a Students know a force has both direction and magnitude.
8.2.c Students know when the forces on an object are balanced, the motion of the object does not change.
8.2.d Students know how to identify separately the two or more forces that are acting on a single static object, including gravity, elastic forces due to tension or compression in matter, and friction.
8.2.e Students know that when the forces on an object are unbalanced, the object will change its velocity (that is, it will speed up, slow down, or change direction).

Figure 1 *When the hills and valleys of one surface stick to the hills and valleys of another surface, friction is created.*

Figure 2 Force and Friction

a The friction between the heavier book and the table is greater than the friction between the lighter book and the table. A harder push is needed to move the heavier book.

b Turning a book on its edge does not change the amount of friction between the table and the book.

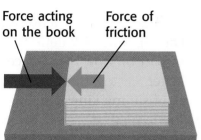

Force acting on the book — Force of friction

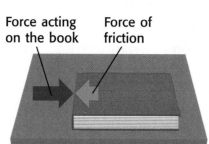

Force acting on the book — Force of friction

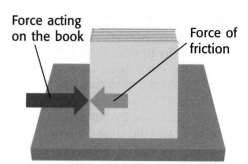

Force acting on the book — Force of friction

The Effect of Material on Friction

The material that makes up a surface affects the magnitude of friction. For example, friction is usually greater between materials that have rough surfaces than it is between materials that have smooth surfaces. A table-tennis ball rolling on carpet slows down and stops because of friction between the ball and the carpet. The amount of friction is large because the carpet has a rough surface. But a table-tennis ball rolling on a wood floor rolls for a long time before stopping. The ball keeps rolling because the wood floor has a smooth surface. So, the amount of friction between the ball and the floor is small.

Standards Check Why does a ball rolling on a carpet slow down and stop? 8.2.e

Quick Lab

Feeling Friction

1. Place a **block of wood with a hook** on a **table.** Attach a **spring scale** to the hook.

2. Gently pull the spring scale horizontally, and record the amount of force needed to keep the block moving at a constant speed. This amount is equal to the amount of friction.

3. Change the surface of the table by spreading a **piece of fabric** on the table. Repeat step 2.

4. Change the surface of the table again by using a **different material.** Repeat step 2.

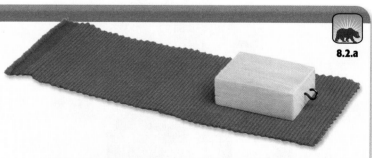

8.2.a

5. What factor caused the amount of friction to differ in each trial?

6. In what direction did the force of friction act? How do you know?

 20 min

Types of Friction

There are two types of friction. The friction observed when you slide books across a tabletop is *kinetic friction*. The other type of friction is *static friction*. You observe static friction when you push on a piece of furniture that you cannot move.

Kinetic Friction

The word *kinetic* means "moving." So, kinetic friction is friction between moving surfaces. The amount of kinetic friction between two surfaces depends in part on how the surfaces move. Surfaces can slide past each other. Or a surface can roll over another surface. Often, the force of sliding kinetic friction is greater than the force of rolling kinetic friction. Thus, things on wheels are often easier to move than things that must be slid along the floor, as **Figure 3** shows.

Kinetic friction is very useful in everyday life. You use sliding kinetic friction when you apply the brakes on a bicycle and when you write with a pencil. Rolling kinetic friction is an important part of almost all means of transportation. Anything that has wheels—bicycles, in-line skates, cars, trains, and planes—uses rolling kinetic friction.

Kinetic friction is often an unbalanced force acting on moving objects. Thus, kinetic friction often changes the velocity of a moving object by slowing down the object.

SCHOOL to HOME

Comparing Friction

Ask an adult at home to sit on the floor. Try to push the adult across the room. Next, ask the adult to sit on a chair that has wheels and to keep his or her feet off the floor. Try pushing the adult and the chair across the room. If you do not have a chair that has wheels, try pushing the adult on different kinds of flooring. In your **Science Journal,** explain why there was a difference between the two trials.

Figure 3   Comparing Kinetic Friction

ⓐ Moving a heavy piece of furniture in your room can be difficult because **the force of sliding kinetic friction is large.**

ⓑ Moving a heavy piece of furniture is easier if you put it on wheels. **The force of rolling kinetic friction is smaller** and easier to overcome.

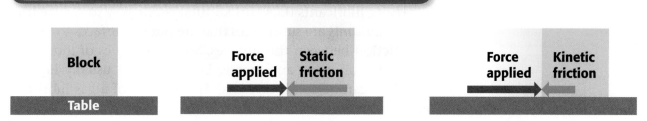

Figure 4 Static Friction

Block

Table

Force applied | **Static friction**

Force applied | **Kinetic friction**

ⓐ There is no friction between the block and the table when no force is applied to the block.

ⓑ If a small force (purple arrow) is applied to the block, the block does not move. The force of static friction (green arrow) balances the force applied.

ⓒ When the force applied to the block is greater than the force of static friction, the block starts moving. When the block starts moving, kinetic friction (green arrow) replaces all of the static friction and opposes the force applied.

Static Friction

Often, a force is applied to an object but does not cause the object to move. The object does not move because the force of static friction is balancing the force applied. Static friction can be overcome by applying a large enough force. As soon as an object starts moving, static friction has gone and has been replaced by kinetic friction. Look at **Figure 4** to understand when static friction affects an object.

The middle image in **Figure 4** shows that the force of static friction is equal in magnitude but opposite in direction to the force applied. So, the forces on the object shown are balanced, and the motion of the object does not change. In fact, some static objects do not move because the force of static friction balances the other forces acting on the object. For example, a ladder leaning against a wall does not move because of static friction between the ladder and the wall and between the ladder and the ground.

Standards Check Suppose that you push on a heavy desk, but it does not move. What force opposes your push? How do you know that the opposing force balances the force that you exert?  **8.2.c, 8.2.d**

Friction: Harmful and Helpful

Friction is both harmful and helpful to you and to the world around you. Friction can cause holes in your socks. Friction by wind and water can cause erosion. On the other hand, friction between your pencil and your paper is needed for the pencil to leave a mark. Without friction, you would slip and fall when you tried to walk. Because friction can be both harmful and helpful, sometimes it should be decreased and sometimes it should be increased.

INTERNET ACTIVITY

Biographies of Physical Scientists

Who made contributions to the understanding of forces? Write a biography of a scientist who studied forces. Go to **go.hrw.com,** and type in the keyword HY7MOTW.

Ways to Reduce Friction

Using lubricants (LOO bri kuhnts) is one way to reduce friction. *Lubricants* are substances that are put on surfaces to reduce the friction between the surfaces. Some examples of lubricants are motor oil, wax, and grease. Lubricants are usually liquids, but they can be solids or gases. An example of a gas lubricant is the air that comes out of the tiny holes on an air-hockey table. **Figure 5** shows one use of a lubricant.

Friction can also be reduced by switching from sliding kinetic friction to rolling kinetic friction. Ball bearings placed between the wheels and axles of in-line skates and bicycles make the wheels turn more easily by reducing friction.

Another way to reduce the magnitude of friction is to smooth surfaces that rub against each other. For example, rough wood on a park bench can snag your clothes or scratch your skin because there is a large amount of friction between you and the bench. Rubbing the bench with sandpaper makes the bench smoother. As a result, the friction between you and the bench is less. So, the bench will no longer snag your clothes or scratch you.

Standards Check How can the magnitude of friction be reduced?
🐻 8.2.a

Figure 5 *When you work on a bicycle, watch out for the chain! You may get dirty from the grease or oil that keeps the chain moving freely. Without this lubricant, friction between the sections of the chain makes riding difficult.*

Ways to Increase Friction

One way to increase friction is to make surfaces rougher. For example, sand spread on icy roads keeps cars from sliding. Baseball players often wear textured batting gloves to increase the friction between their hands and the bat. The increased friction helps stop the bat from flying out of their hands.

Another way to increase friction is to increase the force pushing surfaces together. Suppose that you are sanding a piece of wood. You can sand the wood faster by pressing harder on the sandpaper. Pressing harder increases the force pushing the sandpaper and wood together. So, the friction between the sandpaper and wood increases. **Figure 6** shows another example of pushing on something to increase friction.

Figure 6 *No one likes cleaning dirty pans. To get this job done quickly, press down with the scrubber to increase friction.*

SECTION Review

8.2.a, 8.2.c, 8.2.d, 8.2.e

Summary

- Friction is a force that acts in a direction opposite to the direction of motion.
- Factors that affect the magnitude of friction include the force pushing the surfaces together and the materials that make up the surfaces.
- Kinetic friction is a force that, when unbalanced, can change the velocity of a moving object.
- Static friction can balance other forces and can prevent changes in motion.
- Friction can be helpful or harmful.

Using Vocabulary

1. Write an original definition for *friction*.

Understanding Concepts

2. **Applying** Kinetic friction acts on a baseball player sliding into first base. Will the player's velocity change? Explain your answer in terms of unbalanced forces.

3. **Listing** Name three common lubricants.

4. **Summarizing** Describe two factors that affect the magnitude of friction between two surfaces that are touching.

5. **Identifying** List the two types of friction, and give an example of each.

6. **Justifying** How do you know that forces are balanced when static friction acts on an object?

7. **Concluding** Friction opposes motion. Describe how the direction of the force of kinetic friction is related to the direction of an object's motion.

Critical Thinking

8. **Applying Concepts** Name two ways that friction is harmful and two ways that friction is helpful when you are riding a bicycle.

9. **Making Inferences** Describe a situation in which static friction is useful.

INTERPRETING GRAPHICS Use the image below to answer the next question.

10. **Applying Concepts** Identify the forces acting on the cars, and explain why the cars do not slide down the hill.

Skills Practice Lab

Detecting Acceleration

Have you ever noticed that you can "feel" acceleration? In a car or in an elevator, you may notice changes in speed or direction—even with your eyes closed! You are able to sense these changes because of tiny hair cells in your ears. These cells detect the movement of fluid in your inner ear. The fluid accelerates when you do, and the hair cells send a message about the acceleration to your brain. This message allows you to sense the acceleration. In this activity, you will build a device that detects acceleration. This device is called an *accelerometer* (ak sel uhr AHM uht uhr).

Procedure

1. Cut a piece of string that reaches three-quarters of the way into the container.

2. Use a pushpin to attach one end of the string to the cork or plastic-foam ball.

3. Use modeling clay to attach the other end of the string to the center of the inside of the container lid. The cork or ball should hang no farther than three-quarters of the way into the container.

4. Fill the container with water.

5. Return the lid to the container, and tightly close the lid. The string and cork should be inside the container.

6. Turn the container upside down. The cork should float about three-quarters of the way up inside the container, as shown at left. You are now ready to detect acceleration by using your accelerometer and completing the following steps.

7. Put the accelerometer on a tabletop. The container lid should touch the tabletop. Notice that the cork floats straight up in the water.

8. Now, gently push the accelerometer across the table at a constant speed. Notice that the cork quickly moves in the direction you are pushing and then swings backward. If you did not see this motion, repeat this step until you are sure that you can see the first movement of the cork.

OBJECTIVES

Build an accelerometer.

Explain how an accelerometer shows changes in speed and direction.

MATERIALS

- container, 1 L, with watertight lid
- cork or plastic-foam ball, small
- modeling clay
- pushpin
- scissors
- string
- water

SAFETY

8.1.e Students know changes in velocity may be due to changes in speed, direction, or both.

9. After you are familiar with how to use your accelerometer, try the following changes in motion. For each change, record your observations of the cork's first motion.

  a. As you move the accelerometer across the table, gradually increase its speed.

  b. As you move the accelerometer across the table, gradually decrease its speed.

  c. While moving the accelerometer across the table, change the direction in which you are pushing.

  d. Make any other changes in motion that you can think of. You should make only one change to the motion for each trial.

Analyze the Results

10. **Analyzing Results** When you move the bottle at a constant speed, why does the cork quickly swing backward after it moves in the direction of acceleration?

11. **Explaining Events** The cork moves forward (in the direction you were moving the bottle) when you speed up but moves backward when you slow down. Explain why the cork moves this way. (Hint: Think about the direction of acceleration.)

Draw Conclusions

12. **Making Predictions** Imagine you are holding some helium balloons in a car at a stoplight. Use what you observed with your accelerometer to predict what will happen to the balloons when the car begins moving.

Big Idea Question

13. **Drawing Conclusions** Most cars have a speedometer, a device that shows the speed of the car. How can a speedometer function like an accelerometer? What change in velocity cannot be detected by a speedometer? How can you use a speedometer to tell when unbalanced forces act on a car?

357

Science Skills Activity

Investigation and Experimentation

8.9.e Construct appropriate graphs from data and develop quantitative statements about the relationships between variables.

Constructing and Interpreting Graphs

▶ Tutorial

1 Draw the axes for your graph on a **sheet of graph paper.** The independent variable is often graphed on the x-axis. The dependent variable is often graphed on the y-axis.

2 Determine the scale for the axes, and write the numbers of the scale on the axes. Label the axes with appropriate units.

3 Use the data to place data points at the appropriate coordinates on the graph.

4 Use a **ruler** or a **straight edge** to draw lines connecting the data points. Write the title of your graph at the top of the graph.

5 Use the graph to identify patterns in the data. Calculating the slope can help you develop quantitative statements about the relationship between variables. Changes in the slope show changes in the relationship between variables.

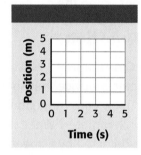

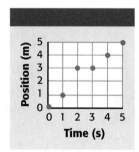

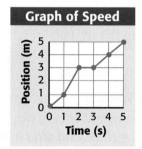

▶ You Try It!

Procedure

1 Use the data in the table at right to construct a graph. The data give the position of a person from a reference point. Use the graph to make observations about the person's motion.

Analysis

2 **Identifying** How many times did the person's speed change? Explain your answer.

3 **Comparing** Develop a quantitative statement about the relationship between time and distance covered during the first 30 s. (Hint: Find the slope of the graph.)

4 **Concluding** During which time period was the person jogging? During which time period was the person standing still? Explain your answers.

Position from a Lamppost	
Time (s)	**Position (m)**
0	0
10	10
20	20
30	30
40	60
50	90
60	110
70	130
80	150
90	150
100	150

Chapter Summary

The Big Idea Forces act on objects and can produce motion.

Section

Vocabulary

1 Measuring Motion

Key Concept Motion can be measured and described in many ways.

- Properties used to describe the motion of an object include a reference point, direction, speed, velocity, and acceleration.
- Average speed can be calculated by dividing total distance by total time.
- A change in velocity is due to a change in speed, direction, or both.
- Speed and acceleration can be represented on graphs.

The velocity of these cars is their speed and their direction of motion.

motion p. 336
average speed p. 338
velocity p. 340
acceleration p. 341

2 What Is a Force?

Key Concept Forces acting on an object can be combined and may cause changes in motion.

- A force is a push or a pull that acts on an object. Forces have magnitude and direction.
- Net force is the combined effect of two or more forces acting on an object.
- Balanced forces do not cause changes in motion.
- Unbalanced forces cause changes in an object's velocity.

The net force on the rope is the combined effect of the forces exerted by the dogs.

force p. 344
newton p. 344
net force p. 345

3 Friction: A Force That Opposes Motion

Key Concept Friction is a force that can balance other forces to prevent motion. Friction is also a force that, when unbalanced, can change the velocity of an object.

- The magnitude of the force of friction can vary.
- Kinetic friction is a force that, when unbalanced, can change the velocity of a moving object.
- Static friction balances an applied force and can prevent motion.
- Friction can be both harmful and helpful.

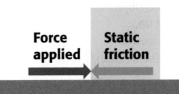

Static friction balances an applied force and prevents motion.

friction p. 350

Chapter Review

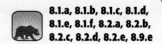

8.1.a, 8.1.b, 8.1.c, 8.1.d,
8.1.e, 8.1.f, 8.2.a, 8.2.b,
8.2.c, 8.2.d, 8.2.e, 8.9.e

Organize

Tri-Fold Review the FoldNote that you created at the beginning of the chapter. Add to or correct the FoldNote based on what you have learned.

Using Vocabulary

1 **Academic Vocabulary** In the sentence "The speed of an object can vary," what does the word *vary* mean?

Complete each of the following sentences by choosing the correct term from the word bank.

friction	acceleration
average speed	velocity
net force	newton

2 ___ opposes motion between surfaces that are touching.

3 The ___ is the unit of force.

4 ___ is determined by combining forces.

5 ___ is the total distance traveled divided by the total time elapsed.

6 ___ may be a change in speed or a change in direction.

Understanding Concepts

Multiple Choice

7 Which of the following changes can happen when the forces on an object are unbalanced?
a. The object speeds up.
b. The object slows down.
c. The object changes direction.
d. All of the above

8 Which of the following is NOT an example of a change in velocity?
a. a person jogging at 3 m/s along a winding path
b. a car stopping at a stop sign
c. a cheetah running 27 m/s east
d. a plane taking off

9 How do you know if the forces on an object are balanced?
a. The object speeds up.
b. The object slows down.
c. The object's motion does not change.
d. The object's direction of motion does not change.

Short Answer

10 **Describing** Describe how to use a reference point and a set of reference directions to define the position of an object.

11 **Justifying** How is it possible to be accelerating and traveling at a constant speed?

12 **Analyzing** Why do you think that arrows of varying lengths are used to represent forces? (Hint: Think about magnitude and direction.)

13 **Summarizing** Describe how to find the cumulative effect of two or more forces acting on an object.

14 **Applying** How can you increase the magnitude of friction between two surfaces? How can you decrease the magnitude of friction?

INTERPRETING GRAPHICS Use the image below to answer the next three questions.

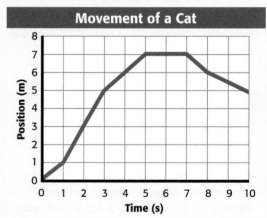

15 **Concluding** During which period of time is the cat standing still?

16 **Analyzing** When is the cat moving with the greatest speed?

17 **Describing** Describe the motion of the cat during the last 3 s.

Writing Skills

18 Creative Writing Write a short story about a group of friends who must work together to overcome friction in three different situations. Be sure to identify the kind of friction involved in each situation.

Critical Thinking

19 Concept Mapping Use the following terms to create a concept map: *speed, velocity, acceleration, force, direction,* and *motion.*

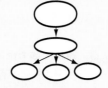

20 Analyzing Ideas Imagine that you walk from your home to a store that is five blocks away. Do you think that your speed will be constant or will vary along the path that you travel? Explain your answer.

21 Identifying Relationships Explain why airplane pilots should know wind velocity and not just wind speed during a flight.

22 Applying Concepts Can balanced forces act on a moving object? Explain your answer, and describe the motion of the object.

23 Analyzing Ideas A rock rolls halfway down a hill and then comes to a stop. What caused the rock to stop moving? Identify two forces acting on the static rock.

INTERPRETING GRAPHICS Use the image below to answer the next question.

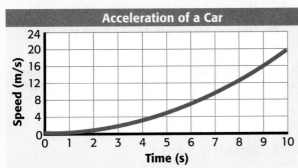

24 Evaluating Data Does the graph show positive acceleration or negative acceleration? Explain your answer

INTERPRETING GRAPHICS Use the diagrams below to answer the next question.

a.
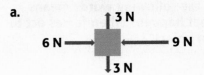

b.

c.
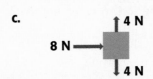

25 Predicting Consequences You know how to find the combined effect of two forces. So, you can also find the combined effect of more than two forces acting on an object. But the process is a little more difficult. Look at the diagrams, and apply what you know about net force to calculate the net force in each diagram. State the cumulative effect of the forces by predicting the direction in which each object will move.

Math Skills

26 Using Equations What is the average speed of a kangaroo that hops 60 m in 5 s?

27 Using Equations Find the distance traveled by a baseball in 1.7 s if the baseball's average speed is 22.4 m/s.

28 Using Equations A car left Sacramento, California, and traveled at an average speed of 95 km/h to Redding, California. The distance between the two cities is 260 km. How many hours was the car traveling?

Challenge

29 Applying Concepts Describe the motion of a bouncing ball. Are unbalanced forces acting on the ball? Explain your answer.

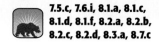
REVIEWING ACADEMIC VOCABULARY

1 Which of the following words means "stress that happens when forces act to stretch an object"?

- **A** drive
- **B** tension
- **C** torque
- **D** energy

2 Which of the following words is the closest in meaning to the word *involve*?

- **A** include
- **B** ascertain
- **C** believe
- **D** accompany

3 In the sentence "By interpreting the data in the graph, the scientist learned that the speed of the car had been constant," what does the word *interpreting* mean?

- **A** figuring out the meaning of
- **B** interacting with
- **C** disposing of
- **D** identifying the parts of

4 Which of the following sets of words best completes the following sentence: "Position ___ relation to a reference point and a set of reference directions."

- **A** defines with
- **B** was defined of
- **C** is defined in
- **D** definition by

5 Which of the following is the noun form of the verb *specify*?

- **A** specific
- **B** specifically
- **C** specified
- **D** specification

REVIEWING CONCEPTS

6 The rate at which an object moves is its speed. If a horse walked 50 m in 68 s, cantered 150 m in 35 s, and galloped 300 m in 22 s, what would its average speed be?

- **A** 0.25 m/s
- **B** 4 m/s
- **C** 6.22 m/s
- **D** 40 m/s

7 What is the difference between speed and velocity?

- **A** Velocity is expressed in m/s. Speed is expressed in m/s^2.
- **B** Speed involves a constant rate of acceleration, and velocity does not.
- **C** Speed is measured by time and distance, but velocity also includes direction.
- **D** Velocity involves moving in a direction in a straight line, and speed does not.

8 A teenager pulls a rope to the left with a force of 12 N. A child pulls on the other end of the rope to the right with a force of 7 N. The child's friend adds a force of 8 N, also pulling to the right. What will happen?

- **A** The net force will be 3 N to the right.
- **B** The net force will be 15 N to the left.
- **C** The net force will be 12 N to the right.
- **D** The net force will be 27 N to the left.

9 Which of the following are forces that act on a person leaning against a pole at a bus stop?

- **A** gravity and newtons
- **B** tension and weight
- **C** tension and kinetic friction
- **D** gravity and static friction

A Graph Showing Speed

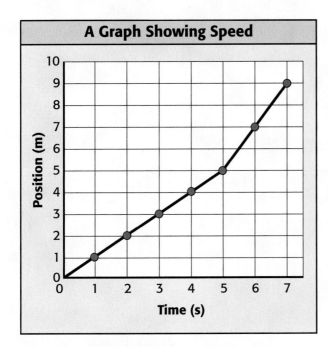

10 The graph above shows a person walking. Which of the following sentences best describes the walker's speed?

A She travels an average of 10 m/s.

B She travels an average of 4 m/s.

C Her rate of speed decreases after 5 s.

D Her rate of speed increases after 5 s.

11 All forces are measured by their direction and their size. Another term for the size of a force is

A circumference.

B magnitude.

C cumulative force.

D velocity.

12 What is matter?

A solid things that you can see and touch

B anything contained in a gravitational field

C anything that has mass and volume

D things with a definite shape and volume

13 Which of the following holds the electrons of an atom around the atom's nucleus?

A strong force

B electromagnetic force

C weak force

D gravitational force

14 What is the function of tendons in the human body?

A They coordinate muscle groups.

B They provide support for the body.

C They connect two muscles.

D They attach muscle to bone.

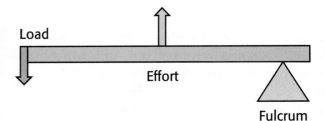

15 The diagram above shows a class-3 lever. Which of the following is an example of a class-3 lever?

A a pencil

B a wheelbarrow

C a see saw

D a stapler

Science in Action

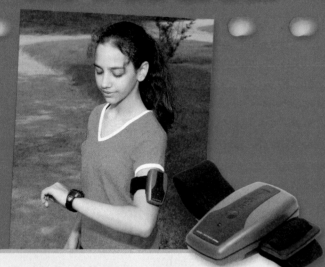

Science, Technology, and Society

GPS Watch System

Some athletes are concerned about knowing their speed during training. To calculate speed, they need to know distance and time. Using a watch to measure time is easy. But determining distance is more difficult. However, a GPS watch system is now available to help with this problem. *GPS* stands for *global positioning system*. A GPS unit, which is worn on an athlete's upper arm, monitors the athlete's position by using signals from satellites. As the athlete moves, the GPS unit calculates the distance traveled. The GPS unit sends a signal to the watch, which keeps the athlete's time. Then, the watch displays the athlete's speed.

Weird Science

Jai Alai: The World's Fastest Sport

Imagine catching a ball that is traveling at a speed of more than 240 km/h (150 mi/h)! If you ever play the sport of jai alai, you may have to catch this ball. Some people think that jai alai is the world's fastest sport. Because the jai alai ball, called a *pelota*, can move so fast, players catch and throw it with a curved device called a *cesta*. The cesta protects a player's hand and allows the player to throw the pelota with a great force.

Math ACTIVITY

Suppose an athlete wishes to finish a 5 K race in under 25 min. The distance of a 5 K is 5 km. (Remember that 1 km = 1,000 m.) If the athlete runs the race at a constant speed of 3.4 m/s, will she meet her goal?

Language Arts ACTIVITY

Do research to find out how the game of jai alai is played. Then, write a short instruction manual that explains the rules of the game to someone who does not know how to play the game.

Duane Flatmo

Kinetic Sculptor So, you think you have seen it all. But have you seen the 350 kg jumble of colorful eyes, ears, teeth, and bicycle parts that moves across beaches? Kinetic sculptor Duane Flatmo created this jumble of body and bicycle parts, which he calls *Extreme Makeover*. It is an entry in the annual Arcata to Ferndale Kinetic Sculpture Race.

Kinetic sculpture is art that moves. The Arcata to Ferndale Race is one of kinetic art's ultimate challenges. The race covers more than 60 km of sand, mud, road, river, and sea. Flatmo has been racing his artwork for more than 20 years, and he knows how to succeed.

Flatmo is one of the region's most distinctive artists. His sculptures are always a highlight of the race. But building a kinetic sculpture is a big project. "I have a love-hate thing with these kinetic sculptures. It's daunting," says Flatmo. To build such a sculpture, you need to mix precision, engineering, and imagination. And you definitely must have a sense of fun. Kinetic sculptures may be a lot of work. But Flatmo always looks forward to building the next one. "You start thinking about how you can outdo what you did the year before," he says.

Social Studies ACTIVITY

A mobile is a kinetic sculpture in which objects hang in a balanced arrangement. Some artists build mobiles that contain origami pieces. Origami is the Japanese art of folding paper into shapes. Learn how to make shapes using origami and then build a mobile using the shapes that you made.

Internet Resources

- To learn more about careers in science, visit www.scilinks.org and enter the SciLinks code HY70225.

- To learn more about these Science in Action topics, visit go.hrw.com and type in the keyword HY7MOTF.

- Check out articles related to this chapter by visiting go.hrw.com. Just type in the keyword HY7MOTC.

Improving Comprehension

Graphic Organizers are important visual tools that can help you organize information and improve your reading comprehension. The Graphic Organizer below is called *combination notes*. Instructions for creating other types of Graphic Organizers are located in the **Study Skills** section of the Appendix.

How to Make Combination Notes

1 Draw a table like the one shown below. Draw the columns to be as long as you want them to be.

2 Write the topic of your notes in the section at the top of the table.

3 In the left column, write important phrases or sentences about the topic. In the right column, draw diagrams or pictures that illustrate the information in the left column.

When to Use Combination Notes

Combination notes let you express scientific information in words and pictures at the same time. Use combination notes to express information that a picture could help explain. The picture could be a diagram, a sketch, or another useful visual representation of the written information in your notes.

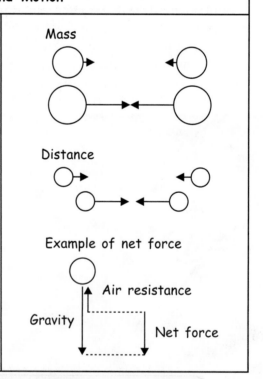

Forces and Motion

Gravity

Mass and **distance** affect the magnitude of gravitational force.

Gravitational force tends to be small when
- masses are small
- distances are large

Gravitational force tends to be large when
- masses are large
- distances are small

Force and Motion
- Objects move according to the net force exerted on them.
- Net force is the sum of all forces acting on an object.
- Newton's laws of motion describe how forces and motion relate.

Mass

Distance

Example of net force
Air resistance
Gravity
Net force

You Try It!

This Reading Strategy can also be used within the chapter that you are about to read. Practice making your own *combination notes* as directed in the Reading Strategies for Section **2** and Section **3**. Record your work in your **Science Journal.**

Unpacking the Standards

The information below "unpacks" the standards by breaking them down into basic parts. The higher-level, academic vocabulary is highlighted and defined to help you understand the language of the standards. "What It Means" restates the standards as simply as possible.

California Standard	Academic Vocabulary	What It Means
8.2.a Students know a force has both direction and magnitude.		A force acts in a particular direction and has a certain size.
8.2.b Students know when an object is subject to two or more forces at once, the result is the cumulative effect of all the forces.		When two or more forces act on an object, the effect on the object is due to the combination of the forces.
8.2.c Students know when the forces on an object are balanced, the motion of the object does not change.		When the forces acting on an object cancel each other out, the object's speed and direction of motion stay the same.
8.2.d Students know how to **identify** separately the two or more forces that are acting on a single static object, including gravity, elastic forces due to **tension** or compression in matter, and friction.	**identify** (ie DEN tuh FIE) to point out or pick out **tension** (TEN shuhn) stress that happens when forces act to stretch an object	You must be able to say what forces are acting on an object that is sitting still. Those forces include the force of attraction between objects that is due to their masses, the forces associated with stretching or squeezing an object, and the force that opposes motion between surfaces that are in contact.
8.2.e Students know that when the forces on an object are unbalanced, the object will change its velocity (that is, it will speed up, slow down, or change direction).		When the forces acting on an object do not cancel each other out, the object will speed up, slow down, or change direction.
8.2.f Students know the greater the mass of an object, the more force is needed to **achieve** the same rate of change in motion.	**achieve** (uh CHEEV) to do; to carry out	Two objects that have different masses can have the same change in motion in the same amount of time if a larger force acts on the more massive object.

The following list identifies other standards that are covered in this chapter and indicates where you can go to see them unpacked: **8.2.g** (Chapter 15).

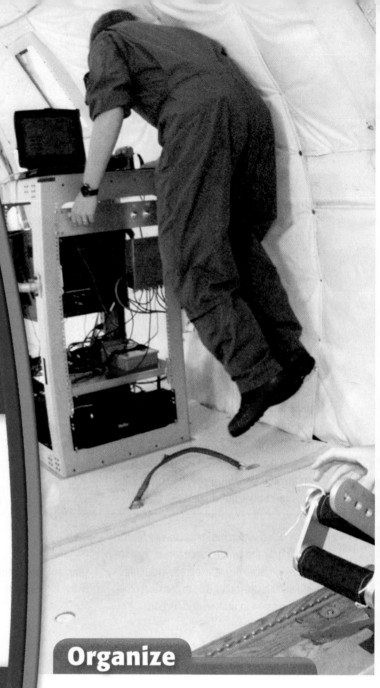

13

Forces and Motion

The Big Idea

Unbalanced forces cause changes in motion that can be predicted and described.

California Standards

Focus on Physical Sciences
8.2 Unbalanced forces cause changes in velocity. (Sections 1, 2, and 3)

Investigation and Experimentation
8.9 Scientific progress is made by asking meaningful questions and conducting careful investigations. (Science Skills Activity)

Math
7.4.2 Algebra and Functions

English–Language Arts
8.2.2 Reading
8.2.1 Writing

About the Photo

To prepare for space flight, astronauts trained in a modified KC-135 cargo airplane. The airplane first flew upward at a steep angle and then flew downward at a steep angle. This motion caused the feeling of reduced gravity inside. Under these conditions, the astronauts in the plane could float and could practice carrying out tasks that they would need to perform when they were in orbit. Because the floating made people queasy, the KC-135 was nicknamed the "Vomit Comet."

Organize

Pyramid

Before you read this chapter, create the FoldNote entitled "Pyramid." Label each side of the pyramid with the title of one of the sections in the chapter. As you read the chapter, add details from each section on the appropriate side of the pyramid.

Instructions for creating FoldNotes are located in the Study Skills section on p. 517 of the Appendix.

Explore Activity

20 min

8.2.e

Gravity and Falling

Gravity is an important force. Gravity keeps Earth in orbit around the sun and keeps objects on Earth from floating away into space. In this activity, you will observe the effect of gravity on a falling object.

Procedure

1. Place a **wide plastic tub** on the floor. Use a **pencil** to punch a small hole in the side of a **paper cup,** near the bottom.

2. Hold your finger over the hole, and fill the cup with **water.** Hold the cup waist high above the tub.

3. Uncover the hole. Record your observations as Trial 1.

4. Predict what will happen to the water if you drop the cup at the same time you uncover the hole.

5. Cover the hole, and refill the cup with water.

6. Uncover the hole, and drop the cup at the same time. Record your observations as Trial 2.

Analysis

7. What differences did you observe in the behavior of the water during the two trials?

8. In Trial 2, how fast did the cup fall compared with how fast the water fell?

9. The cup and water sped up as they fell because an unbalanced force acted on them. What force caused this change in velocity?

10. How did the results of Trial 2 compare with your prediction?

Gravity: A Force of Attraction

Key Concept   Gravity is a force of attraction between objects that is due to their masses.

What You Will Learn

- Gravity affects all matter, including the parts of the solar system.
- Because gravity is a force, it can change the velocity of objects.
- The law of universal gravitation explains how distance, mass, and gravitational force are related.
- The weight of an object depends on gravity, but the mass of the object does not.

Why It Matters

Gravity keeps you on Earth and holds the solar system together.

Vocabulary

- gravity
- weight
- mass

READING STRATEGY

Summarizing   Read this section silently. In pairs, take turns summarizing the material. Stop to discuss ideas and words that seem confusing.

gravity (GRAV i tee) a force of attraction between objects that is due to their masses

▶ Have you ever seen a video of astronauts on the moon? The astronauts, such as the one in **Figure 1,** bounce around like beach balls even though they wear big, bulky spacesuits. Why is leaping on the moon easier than leaping on Earth? The reason is that there is less force pulling the astronauts to the ground when they leap on the moon than when they leap on Earth. **Gravity** is a force of attraction between objects that is due to their masses. The force of gravity can change the motion of an object by changing the object's velocity.

The Effects of Gravity on Matter

All matter has mass. Gravity is a result of mass. Therefore, all matter is affected by gravity. That is, all objects experience an attraction toward all other objects. This gravitational force pulls objects toward each other. For example, gravity between the objects of the solar system holds the solar system together.

Gravity affects smaller objects, too. Right now, because of gravity, you are being pulled toward this book and every other object around you. These objects are also being pulled toward you and toward each other. So, why don't you notice objects moving toward each other? The reason is that the mass of most objects is too small to cause a force large enough to notice. However, you know one object that is massive enough to cause a noticeable attraction—Earth.

Figure 1   *Because the moon has less gravity than Earth does, walking on the moon's surface was a very bouncy experience for the Apollo astronauts.*

Earth's Gravitational Force

Compared with all objects around you, Earth has a huge mass. The gravitational attraction of Earth is thus an important force that you experience all the time. Earth's gravitational force pulls everything toward the center of Earth. Because of this force, the books, tables, and chairs in the room stay in place, and dropped objects fall to Earth rather than move together or toward you. You must apply forces to overcome Earth's gravitational force any time that you lift objects or even parts of your body.

Newton and the Study of Gravity

For thousands of years, people asked two very puzzling questions: Why do objects fall toward Earth, and what keeps the planets moving in the sky? The two questions were treated separately. But in 1665, Sir Isaac Newton, a British scientist, realized that they were two parts of the same question.

The Core of an Idea

The legend is that Newton made the connection between the two questions when he watched a falling apple, as shown in **Figure 2.** He knew that unbalanced forces are needed to change the motion of objects by changing the velocity of the objects. He concluded that an unbalanced force on the apple made the apple fall. And he reasoned that an unbalanced force on the moon kept the moon moving circularly around Earth. Newton said that these two forces are actually the same force—a force that he called *gravity*.

Standards Check How did Newton know that an unbalanced force was acting on the apple and on the moon? **8.2.e**

The Birth of a Law

Newton summarized his ideas about gravity in a law now known as the *law of universal gravitation*. This law describes the relationships between gravitational force, mass, and distance. The law is called *universal* because it is thought to apply to all objects in the universe.

8.2.a Students know a force has both direction and magnitude.
8.2.c Students know when the forces on an object are balanced, the motion of the object does not change.
8.2.d Students know how to identify separately the two or more forces that are acting on a single static object, including gravity, elastic forces due to tension or compression in matter, and friction.
8.2.e Students know that when the forces on an object are unbalanced, the object will change its velocity (that is, it will speed up, slow down, or change direction).
8.2.g Students know the role of gravity in forming and maintaining the shapes of planets, stars, and the solar system.

Figure 2 *Newton realized that the same unbalanced force affected the motions of the apple and the moon.*

The Law of Universal Gravitation

The law of universal gravitation states that all objects in the universe attract each other through gravitational force. The magnitude of the force depends on the masses of the objects and the distance between the objects. Understanding the law is easier if you consider it in two parts.

Part 1: Gravitational Force and Mass

The gravitational force between objects depends on the product of the masses of the objects. So, the gravity between objects increases as the masses of the objects increase, as shown in **Figure 3.** For example, an elephant has a larger mass than a cat does. Thus, gravitational force between an elephant and Earth is greater than the gravitational force between a cat and Earth. So, a cat is much easier to pick up than an elephant! There is also gravity between the cat and the elephant. But that force seems very small because the cat's mass and the elephant's mass are so much smaller than Earth's mass.

This part of the law of universal gravitation also explains why the astronauts on the moon bounce so easily. The moon has less mass than Earth does. Therefore, the moon's gravitational force is less than Earth's. The astronauts bounced around on the moon because they were not being pulled down with as much force as they would have been on Earth.

Standards Check How does mass affect the magnitude of gravitational force? 🐘 **8.2.a**

Figure 3 **How Mass Affects Gravitational Force**

The arrows indicate the gravitational force between two objects. The length of the arrows indicates the magnitude of the force.

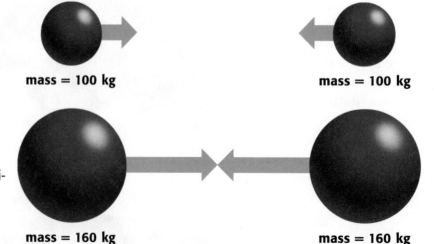

ⓐ Gravitational force is small between objects that have small masses.

mass = 100 kg   mass = 100 kg

ⓑ If the mass of one or both objects increases, the gravitational force pulling them together increases.

mass = 160 kg   mass = 160 kg

Part 2: Gravitational Force and Distance

The force of gravity depends on the distance between two objects. If you jump up, you are pulled back down by Earth's gravitational force. But the sun is more than 300,000 times more massive than Earth. Why doesn't the sun's gravitational force affect you more than Earth's does when you jump up? The reason is that the sun is about 150 million kilometers (93 million miles) away.

The force of gravity changes as distance changes, as shown in **Figure 4.** As the distance between two objects gets larger, the force of gravity gets much smaller. For example, if the distance between two things is doubled, the force of gravity becomes one-fourth as large. **Figure 5** shows how the force of gravity gets smaller as the distance between objects gets larger.

The sun is very far away from you. So, the sun's gravitational force on your body is very small. However, the gravitational force between the sun and the planets is large because they all have such large masses. The large gravitational force of the sun affects the movement of all the planets. This force helps them stay in orbit around the sun. So, the force of gravity has an important role in maintaining the shape of the solar system.

Standards Check Why do the planets in the solar system stay in orbit around the sun? 8.2.g

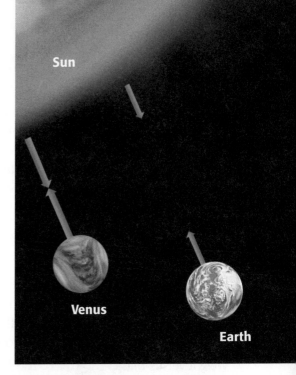

Figure 4 *Venus and Earth have approximately the same mass. But because Venus is closer to the sun, the gravitational force between Venus and the sun is greater than the gravitational force between Earth and the sun.*

Figure 5 How Distance Affects Gravitational Force

The length of the arrows indicates the magnitude of the gravitational force between two objects.

ⓐ Gravitational force is large when the distance between two objects is small.

ⓑ If the distance between two objects increases, the gravitational force pulling them together decreases rapidly.

Weight and Gravitational Force

Gravity is a force of attraction between objects. **Weight** is a measure of the gravitational force on an object. Therefore, weight is expressed in the SI unit of force, the newton (N). When you see or hear the word *weight,* it usually refers to Earth's gravitational force on something. But weight can also be a measure of the gravitational force exerted on things by other planets or even by the moon.

The Differences Between Weight and Mass

Weight is related to mass, but they are not the same. Weight changes when gravitational force changes. **Mass** is a measure of the amount of matter in an object. Mass is usually expressed in kilograms (kg) or grams (g). An object's mass does not change when gravitational force changes. Imagine that an object is moved to a place where it would experience a greater gravitational force than on Earth—such as the planet Jupiter. The object's weight will increase, but its mass will remain the same.

Figure 6 shows the weight and mass of an astronaut on Earth and on the moon. The moon's gravitational force is about one-sixth of Earth's gravitational force. Gravitational force is about the same everywhere on Earth. Because the weight of an object is constant as long as the object remains on Earth, we often get confused about the difference between weight and mass. Be sure you understand the difference!

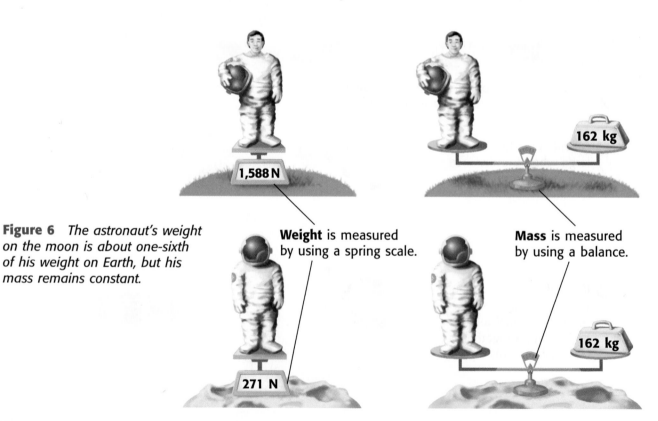

Figure 6 *The astronaut's weight on the moon is about one-sixth of his weight on Earth, but his mass remains constant.*

Weight is measured by using a spring scale.

Mass is measured by using a balance.

1,588 N

271 N

162 kg

162 kg

Gravity and Static Objects

Like all forces, gravity can cause objects to move. But gravity also acts on nonmoving, or *static,* objects. Earth's gravity pulls static objects downward. But they do not move downward, because gravity is balanced by an upward force. For example, imagine a framed picture hanging from a nail. The gravity on the picture is balanced by elastic forces due to tension in the nail. What if you place the same picture on a shelf? Then, the gravity on the picture is balanced by elastic forces due to compression in the shelf. In both cases, the picture is static.

Standards Check Why won't a book resting on a table fall to the ground? What forces are acting on the book? 8.2.c, 8.2.d

weight (WAYT) a measure of the gravitational force exerted on an object; its value can change with the location of the object in the universe

mass (MAS) a measure of the amount of matter in an object

SECTION Review

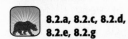 8.2.a, 8.2.c, 8.2.d, 8.2.e, 8.2.g

Summary

- Gravity is a force of attraction between objects that is due to their masses. Gravity can be an unbalanced force that causes changes in velocity.
- Gravity holds the solar system together.
- The law of universal gravitation states that all objects attract each other through gravitational force and that the magnitude of this force depends on the objects' masses and the distance between them.
- Mass is the amount of matter in an object. Weight is a measure of the gravitational force on an object.
- Gravity is often balanced by elastic forces due to tension or compression.

Understanding Concepts

1. **Applying** How does gravity maintain the shape of the solar system?

2. **Identifying** What affects the magnitude of gravitational force?

3. **Describing** In which directions do the gravitational forces act between you and Earth?

4. **Concluding** Describe a situation in which gravity causes a change in velocity. Why does the change in velocity happen?

5. **Summarizing** Explain why Newton knew that an unbalanced force was acting on the moon and on a falling apple.

Critical Thinking

6. **Identifying Relationships** Gravity pulls down on a picture that is hanging from a nail. Why doesn't the motion of the picture change?

7. **Applying Concepts** A cat toy is hanging by a string tied to a doorknob. Identify two separate forces that are acting on the toy.

8. **Making Comparisons** Explain why your weight but not your mass would change if you landed on Mars.

INTERPRETING GRAPHICS Use the figure below to answer the next question.

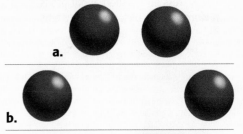

a.

b.

c.

9. **Applying Concepts** Rank the pairs of masses in order of increasing magnitude of gravitational force between the masses.

Internet Resources

For a variety of links related to this chapter, go to www.scilinks.org
Topic: Matter and Gravity
SciLinks code: HY70922

Gravity and Motion

Key Concept Gravity can be an unbalanced force that causes predictable changes in motion.

What You Will Learn

- The acceleration due to gravity is the same for all objects near Earth's surface.
- Air resistance is a force that opposes the motion of objects through air.
- Projectile motion has two components—horizontal motion and vertical motion.

Why It Matters

Gravity affects the motion of everything that you drop or throw.

Vocabulary

- terminal velocity
- free fall
- projectile motion

READING STRATEGY

Graphic Organizer In your **Science Journal,** create Combination Notes that express information about orbits in words and in pictures or diagrams.

Suppose that you dropped a baseball and a marble at the same time. Which do you think would land on the ground first?

In ancient Greece around 400 BCE, a philosopher named Aristotle (AR is TAHT'l) thought that the rate at which an object falls depends on the object's mass. If you asked Aristotle whether the baseball or the marble would land first, he would have said the baseball. But Aristotle never tried dropping objects that have different masses to test his idea about falling objects.

Gravity and Falling Objects

Late in the 16th century, Galileo Galilei (GAL uh LAY oh GAL uh LAY), an Italian scientist, questioned Aristotle's idea about falling objects. Galileo argued that the mass of an object does not affect the time the object takes to fall to the ground, as shown in **Figure 1.** According to one story, Galileo proved his argument by dropping two metal balls of very different masses from the top of the Leaning Tower of Pisa in Italy. The people watching from the ground below were amazed to see the two balls land at the same time. Whether or not this story is true, Galileo's work changed people's understanding of gravity and falling objects.

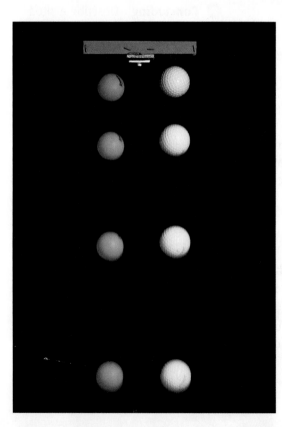

Figure 1 *This stop-action photo shows that a table-tennis ball and a golf ball fall at the same rate even though they have different masses.*

8.2.a Students know a force has both direction and magnitude.
8.2.b Students know when an object is subject to two or more forces at once, the result is the cumulative effect of all the forces.
8.2.e Students know that when the forces on an object are unbalanced, the object will change its velocity (that is, it will speed up, slow down, or change direction).
8.2.f Students know the greater the mass of an object, the more force is needed to achieve the same rate of change in motion.
8.2.g Students know the role of gravity in forming and maintaining the shapes of planets, stars, and the solar system.

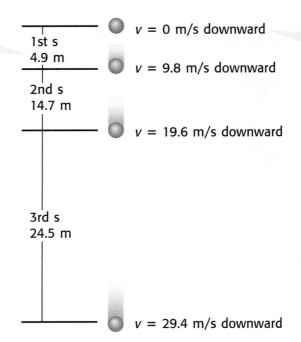

These distances show how far the ball falls in each second. The total distance that the ball falls can be found by adding these numbers.

1st s
4.9 m

2nd s
14.7 m

3rd s
24.5 m

$v = 0$ m/s downward

$v = 9.8$ m/s downward

$v = 19.6$ m/s downward

$v = 29.4$ m/s downward

These numbers show the velocity of the ball after each second.

Figure 2 *A falling object accelerates at a constant rate. The object falls faster and farther each second than it did the second before.*

Gravity and Acceleration

Objects fall to the ground at the same rate because the acceleration due to gravity is the same for all objects near Earth's surface. Why is this true? Acceleration depends on both force and mass. A heavier object experiences a greater gravitational force than a lighter object does. But a heavier object is also harder to accelerate because it has more mass. The extra mass of the heavy object exactly makes up for the additional gravitational force.

Standards Check Why will a baseball and a marble fall at the same rate? 8.2.f

Acceleration and Changes in Velocity

Acceleration is the rate at which velocity changes over time. An object accelerates when the forces on it are unbalanced. Gravity exerts a downward, unbalanced force on falling objects. So, the objects accelerate. Falling objects accelerate toward Earth at a rate of 9.8 meters per second per second. This rate is written as 9.8 m/s². So, for every second that something falls, its downward velocity increases by 9.8 m/s, as shown in **Figure 2.** You can calculate the change in velocity (Δv) of a falling object by using the following equation:

$$\Delta v = g \times t$$

In this equation, g is the acceleration due to gravity. And t is the time the object falls (in seconds). The change in velocity is the difference between the final velocity and the starting velocity. If the object starts at rest, this equation gives you the object's velocity after falling for a certain amount of time.

Calculating Velocity

Use the equation for the change in velocity to solve the following problem. A penny at rest is dropped from the top of a tall stairwell. What is the penny's velocity after it has fallen for 2.5 s?

Figure 3 Effect of Air Resistance on a Falling Object

a The **force of gravity** is pulling down on the apple. If gravity were the only force acting on the apple, the apple would accelerate at a rate of 9.8 m/s².

b The **force of air resistance** is pushing up on the falling apple. This force is subtracted from the force of gravity to yield the net force.

c The **net force** on the falling apple is equal to the force of air resistance subtracted from the force of gravity. Because the net force is not 0 N, the apple accelerates downward. But the apple does not accelerate as fast as it would without air resistance.

Air Resistance and Falling Objects

Try dropping two sheets of paper—one crumpled in a tight ball and the other kept flat. What happened? Does this simple experiment seem to contradict what you just learned about falling objects? The flat paper falls more slowly than the crumpled paper because of air resistance. *Air resistance* is the force that opposes the motion of objects through air.

The magnitude of air resistance acting on an object depends on the size, shape, and speed of the object. Air resistance affects the flat sheet of paper more than the crumpled one. The larger surface area of the flat sheet causes the flat sheet to encounter more air as it falls. Thus there is more air resistance. **Figure 3** shows the effect of air resistance on a falling object.

Standards Check Which two forces combine to determine the net force on a falling object? In which directions do these two forces act? 🐻 **8.2.a, 8.2.b**

Acceleration and Terminal Velocity

As the speed of a falling object increases, air resistance increases. The upward force of air resistance continues to increase until it is equal to the downward force of gravity. At this point, the net force is 0 N, and the object stops accelerating. The object then falls at a constant velocity called the **terminal velocity.**

Terminal velocity can be a good thing. Every year, cars, buildings, and vegetation are severely damaged in hailstorms. The terminal velocity of hailstones is between 5 and 40 m/s, depending on their size. If there were no air resistance, hailstones would hit the ground at velocities near 350 m/s!

terminal velocity (TUHR muh nuhl vuh LAHS uh tee) the constant velocity of a falling object when the force of air resistance is equal in magnitude and opposite in direction to the force of gravity

free fall (FREE FAWL) the motion of a body when only the force of gravity is acting on the body

Free Fall and Air Resistance

Sky divers are often described as being in free fall before they open their parachutes. But this description is not correct. A sky diver is falling through air. As a result, air resistance is always acting on the sky diver.

Something is in **free fall** only if gravity is pulling it down and no other forces are acting on it. Because air resistance is a force, free fall can happen only where there is no air. For example, there is no air in outer space or in a vacuum. The term *vacuum* is used to describe a place in which there is no matter. Vacuum chambers are special containers from which air can be removed to make a vacuum. **Figure 4** shows two objects falling in a vacuum chamber. Because there is no air resistance in a vacuum, the two objects are in free fall.

Standards Check Why can an object falling in a vacuum never reach terminal velocity?  8.2.e

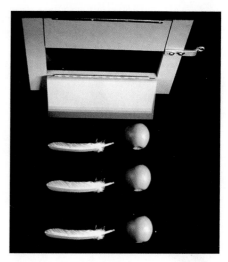

Figure 4 *Air resistance usually causes a feather to fall more slowly than an apple falls. But in a vacuum chamber, a feather and an apple fall with the same acceleration because both are in free fall.*

Quick Lab

Parachutes and Air Resistance

Sky divers use parachutes to increase their air resistance. In this activity, you will explore how air resistance affects falling objects.

8.2.a
8.2.b
8.2.e

▶ Try It!

1. Use **15 cm of string** to tie **four washers** together securely.

2. Choose one person to drop the washers from shoulder height. Observe their motion. Record your observations.

3. As a group, use the materials provided by your teacher to design and build a parachute. These materials may include a **plastic bag**, a **sheet of newspaper, tape**, and **four 30 cm pieces of string**.

4. Have the same person who dropped the washers earlier hold the washers at shoulder height while the other group members hold the parachute open above the washers.

5. Drop the washers and parachute at the same time, and record your observations.

▶ Think About It!

6. How did the motion of the washers differ between the two trials?

7. What forces were acting on the washers and the parachute during the two trials?

8. Were the forces on the washers balanced or unbalanced? How do you know?

9. During which trial was the force of air resistance greater? Explain your answer.

30 min

Figure 5 Projectile Motion

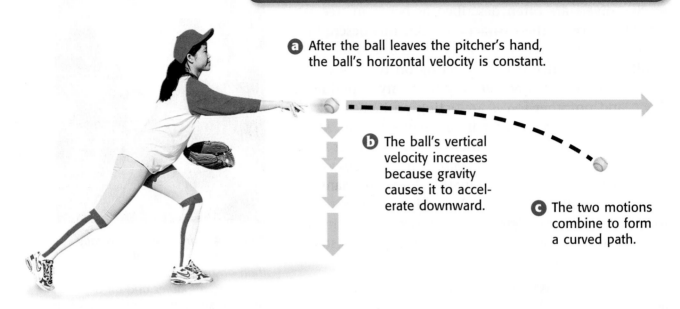

a After the ball leaves the pitcher's hand, the ball's horizontal velocity is constant.

b The ball's vertical velocity increases because gravity causes it to accelerate downward.

c The two motions combine to form a curved path.

Projectile Motion and Gravity

The movement of a hopping grasshopper is an example of projectile motion. **Projectile motion** is the curved path an object follows when it is thrown or propelled near the surface of Earth. Projectile motion is made of two different motions, or movements—horizontal movement and vertical movement. These two movements are separate. So, they have no effect on each other. But when these two movements are put together, they form a curved path, as shown in **Figure 5.** Projectile motion can be seen in the following situations:

- a frog leaping
- water spraying from a hose
- a swimmer diving into water
- balls being juggled

Horizontal Movement

When you throw a ball to a friend, your hand applies a force to the ball that makes the ball begin to move forward. This force gives the ball its horizontal movement, which is movement parallel to the ground. After the ball leaves your hand, no horizontal forces are acting on the ball (ignoring air resistance). Even gravity does not affect the horizontal movement of projectile motion. So, there are no forces to change the ball's horizontal velocity. Thus, the horizontal velocity of the ball remains the same after the ball leaves your hand, as shown in **Figure 5.**

projectile motion (proh JEK tuhl MOH shuhn) the curved path that an object follows when thrown, launched, or otherwise projected near the surface of Earth

Wordwise The prefix *pro-* means "forward." The root *ject-* means "to throw." Other examples are *inject, promote,* and *produce.*

Vertical Movement

Gravity pulls everything on Earth down toward the center of Earth. A ball in your hand doesn't fall down because your hand is holding the ball. After you throw the ball, gravity pulls the ball down. Gravity gives the ball vertical movement, which is movement perpendicular to the ground. Gravity pulls the ball in projectile motion down at an acceleration of 9.8 m/s^2 (if air resistance is ignored). This rate is the same for all falling objects on Earth. **Figure 6** shows that the downward acceleration of a thrown ball and a falling ball are the same.

Because objects in projectile motion accelerate down, you always have to aim above a target if you want to hit it with a thrown or propelled object. For this reason, when you aim an arrow directly at a round bull's-eye, your arrow hits the bottom of the circle rather than the middle of the circle.

Standards Check What force affects the vertical movement of an object in projectile motion? 🐻 **8.2.e**

Orbiting and Gravity

An object is orbiting when it is moving around another object in space. A spacecraft orbiting Earth is moving forward. But the spacecraft is also in free fall toward Earth. **Figure 7** shows how these two movements come together to form an orbit.

The two movements that come together to form an orbit are similar to the horizontal and vertical movements in projectile motion. In fact, you can think of something in orbit as being in projectile motion but never reaching the ground.

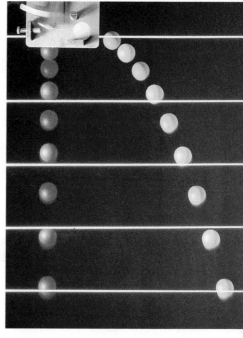

Figure 6 *The two balls have the same acceleration due to gravity even though the yellow ball is in projectile motion and the red ball is not.*

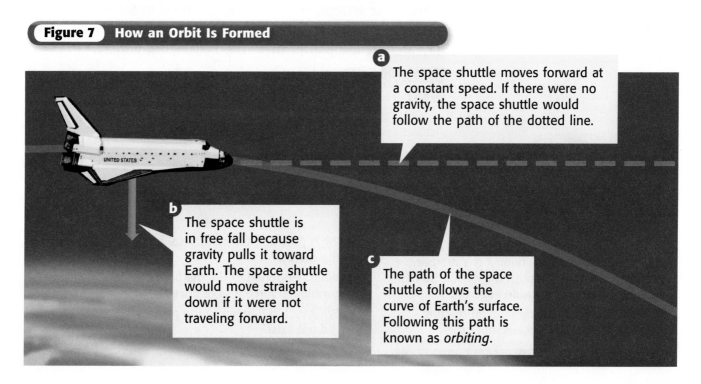

Figure 7 **How an Orbit Is Formed**

a The space shuttle moves forward at a constant speed. If there were no gravity, the space shuttle would follow the path of the dotted line.

b The space shuttle is in free fall because gravity pulls it toward Earth. The space shuttle would move straight down if it were not traveling forward.

c The path of the space shuttle follows the curve of Earth's surface. Following this path is known as *orbiting*.

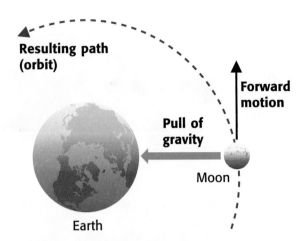

Resulting path (orbit)

Forward motion

Pull of gravity

Moon

Earth

Figure 8 *Gravity changes the straight-line path of the moon into a curved orbit.* **What kind of force provided by gravity keeps the moon in orbit around Earth?**

Orbiting and Centripetal Force

Besides spacecraft, many other things in the universe are in orbit. The moon orbits Earth. Earth and the other planets orbit the sun. Also, many stars orbit large masses in the center of galaxies. The path of an orbiting object is not quite a circle. Instead, the path is an ellipse.

Anything in orbit is always changing direction. An unbalanced force is needed to change the movement of an object. So, there must be an unbalanced force acting on anything in orbit. This unbalanced force that makes things move in an elliptical path (or in a circular path) is called a *centripetal force* (sen TRIP uht'l FOHRS). The word *centripetal* means "toward the center." Gravity provides the centripetal force that keeps things in orbit, as shown in **Figure 8.**

Gravity and the Solar System

Gravity plays an important role in maintaining the shape of the solar system. Gravity between the sun and the planets keeps the planets in orbit around the sun. Gravity provides a centripetal force on the planets. Also, gravity between a planet and its moons keeps the moons in orbit around the planet. Gravity also keeps asteroids in orbit around the sun. And gravity between comets and the sun makes the comets orbit the sun in very long ellipses.

Gravity can also change the movement of very small things in the solar system. For example, the rings of Saturn are made of tiny pieces of ice and dust. These pieces of ice and dust stay around the planet in a ring because of gravity.

Standards Check What helps keep the planets orbiting the sun?
8.2.g

Quick Lab

8.2.g

Circling Marbles

1. Use **tape** to join the ends of a **3 cm × 60 cm strip of poster board** to form a ring.

2. Place the ring on the floor. Put a **marble** inside the ring, and push the marble so that it travels along the inside edge of the ring.

3. While the marble is moving, lift the ring and observe the marble's motion.

4. What provided the centripetal force on the marble?

5. What happened to the marble when the centripetal force was removed?

6. What would happen to the planets if gravity did not exist?

 15 min

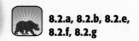
Summary

- Gravity is the force that causes all objects on Earth to accelerate downward at a rate of 9.8 m/s².

- Air resistance slows the acceleration of falling objects. An object falls at its terminal velocity when the upward force of air resistance equals the downward force of gravity.

- An object is in free fall if gravity is the only force acting on it.

- Projectile motion is the curved path that an object follows when thrown or propelled near the surface of Earth.

- Projectile motion has two components: horizontal motion and vertical motion. Gravity affects only the vertical motion of projectile motion.

- Gravity provides the centripetal force that keeps objects in orbit.

- Gravity is the force that keeps the solar system together.

Understanding Concepts

1 Concluding   Suppose that the magnitude of gravity on a falling object is greater than the magnitude of air resistance on the object. What is the cumulative effect of the forces on the object's motion?

2 Analyzing   How does air resistance affect the acceleration of falling objects?

3 Comparing   How does the unbalanced force of gravity affect the horizontal and vertical velocities of an object in projectile motion?

4 Describing   How is the acceleration of falling objects affected by gravity?

5 Justifying   A brick has a greater mass than a sponge has. Why is the acceleration due to gravity the same for both objects?

6 Summarizing   Explain why an object in orbit needs a centripetal force acting on it. In what direction does a centripetal force act?

Critical Thinking

7 Applying Concepts   Think about a sport that uses a ball. Identify four examples from that sport in which an object is in projectile motion.

8 Predicting Consequences   Predict the motion of a planet if gravity between the sun and the planet stopped acting. Explain your prediction.

INTERPRETING GRAPHICS   Use the image below to answer the following question.

9 Applying Concepts   Whenever Jon delivers a newspaper to the Zapanta house, the newspaper lands in the bushes. What should Jon do to make sure the newspaper lands on the porch?

Math Skills

10 Using Equations   A rock at rest falls off a tall cliff. What is the rock's velocity as the rock hits the ground 3.5 s later? Ignore air resistance.

Challenge

11 Making Inferences   The moon has no atmosphere. What would happen if an astronaut on the moon dropped a hammer and a feather at the same time from the same height? Explain your answer.

12 Predicting Consequences   Sky divers must open their parachutes before they reach a certain distance above the ground. Explain why a parachute would be less useful if it were opened too close to the ground.

Internet Resources

For a variety of links related to this chapter, go to www.scilinks.org

Topic: Gravity and Orbiting Objects; Projectile Motion
SciLinks code: HY70692; HY71223

Newton's Laws of Motion

Key Concept Newton's laws of motion describe the relationship between forces and the motion of an object.

What You Will Learn

- Newton's first law of motion states that the motion of an object will change only if unbalanced forces act on the object.
- Newton's second law of motion states that the acceleration of an object depends on the object's mass and on the force exerted on the object.
- Newton's third law of motion states that whenever one object exerts a force on a second object, the second object exerts an equal and opposite force on the first.

Why It Matters

Newton's laws of motion will help you understand why you and the objects around you move in certain ways.

Vocabulary

- inertia

READING STRATEGY

Graphic Organizer In your **Science Journal,** create Combination Notes about Newton's laws of motion.

8.2.c Students know when the forces on an object are balanced, the motion of the object does not change.

8.2.e Students know that when the forces on an object are unbalanced, the object will change its velocity (that is, it will speed up, slow down, or change direction).

8.2.f Students know the greater the mass of an object, the more force is needed to achieve the same rate of change in motion.

Imagine that you are playing softball. The pitch comes in, and—crack—you hit the ball hard! But instead of flying off the bat, the ball just drops to the ground. Is that normal?

You would probably say no. You know that force and motion are related. When you exert a force on a softball by hitting it with a bat, the softball should move. In 1686, Sir Isaac Newton explained this relationship between force and the motion of an object with his three laws of motion.

Newton's First Law

An object at rest remains at rest, and an object in motion remains in motion at constant speed and in a straight line unless acted on by an unbalanced force.

Newton's first law of motion describes the motion of an object that has a net force of 0 N acting on it. This law is easier to understand if you consider its two parts separately.

Part 1: Objects at Rest

An object that is not moving is said to be at rest. A chair on the floor and a golf ball on a tee are examples of objects at rest. Newton's first law states that objects at rest will stay at rest unless they are acted on by an unbalanced force. So, objects will not start moving until a push or a pull is exerted on them. A chair won't slide across the room unless you push the chair. And a golf ball won't move off the tee unless the ball is struck by a golf club, as shown in **Figure 1.**

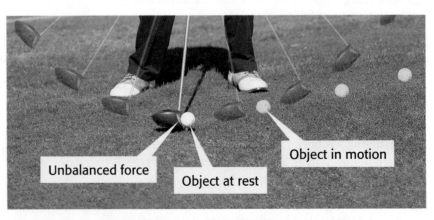

Unbalanced force   Object at rest   Object in motion

Figure 1 *A golf ball will remain at rest on a tee until it is acted on by the unbalanced force of a moving club.*

Part 2: Objects in Motion

The second part of Newton's first law is about objects moving with a certain velocity. Such objects will continue to move forever with the same velocity unless an unbalanced force acts on them.

Think about driving a bumper car at an amusement park. Your ride is pleasant as long as you are driving in an open space. But the name of the game is bumper cars! Sooner or later, you are likely to run into another car, as shown in **Figure 2.** Your bumper car stops when it hits another car. But you continue to move forward until the force from your seat belt stops you.

Friction and Newton's First Law

The motion of an object will not change unless the object is acted on by an unbalanced force. So, you should be able to give your desk a push and send it sliding across the floor. If you push your desk, the desk quickly stops. Why?

The desk stops because an unbalanced force changes its motion. That unbalanced force is friction. Friction changes the motion of objects. The friction between the desk and the floor slows the motion of the desk. Because of friction, observing the effects of Newton's first law is often difficult. For example, friction will cause a rolling ball to slow down and stop.

Standards Check What must be true about the forces acting on an object if the motion of the object does not change? 🐻 **8.2.c**

b The collision changes your car's motion, not your motion. Your motion continues with the same velocity.

a An unbalanced force from another car acts on your car and changes your car's motion.

c Another unbalanced force, from your seat belt, changes your motion.

Figure 2 *Bumper cars let you have fun with Newton's first law.*

Quick Lab

First-Law Skateboard

1. Place an **empty aluminum beverage can** on top of a **skateboard.**

2. Ask a friend to catch the skateboard after you push it. Now, give the skateboard a quick, firm push. What happened to the can?

3. Put the can on the skateboard again.

4. Push the skateboard gently so that it moves quickly but so that the can does not fall.

5. Ask your friend to let the skateboard travel a short distance and then to stop it quickly. What happened to the can?

6. Explain how Newton's first law applies to what happened in each case.

8.2.c
8.2.e

⏱ 15 min

Inertia and Newton's First Law

inertia (in UHR shuh) the tendency of an object to resist being moved or, if the object is moving, to resist a change in speed or direction until an outside force acts on the object

Newton's first law of motion is sometimes called the *law of inertia*. **Inertia** is the tendency of all objects to resist any change in motion. Because of inertia, an object at rest will remain at rest until a force makes it move. Likewise, inertia is the reason that a moving object stays in motion with the same velocity unless a force changes its speed or direction. For example, because of inertia, you slide toward the side of a car when the driver turns a corner. Inertia is also the reason why a plane, car, or bicycle cannot stop immediately.

Standards Check Why must a force be exerted on an object to change its velocity? **8.2.e**

Mass and Inertia

Mass is a measure of inertia. An object that has a small mass has less inertia than an object that has a large mass. So, changing the motion of an object that has a small mass is easier than changing the motion of an object that has a large mass. For example, a softball has less mass and therefore less inertia than a bowling ball. Because the softball has a small amount of inertia, it is easy to pitch a softball and to change its motion by hitting it with a bat. Imagine how difficult it would be to play softball with a bowling ball! **Figure 3** further shows the relationship between mass and inertia.

Figure 3 *Inertia makes it harder to accelerate a car than to accelerate a bicycle. Inertia also makes it easier to stop a moving bicycle than a car moving at the same speed.*

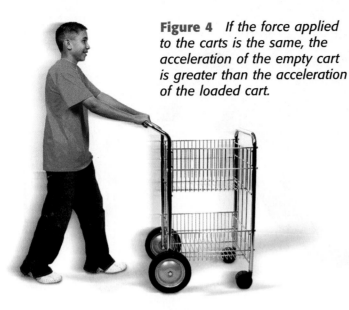

Figure 4 *If the force applied to the carts is the same, the acceleration of the empty cart is greater than the acceleration of the loaded cart.*

Acceleration

Acceleration

Newton's Second Law of Motion

The acceleration of an object depends on the mass of the object and the amount of force applied.

Newton's second law describes the motion of an object when an unbalanced force acts on the object. As with Newton's first law, you should consider the second law in two parts.

Part 1: Acceleration and Mass

Suppose that you are using a cart to help your teacher move some heavy boxes. When the cart is empty, you have to exert only a small force on the cart to accelerate it. But the same amount of force will not accelerate the fully loaded cart as much as the empty cart. **Figure 4** shows part of Newton's second law. The length of the arrows shows the amount of acceleration of the cart. You can see that for the same force, the acceleration of an object decreases as its mass increases. On the other hand, the acceleration of an object increases as its mass decreases.

The acceleration of an object is always in the same direction as the net force applied. The cart in **Figure 4** moved forward because the push was in the forward direction.

Standards Check Describe how the mass of an object is related to the object's acceleration.  **8.2.f**

INTERNET ACTIVITY

Newton's Rap

How do you remember Newton's laws of motion? Create a song or jingle to help you remember Newton's laws of motion. Go to **go.hrw.com,** and type in the keyword HY7FORW.

Figure 5 *The acceleration of a loaded cart will increase when a larger force is exerted on it.*

Acceleration

Acceleration

Part 2: Acceleration and Force

How can you give the loaded cart the same acceleration as the empty cart? You have to exert a greater force on the loaded cart than you exerted on the empty cart. **Figure 5** shows that the loaded cart has a greater acceleration when it is pushed harder. This example shows the other part of Newton's second law. An object's acceleration increases as the force on the object increases. On the other hand, an object's acceleration decreases as the force on the object decreases.

Standards Check Compare the forces needed to give the same rate of change in motion to two objects that have different masses. 🐻 **8.2.f**

Quick Lab

Testing Newton's Second Law

1. Use a **spring scale** to measure the weights of **two objects that have different masses.** Record the weights.

2. Weight is a measure of gravitational force. On which object is gravitational force greater? Which object has the greater mass?

3. Hold the objects about waist high. Make sure that the bottom of each object is the same distance above a **soft surface.**

4. Drop the objects at the same time. Compare the acceleration of each object. (Hint: To compare the accelerations of the objects, consider the order in which the objects hit the ground.)

5. Explain your observations of mass, force, and rate of change in motion in terms of Newton's second law.

8.2.f

⏱ 15 min

Newton's Third Law of Motion

Whenever one object exerts a force on a second object, the second object exerts an equal and opposite force on the first.

Newton's third law can be simply stated as follows: All forces act in pairs. For example, when your hand applies a force to a ball, the ball applies a force that is equal in size and opposite in direction to your hand. The law itself addresses only forces. But the way that force pairs interact changes the movement of objects.

How do forces act in pairs? **Figure 6** shows how one force pair helps move a swimmer through water. Action and reaction force pairs are present even when there is no movement. For example, you apply a force to a chair when you sit on it. Your weight pushing down on the chair is the action force. The reaction force is the force applied by the chair that pushes up on your body. The force applied by the chair is equal in size to your weight but opposite in direction.

Force Pairs Applied to Objects

A force is always applied by one object on another object. This rule is true for all forces, including action and reaction forces. However, action and reaction forces in a pair do not act on the same object. If they did, the net force would always be 0 N. So, nothing would ever move! Look at **Figure 6** again. The action force is applied to the water by the swimmer's hands. But the reaction force is applied to the swimmer's hands by the water. The forces do not act on the same object.

Newton Ball

Play catch with an adult. As you play, discuss how Newton's laws of motion are involved in the game. After you finish your game, make a list of what you discussed in your **Science Journal.**

Figure 6 *The action force and reaction force are a pair. The two forces are equal in size but opposite in direction.*

The action force is the swimmer's hands pushing on the water.

The reaction force is the water pushing on the hands. The reaction force moves the swimmer forward.

Figure 7 Examples of Action and Reaction Force Pairs

The rabbit's legs exert a force on the ground. The ground exerts an equal force on the rabbit's legs and causes the rabbit to accelerate upward.

The space shuttle's thrusters push the exhaust gases downward as the gases push the shuttle upward with an equal force.

The bat exerts a force on the ball and sends the ball flying. The ball exerts an equal force on the bat, but the bat does not move backward because the batter is exerting another force on the bat.

Action and Reaction Force Pairs

Newton's third law states that all forces act in pairs. When a force is exerted, there is always a reaction force. A force never acts by itself. **Figure 7** shows some examples of action and reaction force pairs. In each example, the action force is shown in yellow and the reaction force is shown in red.

Noticing the Effects of a Reaction Force

Another example of a force pair is shown in **Figure 8.** Gravity is a force of attraction between objects that is due to their masses. If you drop a ball, gravity pulls the ball toward Earth. This force is the action force exerted by Earth on the ball. But gravity also pulls Earth toward the ball. The force is the reaction force exerted by the ball on Earth.

It's easy to see the effect of the action force—the ball falls to Earth. Why don't you notice the effect of the reaction force—Earth being pulled upward? To find the answer to this question, think about Newton's second law. It states that the acceleration of an object depends on the force applied to it and on the mass of the object. The force on Earth is equal to the force on the ball. But the mass of Earth is much *larger* than the mass of the ball. Thus, the acceleration of Earth is much *smaller* than the acceleration of the ball. The acceleration of Earth is so small that you can't see or feel the acceleration. So, it is difficult to observe the effect of Newton's third law on falling objects.

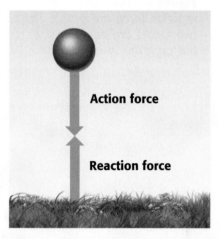

Figure 8 *The force of gravity between Earth and a falling object is a force pair.*

Summary

- Newton's first law of motion states that the motion of an object will not change if the forces on it are balanced.

- Objects at rest will not move unless acted upon by an unbalanced force.

- Objects in motion will continue to move at a constant speed and in a straight line unless acted upon by an unbalanced force.

- Inertia is the tendency of matter to resist a change in motion. Mass is a measure of inertia.

- Newton's second law of motion states that the acceleration of an object depends on the mass of the object and the amount of force applied.

- The greater the mass of an object is, the greater the force needed to achieve the same acceleration.

- Newton's third law of motion states that whenever one object exerts a force on a second object, the second object exerts an equal and opposite force on the first object.

Using Vocabulary

1 Write an original definition for *inertia*.

Understanding Concepts

2 Identifying What are three ways in which the velocity of an object may change when the forces on the object are unbalanced?

3 Describing What does Newton's first law of motion state about objects on which forces are balanced?

4 Summarizing Use Newton's second law of motion to describe the relationship between force, mass, and acceleration.

5 Concluding What would happen if there were no friction between a rolling ball and the ground? Explain your answer.

Critical Thinking

6 Applying Concepts When a truck pulls a trailer, the trailer and truck accelerate forward even though the action and reaction forces are the same size but are in opposite directions. Why don't these forces balance each other?

7 Making Inferences Use Newton's first law of motion to explain why air bags in cars are important during head-on collisions.

INTERPRETING GRAPHICS Use the image below to answer the next question.

8 Analyzing Processes Use Newton's third law of motion to describe the forces represented by the arrows.

Challenge

9 Applying Concepts Imagine that you are pulling a wagon while your friend sits in the wagon. Soon after, your friend's brother wants to ride, too. After your friend's brother joins your friend, you pull the wagon with the same force as you did before. Compare the acceleration of the wagon before your friend's brother climbed in with the acceleration of the wagon after he climbed in. What must you do to give the wagon containing both people the same acceleration as you gave the wagon when only your friend was in it? Explain your reasoning.

Skills Practice Lab

OBJECTIVES

Observe several effects of inertia.

Describe how balanced and unbalanced forces affect the motion of objects.

MATERIALS

Station 1
- egg, hard-boiled
- egg, raw

Station 2
- card, index
- coin
- cup, plastic

Station 3
- mass, hanging, 1 kg
- meterstick
- scissors
- thread, spool

SAFETY

8.2.c Students know when the forces on an object are balanced, the motion of the object does not change.
8.2.e Students know that when the forces on an object are unbalanced, the object will change its velocity (that is, it will speed up, slow down, or change direction).

Exploring Inertia

Inertia is a property of all matter, from small particles of dust to enormous planets and stars. In this lab, you will investigate the inertia of various shapes and kinds of matter. Keep in mind that each investigation requires you to either overcome or use the object's inertia.

Station 1: Magic Eggs

Ask a Question

1 There are two unmarked eggs at this station. The masses of the two eggs are about the same. Without breaking them open, how can you tell which egg is raw (liquid inside) and which egg is hard-boiled (solid all the way through)?

Form a Hypothesis

2 Before you do anything to either egg, make some predictions. Will there be any difference in the way the two eggs spin? Which egg will be easier to stop?

Test the Hypothesis

3 First, spin one egg. Then, place your finger on it gently to make it stop spinning. Record your observations.

4 Repeat step 3 with the second egg.

5 Compare your predictions with your observations. (Repeat steps 3 and 4 if necessary.)

6 Which egg is hard-boiled, and which one is raw? Explain.

Analyze the Results

7 **Explaining Events** Explain why the eggs behave differently when you spin them even though they should have the same inertia. (Hint: Think about what happens to the liquid inside the raw egg.)

Draw Conclusions

8 **Drawing Conclusions** Explain why the eggs react differently when you try to stop them.

Station 2: Coin in a Cup

Procedure

9 At this station, you will find a coin, an index card, and a plastic cup. Place the card over the cup. Then, place the coin on the card over the center of the cup, as shown below.

10 Write down a method for getting the coin into the cup without touching the coin and without lifting the card.

11 Try your method. If it doesn't work, try again until you find a method that does work.

Analyze the Results

12 **Describing Events** Use Newton's first law of motion to explain why the coin falls into the cup if you remove the card quickly.

Draw Conclusions

13 **Defending Conclusions** Explain why pulling on the card slowly will not work even though the coin has inertia. (Hint: Friction is a force.)

Station 3: The Magic Thread

Procedure

14 At this station, you will find a spool of thread and a mass hanging from a strong string. Cut a piece of thread about 40 cm long. Tie the thread around the bottom of the mass, as shown at right.

15 Pull gently on the end of the thread. Observe what happens, and record your observations.

16 Stop the mass from moving. Now, hold the end of the thread so that there is a lot of slack between your fingers and the mass.

17 Give the thread a quick, hard pull. You should observe a very different event. Record your observations. Throw away the thread.

Analyze the Results

18 **Analyzing Results** Use Newton's first law of motion to explain why a hard pull breaks the thread and a gentle pull does not.

Draw Conclusions

19 **Applying Conclusions** Both moving and nonmoving objects have inertia. Explain why throwing a bowling ball and catching a thrown bowling ball are hard.

Big Idea Question

20 **Evaluating Results** Explain your observations in the lab in terms of balanced and unbalanced forces. When were the forces on the objects balanced? What happened when the forces became unbalanced?

Science Skills Activity

Investigation and Experimentation
8.9.f Apply simple mathematical relationships to determine a missing quantity in a mathematic expression, given the two remaining terms (including speed = distance/time, density = mass/volume, force = pressure × area, volume = area × height).

Finding a Missing Quantity

▶ Tutorial

Procedure

Simple mathematical relationships can be used to help find a missing quantity when all but one of the terms are known. An equation that has three terms that can all change in value is called a *three-variable equation.* The equation to find the velocity of falling objects is an example of a three-variable equation.

1 The equation for the velocity of falling objects is arranged to find the change in velocity.

$$\Delta v = g \times t$$

2 To find time, rearrange the equation by dividing both sides by acceleration due to gravity.

$$t = \frac{\Delta v}{g}$$

3 The acceleration due to gravity on Earth is always 9.8 m/s². But the acceleration due to gravity varies between different planets and moons. To rearrange the original equation to find the acceleration due to gravity, divide both sides of the original equation by time.

$$g = \frac{\Delta v}{t}$$

Analysis

4 **Using Equations** To determine which form of a three-variable equation you need to use to solve a problem, read the problem carefully. The problem will ask you to find a missing quantity. Make sure you use the form of the three-variable equation that has the missing quantity you are looking for isolated by itself on one side of the equals sign.

▶ You Try It!

Procedure

Use the equation for the velocity of falling objects to answer the following questions. Show all of your work, including the work you did to rearrange the equation, if necessary.

Analysis

1 **Using Equations** A marble at rest is dropped from the top of a building. Find the marble's velocity after it has fallen for 3 s. Ignore air resistance.

2 **Using Equations** The same marble hits the ground with a velocity of 44.1 m/s. How much time was the marble falling? Ignore air resistance.

3 **Using Equations** An acorn at rest falls from an oak tree. The acorn hits the ground with a velocity of 14.7 m/s. How much time was the acorn falling? Ignore air resistance.

4 **Using Equations** Suppose that an astronaut drops a golf ball on the moon. The golf ball falls for 2 s and hits the surface of the moon with a velocity of 3.2 m/s. Find the acceleration due to gravity on the moon.

5 **Using Equations** Imagine that a rover on the surface of Mars films a rock falling off a cliff. The rock lands with a velocity of 9.25 m/s after falling for 2.5 s. Find the acceleration due to gravity on Mars.

Chapter Summary

go.hrw.com
SUPER SUMMARY
KEYWORD:HY7FORS

The Big Idea
Unbalanced forces cause changes in motion that can be predicted and described.

Section	Vocabulary

1 Gravity: A Force of Attraction

Gravity can change the movement of an object.

Key Concept Gravity is a force of attraction between objects that is due to their masses.

- Gravity affects all matter, including the parts of the solar system.
- Because gravity is a force, it can change the velocity of objects.
- The law of universal gravitation explains how distance, mass, and gravitational force are related.
- The weight of an object depends on gravity, but the mass of the object does not.

gravity p. 370
weight p. 374
mass p. 374

2 Gravity and Motion

Key Concept Gravity can be an unbalanced force that causes predictable changes in motion.

- The acceleration due to gravity is the same for all objects near Earth's surface.
- Air resistance is a force that opposes the motion of objects through air.
- Projectile motion has two components—horizontal motion and vertical motion.

The two components of projectile motion combine to form a curved path.

terminal velocity p. 378
free fall p. 379
projectile motion p. 380

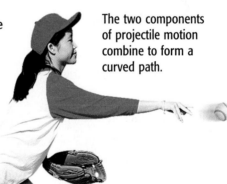

3 Newton's Laws of Motion

Acceleration depends on mass and force.

Key Concept Newton's laws of motion describe the relationship between forces and the motion of an object.

- Newton's first law of motion states that the motion of an object will change only if unbalanced forces act on the object.
- Newton's second law of motion states that the acceleration of an object depends on the object's mass and on the force exerted on the object.
- Newton's third law of motion states that whenever one object exerts a force on a second object, the second object exerts an equal and opposite force on the first.

inertia p. 386

Chapter Review

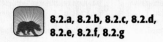

8.2.a, 8.2.b, 8.2.c, 8.2.d,
8.2.e, 8.2.f, 8.2.g

Organize

Pyramid Review the FoldNote that you created at the beginning of the chapter. Add to or correct the FoldNote based on what you have learned.

Using Vocabulary

1 **Academic Vocabulary** In the sentence "Gravity has an important role in maintaining the shape of the solar system," what does the word *role* mean?
a. a part played by an actor
b. a function
c. a socially expected behavior pattern
d. a character assigned or taken on

Complete each of the following sentences by choosing the correct term from the word bank.

gravity	projectile motion
inertia	terminal velocity
mass	weight

2 An object in motion has ___, so it tends to stay in motion.

3 An object is falling at its ___ if it falls at a constant velocity.

4 ___ is a measure of the gravitational force on an object.

Understanding Concepts

Multiple Choice

5 The gravitational force between 1 kg of lead and Earth is ___ the gravitational force between 1 kg of marshmallows and Earth.
a. greater than   c. the same as
b. less than   d. None of the above

6 Newton's first law of motion applies to
a. moving objects.
b. objects that are not moving.
c. objects that are accelerating.
d. Both (a) and (b)

7 To accelerate two objects at the same rate, the force used to push the object that has more mass should be
a. smaller than the force used to push the object that has less mass.
b. larger than the force used to push the object that has less mass.
c. the same as the force used to push the object that has less mass.
d. equal to the object's weight.

Short Answer

8 **Identifying** Give an example of an object that is in free fall.

9 **Summarizing** Describe how the cumulative effect of gravity and air resistance is related to an object's terminal velocity.

10 **Describing** Explain why friction changes the velocity of objects and why friction can make observing Newton's first law of motion difficult.

11 **Concluding** What would happen to the magnitude of the gravitational force between the sun and Earth if Earth were placed in Pluto's orbit?

12 **Analyzing** Explain why action and reaction forces do not cancel out, even though they have equal magnitudes and act in opposite directions.

INTERPRETING GRAPHICS Use the image below to answer the next two questions.

13 **Identifying** The arrows in the image indicate two separate forces that are acting in the upward and downward directions on the static light bulb. Identify these two forces.

14 **Justifying** Are the forces on the light bulb balanced or unbalanced? Explain your answer by considering the motion of the light bulb.

INTERPRETING GRAPHICS Use the table below to answer the next question.

Force	Acceleration
35 N	5 m/s^2
70 N	10 m/s^2
105 N	15 m/s^2

15 **Evaluating** The table shows the acceleration produced by applying different forces on a 7 kg mass. Assuming that the pattern continues, predict what force would be needed to produce an acceleration of 25 m/s^2.

Writing Skills

16 **Writing a Biography** Describe the significance of Newton's *Principia* books. Describe what information was presented in *Principia* and why this information was important to scientists everywhere.

Critical Thinking

17 **Concept Mapping** Use the following terms to create a concept map: *gravity, free fall, terminal velocity, projectile motion,* and *air resistance.*

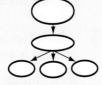

18 **Identifying Relationships** During a space-shuttle launch, about 830,000 kg of fuel are burned in 8 min. The fuel provides the shuttle with a constant thrust, or forward force. How does Newton's second law of motion explain why the shuttle's acceleration increases as the fuel is burned?

19 **Applying Concepts** Suppose that you are standing on a skateboard and you toss a backpack full of books toward your friend. What do you think will happen to you? Explain your answer in terms of Newton's third law of motion.

INTERPRETING GRAPHICS Use the image below to answer the next two questions.

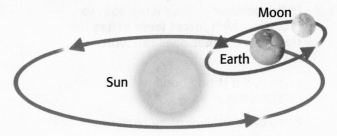

20 **Applying Concepts** The image shows the paths of Earth and the moon. Explain how you can use the image to prove that Earth and the moon are accelerating.

21 **Identifying Relationships** Identify the forces responsible for maintaining the relative positions of these bodies in the solar system.

INTERPRETING GRAPHICS Use the image at the right to answer the next two questions.

22 **Applying Concepts** The arrows in the image show the force of gravity and the force of air resistance on an acorn. Is the acorn accelerating? Explain your answer.

23 **Making Inferences** Under what conditions would the acorn stop accelerating yet still continue to fall?

Math Skills

24 **Using Equations** A rock falls from rest off a cliff and hits the ground in 1.5 s. Without considering air resistance, determine the rock's velocity as the rock hits the ground.

Challenge

25 **Forming Hypotheses** Suppose that you are looking at an orange tree. Several oranges are hanging from the tree. Suddenly, an orange falls to the ground. Form a hypothesis that explains why the orange fell. Use Newton's first law of motion in your hypothesis.

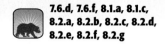
REVIEWING ACADEMIC VOCABULARY

1 In the sentence "They were able to identify which forces were acting on the object," what does the word *identify* mean?

A to feel a strong bond with somebody or something

B to consider two or more things as being the same

C to point out or pick out

D to be aware of a difference between two things

2 Which of the following words means "stress that happens when forces act to stretch an object"?

A extended

B elasticity

C tension

D withheld

3 In the sentence "The greater the mass of an object the more force is needed to achieve the same rate of change in motion," what does the word *achieve* mean?

A do

B finish

C win

D persist

4 In the sentence "Gravity is one of the factors that helps to maintain the shapes of the planets, stars, and solar system," what does the word *maintain* mean?

A argue

B keep the same

C provide

D repair

REVIEWING CONCEPTS

5 The magnitude of the gravitational force between two bodies depends upon

A the velocity of the bodies and the friction between them.

B the size of the bodies and their position relative to Earth.

C the weight of the bodies and how quickly they are moving.

D the mass of the bodies and the distance between them.

6 If we observe a book resting on a table, which of the following can we conclude is true?

A A force greater than gravity is necessary to move an object at rest.

B Earth's gravitational force is balanced by the upward force of the table.

C The attraction between the book and the table is greater than gravity.

D Gravity does not affect small objects, only massive bodies.

7 Which forces most strongly affect a picture hanging on a nail on the wall?

A compression and tension

B gravity and friction

C tension and gravity

D friction and compression

8 What is the role of gravity in our solar system?

A Gravity pushes the planets farther and farther apart.

B Gravity pulls planets closer and closer to the sun.

C Gravity keeps the planets in orbit around the sun.

D Gravity is created by the sun, which attracts the planets.

9 Newton's first law explains inertia. What effect does inertia have on a static object?

A Static objects are not affected by inertia.

B Inertia causes a static object to have more mass than a moving one.

C Inertia causes the object to begin moving when acted upon by balanced forces.

D Due to inertia, the object will remain at rest until acted upon.

10 What is the best explanation for why this picture is an example of projectile motion?

A The runner jumps higher than the hurdle.

B The runner has greater horizontal velocity than vertical velocity.

C The runner has both horizontal and vertical motion.

D The runner has both vertical motion and gravity.

11 Two objects in motion have different masses. How does this difference affect the force needed to achieve the same rate of change?

A The object with less mass will require more force to achieve the same rate of change.

B Force does not affect the rate of change of an object.

C It will take the same amount of force to achieve the same rate of change for the two objects.

D The object with greater mass will require more force to achieve the same rate of change.

REVIEWING PRIOR LEARNING

12 Which of the following structures absorbs rays of light in the human eye, so that we are able to see objects?

A the retina

B the magnifier

C the lens

D the cornea

1	2	3
4	5	6
7	8	9

13 Use the diagram above to answer the following question. If you begin in box 5 and move one box down, one box to the right, and two boxes up, what will your final position be?

A box 1

B box 3

C box 7

D box 9

14 Light shines less brightly through colored glass than through colorless glass. This phenomenon is an example of

A reflection.

B refraction.

C transmission.

D absorption.

15 Imagine that a sprinter ran 200 m in 40 s. What was the sprinter's average speed?

A 0.5 m/s

B 5 m/s

C 160 m/s

D 240 m/s

Science in Action

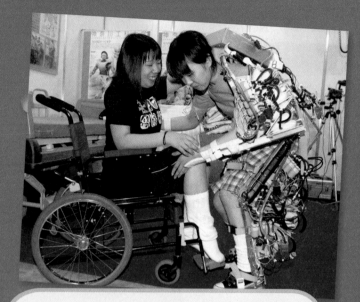

Scientific Discoveries

The Millennium Bridge

You may have heard the children's song "London Bridge Is Falling Down." London Bridge never fell. But some people who walked on the Millennium Bridge thought that it might fall instead! The Millennium Bridge is a pedestrian bridge in London, England. The bridge opened on June 10, 2000, and more than 80,000 people crossed it that day. Immediately, people noticed something wrong—the bridge was swaying! The bridge was closed after two days so that engineers could determine what was wrong. After much research, the engineers learned that the force of the footsteps of the people crossing the bridge caused the bridge to sway.

Language Arts ACTIVITY

Imagine that you were in London on June 10, 2000, and walked across the Millennium Bridge. Write a one-page story about what you think it was like on the bridge that day.

Science, Technology, and Society

Power Suit for Lifting Patients

Imagine visiting a hospital and seeing someone who looked half human and half robot. No, it isn't a scene from a science fiction movie—it is a new invention that may someday help nurses lift patients easily. The invention, called a *power suit,* is a metal framework that a nurse would wear on his or her back. The suit calculates how much force a nurse needs to lift a patient, and then the robotic joints on the suit help the nurse exert the right amount of force. The suit will also help nurses avoid injuring their backs.

Math ACTIVITY

The pound (symbol £) is the currency in England. Suppose that the inventor sells the suit for £1,200. How much does the suit cost in dollars if $1 is equal to £0.55?

Steve Okamoto

Roller Coaster Designer Roller coasters have fascinated Steve Okamoto ever since his first ride on one. "I remember going to Disneyland as a kid. My mother was always upset with me because I kept looking over the sides of the rides, trying to figure out how they worked," he says. To satisfy his curiosity, Okamoto became a mechanical engineer. Today, he works for a company based in San Jose, California, that designs rides for amusement parks all over the world.

Roller coasters really do coast along the track. A motor pulls the cars up a high hill to start the ride. After that, the cars are powered only by gravity. Designing a successful roller coaster is not a simple task. Okamoto has to calculate the cars' speed and acceleration on each part of the track. He must also consider the safety of the ride and the strength of the structure that supports the track.

Social Studies ACTiViTY

Research the history of roller coasters to learn how roller coaster design has changed over time. Make a poster to summarize your research.

Internet Resources

- To learn more about careers in science, visit www.scilinks.org and enter the SciLinks code HY70225.

- To learn more about these Science in Action topics, visit go.hrw.com and type in the keyword HY7FORF.

- Check out articles related to this chapter by visiting go.hrw.com. Just type in the keyword HY7FORC.

Improving Comprehension

Graphic Organizers are important visual tools that can help you organize information and improve your reading comprehension. The Graphic Organizer below is called an *idea wheel*. Instructions for creating other types of Graphic Organizers are located in the **Study Skills** section of the Appendix.

How to Make an Idea Wheel

1 Draw a circle. Draw a larger circle around the first circle. Divide the ring between the circles into sections by drawing lines from one circle to the other across the ring. Divide the ring into as many sections as you want.

2 Write a main idea or topic in the smaller circle. Label each section in the ring with a category or characteristic of the main idea.

3 In each section of the ring, include details that are unique to the topic.

When to Use an Idea Wheel

An idea wheel is an effective type of visual organization in which ideas in science can be divided into categories or parts. It is also a useful way to illustrate characteristics of a main idea or topic. As you read, look for topics that are divided into ideas or categories, that can be organized around an idea wheel.

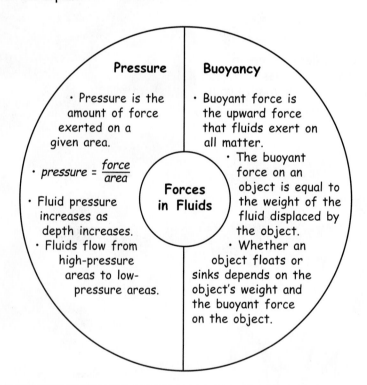

Pressure

- Pressure is the amount of force exerted on a given area.
- $pressure = \dfrac{force}{area}$
- Fluid pressure increases as depth increases.
- Fluids flow from high-pressure areas to low-pressure areas.

Forces in Fluids

Buoyancy

- Buoyant force is the upward force that fluids exert on all matter.
- The buoyant force on an object is equal to the weight of the fluid displaced by the object.
- Whether an object floats or sinks depends on the object's weight and the buoyant force on the object.

You Try It!

This Reading Strategy can also be used within the chapter that you are about to read. Practice making your own *idea wheel* as directed in the Reading Strategy for Section **2**. Record your work in your **Science Journal**.

Unpacking the Standards

The information below "unpacks" the standards by breaking them down into basic parts. The higher-level, academic vocabulary is highlighted and defined to help you understand the language of the standards. "What It Means" restates the standards as simply as possible.

California Standard	Academic Vocabulary	What It Means
8.8.a Students know density is mass per unit volume.		Density is the amount of matter in a given amount of space.
8.8.b Students know how to calculate the density of substances (regular and irregular solids and liquids) from measurements of mass and volume.		You must know how to figure out the density of substances—including solids that have uniform shapes, solids that vary in shape, and liquids—from measurements of mass and volume.
8.8.c Students know the buoyant force on an object in a fluid is an upward force equal to the weight of the fluid the object has **displaced.**	**displace** (dis PLAYS) to take the place of; to move aside	Students know that the upward force on an object in a liquid or a gas is equal to the weight of the liquid or the gas that has been pushed out of the way by the object.
8.8.d Students know how to **predict** whether an object will float or sink.	**predict** (pree DIKT) to say ahead of time	You must know how to figure out in advance whether an object will float or sink.

Forces in Fluids

The Big Idea

Forces in fluids are related to pressure and density and can affect the motion of objects in the fluid.

 California Standards

Focus on Physical Sciences
8.8 All objects experience a buoyant force when immersed in a fluid. (Sections 1 and 2)

Investigation and Experimentation
8.9 Scientific progress is made by asking meaningful questions and conducting careful investigations. (Sections 1 and 2; Science Skills Activity)

Math
7.4.2 Algebra and Functions

English–Language Arts
8.2.2 Reading
8.1.1 Writing

About the Photo

If you have ever flown a kite or gone swimming, you have experienced forces that are exerted by fluids. Of course, your kite would not last long in the 555 km/h (about 346 mi/h) winds that these six fans generate. Each fan is 40 ft in diameter! This wind tunnel is located at NASA Ames Research Center in Moffett Field, California. It is used to study the effects of the forces that air exerts on objects, such as airplanes and trucks.

Organize

Two-Panel Flip Chart

Before you read this chapter, create the FoldNote entitled "Two-Panel Flip Chart." Label the first flap "Floating," and label the second flap "Sinking." As you read the chapter, write what you learn about each topic under the appropriate flap.

Instructions for creating FoldNotes are located in the Study Skills section on p. 520 of the Appendix.

Explore Activity

20 min

Floating and Density Changes

In this activity, you will observe how an increase in the density of a fluid affects how an object floats.

Procedure

1. Cut a **straw** in half lengthwise.

2. Insert a **marble-sized lump of clay** into one end of one of the pieces of straw.

3. Use a **ruler** and **marker** to create a scale along the length of the straw.

4. Fill a **plastic cup** three-quarters full with **water**. Place the straw in the water, clay end first. If the clay touches the bottom of the cup, remove some clay from the straw. The straw and clay should float at least slightly above the bottom of the cup.

5. Record the water level shown on the straw's scale.

6. Using a **plastic spoon,** add several spoonfuls of **salt** to the water, and stir to dissolve. Record the new water level shown on the straw's scale.

8.8.c
8.8.d

Analysis

7. What happened to the straw setup when the salt was added to the water?

8. How did adding salt affect the water's density?

9. Explain how increasing a fluid's density affects how an object floats.

Forces in Fluids **405**

Fluids and Pressure

Key Concept Fluid is a nonsolid state of matter. All fluids can flow and exert pressure evenly in all directions.

You have something in common with a dog, a sea gull, and a dolphin. You and all of these other living things spend a lifetime moving through fluids. A **fluid** is any material that can flow and that takes the shape of its container. Liquids and gases are fluids. For example, you could fill a fishbowl with water or with air. Each would take the shape of the bowl. Fluids can flow because the particles in fluids move past one another easily.

Fluids and Pressure

You have probably heard the terms *air pressure* and *water pressure*. Air and water are both fluids. All fluids exert pressure. So, what is pressure? When you pump up a bicycle tire, you push air into the tire. And like all matter, air is made of tiny particles that are constantly moving. Look at **Figure 1.** Inside the tire, the air particles bump against one another and against the walls of the tire. The bumping of particles creates a force on the tire. The amount of force exerted on a given area is **pressure.** So, any force, such as the weight of an object, acting on an area creates pressure.

Calculating Pressure

Pressure can be calculated by using the following equation:

$$pressure = \frac{force}{area}$$

The SI unit for pressure is the **pascal.** One pascal (1 Pa) is the force of one newton exerted over an area of one square meter (1 N/m^2).

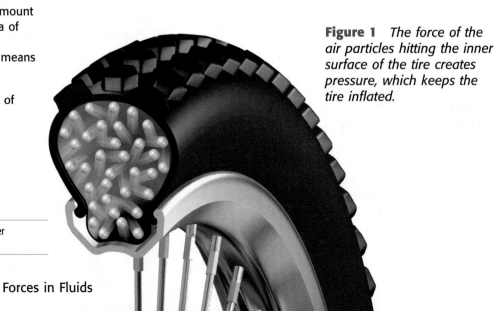

Figure 1 *The force of the air particles hitting the inner surface of the tire creates pressure, which keeps the tire inflated.*

Pressure, Force, and Area

What is the pressure exerted by a book that has an area of 0.2 m² and a weight of 10 N?

Step 1: Write the equation for pressure.

$$pressure = \frac{force}{area}$$

Step 2: Replace force and area with the values given, and solve. (Hint: Weight is a measure of gravitational force.)

$$pressure = \frac{10 \text{ N}}{0.2 \text{ m}^2} = 50 \text{ N/m}^2 = 50 \text{ Pa}$$

The equation for pressure can be rearranged to find force or area, as shown below.

$force = pressure \times area$ *(Rearrange by multiplying by area.)*

$area = \dfrac{force}{pressure}$ *(Rearrange by multiplying by area and then dividing by pressure.)*

Now It's Your Turn

1. Find the pressure exerted by a 3,000 N crate that has an area of 2 m².
2. Find the weight of a rock that has an area of 10 m² and that exerts a pressure of 250 Pa.

Pressure and Bubbles

When you pour a carbonated liquid into a glass, you can see gas bubbles in the liquid. Why are the bubbles round? The shape of the bubbles depends partly on an important property of fluids: Fluids exert pressure evenly in all directions. The gas in the bubble exerts pressure evenly in all directions. So, the bubble expands in all directions to make a round shape.

Atmospheric Pressure

The *atmosphere* is the layer of nitrogen, oxygen, and other gases that surrounds Earth. Earth's atmosphere is held in place by gravity, which pulls the gases toward Earth. The pressure caused by the weight of the atmosphere is called **atmospheric pressure.**

Atmospheric pressure is exerted on everything on Earth, including you. At sea level, the atmosphere exerts a pressure of about 101,300 N on every square meter, or 101,300 Pa. So, there is a weight of about 10 N (about 2 lb) on every square centimeter of your body. Why don't you feel this crushing pressure? Like the air inside a balloon, the fluids inside your body exert pressure. This pressure inside your body acts against the atmospheric pressure. **Figure 2** can help you understand why you don't feel the pressure.

atmospheric pressure
(AT mahs FIR ik PRESH uhr) the pressure caused by the weight of the atmosphere

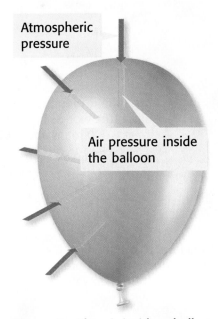

Atmospheric pressure

Air pressure inside the balloon

Figure 2 *The air inside a balloon exerts pressure that keeps the balloon inflated against atmospheric pressure. Similarly, fluid inside your body exerts pressure that acts against atmospheric pressure.*

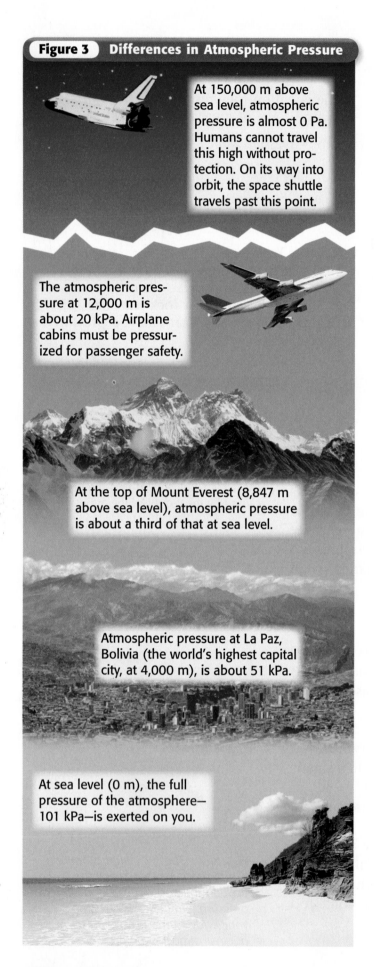

Figure 3 Differences in Atmospheric Pressure

At 150,000 m above sea level, atmospheric pressure is almost 0 Pa. Humans cannot travel this high without protection. On its way into orbit, the space shuttle travels past this point.

The atmospheric pressure at 12,000 m is about 20 kPa. Airplane cabins must be pressurized for passenger safety.

At the top of Mount Everest (8,847 m above sea level), atmospheric pressure is about a third of that at sea level.

Atmospheric pressure at La Paz, Bolivia (the world's highest capital city, at 4,000 m), is about 51 kPa.

At sea level (0 m), the full pressure of the atmosphere—101 kPa—is exerted on you.

Variation of Atmospheric Pressure

The atmosphere stretches about 150 km above Earth's surface. However, about 80% of the atmosphere's gases are found within 10 km of Earth's surface. At the top of the atmosphere, pressure is almost nonexistent. The pressure is close to 0 Pa because there are fewer gas particles and they rarely collide. The small number of gas particles is one of the reasons it is harder to breathe at high altitudes. There isn't as much air! Mount Everest in south-central Asia is the highest point on Earth. At the top of Mount Everest, atmospheric pressure is about 33,000 Pa, or 33 kilopascals (33 kPa). People who climb Mount Everest bring oxygen tanks to help them breathe at that altitude. At sea level, atmospheric pressure is about 101 kPa.

Atmospheric Pressure and Depth

Take a look at **Figure 3.** Notice how atmospheric pressure changes as you travel through the atmosphere. As you travel farther down into Earth's atmosphere, pressure increases. In other words, the pressure increases as the atmosphere gets "deeper." An important point to remember about fluids is that pressure varies depending on depth. At lower levels of the atmosphere, more fluid from above is being pulled by Earth's gravitational force. So, there is more pressure at lower levels of the atmosphere.

Pressure Changes and Your Body

So, what happens to your body when atmospheric pressure changes? If you travel to higher or lower points in the atmosphere, the fluids in your body have to adjust to maintain equal pressure. You have experienced this adjustment if your ears have "popped" when you were in a plane taking off or were in a car traveling down a steep mountain road. The "pop" happens because of pressure changes in air chambers behind your eardrums.

Water Pressure

Water is a fluid. So, like the atmosphere, water exerts pressure. Also, water pressure increases as depth increases, as shown in **Figure 4.** As a diver goes deeper into the water, pressure increases. The pressure increases because more water above the diver is being pulled by Earth's gravitational force. Also, the atmosphere presses down on the water. So the total pressure on the diver includes water pressure and atmospheric pressure.

Water Pressure and Depth

Like atmospheric pressure, water pressure depends on depth. Water pressure does not depend on the total amount of fluid present. A person swimming 3 m below the surface of a small pond feels the same pressure as a person swimming 3 m below the surface of a large lake. There is more water in the lake than there is in the pond, but the pressure on the swimmer in the pond is the same as the pressure on the swimmer in the lake.

Density and Water Pressure

Water is about 1,000 times as dense as air. *Density* is the amount of matter in a given volume, or mass per unit volume. Because water is denser than air, a certain volume of water has more mass—and weighs more—than the same volume of air. So, water exerts more pressure than air does.

For example, if you walk up 3 flights of stairs, the decrease in atmospheric pressure is too small to notice. But if you dive underwater the same distance, the pressure on you increases to 201 kPa, which is almost twice the atmospheric pressure at the surface of the water!

Standards Check Why does water exert more pressure than air? 🐻 8.8.a

Figure 4 Differences in Water Pressure

Pressure exerted on a diver 10 m below the water's surface is twice the pressure at the surface.

At 500 m below the surface, pressure is about 5,000 kPa. Divers at or below this level must wear special suits to survive the pressure.

The wreck of the *Titanic* is 3,660 m below the surface. The water pressure at this depth is 36,600 kPa.

The viper fish lives 8,000 m below the ocean's surface. No fish are found below this level. Water pressure at this depth is 80,000 kPa.

In 1960, the *Trieste* descended to the deepest part of the ocean (11,000 m), where the pressure is 110,000 kPa.

8.8.a

Quick Lab

Forces on Fluids

1. Fill a **plastic bottle** with **water**.

2. Place a **sealed plastic pipette bulb** into the bottle. Tightly screw the **cap** onto the bottle.

3. Squeeze and release the sides of the bottle several times. Look closely at the bulb, and record your observations.

4. You exerted a force on the water in the bottle. Why was a force also exerted on the air in the bulb?

5. How did squeezing the bottle affect the density of the air in the bulb? Explain your answer.

🕐 **10 min**

Pressure Differences and Fluid Flow

When you drink through a straw, you remove some of the air in the straw. Because there is less air inside the straw, the pressure in the straw is reduced. But the atmospheric pressure on the surface of the liquid remains the same. Thus, there is a difference between the pressure inside the straw and the pressure outside the straw. The outside pressure forces the liquid up the straw and into your mouth. So, just by drinking through a straw, you can observe an important property of fluids: Fluids flow from areas of high pressure to areas of low pressure.

Pressure Differences and Breathing

Take a deep breath—fluid is flowing from high to low pressure! When you inhale, a muscle moves down in your chest. This movement makes the space in your chest bigger. So your lungs have room to expand. This expansion lowers the pressure in your lungs. The pressure in your lungs becomes lower than the air pressure outside your lungs. Then air flows into your lungs—from high to low pressure. **Figure 5** shows the reverse process when you exhale. Exhaling also causes fluids to flow from high to low pressure. When you exhale, the air in your lungs flows out from a region of high pressure (inside your chest) to a region of lower pressure (outside your body).

Figure 5 Exhaling, Pressure, and Fluid Flow

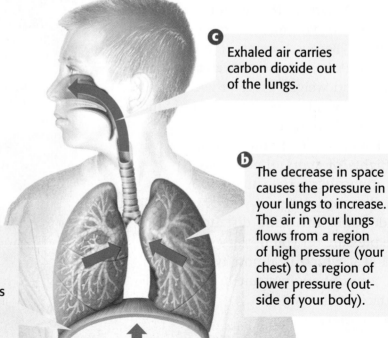

c Exhaled air carries carbon dioxide out of the lungs.

b The decrease in space causes the pressure in your lungs to increase. The air in your lungs flows from a region of high pressure (your chest) to a region of lower pressure (outside of your body).

a When you exhale, a muscle in your chest moves upward and decreases the space in your chest.

Pressure Differences and Tornadoes

Look at the tornado in **Figure 6.** Some of the damaging winds caused by tornadoes are the result of pressure differences. The air pressure inside a tornado is very low. Because the air pressure outside the tornado is higher than the pressure inside, air rushes into the tornado. The rushing air causes objects to be pushed into the tornado as though the tornado were a giant vacuum cleaner. The winds are usually very strong and affect the area around the tornado. So sometimes, the winds damage trees and buildings that are not even in the direct path of the tornado.

Figure 6 *Pressure differences in tornadoes make tornadoes like giant vacuum cleaners.*

SECTION Review

 8.8.a, 8.9.f

Summary

- A fluid is any material that flows and that takes the shape of its container.
- Pressure is the amount of force exerted on a given area.
- Moving particles of matter create pressure by colliding with one another and with the walls of their container.
- Atmospheric pressure is the pressure caused by the weight of the atmosphere.
- Fluid pressure increases as depth increases.
- Because water is denser than air, water exerts more pressure than air does.
- Fluids flow from areas of high pressure to areas of low pressure.

Understanding Concepts

1 **Describing** How do fluids exert pressure on a container?

2 **Applying** Why are you not crushed by atmospheric pressure?

3 **Analyzing** Explain why atmospheric pressure changes as depth changes.

4 **Describing** Describe density in terms of mass and volume.

Critical Thinking

5 **Making Inferences** When airplanes fly high in the atmosphere, why must they be pressurized for passenger safety?

6 **Applying Concepts** Explain why drinking through a straw shows that fluids flow from areas of high pressure to areas of low pressure.

7 **Making Comparisons** Explain why the density of ocean water is greater than the density of tap water.

Math Skills

8 **Using Equations** The water in a glass has a weight of 2.4 N. The bottom of the glass has an area of 0.012 m². What is the pressure exerted by the water on the bottom of the glass?

9 **Using Equations** What force is exerted on 2.5 m² if the pressure is 99,500 Pa?

Challenge

10 **Identifying Relationships** Mercury is a liquid that has a density of 13.5 g/mL. Water has a density of 1.0 g/mL. Equal volumes of mercury and water are in identical containers. Explain why the pressures exerted on the bottoms of the containers are different.

Internet Resources

For a variety of links related to this chapter, go to www.scilinks.org
Topic: Fluids and Pressure
SciLinks code: HY70586

Buoyancy and Density

Key Concept Buoyant force and density affect whether an object will float or sink in a fluid.

What You Will Learn

- All fluids exert an upward buoyant force on objects in the fluid.
- The buoyant force on an object is equal to the weight of the fluid displaced by the object.
- An object will float or sink depending on the relationship between the object's weight, buoyant force, and overall density.
- Density can be calculated from measurements of mass and volume. The overall density of an object can be changed by changing the object's shape, mass, or volume.

Why It Matters

Understanding buoyant force and density will help you predict whether an object will float or sink in a fluid.

Vocabulary

- buoyant force
- Archimedes' principle

READING STRATEGY

Graphic Organizer In your **Science Journal,** create an Idea Wheel about the factors that affect density.

8.8.a Students know density is mass per unit volume.

8.8.b Students know how to calculate the density of substances (regular and irregular solids and liquids) from measurements of mass and volume.

8.8.c Students know the buoyant force on an object in a fluid is an upward force equal to the weight of the fluid the object has displaced.

8.8.d Students know how to predict whether an object will float or sink.

▶ Why does ice float on water? Why doesn't it sink? Imagine that you use a straw to push an ice cube underwater. Then, you remove the straw. A force pushes the ice up to the water's surface. The force, called **buoyant force,** is the upward force that fluids exert on all matter.

Buoyant Force and Fluid Pressure

Look at **Figure 1.** Water exerts fluid pressure on all sides of an object. The pressure that is applied horizontally on one side of the object is equal to the pressure applied on the other side. These equal pressures balance one another. So, the only fluid pressures that may change the net force on the object are at the top and at the bottom. Pressure increases as depth increases. So, the pressure at the bottom of the object is greater than the pressure at the top. This difference in pressure is shown by the different lengths of the arrows in **Figure 1.** The water applies a net upward force on the object. This upward force, which is caused by differences in pressure, is buoyant force.

Standards Check Why is the pressure at the bottom of an object in a fluid greater than the pressure at the top of the object? 🐻 **8.8.c**

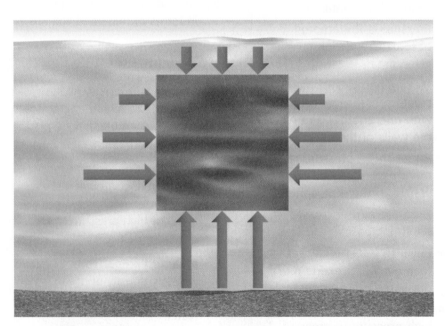

Figure 1 *There is more pressure at the bottom of an object because pressure increases with depth. This difference in pressure results in an upward buoyant force on the object.*

Finding the Buoyant Force

8.8.c

1. Use **string** to attach a ball of **modeling clay** to a **spring scale.** Record the weight of the clay.

2. Slowly lower the clay into a **tub** filled with **water.** Do not let the spring scale get wet. Record how the reading changes as the clay enters the water.

3. Record the reading on the scale when the clay is completely underwater.

4. Explain why the reading changed as the clay entered the water.

5. Calculate the buoyant force when the clay was completely underwater.

6. How does the buoyant force relate to the water that was displaced by the clay?

15 min

Determining Buoyant Force

Archimedes (AHR kuh MEE DEEZ) was a Greek mathematician who lived in the third century BCE. He discovered how to find buoyant force. **Archimedes' principle** states that the buoyant force on an object in a fluid is an upward force equal to the weight of the fluid that the object takes the place of, or *displaces.* Suppose the block in **Figure 2** displaces 250 mL of water. The weight of 250 mL of water is about 2.5 N. The weight of the displaced water is equal to the buoyant force acting on the block. So, the buoyant force on the block is 2.5 N. Notice that you need to know only the weight of the water that is displaced to find the buoyant force. You do not need to know the weight of the block. But in order to predict if an object will float or sink, you need to consider the weights of both the displaced water and the object.

Standards Check Explain how displacement is used to determine buoyant force. 8.8.c

buoyant force (BOY uhnt FAWRS) the upward force that keeps an object immersed in or floating on a liquid

Archimedes' principle (AHR kuh MEE DEEZ PRIN suh puhl) the principle that states that the buoyant force on an object in a fluid is an upward force equal to the weight of the volume of fluid that the object displaces

Wordwise **displace**
The prefix *dis-* means "away" or "in different directions."

Figure 2 *As a block is lowered into a container of water, the block displaces a certain volume of water. Then, this same volume of water flows into a smaller container.* **What does the weight of displaced water in the smaller container represent?**

Weight Versus Buoyant Force

An object in a fluid will sink if the object's weight is greater than the buoyant force (the weight of the fluid that the object displaces). An object floats only when the buoyant force on the object is equal to the object's weight.

Sinking

The rock in **Figure 3** weighs 75 N. It displaces 5 L of water. Archimedes' principle states that the buoyant force is equal to the weight of the displaced water—about 50 N. The rock's weight is greater than the buoyant force. So, the rock sinks.

Floating

The fish in **Figure 3** weighs 12 N. It displaces a volume of water that weighs 12 N. Because the fish's weight is equal to the buoyant force, the fish floats in the water. In fact, the fish is suspended in the water as it floats.

Now, look at the duck. The duck weighs 9 N. The duck floats. So, the buoyant force on the duck must equal 9 N. But only part of the duck has to be below the surface to displace 9 N of water. So, the duck floats on the surface of the water.

Buoying Up

If it dives underwater, the duck will displace more than 9 N of water. So, the buoyant force on the duck will be greater than the duck's weight. When the buoyant force on the duck is greater than the duck's weight, the duck is *buoyed up* (pushed up). An object is buoyed up until the part of the object underwater displaces an amount of water that equals the object's entire weight. Thus, an ice cube pops to the surface when it is pushed to the bottom of a glass of water.

Standards Check   What causes an object to buoy up?   **8.8.c**

Figure 3 *Will an object sink or float? The answer depends on the amount of buoyant force in relation to the object's weight.*

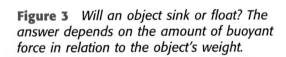

Weight = 12 N
Buoyant force = 12 N
Fish floats and is suspended in the water.

Weight = 9 N
Buoyant force = 9 N
Duck floats on the surface.

Weight = 75 N
Buoyant force = 50 N
Rock sinks.

Density and Floating

Think again about the rock in the lake. The rock displaces 5 L of water. But volumes of solids are measured in cubic centimeters (cm³). Because 1 mL is equal to 1 cm³, the volume of the rock is 5,000 cm³. But 5,000 cm³ of rock weighs more than an equal volume of water. So, the rock sinks. Because mass is proportional to weight, you can say that the rock has more mass per volume than water has. Mass per unit volume is density. The rock sinks because it is denser than water. The duck floats because it is less dense than water is. The density of the fish is equal to the density of the water.

Standards Check Explain why volume and mass affect whether an object will sink or float in water. 🐾 **8.8.a, 8.8.d**

More Dense Than Air

Why does an ice cube float on water but not in air? An ice cube floats on water because ice is less dense than water. But most substances are *more* dense than air. So, there are few substances that float in air. An ice cube is more dense than air, so ice doesn't float in air.

Less Dense Than Air

One substance that is less dense than air is helium, a gas. In fact, helium has one-seventh the density of air under normal conditions. So, helium floats in air. Because it floats in air, helium is used in parade balloons, such as the one shown in **Figure 4.**

Figure 4 *Helium in a balloon floats in air for the same reason that an ice cube floats on water: the helium is less dense than the surrounding fluid.*

MATH FOCUS

Finding Density

Find the density of a rock that has a mass of 10 g and a volume of 2 cm³.

Step 1: Write the equation for density. Density is calculated by using this equation:

$$density = \frac{mass}{volume}$$

Step 2: Replace mass and volume with the values in the problem, and solve.

$$density = \frac{10\ g}{2\ cm^3} = 5\ g/cm^3$$

Now It's Your Turn

1. What is the density of a 20 cm³ object that has a mass of 25 g?
2. A 546 g fish displaces 420 mL of water. What is the density of the fish? (Note: 1 mL = 1 cm³.)
3. A beaker holds 50 mL of a slimy green liquid. The mass of the liquid is 163 g. What is the density of the liquid?

Determining Density

To determine the density of an object, you need to know the object's mass and volume. You can use a balance to measure the mass of an object. But finding the volume of the object takes a little more work.

Volume of a Regular Solid

Some solids, such as cubes or rectangular blocks, have regular shapes. To find the volume of one of these objects, use a ruler to measure the length of each side. Then, multiply the three lengths together to find the volume of the object.

Volume of an Irregular Solid

Many things do not have a regular shape. So, you cannot easily calculate the volume of these objects. Instead, you can find the volume through water displacement. By measuring the volume of water that the object pushes aside, you find the volume of the object itself.

Standards Check Compare the methods for finding the volume of a regular solid and the volume of an irregular solid. 🐻 **8.8.b**

Trapped with No Bottle
You are stranded on a desert island and want to send a distress message in a bottle. But you do not have any bottles! Go to **go.hrw.com,** and type in the keyword HY7FLUW.

Quick Lab

Will It Sink or Float?

In this activity, you will predict whether an object will sink or float, plan a procedure to determine the density of the object, and test your prediction.

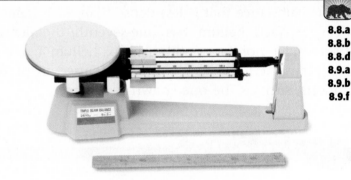

▶ **Try It!**

1. Examine a **regular solid.**

2. Predict whether the object will sink or float in water.

3. Plan an investigation to determine the density of the object and to test your prediction. Materials that may be helpful include a **metric ruler,** a **balance,** an appropriate formula for volume, a **plastic tub,** and **water.**

4. Record the steps that you plan to follow, and show your procedure to your teacher. If your procedure is approved, conduct your investigation. Record all of your data.

▶ **Think About It!**

5. Was your prediction correct?

6. Explain how you can use densities to better predict whether an object will sink or float in a fluid.

7. Evaluate the accuracy of your data based on how the solid behaved when placed in water.

8.8.a
8.8.b
8.8.d
8.9.a
8.9.b
8.9.f

 25 min

Figure 5 *A block of steel is denser than water, so the block sinks. But shaping that block of steel into a hollow form results in less overall density. So, the ship floats.*

Changing Overall Density

Steel is almost 8 times denser than water. Yet huge steel ships cruise the oceans with ease. But hold on! You just learned that substances that are denser than water will sink in water. So, how does a steel ship float?

Changing the Shape

The secret of how a ship floats is in the shape of the ship, as shown in **Figure 5**. What if a ship were just a big block of steel? If you put that block into water, the block would sink because it is denser than water. So, ships are built with a hollow shape. Imagine that the amount of steel in the ship is equal to the amount in the block. The hollow shape increases the volume of the ship. Remember that density is mass per unit volume. As volume increases, density decreases if the mass stays the same. So, an increase in the ship's volume leads to a decrease in the ship's density. Thus, ships made of steel float because their *overall density* is less than the density of water.

Most ships are built to displace more water than is necessary for the ships to float. Ships are made this way so that they will not sink when people and cargo are loaded on the ships.

Quick Lab

Ship Shape 8.8.a 8.8.d

1. Roll a **piece of clay** into a ball the size of a golf ball, and drop it into a **container of water.** Record your observations.

2. With your hands, flatten the ball of clay until it is a bit thinner than your little finger, and press it into the shape of a bowl or canoe.

3. Gently place the clay boat in the water. Record your observations.

4. How does the change of shape affect the buoyant force on the clay? How is that change related to the overall density of the clay boat? Record your answers.

⏱ **15 min**

Figure 6 **Controlling Density Using Ballast Tanks**

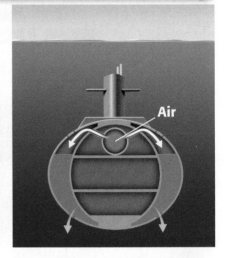

When a submarine is floating on the ocean's surface, its ballast tanks are filled mostly with air.

Vent holes on the ballast tanks are opened to allow the submarine to dive. Air escapes as the tanks fill with water.

Vent holes are closed, and compressed air is pumped into the ballast tanks to force the water out, so the submarine rises.

Changing the Mass

A submarine is a special kind of ship that can travel both on the surface of the water and underwater. Submarines have *ballast tanks* that can be opened to allow sea water to flow in. As water is added, the submarine's mass increases, but its volume stays the same. The submarine's overall density increases so that it can dive under the surface. Crew members control the amount of water taken in. In this way, they control how dense the submarine is and how deep it dives. Compressed air is used to blow the water out of the tanks so that the submarine can rise. Study **Figure 6** to learn how ballast tanks work.

Changing the Volume

Like a submarine, some fish adjust their overall density to stay at a certain depth in the water. Most bony fishes have an organ called a *swim bladder,* shown in **Figure 7.** This swim bladder is filled with gases that are produced in a fish's blood. The inflated swim bladder increases the fish's volume, which decreases the fish's overall density. Thus, the fish does not sink in the water. The fish's nervous system controls the amount of gas in the bladder. Some fish, such as sharks, do not have a swim bladder. These fish must swim constantly to keep from sinking.

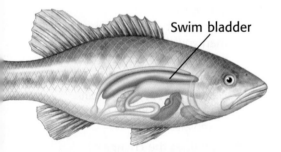

Swim bladder

Figure 7 *Most bony fishes have an organ called a* swim bladder *that allows them to adjust their overall density.*

Standards Check How does a swim bladder enable a fish to float?
🐻 **8.8.d**

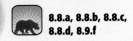
Summary

- All fluids exert an upward force called *buoyant force*.
- Buoyant force is caused by differences in fluid pressure.
- Archimedes' principle states that the buoyant force on an object is equal to the weight of the fluid displaced by the object.
- Any object that is denser than the surrounding fluid will sink. An object that is less dense than the surrounding fluid will float.
- The overall density of an object can be changed by changing the object's shape, mass, or volume.

Using Vocabulary

1. Use *buoyant force* and *Archimedes' principle* in the same sentence.

Understanding Concepts

2. **Applying** Explain how differences in fluid pressure create a buoyant force on an object.

3. **Concluding** How does an object's density help you determine whether the object will sink or float in water?

4. **Demonstrating** Name three methods that can be used to change the overall density of an object.

Critical Thinking

5. **Applying Concepts** An object weighs 20 N. It displaces a volume of water that weighs 15 N.
   a. What is the buoyant force on the object?
   b. Will this object float or sink in water? Explain your answer.

6. **Predicting Consequences** Iron has a density of 7.9 g/cm³. Mercury is a liquid that has a density of 13.5 g/cm³. Will iron float or sink in mercury? Explain your answer.

INTERPRETING GRAPHICS
The table below shows the mass and volume of three objects. Use the table below to answer the next two questions.

Mass and Volume Measurements		
Object	mass (g)	volume (cm³)
1	44.0	3,354.0
2	81.3	6.0
3	3.0	2,260.0

7. **Evaluating Data** Calculate the density of each object.

8. **Predicting Consequences** Predict whether each object will sink or float in water. (Hint: The density of liquid water is 1.00 g/cm³.)

Math Skills

9. **Using Equations** What is the density of an object that has a mass of 184 g and a volume of 50 cm³?

10. **Using Equations** What is the volume of a solid lead ball that has a mass of 454 g? (Hint: The density of solid lead is 11.35 g/cm³.)

11. **Using Equations** What is the mass of a sponge that has a density of 0.25 g/cm³ and a volume of 60 cm³?

Challenge

12. **Evaluating Hypotheses** Imagine that your brother tells you that all heavy objects sink in water. Do you agree or disagree with his statement? Explain your answer in terms of overall density, volume, and buoyant force.

13. **Predicting Consequences** What will happen to the density of a gas if the mass of gas doubles and the volume of the gas is cut in half?

Internet Resources

For a variety of links related to this chapter, go to www.scilinks.org

Topic: Buoyant Force; Undersea Technology in California

SciLinks code: HY70202; HY7C13

Skills Practice Lab

Fluids, Force, and Floating

Calculate the buoyant force on an object.

Compare the buoyant force on an object with its weight.

MATERIALS

- balance
- mass set
- pan, rectangular baking
- paper towels
- ruler, metric
- tub, plastic, large, rectangular
- water

SAFETY

Why do some objects sink in fluids but others float? In this lab, you will determine that an object floats when its weight equals the buoyant force exerted by the surrounding fluid.

Procedure

1 Copy the table shown below.

Measurement	Trial 1	Trial 2
Length (l), cm		
Width (w), cm		
Initial height (h_1), cm		
Initial volume (V_1), cm^3 $V_1 = l \times w \times h_1$		
New height (h_2), cm		
New total volume (V_2), cm^3 $V_2 = l \times w \times h_2$		
Displaced volume (ΔV), cm^3 $\Delta V = V_2 - V_1$		
Mass of displaced water, g $m = \Delta V \times 1$ g/cm^3		
Weight of displaced water, N (buoyant force)		
Weight of pan and masses, N		

DO NOT WRITE IN BOOK

2 Fill the tub half full with water. Measure (in centimeters) the length, width, and initial height of the water. Record your measurements in the table.

3 Use the equation given in the table to determine the initial volume of water in the tub. Record your results in the table.

4 Place the pan in the water, and place masses in the pan, as shown on the next page. Keep adding masses until the pan sinks to about three-quarters of its height. Record the new height of the water in the table. Then, use this value to determine and record the new total volume of water plus the volume of water displaced by the pan.

8.8.c Students know the buoyant force on an object in a fluid is an upward force equal to the weight of the fluid the object has displaced.
8.8.d Students know how to predict whether an object will float or sink.

5 Determine the volume of the water that the pan and masses displaced, and record this value in the table. The displaced volume is equal to the new total volume minus the initial volume.

6 Determine the mass of the displaced water by multiplying the displaced volume by its density (1 g/cm³). Record the mass in the table.

7 Divide the mass by 100. The value that you get is the weight of the displaced water in newtons (N), which is equal to the buoyant force. Record the weight of the displaced water in the table.

8 Remove the pan and masses, and dry them off. Use the balance to determine their total mass (in grams). Convert the mass to weight (N), as you did in step 7. Record the weight of the masses and pan in the table.

9 Place the empty pan in the tub. Perform a second trial by repeating steps 4–8. This time, add masses until the pan is just about to sink.

Analyze the Results

10 **Identifying Patterns**   Compare the buoyant force (the weight of the displaced water) with the weight of the pan and masses for both trials.

11 **Examining Data**   How did the buoyant force differ between the two trials? Explain.

Draw Conclusions

12 **Drawing Conclusions**   Use your observations to predict what will happen if you add even more mass to the pan than you did in the second trial. Explain your answer in terms of buoyant force.

13 **Making Predictions**   What will happen if you put the masses in the water without the pan? What difference does the pan's shape make?

Big Idea Question

14 **Identifying Relationships**   Explain the relationship between density and buoyant force. How do density and buoyant force affect whether an object will float or sink?

421

Science Skills Activity

Investigation and Experimentation
8.9.f Apply simple mathematical relationships to determine a missing quantity in a mathematic expression, given the two remaining terms (including speed = distance/time, density = mass/volume, force = pressure × area, volume = area × height).

Finding a Missing Quantity

▶ Tutorial

Procedure

Simple mathematical relationships can be used to help find a missing quantity when all but one of the terms are known. An equation that has three terms that can all change in value is called a *three-variable equation*. The equation for pressure is an example of a three-variable equation.

1 The equation for pressure is arranged to find pressure.

$$pressure = \frac{force}{area}$$

2 To find force, rearrange the equation by multiplying both sides by area.

$$force = pressure \times area$$

3 To find area, rearrange the equation for force shown in step 2 by dividing both sides by pressure.

$$area = \frac{force}{pressure}$$

Analysis

4 **Using Equations** To determine which form of a three-variable equation you need to use to solve a problem, read the problem carefully. The problem will ask you to find a missing quantity. This missing quantity will be one of the three variables. Make sure to use the form of the three-variable equation in which the missing quantity that you are trying to find appears by itself on one side of the equals sign. This form of the equation will solve for the missing quantity that the problem is asking you to find.

▶ You Try It!

Procedure

Use the correct form of the equation for pressure to answer the following questions. Show all of your work. Include the work that you do to rearrange the equation when necessary.

Analysis

1 **Using Equations** Suppose you buy a small water bed that has an area of 2.6 m² and that weighs 1,025 N. Find the pressure that the water bed exerts on the floor. (Hint: Weight is a measure of gravitational force.)

2 **Using Equations** Find the area of a stepping stone that weighs 1.2 N and exerts a pressure of 13 Pa.

3 **Using Equations** Find the weight of a filing cabinet that exerts a pressure of 150 Pa and that has an area of 0.5 m².

4 **Using Equations** The block of wood shown below is 0.055 m long, 0.040 m wide, and 0.020 m tall. If the block weighs 44 N, what amount of pressure does the block exert as it rests on its largest side, as shown below? (Hint: *area = length × width*.)

Chapter Summary

The Big Idea
Forces in fluids are related to pressure and density and can affect the motion of objects in the fluid.

Section

Vocabulary

1 Fluids and Pressure

Key Concept Fluid is a nonsolid state of matter. All fluids can flow and exert pressure evenly in all directions.

- Pressure is the amount of force exerted on a given area.
- Fluid pressure increases as depth increases.
- Density is mass per unit volume. Because water is denser than air, water exerts more pressure than air does.
- Fluids flow from areas of high pressure to areas of low pressure.

The force of air particles hitting the inner surface of a tire creates pressure.

fluid p. 406
pressure p. 406
pascal p. 406
atmospheric pressure p. 407

2 Buoyancy and Density

Key Concept Buoyant force and density affect whether an object will float or sink in a fluid.

- All fluids exert an upward buoyant force on objects in the fluid.
- The buoyant force on an object is equal to the weight of the fluid displaced by the object.
- An object will float or sink depending on the relationship between the object's weight, buoyant force, and overall density.
- Density can be calculated from measurements of mass and volume. The overall density of an object can be changed by changing the object's shape, mass, or volume.

Submarines adjust their overall density by using ballast tanks. This change in density allows them to sink or float.

buoyant force p. 412
Archimedes' principle p. 413

Chapter Review

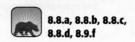

8.8.a, 8.8.b, 8.8.c, 8.8.d, 8.9.f

Organize

Two-Panel Flip Chart Review the FoldNote that you created at the beginning of the chapter. Add to or correct the FoldNote based on what you have learned.

Using Vocabulary

1 **Academic Vocabulary** Choose the appropriate form of the word *displace* for the following sentence: "The buoyant force on an object is equal to the weight of the fluid that the object ___."
a. displace.
b. displaces.
c. displacing.
d. was displaced.

Correct each statement by replacing the underlined term.

2 A unit used to express atmospheric pressure is the <u>fluid</u>.

3 A <u>pascal</u> can be a liquid or a gas.

4 <u>Buoyant force</u> on an object is caused by the weight of the air above the object.

5 <u>Atmospheric pressure</u> is the upward force that fluids exert on objects.

Understanding Concepts

Multiple Choice

6 An object that is surrounded by a fluid will displace a volume of fluid that is
a. equal to the object's own volume.
b. less than the object's own volume.
c. greater than the object's own volume.
d. denser than the object itself.

7 Materials that can flow to fit their containers include
a. gases.
b. liquids.
c. both gases and liquids.
d. gases, liquids, and solids.

8 If an object weighing 50 N displaces a volume of water that weighs 10 N, what is the buoyant force on the object?
a. 60 N
b. 50 N
c. 40 N
d. 10 N

9 Fluid pressure is always directed
a. up.
b. down.
c. sideways.
d. in all directions.

10 A helium-filled balloon floats in air because
a. there is more air than helium.
b. helium is less dense than air.
c. helium is as dense as air.
d. helium is denser than air.

Short Answer

11 **Applying** Why are bubbles round?

12 **Analyzing** In what way are tornadoes like giant vacuum cleaners?

INTERPRETING GRAPHICS Use the image below to answer the next two questions.

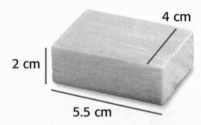

4 cm

2 cm

5.5 cm

13 **Applying** The mass of the object above is 220 g. What is the object's density?

14 **Concluding** Will this object sink or float in water? Explain your answer.

Writing Skills

15 Communicating Concepts Write an essay that clearly explains to a 3rd grade student why objects float or sink. Your essay should include a thesis statement and evidence that supports your ideas. Finally, make sure that your essay has a conclusion sentence.

Critical Thinking

16 Concept Mapping Use the following terms to create a concept map: *fluid, pressure, density, Archimedes' principle, pascals,* and *buoyant force.*

INTERPRETING GRAPHICS Use the diagram of the iceberg below to answer the next three questions.

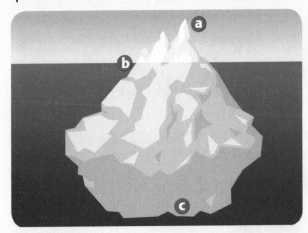

17 Applying Concepts At what point (**a, b,** or **c**) is water pressure greatest on the iceberg?

18 Evaluating Data How much of the iceberg has a weight equal to the buoyant force?
a. all of the iceberg
b. the section from **a** to **b**
c. the section from **b** to **c**
d. None of the above

19 Making Comparisons Compare the density of ice with the density of water. Explain your answer in terms of mass and volume.

20 Making Comparisons Will a ship loaded with beach balls float higher or lower in the water than an empty ship will? Explain your answer.

21 Applying Concepts Inside all vacuum cleaners is a high-speed fan. Explain how this fan causes the vacuum cleaner to pick up dirt.

22 Evaluating Data Is water pressure greater at a depth of 1 m in a large lake or at a depth of 2 m in a small pond? Explain your answer.

INTERPRETING GRAPHICS Use the image below to answer the next two questions.

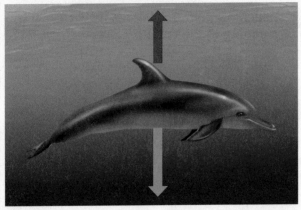

23 Applying Concepts Identify the force that each arrow represents.

24 Evaluating Data Will this dolphin float on the surface of the water, sink, or be suspended in the water? Explain your answer.

Math Skills

25 Using Equations Calculate the area of a 1,500 N object that exerts a pressure of 500 Pa (500 N/m²). Then, calculate the pressure that the same object exerts over twice that area.

Challenge

26 Evaluating Hypotheses A 600 N girl on stilts says to two 600 N boys who are sitting on the ground, "I am exerting over twice as much pressure as the two of you are exerting together!" Could this statement be true? Explain your reasoning.

Standards Assessment

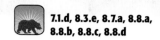

REVIEWING ACADEMIC VOCABULARY

1 Choose the appropriate form of the word *displace* for the following sentence: "When the volume of an object is not easily calculated, you can find the object's volume by using ___."?

A displace

B displacing

C displacement

D displaced

2 Which of the following words is closest in meaning to the word *predict*?

A apply

B explain

C say ahead of time

D identify

3 In the sentence "The weight of the displaced water is equal to the buoyant force acting on the object," what does the word *displaced* mean?

A assigned to

B moved aside

C changed

D adapted to

4 Which of the following words means "the amount of space that an object contains or takes up"?

A width

B length

C force

D volume

REVIEWING CONCEPTS

5 Which procedure allows you to determine the volume of an irregularly shaped object?

A Divide the density of the object by the mass of the object.

B Calculate the water pressure around the object.

C Measure the amount of water displaced by the object.

D Multiply the width, length, and height of the object.

6 Which of the following is the correct way to find the density of an object?

A Divide the mass of the object by the volume of the object.

B Multiply the mass of the object by the volume of the object.

C Measure the buoyant force that is acting on the object

D Measure the weight of the water displaced by the object.

Mass and Volume Measurements		
Object	Mass (g)	Volume (cm³)
1	12	4
2	790	100
3	88	11
4	5	50

7 The table above shows mass and volume measurements for four objects. Which of these objects will float in water, given that the density of liquid water is 1 g/cm³?

A Object 1

B Object 2

C Object 3

D Object 4

8 A submarine can travel on the surface of water and underwater. How does a submarine dive underwater?

A Water is added to special tanks in the submarine to increase its mass and therefore its overall density.

B Air is released from special tanks in the submarine to increase its volume.

C Special mechanisms change the submarine's shape and allow it to dive.

D The density of the submarine increases and the water pressure decreases when it dives.

9 You push a ball under water in a swimming pool. When you let go of the ball, it pops back to the surface. Which of the following is the force that is responsible for this phenomenon?

A water pressure

B buoyant force

C gravity

D density

10 A toy submarine that has a mass of 1,200 g displaces 1,000 mL of water. What is the density of the toy submarine?

A 0.83 g/cm^3

B 1.2 g/cm^3

C 200 g/cm^3

D 2,200 g/cm^3

11 A rock weighs 30 N. It displaces a volume of water that weighs 5 N. What is the buoyant force on the object?

A 5 N

B 6 N

C 30 N

D 35 N

REVIEWING PRIOR LEARNING

12 Which structure in a eukaryotic cell liberates energy for the work that the cell does?

A nucleus

B vacuole

C centrosome

D mitochondrion

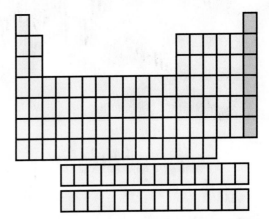

13 Which class of elements is in the shaded region of the periodic table diagram above?

A metals

B metalloids

C noble gases

D halogens

14 Which of the following best describes the behavior of atoms in a solid?

A widely separated

B loosely connected

C locked in position

D slide past each other

Standards Assessment

Science in Action

Science, Technology, and Society

Deep Flight

Imagine that you are the pilot of a revolutionary undersea vessel that can dive, spin, and turn just like an airplane. Can a craft be designed to "fly" underwater? Engineer Graham Hawkes decided to find out.

In 1996, Hawkes launched his first winged submersible at Monterey Bay, California. He called it *Deep Flight 1*. Since then, Hawkes has created several other submersibles that look like small airplanes with stubby wings. *Deep Flight* submersibles cost a lot less than submarines, and their battery-powered motor lets you cruise along at 9 km/h!

Math ACTIVITY

At an average speed of 9 km/h, how long would it take a *Deep Flight* submersible to "fly" underwater from Los Angeles, California, to Catalina Island—a distance of 35.2 km?

Science Fiction

"Wet Behind the Ears"
by Jack C. Haldeman II

Willie Joe Thomas cheated to get a swimming scholarship. Now, he is faced with a major swim meet, and his coach told him that he has to swim or be kicked off the team. Willie Joe could lose his scholarship.

One day, Willie Joe's roommate, Frank, announces that he has developed a new "sliding compound." Frank said something about using the compound to make ships go faster. So, Willie Joe thought, If it works for ships, it might work for swimmers.

See what happens when Willie Joe tries to save his scholarship by using Frank's compound at the swim meet. Read "Wet Behind the Ears," by Jack C. Haldeman II in the *Holt Anthology of Science Fiction*.

Language Arts ACTIVITY

Analyze the story structure of "Wet Behind the Ears." In your analysis, identify the introduction, the rising action, the climax, and the denouement. Summarize your analysis in a chart.

Alisha Bracken

Scuba Instructor Alisha Bracken first started scuba diving in her freshman year of college. Her first dives were in a saltwater hot spring near Salt Lake City, Utah. "It was awesome," Bracken says. "There were nurse sharks, angelfish, puffer fish, and brine shrimp!" Bracken enjoyed her experience so much that she wanted to share it with other people. The best way to do that was to become an instructor and teach other people to dive.

Bracken says that one of the biggest challenges of being a scuba instructor is teaching people to adapt and function in a foreign environment. She believes that learning to dive properly is important not only for the safety of the diver but also for the protection of the underwater environment. She relies on science principles to help teach people how to control their movements and protect the natural environment. "Buoyancy is the foundation of teaching people to dive comfortably," she explains. "Without it, we cannot float on the surface or stay off the bottom. Underwater life can be damaged if students do not learn and apply the concepts of buoyancy."

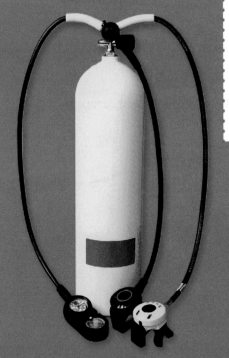

Social Studies ACTiViTY

Sometimes, scuba divers and other underwater explorers investigate shipwrecks on the bottom of the ocean. Research the exploration of a specific shipwreck. Make a poster showing what artifacts were retrieved from the shipwreck and what was learned from the exploration.

Internet Resources

- To learn more about careers in science, visit www.scilinks.org and enter the SciLinks code HY70225.
- To learn more about these Science in Action topics, visit go.hrw.com and type in the keyword HY7FLUF.
- Check out articles related to this chapter by visiting go.hrw.com. Just type in the keyword HY7FLUC.

UNIT 6

TIMELINE

Studying the Universe

In this unit, you will learn about the universe. Long before science was called *science*, people looked up at the night sky and tried to make sense of the twinkling lights above. Today, astronomers have discovered a universe that is far more curious and complex than their predecessors could have imagined. This timeline shows some of the events leading to our current understanding of the universe and of our solar system.

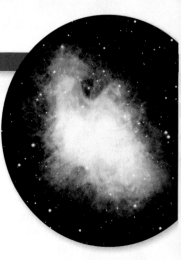

1054

Chinese and Korean astronomers record the appearance of a supernova, an exploding star. Strangely, no European observations of this event have ever been found.

The Crab Nebula

Andromeda Galaxy

1924

An astronomer named Edwin Hubble confirms the existence of other galaxies.

1983

Sally Ride becomes the first American woman to travel in space.

1582

Ten days are dropped from October as the Julian calendar is replaced by the Gregorian calendar.

1666

Using a prism, Isaac Newton discovers that white light is composed of different colors.

1898

The War of the Worlds, by H. G. Wells, is published.

1958

The National Aeronautics and Space Administration (NASA) is established to oversee the exploration of space.

1970

Apollo 13 is damaged shortly after leaving orbit. The spacecraft's three astronauts navigate around the moon to return safely to Earth.

1977

Voyager 1 and *Voyager 2* are launched on missions to Jupiter, Saturn, and beyond. Now, more than 10 billion kilometers away from Earth, they are still sending back information about space.

Voyager 2

1992

Astronomers discover the first planet outside the solar system.

1998

John Glenn becomes the oldest human in space. His second trip into space comes 36 years after he became the first American to orbit Earth.

2003

Astronomers discover three distant quasars that date back to a time when the universe was only 800 million years old. It takes light 13 billion years to reach Earth from the farthest of the three quasars.

Improving Comprehension

Graphic Organizers are important visual tools that can help you organize information and improve your reading comprehension. The Graphic Organizer below is called a *pyramid chart*. Instructions for creating other types of Graphic Organizers are located in the **Study Skills** section of the Appendix.

How to Make a Pyramid Chart

1. Draw a triangle that is divided into sections like the one shown below. Draw as many sections as you need to draw.

2. Draw a box to the left of the triangle, as shown in the example. Write the topic of your pyramid chart in the box.

3. In each section of your triangle, write information about the topic in the appropriate level of the pyramid.

When to Use a Pyramid Chart

A pyramid chart is used to organize information in a hierarchy of magnitude or detail. As the shape of the pyramid suggests, the pyramid's bottom level contains information that is largest in terms of magnitude and broadest, or least specific, in terms of detail. As you read about science, look for information that you can organize into a hierarchy.

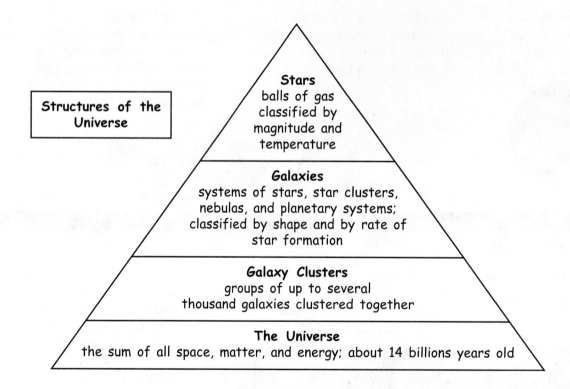

Structures of the Universe

Stars
balls of gas classified by magnitude and temperature

Galaxies
systems of stars, star clusters, nebulas, and planetary systems; classified by shape and by rate of star formation

Galaxy Clusters
groups of up to several thousand galaxies clustered together

The Universe
the sum of all space, matter, and energy; about 14 billions years old

You Try It!

This Reading Strategy can also be used within the chapter that you are about to read. Practice making your own *pyramid chart* as directed in the Reading Strategy for Section 1. Record your work in your Science Journal.

Unpacking the Standards

The information below "unpacks" the standards by breaking them down into basic parts. The higher-level, academic vocabulary is highlighted and defined to help you understand the language of the standards. "What It Means" restates the standards as simply as possible.

California Standard	Academic Vocabulary	What It Means
8.2.g Students know the **role** of gravity in forming and **maintaining** the shapes of planets, stars, and the solar system.	**role** (ROHL) a part or function; purpose **maintain** (mayn TAYN) to keep the same	You must know how the force of attraction between objects that is due to their masses affects the shapes of planets, stars, and the solar system.
8.4.a Students know galaxies are clusters of billions of stars and may have different shapes.		Galaxies are groups of billions of stars and may have different shapes.
8.4.b Students know that the Sun is one of many stars in the Milky Way galaxy and that stars may differ in size, temperature, and color.		The sun is one of many stars in the Milky Way galaxy. Stars may differ in size, temperature, and color.
8.4.c Students know how to use astronomical units and light years as measures of distances between the Sun, stars, and Earth.		You must know how to use the distance between Earth and the sun and the distance that light can travel in one year to measure distances between the sun, stars, and Earth.
8.4.d Students know that stars are the **source** of light for all bright objects in outer space and that the Moon and planets shine by reflected sunlight, not by their own light.	**source** (SAWRS) the thing from which something else comes	Stars are the only objects in space that generate light. All other bright objects in outer space, such as the moon and planets, shine because they reflect light from the sun. They do not make their own light.

Stars, Galaxies, and the Universe

The Big Idea

The structure and composition of the universe can be learned by studying stars and galaxies and their evolution.

California Standards

Focus on Physical Sciences
8.2 Unbalanced forces cause changes in velocity. (Section 4)
8.4 The structure and composition of the universe can be learned from studying stars and galaxies and their evolution. (Sections 1, 2, 3, and 4)

Investigation and Experimentation
8.9 Scientific progress is made by asking meaningful questions and conducting careful investigations. (Science Skills Activity)

Math
8.15.0 Algebra 1

English–Language Arts
8.2.2 Reading
8.2.1 Writing

About the Photo

This image, taken by NASA's *Hubble Space Telescope,* shows a near collision between two spiral galaxies—the larger NGC 2207 galaxy on the left and the smaller IC 2163 galaxy on the right. Gravitational forces from NGC 2207 have changed the shape of IC 2163. Stars and gas from IC 2163 form long streamers that extend outward from the galaxy for a hundred thousand light-years.

Organize

Three-Panel Flip Chart

Before you read this chapter, create the FoldNote entitled "Three-Panel Flip Chart." Label the flaps of the three-panel flip chart with "Stars," "Galaxies," and "The universe." As you read the chapter, write information about each topic under the appropriate flap.

Instructions for creating FoldNotes are located in the Study Skills section on p. 519 of the Appendix.

Explore Activity

15 min

Exploring the Movement of Galaxies in the Universe

In this activity, you will explore why distant galaxies appear to be moving away from the Milky Way galaxy faster than galaxies close to the Milky Way galaxy are.

Procedure

1. Using **scissors,** cut a thick **rubber band** so that it is at least 4 cm long.

2. Using a **metric ruler** to obtain accurate measurements and a **marker,** draw five ovals 1 cm apart from each other on the rubber band. Label the ovals "A" through "E" from left to right. Oval A represents the Milky Way galaxy, and ovals B through E represent galaxies at various distances from the Milky Way galaxy.

3. Stretch the rubber band to double its original length so that the ovals are 2 cm apart.

8.4.a

4. Stretch the rubber band again—if possible— so that it is triple its original length and the ovals are 3 cm apart.

Analysis

5. How did the distances between galaxies increase as the rubber band was stretched?

6. How did the distances between each pair of galaxies change? Explain your answer.

Stars

Key Concept Stars differ in size, color, temperature, brightness, and age. Scientists use these differences to classify stars.

▶ Most stars appear as faint dots of light in the night sky. But stars are actually huge, hot, and bright balls of gas that are trillions of kilometers from Earth. How do astronomers learn about stars, which are too far away to visit? They study starlight!

Color of Stars

Look at the flames on the candle and on the Bunsen burner shown in **Figure 1.** Which flame is hotter? How can you tell? The blue flame of the Bunsen burner is much hotter than the yellow flame of the candle. Scientists know that the color of a star indicates the star's temperature in the same way that the color of a flame indicates how hot the flame is. Red stars are the coolest, and blue stars are the hottest. Other stars have colors that fall between red and blue.

If you look carefully at the night sky, you might notice that stars are different colors. Betelgeuse (BET'l JOOZ), which is red, and Rigel (RIE juhl), which is blue, are the stars that form two corners of the constellation Orion (oh RIE uhn), shown in **Figure 1.** Because these two stars differ in color, we can conclude that they differ in temperature, too.

Standards Check What is the relationship between the color and temperature of a star? **8.4.b**

Figure 1 *The blue flame of the Bunsen burner is hotter than the yellow flame of the candle. Similarly, the blue star Rigel is hotter than the red star Betelgeuse.*

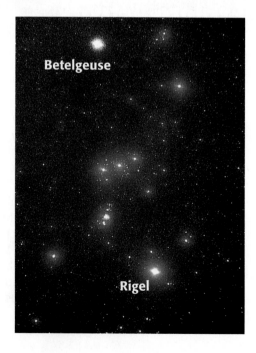

Betelgeuse

Rigel

Composition of Stars

To learn what stars are made of, astronomers study the light from stars. When you look at white light through a glass prism, you see a rainbow of colors called a **spectrum** (plural, *spectra*). The spectrum consists of millions of colors, including red, orange, yellow, green, blue, and violet. Astronomers use an instrument called a *spectroscope* to separate a star's light into a spectrum. The spectrum gives astronomers information about the composition and temperature of a star.

spectrum (SPEK truhm) the band of colors produced when white light passes through a prism

Types of Spectra

A hot, solid object, such as the glowing wire inside a light bulb, gives off a *continuous spectrum,* shown in **Figure 2.** A continuous spectrum shows all of the colors. However, hot gases emit only certain wavelengths of light, or colors. When a chemical element emits light, only some colors in the spectrum show up. All of the other colors are missing. The colors that appear are called *emission lines.* Every element has a unique set of bright emission lines that act like a fingerprint for that element. **Figure 3** shows emission spectra for four elements.

Trapping the Light: Cosmic Detective Work

The center of a star is so hot that, like a light bulb, it produces white light. However, the cooler atmosphere of a star absorbs rather than emits colors of light. Therefore, the spectrum of a star is called an *absorption spectrum.* An absorption spectrum is produced when light from a hot solid or dense gas passes through a less dense, cooler gas. The cooler gas absorbs certain portions of the spectrum. Thus, the black lines of a star's spectrum represent portions of the spectrum that are absorbed by the star's atmosphere. **Figure 2** shows the absorption spectrum for the element hydrogen.

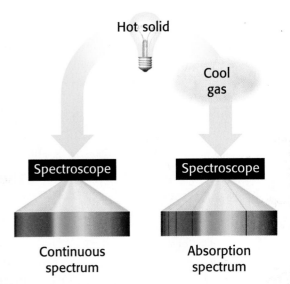

Figure 2 *A continuous spectrum (left) shows all colors, while an absorption spectrum (right) shows which wavelengths of light are absorbed. Black lines appearing in the spectrum show which wavelengths are absorbed.*

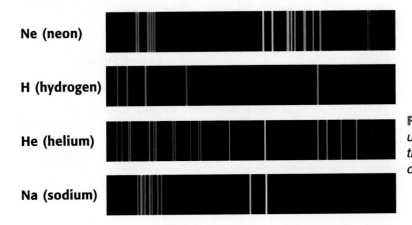

Figure 3 *Neon gas produces a unique set of emission lines, as do the elements hydrogen, helium, and sodium.*

Absorption Spectrum of the Sun

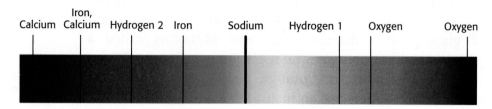

Calcium | Iron, Calcium | Hydrogen 2 | Iron | Sodium | Hydrogen 1 | Oxygen | Oxygen

Identifying Elements by Using Dark Lines

The spectrum produced by the absorption of light can be read to determine the elements in a star's atmosphere. The pattern of lines in a star's absorption spectrum is unique to that star and to the stage that the star occupies in its life cycle.

If a star were made of one element, we could easily identify the element from the star's absorption spectrum. But a star is a mixture of elements, and all of the different lines for a star's elements appear together in its spectrum, as **Figure 4** shows. Often, sorting the patterns is a puzzle.

The Types of Elements in a Star

Stars are made of mostly hydrogen and helium gases. But stars also have traces of many other elements. Carbon, nitrogen, and oxygen are the most common of these elements. Stars also contain calcium, iron, and sodium. In fact, all of the elements in your body that are heavier than hydrogen were once a part of a star! **Table 1** lists the types of elements that make up stars of various temperatures.

Standards Check What are two elements that commonly make up stars? 8.4.b

Table 1	Types of Stars			
Class	Color	Surface temperature (°C)	Elements detected	Examples of stars
O	blue	above 30,000	helium	10 Lacertae
B	blue-white	10,000 to 30,000	helium and hydrogen	Rigel and Spica
A	blue-white	7,500 to 10,000	hydrogen	Vega and Sirius
F	yellow-white	6,000 to 7,500	hydrogen and heavier elements	Canopus and Procyon
G	yellow	5,000 to 6,000	calcium and other heavy elements	the sun and Capella
K	orange	3,500 to 5,000	calcium and molecules	Arcturus and Aldebaran
M	red	less than 3,500	molecules	Betelgeuse and Antares

Classifying Stars

In the 1800s, astronomers started to collect and classify the spectra of many stars. At first, they assigned letters to each type of spectrum. They classified stars according to the elements that the stars contained. Later, scientists realized that using temperature would be a better way to classify stars.

Differences in Temperature

Stars are now classified by how hot they are. Temperature differences between stars result in color differences that you can see. For example, class O stars are blue—the hottest stars. Look at **Table 1.** Notice that the stars are arranged in order from highest temperature to lowest temperature.

Differences in Brightness

Using only their eyes, early astronomers created a system to classify stars based on brightness. They called the brightest stars in the sky *first-magnitude* stars and the dimmest stars *sixth-magnitude* stars. But when astronomers began to use telescopes, they found many stars that had been too dim to see with only the eye. Rather than replacing the old system of magnitudes, astronomers added to it. Positive numbers represent dim stars, and negative numbers represent bright stars. For example, by using large telescopes, astronomers can see stars as dim as 30th magnitude. These stars are less than one-billionth as bright as the dimmest stars visible to the naked eye. And the brightest star in the night sky, Sirius (SIR ee uhs), has a magnitude of −1.4. The Big Dipper, shown in **Figure 5,** contains both bright stars and dim stars.

Standards Check Explain how astronomers use both positive numbers and negative numbers to describe brightness. 8.4.b

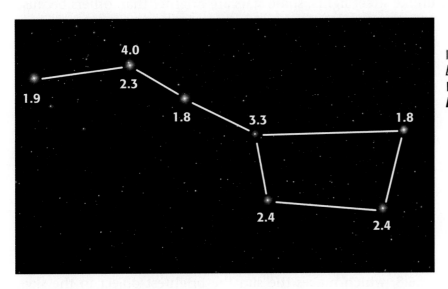

Figure 5 *The Big Dipper contains both bright stars and dim stars.* **What is the magnitude of the brightest star in the Big Dipper?**

Figure 6 *You can estimate how far away each street light is by looking at its apparent brightness.*

apparent magnitude (uh PER uhnt MAG nuh TOOD) the brightness of a star as seen from Earth

absolute magnitude (AB suh LOOT MAG nuh TOOD) the brightness that a star would have at a distance of 32.6 light-years from Earth

Starlight, Star Bright

Magnitude is used to compare the brightness of one object with the brightness of another object. For every five-point difference in magnitude, brightness changes by a multiplication factor of 100. The brightest blue stars, for example, have an absolute magnitude of −10. The sun has an absolute magnitude of about +5. How many times as bright as the sun is a blue star?

How Bright Is That Star?

If you look at a row of street lights, do all of the lights look the same? Of course not! As **Figure 6** shows, the nearest ones look brightest, and the farthest ones look dimmest.

Apparent Magnitude

The brightness of a star is called **apparent magnitude.** Brightness is proportional to the inverse of the square of the distance. Thus, a light that is half as far away as another light is 4 times brighter than the other light. So, a light that is 10 m away from you will appear 4 (2×2, or 2^2) times brighter than a light that is 20 m away from you. The same light will appear 9 (3×3, or 3^2) times brighter than a light that is 30 m away. But unlike street lights, some stars are brighter than others because of their size or energy output, not because of their distance from Earth. So, how can you tell how bright a star is?

Standards Check What is apparent magnitude? 📖 **8.4.b**

Absolute Magnitude

Astronomers use a star's apparent magnitude and distance from Earth to calculate the star's absolute magnitude. **Absolute magnitude** is a measure of how bright a star would be if the star were 32.6 light-years from Earth. If all stars were the same distance away, their absolute magnitudes would be the same as their apparent magnitudes. The absolute magnitude of the sun, for example, is +4.8, which is ordinary for a star. But because the sun is so close to Earth, its apparent magnitude is −26.8, which makes the sun the brightest object in the sky.

Distance to the Stars

Because stars are so far away, astronomers use a unit called the *light-year* to measure the distance from Earth to the stars. A **light-year** is the distance that light travels in one year. Obviously, it is easier to describe the distance to the North Star as 431 light-years than as 4,080,000,000,000,000 km. But how do astronomers measure a star's distance from Earth?

As Earth revolves around the sun, stars close to Earth seem to move and distant stars seem to stay in one place. The apparent shift in position of a star is called **parallax.** In **Figure 7,** the big star on the left when seen from Earth in July appears to shift to the right when seen in January. This shift can be seen only through telescopes. Astronomers use parallax and simple trigonometry to find the actual distance to stars that are close to Earth.

Standards Check Explain why astronomers use light-years rather than kilometers to measure distances from Earth to stars. 🐻 8.4.c

Motions of Stars

As you know, daytime and nighttime are caused by the rotation of Earth. Earth's tilt and revolution around the sun cause the seasons. During each season, Earth faces a different part of the sky at night. Look at **Figure 7** again. In January, Earth's night side faces a different part of the sky than it faces in July. Therefore, you see a different set of constellations at different times of the year.

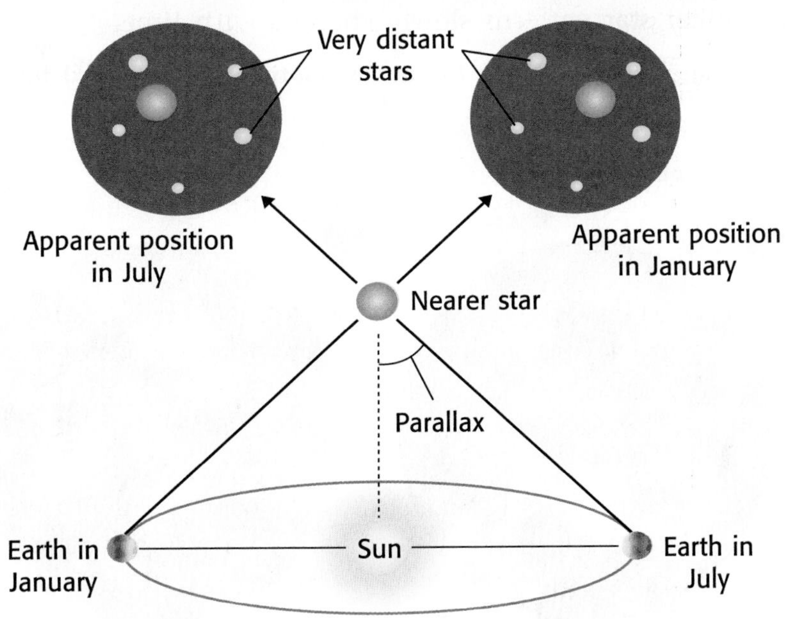

light-year (LIET YIR) the distance that light travels in one year; about 9.46 trillion kilometers

parallax (PAR uh LAKS) an apparent shift in the position of an object when viewed from different locations

Quick Lab

Demonstrating Parallax   8.4.c

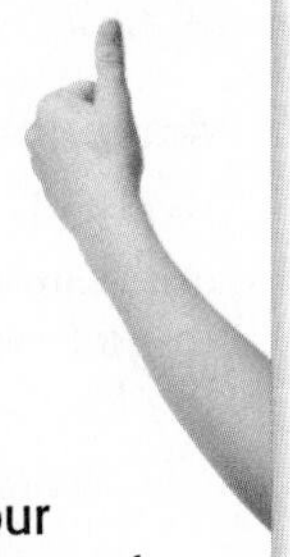

1. Hold your thumb in front of your face at arm's length.

2. Close one eye, and use your thumb to cover an object some distance away.

3. Without moving your head, open your eye and close the other eye. What seems to happen to your thumb relative to the object that you covered in step 2?

4. Now, bring your thumb close to your face, and repeat steps 2 and 3.

5. How does this activity demonstrate parallax?

🕐 10 min

Figure 7   Measuring a Star's Parallax

Very distant stars

Apparent position in July

Apparent position in January

Nearer star

Parallax

Earth in January

Sun

Earth in July

Figure 8 *As Earth rotates on its axis, the stars appear to rotate counterclockwise around Polaris.*

The Apparent Motion of Stars

Because of Earth's rotation, the sun appears to move across the sky. Likewise, if you look at the night sky long enough, the stars also appear to move. In fact, at night you can observe that the whole sky is rotating above us. Look at **Figure 8.** All of the stars that you see appear to rotate around Polaris, the North Star, which is almost directly above Earth's North Pole. Because of Earth's rotation, all of the stars in the sky appear to make one complete circle around Polaris every 24 h.

The Actual Motion of Stars

You now know that the apparent motion of the sun and stars in the sky is due to Earth's rotation and its revolution around the sun. But each star is also moving in space. Because stars are so distant, however, their actual motion is hard to see. If you could put thousands of years into one hour, a star's movement would be obvious. **Figure 9** shows how the shape of familiar star patterns slowly changes with time.

Standards Check Why is the actual motion of stars hard to see?
🐻 **8.4.b**

Astronomer Biographies
Write a biography of an interesting astronomer. Go to **go.hrw.com,** and type in the keyword HY7UNVW.

Figure 9 *Over time, the shapes of star patterns, such as the Big Dipper and other patterns, change.*

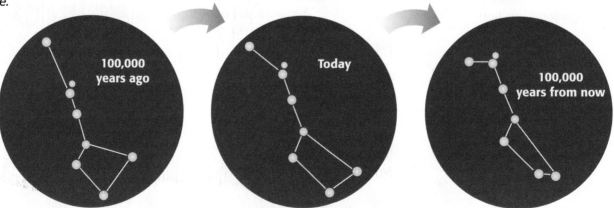

100,000 years ago

Today

100,000 years from now

Summary

- The color of a star depends on the temperature of the star. Blue stars are hottest. Red stars are coolest.

- The spectrum of a star shows which elements make up a star's atmosphere.

- Apparent magnitude is the brightness of a star as seen from Earth. Absolute magnitude is a measure of how bright a star would be if the star were 32.6 light-years from Earth.

- Astronomers use parallax and trigonometry to measure distances to stars that are close to Earth. They use light-years to describe those distances.

- Stars appear to move because of Earth's rotation. The actual motion of stars is hard to see because stars are so distant.

Using Vocabulary

1. Use *apparent magnitude* and *absolute magnitude* in the same sentence.

2. Use *spectrum, light-year,* and *parallax* in separate sentences.

Understanding Concepts

3. **Analyzing**   Explain how color indicates the temperature of a star.

4. **Summarizing**   How do astronomers use spectra to determine the composition of a star?

5. **Identifying**   What two elements are most commonly found in stars?

6. **Comparing**   Compare the absolute magnitude of stars with the apparent magnitude of stars.

7. **Summarizing**   How do astronomers measure distances from Earth to stars?

8. **Analyzing**   Explain why astronomers use light-years to describe distances from Earth to stars.

9. **Summarizing**   Explain why stars appear to move in the sky.

Critical Thinking

10. **Making Comparisons**   Compare a continuous spectrum with an absorption spectrum. Then, explain how an absorption spectrum can identify the elements in a star's atmosphere.

11. **Identifying Relationships**   The apparent magnitude of the sun is −26.8, while the absolute magnitude of the sun is +4.8. Explain why.

12. **Applying Concepts**   If a certain star displayed a large parallax, what could you say about the star's distance from Earth?

Math Skills

13. **Making Calculations**   How many times as bright as a light that is 90 m away from you does a light that is 10 m away from you appear? Show your work.

Challenge

INTERPRETING GRAPHICS   Use the illustrations below to answer the next question.

14. **Evaluating Data**   If all of the stars appear to make one complete circle around Polaris every 24 h, approximately how much time has passed between the illustration of the sky on the left and the illustration of the sky on the right?

Internet Resources

For a variety of links related to this chapter, go to www.scilinks.org

Topic: Stars
SciLinks code: HY71448

The Life Cycle of Stars

Key Concept   Stars vary in mass, size, brightness, color, and temperature, and these variations are related to the stars' life cycles.

Because stars can exist for billions of years, scientists cannot observe a star throughout its entire life. Therefore, scientists have developed theories about the life cycle of stars by studying large numbers of stars in different stages of development.

Types of Stars

Stars can be classified by mass, size, brightness, color, temperature, composition, and age. A star can be classified as one type of star early in its life cycle and as a different type of star as it ages. A star is classified differently as its properties change. Its properties most often relate to whether the star can generate energy by nuclear fusion. The fast-expanding gas clouds shown in **Figure 1** contain the material of a dying star.

The Life Cycle of Sunlike Stars

Like the stages in all natural cycles, the stages in a star's life progress from birth to death. The following paragraphs describe the stages in the life cycle of a sunlike star.

Protostars

A star begins its life as a ball of gas and dust. Gravity pulls the gas and dust into a sphere. As the sphere becomes denser, it gets hotter and eventually reaches a temperature of about 10,000,000°C in its center. As hydrogen combines into helium, energy is released in a process called *nuclear fusion.*

Figure 1   *When sunlike stars die, they throw most of their material outward.*

8.4.b Students know that the Sun is one of many stars in the Milky Way galaxy and that stars may differ in size, color, and temperature.

Main-Sequence Stars

After a sunlike star forms, it enters the **main sequence,** the second and longest stage of its life cycle. During this stage, energy is generated in the core of the star as hydrogen atoms fuse into helium atoms. The size of a main-sequence star changes very little as long as the star has a continuous supply of hydrogen nuclei to fuse into helium nuclei.

Standards Check Describe a star in the main sequence. 🐻 **8.4.b**

Giants and Supergiants

When a main-sequence star uses all of the hydrogen in its core, helium begins to fuse, the center of the star shrinks, and the atmosphere of the star grows very large and cools. The star may become a red giant or red supergiant, such as Antares, shown in **Figure 2.**

White Dwarfs

In the final stage of its life cycle, a sunlike star becomes a white dwarf. A white dwarf is a small, hot, and dim star that is the leftover center of a red giant. A white dwarf no longer generates energy by nuclear fusion. It slowly cools and becomes smaller. A white dwarf can shine for billions of years.

main sequence (MAYN SEE kwuhns) the location on the H-R diagram where most stars lie; it has a diagonal pattern from the lower right (low temperature and luminosity) to the upper left (high temperature and luminosity)

Figure 2 *The red supergiant Antares is shown above. Red supergiants are at least 100 times as large as the sun.*

Quick Lab

Making a Star Movie

A single star can appear very different at different stages in its life. One way to model this life cycle is to make a flip-chart movie that shows the process.

8.4.b

▶ Try It!

1. Using a **marker** or **colored pencils,** draw the stages in the life cycle of a star on the corners of the pages of a **spiral notebook.** Be sure to match the color of the star with the star's correct stage of life.

2. Use as many pages as necessary to illustrate each stage in the star's life. The star will form from a cloud of gas and dust, will become a main-sequence star, will change into a red giant or red supergiant, and eventually will become a white dwarf.

3. If you want, you may read the rest of the section and choose to draw a supernova, a neutron star, a pulsar, or a black hole.

4. When you have completed your illustrations, take the notebook in your left hand. Using the thumb and first finger of your right hand, flip the pages so that they pass before your eyes like the images on a movie screen.

▶ Think About It!

5. Which stage of a star's life cycle did you use the most pages to illustrate?

6. During which stage of its life cycle was the star the largest? During which stage was the star the smallest? During which stage was the star the brightest? Finally, during which stage was the star the dimmest?

🕐 **30 min**

A Tool for Studying Stars

In 1911, a Danish astronomer named Ejnar Hertzsprung (IE nahr HERTS sproong) compared the brightness and temperature of stars on a graph. Two years later, Henry Norris Russell, an American astronomer, made some similar graphs. Although these astronomers used different data, their results were similar. The combination of their ideas is now called the *Hertzsprung-Russell diagram,* or *H-R diagram.* The **H-R diagram** is a graph that shows the relationship between the surface temperature and absolute magnitude of a star. Over the years, the H-R diagram has become a tool for studying the life cycles of stars. It shows not only how stars are classified by brightness and temperature but also how stars change over time.

H-R diagram (AYCH AHR DIE uh GRAM) Hertzsprung-Russell diagram, a graph that shows the relationship between a star's surface temperature and absolute magnitude

Figure 3 *The stages of a star's life cycle—and a star's properties at each stage in its life cycle—can be plotted on the Hertzsprung-Russell diagram.*

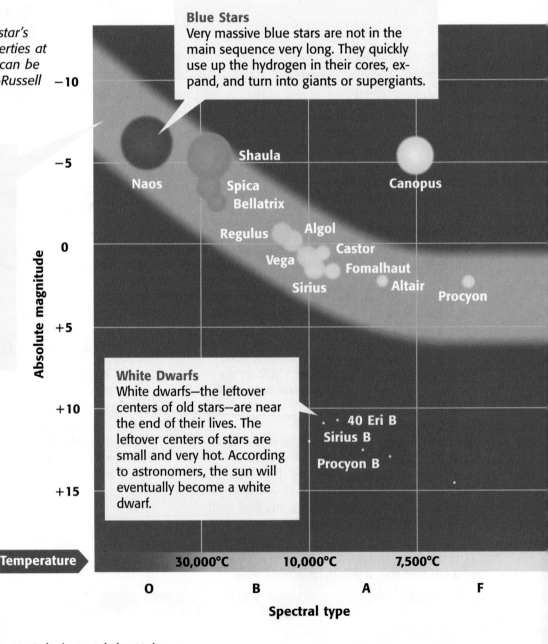

Blue Stars
Very massive blue stars are not in the main sequence very long. They quickly use up the hydrogen in their cores, expand, and turn into giants or supergiants.

Main-Sequence Stars
Stars on the main sequence form a band that runs across the H-R diagram. The sun is a main-sequence star. The sun has been shining for about 5 billion years. Scientists think that the sun is in the middle of its life and will remain on the main sequence for another 5 billion years.

White Dwarfs
White dwarfs—the leftover centers of old stars—are near the end of their lives. The leftover centers of stars are small and very hot. According to astronomers, the sun will eventually become a white dwarf.

Naos   Shaula   Spica   Bellatrix   Canopus   Regulus   Algol   Vega   Castor   Fomalhaut   Sirius   Altair   Procyon

40 Eri B   Sirius B   Procyon B

Absolute magnitude
−10
−5
0
+5
+10
+15

Temperature   30,000°C   10,000°C   7,500°C

O   B   A   F

Spectral type

The H-R Diagram

The modern H-R diagram is shown in **Figure 3.** Temperature appears along the bottom of the diagram, and absolute magnitude, or brightness, appears along the left side. Hot (blue) stars are on the left, and cool (red) stars are on the right. Bright stars are at the top, and dim stars are at the bottom. The diagonal pattern, where most stars lie, represents the main sequence. A star spends most of its lifetime in the main sequence. As main-sequence stars age, they move up and to the right on the H-R diagram to become giants or supergiants. Then, they move to the left and down to become white dwarfs if their mass is eight times the sun or less.

Standards Check Explain how the H-R diagram can be used to determine the temperature and brightness of stars. 🐻 **8.4.b**

Giants and Supergiants
When a star runs out of hydrogen in its core, the center of the star shrinks inward and the outer parts expand outward. For a star that is the size of our sun, the star's atmosphere grows very large and becomes cool. When this change happens, the star becomes a red giant. If the star is very massive, it becomes a red supergiant.

The Sun
The sun is an average star. It is a main-sequence star and is located in the middle of the diagram. The sun is 1 solar diameter and has 1 solar mass. Other stars can be measured against the sun in terms of size, mass, and brightness.

Red Dwarfs
At the lower end of the main sequence are red dwarfs, which are low-mass stars. Low-mass stars remain on the main sequence for a long time. The stars that have the lowest mass are among the oldest stars in the universe.

The Aging of Massive Stars

Massive stars use their hydrogen much faster than stars like the sun do. As a result, massive stars generate more energy than stars like the sun do and are very hot! However, massive stars have shorter lives than other stars do. Massive stars also tend to meet very dramatic ends.

Supernovas

At the end of its life, a massive star may explode in a large, bright flash called a *supernova*. A **supernova** is a gigantic explosion in which a massive star collapses and its outer layers are blasted into space. The ringed structure shown in **Figure 4** is the remains of a supernova. Stars that are more massive than 8 times as massive as the sun may explode with such intensity that they may become neutron stars, pulsars, and black holes.

Neutron Stars

Following a supernova, the center of the collapsed star may contract into a very small but very dense ball of neutrons. This dense ball of neutrons is called a *neutron star.* A single teaspoon of matter from a neutron star would weigh 100 million metric tons on Earth. A neutron star that has more mass than the sun does may have a diameter of only about 20 km but may emit the same amount of energy that 100,000 suns would.

Pulsars

If a neutron star is spinning, it is called a *pulsar.* Pulsars send out beams of radiation that sweep across space in much the same way that the beam of a lighthouse sweeps over the ocean. Every time the beam sweeps by Earth, it is detected by radio telescopes as rapid clicks, or pulses.

Figure 4 *Supernova 1987A was the first supernova to be visible to the unaided eye in 400 years. The first image shows what the original star must have looked like only a few hours before the explosion. Today, the star's remains form a double ring of gas and dust, as shown in the image on the right.*

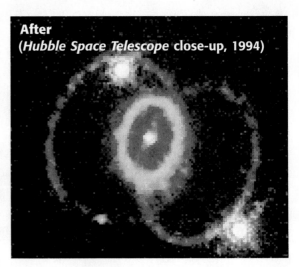

Black Holes

If the center of a collapsed star has a mass that is several times the mass of the sun, the star may contract further because of the strength of its gravity. The force of the contraction crushes the dense center of the star and leaves a black hole. A *black hole* is an object that is so dense and massive that light cannot escape its gravity.

Because black holes do not give off light, locating them is difficult. If a star is nearby, some gas or dust from the star will spiral into the black hole and give off X rays. These X rays allow astronomers to detect the presence of black holes.

Standards Check What is a black hole? How do astronomers detect the presence of black holes? **8.4.b**

SECTION Review

 8.4.b

Summary

- New stars form from gas and dust, which are pulled into a sphere by gravity.

- Some types of stars include main-sequence stars, giants, supergiants, and white dwarfs.

- Most stars, including the sun, are main-sequence stars.

- The H-R diagram shows the brightness of a star relative to the temperature of the star. It also shows the life cycle of stars.

- Massive stars can explode in a large, bright flash called a *supernova.* Their cores can change into neutron stars or black holes.

Using Vocabulary

1 Use *H-R diagram* and *main sequence* in the same sentence.

Understanding Concepts

2 **Applying** Explain the process by which new stars form.

3 **Arranging** Arrange the following stars in the order that reflects the life cycle of a star: white dwarf, red giant, and main-sequence star.

4 **Analyzing** In main-sequence stars, how does brightness relate to temperature?

5 **Applying** Explain what happens when a massive star ends its life as a supernova.

6 **Comparing** Compare a neutron star and a pulsar.

7 **Summarizing** How can the center of a collapsed star form a black hole?

Critical Thinking

8 **Evaluating Data** How does the H-R diagram explain the life cycle of a star?

9 **Identifying Relationships** Why do massive stars have shorter lives than other stars do?

10 **Analyzing Processes** Describe what might happen to a star after it explodes as a supernova.

Challenge

11 **Evaluating Hypotheses** An astronomer hypothesizes that gas and dust from a star are being drawn into a black hole. How can the astronomer test his or her hypothesis to see if the hypothesis is correct?

Internet Resources

For a variety of links related to this chapter, go to www.scilinks.org

Topic: Supernovas
SciLinks code: HY71482

Galaxies

Key Concept Galaxies contain billions of stars and have different shapes.

What You Will Learn

- The three types of galaxies are spiral galaxies, elliptical galaxies, and irregular galaxies.
- Galaxies are composed of stars, planetary systems, nebulas, and star clusters.
- Looking at distant galaxies reveals what young galaxies looked like.

Why It Matters

The structure and composition of galaxies give clues to the structure and composition of the universe.

Vocabulary

- galaxy
- nebula

READING STRATEGY

Graphic Organizer In your **Science Journal,** make a Comparison Table that compares various characteristics of the different types of galaxies.

galaxy (GAL uhk see) a collection of stars, dust, and gas bound together by gravity

Large groups of stars, dust, and gas are called **galaxies.** Galaxies come in a variety of sizes and shapes. The largest galaxies contain more than a trillion stars. Astronomers don't count the stars, of course. They estimate how many sun-sized stars a galaxy contains by studying the size and brightness of the galaxy.

Types of Galaxies

The light from individual stars in another galaxy comes to Earth from so far away that the light blurs together. From Earth, other galaxies look cloudy and have a spiral shape, a round or oval shape, or no definite shape. Astronomers classify a galaxy as a spiral, elliptical, or irregular galaxy according to its shape. They also classify a galaxy by the energy that it emits or by the rate of star formation.

Spiral Galaxies

When someone says the word *galaxy,* most people probably think of a spiral galaxy. *Spiral galaxies,* such as the Andromeda galaxy, shown in **Figure 1,** have a bulge at the center and spiral arms. The spiral arms are made up of gas, dust, and new stars that have formed in these dense regions of gas and dust.

Standards Check What are two characteristics of spiral galaxies?
 8.4.a

Figure 1 Types of Galaxies

Spiral Galaxy
The Andromeda galaxy is a spiral galaxy that looks similar to what our galaxy, the Milky Way, is thought to look like.

8.4.a Students know galaxies are clusters of billions of stars and may have different shapes.
8.4.b Students know that the Sun is one of many stars in the Milky Way galaxy and that stars may differ in size, temperature, and color.

The Milky Way

The galaxy in which we live is a spiral galaxy called the *Milky Way*. The Milky Way consists of about 200 billion stars, including the sun. The sun is located about two-thirds of the way between the center of the galaxy and the galaxy's edge. From Earth, the edge of the Milky Way is seen as a bright band of stars that cuts across the night sky.

Elliptical Galaxies

Because most elliptical galaxies are round or oval, they can be thought of as "cosmic snowballs," as **Figure 1** shows. However, some elliptical galaxies are slightly flattened, but not as much as spiral galaxies are. Unlike spiral galaxies, whose gas clouds are still forming stars, elliptical galaxies seem to have stopped making new stars more than 10 billion years ago. Elliptical galaxies are among the largest galaxies in the universe. They can contain up to 5 trillion stars! Evidence suggests that many large elliptical galaxies form by the merging of smaller galaxies.

Irregular Galaxies

Irregular galaxies are galaxies that have no definite shape. The smallest irregular galaxies have only about 10 million stars. The largest irregular galaxies can contain several billion stars. Irregular galaxies form new stars slowly. Some irregular galaxies form when galaxies collide.

The Milky Way is consuming a pair of nearby irregular galaxies called the *Magellanic Clouds*. The Large Magellanic Cloud is shown in **Figure 1**. It is located about 190,000 light-years from Earth and is visible by eye from the southern hemisphere.

Elliptical Galaxy
Unlike the Milky Way, the galaxy known as M87, an elliptical galaxy, has no spiral arms.

Irregular Galaxy
The Large Magellanic Cloud, an irregular galaxy, is located within our galactic neighborhood.

Contents of Galaxies

Galaxies contain not only stars and planetary systems. Large features, such as the gas clouds and star clusters shown in **Figure 2,** are also located within galaxies.

Gas Clouds

nebula (NEB yu luh) a large cloud of gas and dust in interstellar space; a region in space where stars are born

The Latin word for "cloud" is *nebula*. In space, **nebulas** (or nebulae) are large clouds of gas and dust that are the birthplaces of stars. **Figure 2** shows part of the Eagle nebula. Some types of nebulas glow. Other types absorb light and hide stars. Still other nebulas reflect starlight.

Star Clusters

A *globular cluster* is a highly concentrated group of stars that looks like a ball, as **Figure 2** shows. A globular cluster may have up to 1 million stars. All of these stars formed at the same time from the same nebula and orbit a galaxy as a group. Globular clusters are located in a spherical *halo* that surrounds spiral galaxies, such as the Milky Way. Globular clusters are also common near some elliptical galaxies.

Open clusters are groups of 100 to 1,000 stars that are close together relative to other stars. Open clusters are usually located along the disk of a spiral galaxy. All of the stars in an open cluster formed at the same time from the same nebula. Newly formed open clusters have many bright blue stars, as **Figure 2** shows.

Figure 2 Gas Clouds and Star Clusters

Part of a nebula in which stars are born is shown here. The fingerlike shape to the left of the bright star is slightly wider than our solar system.

We can see the open cluster Pleiades without a telescope.

Omega Centauri is the largest globular cluster in the Milky Way. It contains 5 million to 10 million stars.

Quasars

Quasars are among the most distant objects in the universe. In fact, quasars are so distant that they cannot be photographed clearly. Quasars are starlike sources of energy that are located in the centers of galaxies. They generate energy at a high rate and are among the most powerful energy sources in the universe. Some scientists think that quasars may be caused by massive black holes in the cores of galaxies. **Figure 3** shows a quasar that is 6 billion light-years from Earth.

Standards Check How do quasars differ from galaxies? 8.4.a

Origin of Galaxies

Scientists investigate the early universe by observing objects that are extremely far away in space. Because light takes time to travel through space, looking through a telescope is like looking back in time. Looking at distant galaxies reveals what early galaxies looked like. This information gives scientists ideas about how galaxies form and how galaxies change over time.

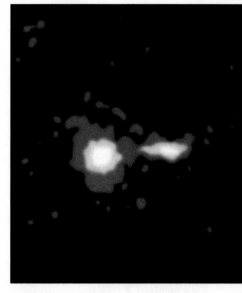

Figure 3 *The quasar known as PKS 0637-752 radiates with the power of 10 trillion suns.*

SECTION Review

8.4.a, 8.4.b

Summary

- Astronomers classify galaxies by shape. The three types of galaxies are spiral galaxies, elliptical galaxies, and irregular galaxies.

- Some galaxies contain nebulas and star clusters.

- A nebula is a cloud of gas and dust. A globular cluster is a highly concentrated group of stars. An open cluster is a group of stars that are relatively close together.

- Scientists look at distant galaxies to see what early galaxies looked like.

Using Vocabulary

1. Use the following terms in the same sentence: *galaxy* and *nebula.*

Understanding Concepts

2. **Summarizing** Briefly describe the differences between spiral, elliptical, and irregular galaxies.

3. **Listing** List four facts about the Milky Way. Include the location of the sun in the Milky Way.

4. **Comparing** Compare a nebula with a star cluster.

5. **Identifying** In which types of galaxy are globular clusters most likely to be found?

6. **Applying** Explain how scientists see what early galaxies looked like.

Critical Thinking

7. **Making Comparisons** Describe the difference between a globular cluster and an open cluster.

8. **Identifying Relationships** Explain how looking through a telescope is like looking back in time.

Challenge

9. **Applying Concepts** Explain why looking at distant galaxies gives scientists an idea about how galaxies change over time.

Internet Resources

For a variety of links related to this chapter, go to www.scilinks.org

Topic: Galaxies
SciLinks code: HY70632

Formation of the Universe

Key Concept Every object in the universe is part of a larger system, and the force of gravity acts within each system.

▶ Imagine an explosion, bright lights, and intense energy. Does that scene sound like an action movie? This scene could also describe a theory about the formation of the universe.

The study of the origin, structure, processes, and evolution of the universe is called *cosmology*. Like other scientific theories, theories about the beginning and end of the universe must be tested by observations or experiments.

The Big Bang Theory

To understand how the universe formed, scientists study the movement of galaxies. Careful measurements have shown that most galaxies are moving away from each other and that the universe is expanding.

Having discovered that the universe is expanding, scientists have worked backward in time to figure out how the universe formed. If a movie of the formation of the universe ran backward, the universe would appear to be contracting. All matter would eventually come together into a very small volume. Thinking about what would happen if all of the matter in the universe were squeezed into such a small space has led scientists to a theory that describes how the universe formed. This theory, known as the **big bang theory,** is the standard model used to explain the expansion of the universe.

Figure 1 *Most astronomers think that the big bang caused the universe to expand in all directions.*

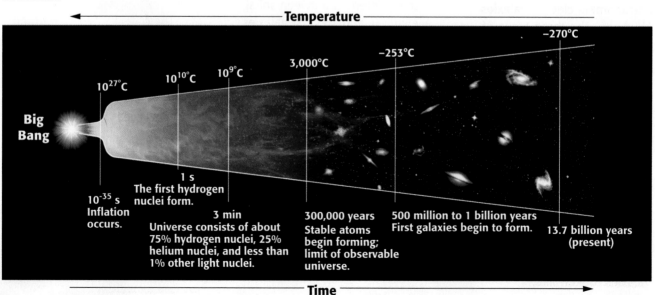

Temperature

10^{27}°C $\quad$ 10^{10}°C $\quad$ 10^{9}°C $\quad$ 3,000°C $\quad$ −253°C $\quad$ −270°C

Big Bang

10^{-35} s
Inflation occurs.

1 s
The first hydrogen nuclei form.

3 min
Universe consists of about 75% hydrogen nuclei, 25% helium nuclei, and less than 1% other light nuclei.

300,000 years
Stable atoms begin forming; limit of observable universe.

500 million to 1 billion years
First galaxies begin to form.

13.7 billion years (present)

Time

A Tremendous Explosion

According to the big bang theory, about 14 billion years ago, all of the contents of the universe were compressed under tremendous pressure, at high temperature and high density, into an extremely small volume. Then, the universe rapidly expanded and cooled. Within the first three minutes of this "big bang," the initial elements, forces of nature—including gravity—and the seeds of galaxy formation were determined. **Figure 1** illustrates the timeline of the big bang.

Standards Check According to the big bang theory, how did the universe form? **8.4.a**

Cosmic Background Radiation

In 1964, scientists noticed that radio "noise" was coming from all directions in space. This "noise" is the *cosmic background radiation* left over from the big bang. According to the big bang theory, the energy from the original explosion was distributed in every direction as the universe expanded. The distribution of this energy is similar to the transfer of heat from a kitchen oven. When an oven door is left open after the oven has been used, thermal energy is transferred throughout the kitchen, and the oven cools. Eventually, the room and the oven become the same temperature.

8.2.g Students know the role of gravity in forming and maintaining the shapes of planets, stars, and the solar system.
8.4.a Students know galaxies are clusters of billions of stars and may have different shapes.

big bang theory (BIG BANG THEE uh ree) the theory that all matter and energy in the universe was compressed into an extremely small volume that 13 billion to 15 billion years ago exploded and began expanding in all directions

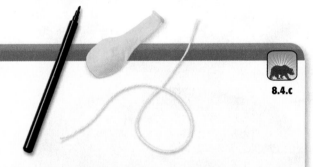

Quick Lab

The Expanding Universe

Use a balloon as a model to show that all objects in the universe are moving away from each other.

8.4.c

▶ Try It!

1. Use a **marker** to make three dots in a row on a noninflated **balloon.** Label the dots "A," "B," and "C." Dot B should be closer to dot A than to dot C.

2. Blow up the balloon just until it is taut. Pinch the balloon to keep it inflated, but do not tie the neck.

3. Use **string** and a **metric ruler** to measure the distances between dots A and B, B and C, and A and C.

4. With the balloon still inflated, blow into the balloon until its diameter is twice as large.

5. Measure the distances between dots A and B, B and C, and A and C. For each pair of dots, subtract the original distances measured in step 3 from the new distances. Then, divide by 2. This calculation will give you the rate of change for each pair of dots.

▶ Think About It!

6. Which pair of dots experienced the greatest rate of change?

7. Suppose that dot A represents Earth in the Milky Way and dots B and C represent galaxies. How does the rate at which galaxies are moving away from us relate to how far the galaxies are from Earth in the Milky Way?

 15 min

Figure 2 *Every object in the universe is part of a larger system.* ***Beginning at the bottom of the figure, explain how each system is part of the larger system above it.***

Gravity and the Universe

You have learned that all objects experience an attraction toward all other objects and that gravitational attraction pulls objects toward one another. After the big bang, gravitational attraction caused the matter distributed throughout the universe to form galaxies. The mutual attraction between galaxies caused galaxies to cluster. Even though the distances between galaxy clusters are very large, gravity still acts between them. Because gravity acts over such great distances, gravity controls the size and shape of the universe.

Standards Check How is gravity related to the shape and size of the universe. 🐻 **8.2.g**

A Cosmic Repetition

As **Figure 2** shows, every object in the universe is part of a larger system, and the force of gravity acts within each system. The largest structures are clusters of galaxies. Each galaxy cluster can contain up to several thousand galaxies, and galaxies are composed of stars and planets. Galaxies such as the Milky Way include planetary systems, such as our solar system. Earth is part of our solar system.

How Old Is the Universe?

Astronomers can estimate the age of the universe by studying white dwarfs, the oldest stars in the Milky Way. White dwarfs are the burned-out cores of stars that started out with masses that were less than 8 times the mass of the sun. These stars have cores of carbon and oxygen at the end of the red giant phase and lose their atmospheres in the planetary nebula stage. The planetary nebula stage is a stage in which the hot central region of a star drives off the star's cooler atmosphere over a period of a few thousand years. Once the star's atmosphere is lost, all that is left is the carbon-oxygen core—a white dwarf—which is tiny, hot, and dense.

The oldest white dwarfs are 12 billion to 13 billion years old. Because it took about 1 billion years after the big bang for the first white dwarfs to form from the first stars, the universe must be approximately 14 billion years old.

Figure 3 shows galaxies far from Earth. Astronomers think that these galaxies are some of the oldest objects in the universe.

A Forever-Expanding Universe?

Astronomical data show that the matter making up stars and planets is only about 4% of the total matter in the universe. Another 23% of the universe consists of what astronomers call *dark matter*. Dark matter does not give off light but has gravity and can be detected indirectly. The remainder of the universe is composed of what astronomers call *dark energy*. Dark energy seems to be accelerating the expansion of the universe and counteracting the effect of gravity. The discovery of dark energy is so recent that astronomers don't know the properties of dark energy yet.

One possible scenario for the future of the universe is that the expansion rate will keep growing. Thus, stars will age and die, and the universe will probably become cold and dark after many billions of years. Even after the universe becomes cold and dark, it will keep expanding forever.

Figure 3 *Distant galaxies in the universe, such as the galaxies shown here, may have formed less than 1 billion years after the big bang.*

SECTION Review

 8.2.g, 8.4.a

Summary

- According to the big bang theory, the universe began with a tremendous explosion about 14 billion years ago.
- The presence of cosmic background radiation helps support the big bang theory.
- Scientists use white dwarfs to estimate the age of the universe.
- The universe is composed of matter, dark matter, and dark energy.
- Scientists think that the universe may expand forever.

Using Vocabulary

1. Write an original definition for the *big bang theory*.

Understanding Concepts

2. **Summarizing** How is gravity related to the big bang?

3. **Applying** How does the presence of cosmic background radiation support the big bang theory?

4. **Summarizing** Describe the structure of the universe.

5. **Analyzing** What will happen to the universe if it expands forever?

Critical Thinking

6. **Analyzing Ideas** Explain why astronomers use white dwarfs to date the universe?

INTERPRETING GRAPHICS Use the illustration below to answer the next question.

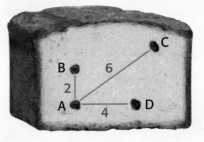

7. **Evaluating Data** If distances AB, AC, and AD double, how fast will raisins B, C, and D be moving away from raisin A? Answer in centimeters per second (cm/s).

Using Scientific Methods

Skills Practice Lab

Star Colors: Red Hot, or Not?

When you look at the night sky, some stars are brighter than others. Some are even different colors. For example, Betelgeuse, a bright star in the constellation Orion, glows red. Sirius, one of the brightest stars in the sky, glows bluish white. Astronomers use color to estimate the temperature of stars. In this activity, you will experiment with a light bulb and some batteries to discover what the color of a glowing object reveals about the temperature of the object.

OBJECTIVES

Discover what the color of a glowing object reveals about the temperature of the object.

Describe how the color and temperature of a star are related.

MATERIALS

- battery, D cell (2)
- battery, D cell, weak
- flashlight bulb
- tape, electrical
- wire, insulated copper, with ends stripped, 20 cm long (2)

SAFETY

Ask a Question

1. How are the color and temperature of a star related?

Form a Hypothesis

2. On a sheet of paper, change the question above into a statement that gives your best estimate about the relationship between the color and temperature of a star.

8.4.b Students know that the Sun is one of many stars in the Milky Way galaxy and that stars may differ in size, temperature, and color.

Investigation and Experimentation
8.9.a Plan and conduct a scientific experiment to test a hypothesis.

Test the Hypothesis

3 Tape one end of an insulated copper wire to the positive pole of the weak D cell. Tape one end of the second wire to the negative pole.

4 Touch the free end of each wire to the light bulb. Hold one of the wires against the bottom tip of the light bulb. Hold the second wire against the side of the metal portion of the bulb. The bulb should light.

5 Record the color of the filament in the light bulb. Carefully touch your hand to the bulb. Observe the temperature of the bulb. Record your observations.

6 Using one of the two fresh D cells, repeat steps 3–5.

7 Use the electrical tape to connect the two fresh D cells so that the positive pole of the first cell is connected to the negative pole of the second cell.

8 Using the fresh D cells that are taped together, repeat steps 3–5.

Analyze the Results

9 **Describing Events** What was the color of the filament in each of the three trials? For each trial, compare the temperature of the bulb with the temperature of the bulb in the other two trials.

10 **Analyzing Results** What information does the color of a star tell you about the star?

11 **Classifying Data** What color are stars that have relatively high surface temperatures? What color are stars that have relatively low surface temperatures?

Draw Conclusions

12 **Applying Conclusions** Arrange the following stars in order from highest to lowest surface temperature: Sirius, which is bluish white; Aldebaran, which is orange; Procyon, which is yellow-white; Capella, which is yellow; and Betelgeuse, which is red.

Big Idea Question

13 **Applying Conclusions** What does the yellow color of the sun tell you about the surface temperature of the sun?

Science Skills Activity

 Investigation and Experimentation
8.9.e Construct appropriate graphs from data and develop quantitative statements about the relationships between variables.

Constructing a Line Graph

▶ Tutorial

1 Follow these steps to build your graph.
- Draw the axes for your graph on a sheet of graph paper.
- Label the *x*-axis in terms that describe the types of data. Usually, the independent variable is placed on the *x*-axis.
- Write the numbers of the scale next to the tick marks of the axis.
- Title the *x*-axis.
- Determine a scale for the *y*-axis that includes the range of your data.
- Write the numbers of the scale next to the tick marks of the axis.
- Title the *y*-axis.
- Write the title of your graph on the top of the graph.

2 Follow these steps to plot your data.
- Plot a series of points by using your data. Each point indicates an (x, y) coordinate on the graph.
- On the graph, draw a line through all of the points that you have plotted.

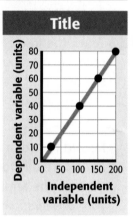

▶ You Try It!

Procedure

Use the data in **Table 1** to construct a line graph. Then, use the graph to make observations about the relationship between the velocity of a galaxy cluster and the galaxy cluster's distance from Earth. This graph is known as a *Hubble diagram.*

Analysis

1 Identifying Write a statement that describes the relationship between the velocity of a galaxy cluster and its distance from Earth.

2 Comparing Compare the ratio of the distance between the galaxy cluster Virgo and Earth to Virgo's velocity with the ratio of the distance between the galaxy cluster Hydra and Earth to Hydra's velocity. What does the comparison in ratios tell you about the line that you will plot on your graph?

3 Evaluating If a galaxy cluster is more than 1,980 million light-years from Earth, at what velocity is that galaxy cluster moving?

Table 1	Galaxy Clusters	
Galaxy cluster	**Distance (in millions of light-years)**	**Velocity (km/s)**
Virgo	39	1,200
Ursa Major	500	15,000
Corona Borealis	700	22,000
Boötes	1,250	39,000
Hydra	1,980	61,000

Chapter Summary

go.hrw.com
SUPER SUMMARY
KEYWORD: HY7UNVS

The Big Idea
The structure and composition of the universe can be learned by studying stars and galaxies and their evolution.

Section

Vocabulary

1 Stars

Key Concept Stars differ in size, color, temperature, brightness, and age. Scientists use these differences to classify stars.

- Stars differ in size, temperature, composition, brightness, and color.
- Distances between stars are enormous and are measured in light-years.

Spectroscope

The absorption spectrum of a star tells you the star's composition.

spectrum p. 437
apparent magnitude p. 440
absolute magnitude p. 440
light-year p. 441
parallax p. 441

2 The Life Cycle of Stars

Key Concept Stars vary in mass, size, brightness, color, and temperature, and these variations are related to the stars' life cycles.

- During star formation, gravity pulls dust and gas into a sphere, and when the sphere gets dense enough, nuclear fusion begins.
- The stages of a star's life cycle and the star's properties at each stage can be plotted on the H-R diagram.

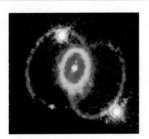
Many massive stars end their lives as supernovas.

main sequence p. 445
H-R diagram p. 446
supernova p. 448

3 Galaxies

Key Concept Galaxies contain billions of stars and have different shapes.

- The three types of galaxies are spiral galaxies, elliptical galaxies, and irregular galaxies.
- Galaxies are composed of stars, planetary systems, nebulas, and star clusters.
- Looking at distant galaxies reveals what young galaxies looked like.

The Andromeda galaxy is a spiral galaxy.

galaxy p. 450
nebula p. 452

4 Formation of the Universe

Key Concept Every object in the universe is part of a larger system, and the force of gravity acts within each system.

- The big bang theory is the standard theory to explain the formation of the universe.
- Gravity controls the size and shape of the universe.

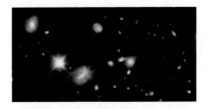
The universe contains billions of galaxies.

big bang theory p. 455

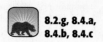

Organize

Three-Panel Flip Chart Review the FoldNote that you created at the beginning of the chapter. Add to or correct the FoldNote based on what you have learned.

Using Vocabulary

1. **Academic Vocabulary** Which of the following words is the closest in meaning to the word *structure?*
   a. outline   c. arrangement
   b. surface   d. shape

Correct each statement by replacing the underlined term.

2. <u>Absolute magnitude</u> is the brightness of a star as seen from Earth.

3. The distance that light travels in space in 1 year is called <u>parallax</u>.

4. The <u>main sequence</u> is a graph that shows the relationship between the surface temperature and absolute magnitude of a star.

Understanding Concepts

Multiple Choice

5. Which of the following stars has the highest surface temperature?
   a. a red star   c. a yellow star
   b. a blue star   d. an orange star

6. Approximately how many kilometers does a light-year equal?
   a. 9.46 trillion   c. 9.46 quadrillion
   b. 9.46 million   d. 9.46 billion

7. The sun is just one of many stars in the Milky Way. Which type of star is the sun?
   a. a neutron star   c. a main-sequence star
   b. a white dwarf   d. a red giant

8. The Milky Way is an example of a(n)
   a. elliptical galaxy.   c. irregular galaxy.
   b. lenticular galaxy.   d. spiral galaxy.

9. Which of the following contain billions of stars and may have different shapes?
   a. open clusters   c. nebulas
   b. galaxies   d. globular clusters

Short Answer

10. **Classifying** Describe how scientists classify stars.

11. **Applying** Explain why astronomers use light-years to estimate the distance between Earth and stars.

12. **Listing** List the stages in the life cycle of a star in the order in which they happen.

13. **Analyzing** Explain the role of nuclear fusion in the life cycle of a star.

14. **Comparing** Compare spiral galaxies, elliptical galaxies, and irregular galaxies.

15. **Describing** Describe the Milky Way, including the sun's position in the Milky Way.

16. **Applying** Explain how the presence of cosmic background radiation supports the big bang theory.

17. **Comparing** Compare dark matter with dark energy.

Writing Skills

18. **Creative Writing** Imagine that you are an astronomer who has made a new discovery either in the Milky Way or in another part of the universe. You may have discovered a star, a star cluster, a nebula, a black hole, or a galaxy. Describe your discovery in the form of a short story. Be sure to describe the way in which you made your discovery.

Critical Thinking

19. **Concept Mapping** Use the following terms to create a concept map: *main-sequence star, nebula, red giant, white dwarf, neutron star,* and *black hole.*

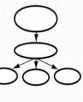

20 Evaluating Data You are looking at a star through a telescope in January. There is a small shift in the star's apparent position compared to when you looked at the same star through a telescope in July. What can you conclude about the distance of the star from Earth?

21 Making Comparisons Explain the differences between main-sequence stars, giant stars, and white dwarfs.

22 Evaluating Conclusions While looking through a telescope, you see a galaxy that doesn't appear to contain any blue stars. What kind of galaxy is the galaxy most likely to be? Explain your answer.

23 Evaluating Sources According to the big bang theory, how did the universe begin?

INTERPRETING GRAPHICS Use the graph below to answer the next two questions.

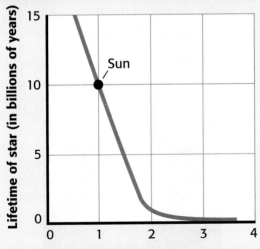

Relationship Between Age and Mass of a Star

Lifetime of star (in billions of years) vs. Mass of star (relative to sun's mass)

24 Identifying Relationships Which star would live longer: a star that has half the mass of the sun or a star that has 2 times the mass of the sun? Explain your answer.

25 Applying Concepts Approximately how long would a main-sequence star that has a mass of about 1.5 times the mass of the sun live?

INTERPRETING GRAPHICS The graph below shows Hubble's law, which relates how far galaxies are from Earth and how fast they are moving away from Earth. Use the graph below to answer the next two questions.

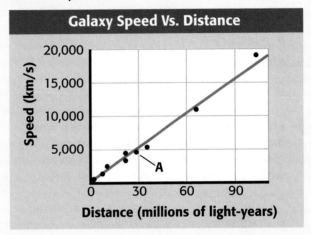

Galaxy Speed Vs. Distance

Speed (km/s) vs. Distance (millions of light-years)

26 Evaluating Data If a galaxy is moving away from Earth at 15,000 km/s, how far from Earth is the galaxy?

27 Evaluating Data If a galaxy is 60 million light-years from Earth, how fast is it moving away from Earth?

Math Skills

28 Making Calculations One star has a magnitude of -5, and another star has a magnitude of $+15$. How much brighter than the star that has the magnitude of $+15$ is the star that has the magnitude of -5?

Challenge

29 Applying Concepts There are more low-mass stars than high-mass stars in the universe. Given this information, do you think that more stars will end their lives as white dwarfs or in supernovas?

30 Making Inferences What is the relationship between gravity and the unknown material that astronomers call *dark energy*?

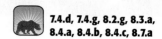
REVIEWING ACADEMIC VOCABULARY

1 Which of the following words means "a whole that is built or put together from parts"?

A structure

B identity

C concept

D cycle

2 Choose the appropriate form of the word *maintain* for the following sentence: "She _____ a B average at school, even while she was in the play."

A maintaining

B maintains

C maintained

D maintenance

3 In the sentence "Scientists study the universe by studying the evolution of stars," what does the word *evolution* mean?

A the pattern of change and growth

B the process by which species develop

C the way characteristics are passed along

D the advancement of life in space

4 Which of the following words is the closest in meaning to the word *role*?

A spin

B personality

C tumble

D function

REVIEWING CONCEPTS

5 What is the unit that astronomers use to measure the distances between Earth and stars called?

A apparent magnitude

B absolute magnitude

C light-year

D parallax

6 Which of the following stars has the coolest temperature?

A a blue-white star

B a yellow star

C a yellow-white star

D an orange star

7 What do scientists learn by studying the pattern of lines in a star's absorption spectrum?

A the brightness of the star

B the elements of the star

C the distance of the star from Earth

D the size of the star

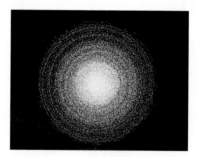

8 The picture above shows an example of

A an elliptical galaxy.

B an irregular galaxy.

C a supernova.

D a spiral galaxy.

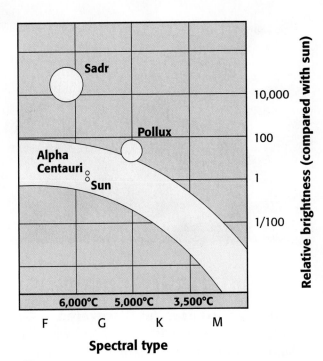

Relative brightness (compared with sun)

10,000

100

1

1/100

Sadr

Pollux

Alpha
Centauri °
° Sun

6,000°C   5,000°C   3,500°C
F   G   K   M

Spectral type

9 **Which statement about the H-R diagram above is true?**

A Alpha Centauri is hotter and brighter than the sun.

B Sadr is cooler but brighter than the star Pollux.

C Pollux is the hottest star shown in the graph.

D Sadr is the hottest star shown in the graph.

10 **The universe contains galaxies, stars, and planets. How does gravity affect these bodies in space?**

A Gravity pulls bodies away from each other.

B Gravity organizes bodies into nebulas, galaxies, and planetary systems.

C Gravity attracts bodies with similar compositions to each other.

D Gravity causes bodies to be scattered randomly throughout the universe.

REVIEWING PRIOR LEARNING

11 **Which of the following particles is always found in the nucleus of an atom?**

A protons

B neutrons

C electrons

D positrons

12 **Which group in the periodic table contains helium?**

A Group 18, the noble gases

B Group 13, the boron group

C Group 15, the nitrogen group

D Group 1, the alkali metals

13 **How do geologists measure the precise age of Earth?**

A by measuring the erosion of land formations

B by analyzing the fossil record

C by measuring the temperature of Earth's mantle

D by measuring the radioactive decay of natural elements

14 **Cyanobacteria were some of the first organisms to appear on Earth. What is the most significant way in which these bacteria affected life on Earth?**

A They were a predator that preyed on organisms that threatened to cause the extinction of other species.

B They released oxygen through photosynthesis, which led to the formation of the ozone layer.

C They were a primary food source for producers.

D They floated on water, shielding other organisms from the sun's radiation.

Science in Action

LBV 1806-20

The Sun

Weird Science

Holes Where Stars Once Were

An invisible phantom lurks in space, ready to swallow everything that comes near it. Once trapped in the phantom's grasp, matter is stretched, torn, and crushed into oblivion. Does this tale sound like a horror story? Guess again!

Scientists call this phantom a *black hole*. As a star runs out of fuel, it cools and eventually collapses under the force of its own gravity. If the collapsing star is massive enough, it may shrink to become a black hole. The gravitational attraction that results is so strong that even light cannot escape! Many astronomers think that black holes lie at the heart of many galaxies. Some scientists think that there is a giant black hole at the center of the Milky Way.

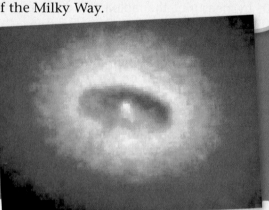

Scientific Discoveries

The Brightest Star Yet Discovered

Imagine a star that is at least 150 times as large as our sun and perhaps as much as 40 million times as bright! In January 2004, a team of astronomers from the University of Florida announced the discovery of such a star. The star is LBV 1806-20, and it may be the brightest star that astronomers have discovered to date.

LBV 1806-20 is located on the other side of the Milky Way galaxy, approximately 45,000 light-years from our solar system. It is what astronomers call a *luminous blue variable star*. Luminous blue variable stars are somewhat rare, are massive, and have short life spans. In fact, LBV 1806-20 is estimated to be less than 2 million years old. In contrast, our sun is 5 billion years old. For astronomers, the large size of LBV 1806-20 remains a mystery. Astronomers think that a supernova slammed together the gases in a molecular cloud to form the massive LBV 1806-20.

Language Arts ACTIVITY

Imagine that you are an astronomer watching a black hole form. In your **Science Journal**, write a short story that describes what you would see during the formation of a black hole.

Math ACTIVITY

If LBV 1806-20 is 45,000 light-years from our solar system, how many kilometers from our solar system is LBV 1806-20? (Hint: One light-year is equal to 9.46 trillion kilometers.)

Sandra Faber

Astronomer What do you do when you send a telescope into space and then find out that the telescope is broken? You call Sandra Faber, Ph.D. Faber is a professor of astronomy at the University of California, Santa Cruz (UCSC). After the *Hubble Space Telescope* went into orbit in April 1990, scientists found that the images collected by the telescope were not turning out as expected. Because Faber was part of a team in charge of the Wide Field Planetary Camera, a device on NASA's Hubble, they decided to use the camera to test the telescope and determine what was wrong.

To perform the test, Faber and her team pointed *Hubble* toward a bright star and took several photos. Information from those photos allowed the team to create a model of what was wrong. After members of the team reported their findings of error and presented the model to NASA, Faber and a group of other experts began to correct the problem. The group's efforts were a success. *Hubble* was put back into operation in December 1993 so that astronomers could continue researching stars and other objects in space.

Social Studies ACTIVITY

Research the history of the telescope. Make a timeline that includes the dates of major events in telescope history. For example, your timeline could include the first use of a telescope to see the rings of Saturn.

Internet Resources

- To learn more about careers in science, visit www.scilinks.org and enter the SciLinks code HY70225.

- To learn more about these Science in Action topics, visit go.hrw.com and type in the keyword HY7UNVF.

- Check out articles related to this chapter by visiting go.hrw.com. Just type in the keyword HY7UNVC.

Improving Comprehension

Graphic Organizers are important visual tools that can help you organize information and improve your reading comprehension. The Graphic Organizer below is called a *concept map*. Instructions for creating other types of Graphic Organizers are located in the **Study Skills** section of the Appendix.

How to Make a Concept Map

❶ Identify main ideas from the text, and write the ideas as short phrases or single words.

❷ Select a main concept. Place this concept at the top or center of a piece of paper.

❸ Place other ideas under or around the main concept based on their relationship to the main concept. Draw a circle around each idea.

❹ Draw lines between the concepts, and add linking words to connect the ideas.

When to Use a Concept Map

Concept maps are useful when you are trying to identify how several ideas are connected to a main concept. Concept maps may be based on vocabulary terms or on main topics from the text. The concept map below shows how the important concepts of this chapter are related. As you read about science, look for terms that can be organized in a concept map.

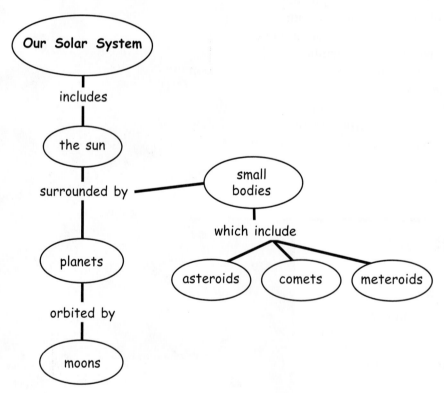

You Try It!

This Reading Strategy can also be used within the chapter that you are about to read. Practice making your own *concept map* as directed in the Reading Strategy for Section ❶. Record your work in your **Science Journal**.

Unpacking the Standards

The information below "unpacks" the standards by breaking them down into basic parts. The higher-level, academic vocabulary is highlighted and defined to help you understand the language of the standards. "What It Means" restates the standards as simply as possible.

California Standard	Academic Vocabulary	What It Means
8.2.g Students know the **role** of gravity in forming and **maintaining** the shapes of planets, stars, and the solar system.	**role** (ROHL) a part or function; purpose **maintain** (mayn TAYN) to keep the same	You must know how the force of attraction between objects that is due to their masses affects the shapes of planets, stars, and the solar system.
8.4.b Students know that the Sun is one of many stars in the Milky Way galaxy and that stars may differ in size, temperature, and color.		The sun is one of many stars in the Milky Way galaxy. Stars may differ in size, temperature, and color.
8.4.c Students know how to use astronomical units and light years as measures of distances between the Sun, stars, and Earth.		You must know how to use the distance between Earth and the sun and the distance that light can travel in one year to measure distances between the sun, stars, and Earth.
8.4.d Students know that stars are the **source** of light for all bright objects in outer space and that the Moon and planets shine by reflected sunlight, not by their own light.	**source** (SAWRS) the thing from which something else comes	Stars are the only objects in space that generate light. All other bright objects in outer space, such as the moon and planets, shine because they reflect light from the sun. They do not make their own light.
8.4.e Students know the appearance, general composition, relative position and size, and motion of objects in the solar system, including planets, planetary satellites, comets, and asteroids.		You must know characteristics of objects in the solar system, including planets, moons, comets, and asteroids. These characteristics include how the objects look, what they are made of, where they are located, how big they are, and how they move.

16

Our Solar System

The Big Idea

The solar system contains a variety of objects that differ in size, appearance, and composition.

California Standards

Focus on Physical Sciences
8.2 Unbalanced forces cause changes in velocity. (Sections 1 and 4)
8.4 The structure and composition of the universe can be learned from studying stars and galaxies and their evolution. (Sections 1, 2, 3, 4, and 5)

Investigation and Experimentation
8.9 Scientific progress is made by asking meaningful questions and conducting careful investigations. (Science Skills Activity)

Math
8.4.0 Using Equations

English–Language Arts
8.2.2 Reading
8.2.1 Writing

About the Photo

This color view of the planet Saturn and its rings was captured by the *Cassini* spacecraft from a distance of more than 6 million kilometers in 2004. In the left side of the view, Saturn's shadow obscures the rings. In the right side of the view, the dark shadows of the rings curve across the top of the planet. The inset shows a false-color image of a brightly-colored thunderstorm in Saturn's southern hemisphere.

Organize

Booklet

Before you read this chapter, create the FoldNote entitled "Booklet." On the front cover, title the booklet "Our Solar System." Label each page of the booklet with a name of a planet in our solar system. As you read the chapter, fill in the booklet with details about the planets.

Instructions for creating FoldNotes are located in the Study Skills section on p. 518 of the Appendix.

8.4.c
8.4.e

Explore Activity

Measuring Space

Do the following activity to get a better idea of the size of our solar neighborhood.

Procedure

1. Use a **meterstick** and some **chalk** to draw a line 2 m long on a **chalkboard** or **sidewalk.** Draw a large dot at one end of the line. This dot represents the sun.

2. Draw smaller dots on the line to represent the relative distance of each of the bodies from the sun, based on information in the table.

Analysis

3. What do you notice about the distances between the bodies?

Body	Distance from sun	
	Millions of km	Scaled to cm
Mercury	57.9	2
Venus	108.2	4
Earth	149.6	5
Mars	227.9	8
Jupiter	778.4	26
Saturn	1,424.0	48
Uranus	2,827.0	97
Neptune	4,499.0	151
Pluto	5,943.0	200

A Solar System Is Born

Key Concept The solar system formed as a result of gravitational attraction in the solar nebula.

nebula (NEB yu luh) a large cloud of gas and dust in interstellar space; a region in space where stars are born

▶ The solar system includes a star we call the *sun*, nine planets, many moons that orbit planets, and other small bodies that travel around the sun. For more than 4.5 billion years, planets have been orbiting the sun. But how did the solar system come to be?

The Solar Nebula

All of the ingredients for building planets, moons, and stars are found in the vast, seemingly empty regions of space between the stars. Just as there are clouds in the sky, there are clouds in space. These clouds are called *nebulas.* **Nebulas** (or *nebulae*) are mixtures of gases—mainly hydrogen and helium—and dust made of elements such as carbon and silicon. Although nebulas are normally dark and invisible to optical telescopes, they can be seen when nearby stars illuminate them. So, how can a cloud of gas and dust such as the Horsehead Nebula, shown in **Figure 1,** form stars and planets? To answer this question, you must explore two factors that interact in nebulas—gravity and pressure.

Gravity Pulls Matter Together

The gas and dust that make up nebulas are made of matter. The matter of a nebula is held together by the force of gravity. In most nebulas, there is a lot of space between the particles. In fact, nebulas are less dense than air! Thus, the gravitational attraction between the particles in a nebula is very weak. The force is just enough to keep the nebula from drifting apart.

Standards Check Explain how gravity holds matter together in a nebula. 🐻 **8.2.g**

Figure 1 *The Horsehead Nebula is a cold, dark cloud of gas and dust. Observations suggest that it is also a site where stars form.*

Figure 2 Gravity and Pressure in a Nebula

1 Gravity causes the particles in a nebula to be attracted to each other.

2 As particles move closer together, collisions cause pressure to increase and particles are pushed apart.

3 If the inward force of gravity is balanced by outward pressure, the nebula becomes stable.

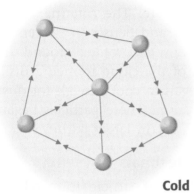

Cold

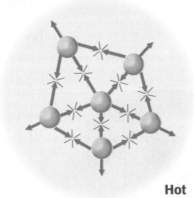

Hot

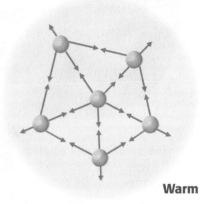

Warm

Pressure Pushes Matter Apart

If gravity pulls on all of the particles in a nebula, why don't nebulas slowly collapse? The answer has to do with the relationship between temperature and pressure in a nebula. *Temperature* is a measure of the average kinetic energy, or the energy of motion, of the particles in an object. If the particles in a nebula have little kinetic energy, they move slowly and the temperature of the cloud is very low. If the particles move fast, the temperature of the cloud is high. As particles move around, they sometimes crash into each other. As shown in **Figure 2,** these collisions cause particles to push away from each other, which creates *pressure*. If you have ever blown up a balloon, you understand how pressure works—pressure within the balloon keeps a balloon from collapsing. In a nebula, outward pressure balances the inward gravitational pull and keeps the cloud from collapsing.

Upsetting the Balance

The balance between gravity and pressure in a nebula can be upset if two nebulas collide or if a nearby star explodes. These events compress, or push together, small regions of a nebula. These regions can become so dense that they contract under their own gravity. As the matter collapses inward, the temperature increases and the stage is set for stars to form. The **solar nebula**—the cloud of gas and dust that formed our solar system—may have formed in this way.

Standards Check Explain how a nebula can become unstable.
 8.2.g

solar nebula (SOH luhr NEB yu luh) a rotating cloud of gas and dust from which the sun and planets formed

8.2.g Students know the role of gravity in forming and maintaining the shapes of planets, stars, and the solar system.
8.4.b Students know that the Sun is one of many stars in the Milky Way galaxy and that stars may differ in size, temperature, and color.
8.4.c Students know how to use astronomical units and light years as measures of distance between the Sun, stars, and Earth.
8.4.d Students know that stars are the source of light for all bright objects in outer space and that the Moon and planets shine by reflected sunlight, not by their own light.

Figure 3 The Formation of the Solar System

1 The young solar nebula begins to collapse.

2 The solar nebula rotates, flattens, and becomes warmer near its center.

3 Planetesimals begin to form within the swirling disk.

4 As the largest planetesimals grow in size, their gravity attracts more gas and dust.

5 Smaller planetesimals collide with the larger ones, and planets begin to grow.

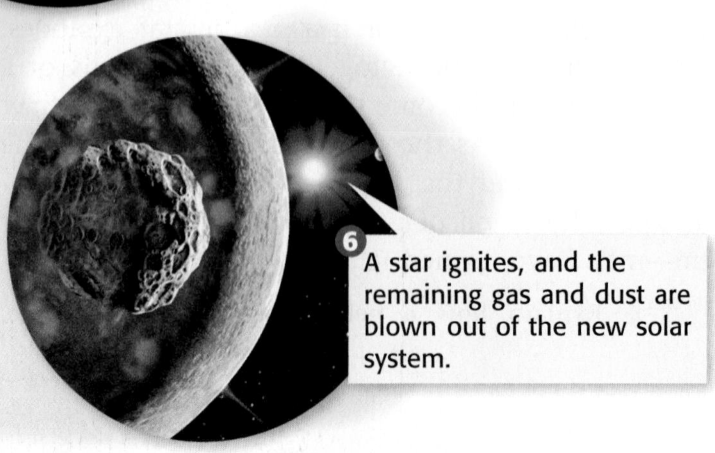

6 A star ignites, and the remaining gas and dust are blown out of the new solar system.

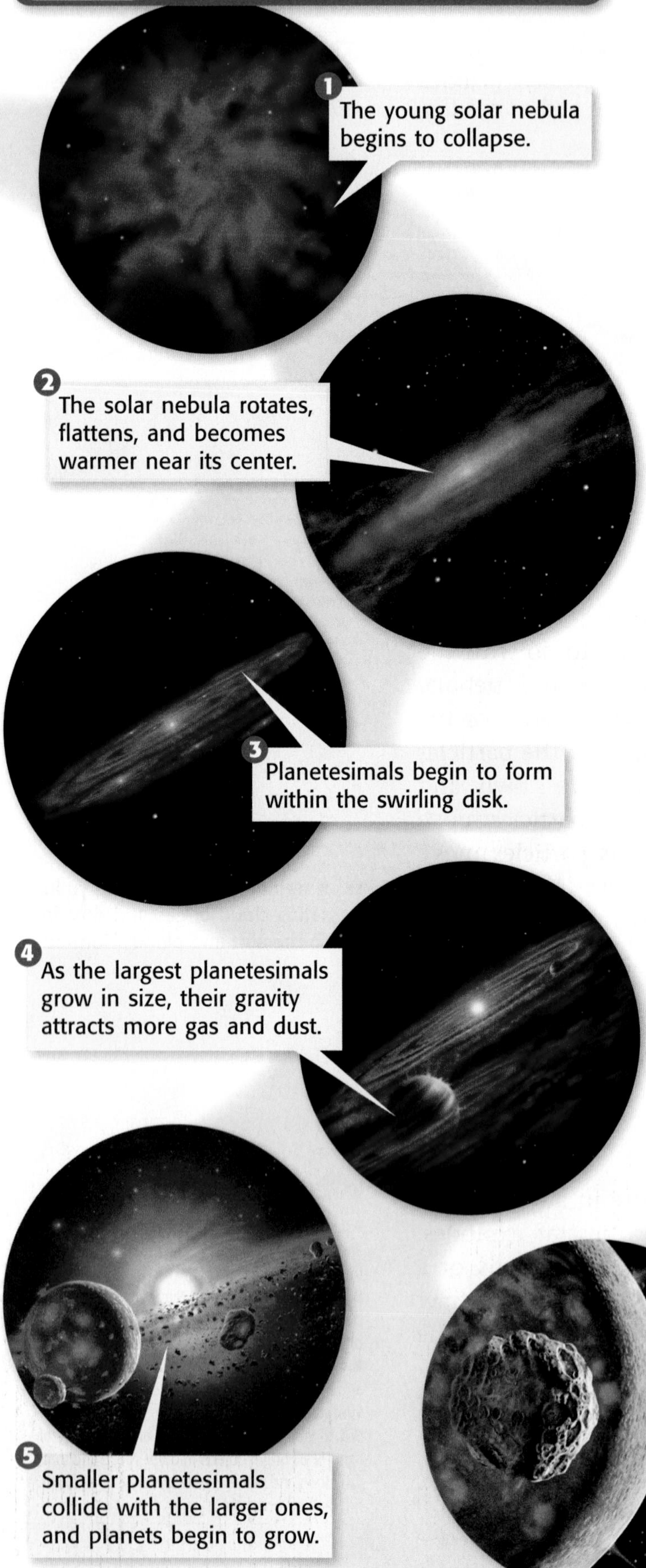

How the Solar System Formed

The events that may have led to the formation of the solar system are shown in **Figure 3.** As the solar nebula collapsed, it began to rotate. The rotating cloud became hotter and denser in its center. The gas and dust that rotated around the central part of the cloud formed a disk. This disk began to cool enough for dust particles to form. These particles began to collide and form larger particles.

From Planetesimals to Planets

The collision of particles formed bodies the size of boulders and asteroids. These small bodies are called *planetesimals.* The size of planetesimals depended on their distance from the center of the solar nebula.

The size of planetesimals continued to increase until their gravity became strong enough to pull in the solid matter near their orbit. In this way, planetesimals grew into protoplanets. Eventually, the protoplanets became large enough to form planets and moons.

Matter in the solar nebula was pulled together by gravity into spheres. The sun, the planets, and most moons are spherical because a sphere is the only geometric form in which all points on the surface are an equal distance from the center.

Standards Check Explain why objects in the solar nebula became spherical. **8.2.g**

The Birth of a Star

As the planets were forming, gas and dust near the center of the solar nebula grew denser and denser. The center became so dense and hot that hydrogen atoms began to fuse, or join, to form helium. Fusion released huge amounts of energy and created enough outward pressure to balance the inward pull of gravity. At this point, when the gas stopped collapsing, our sun was born and the new solar system had formed.

Standards Check Explain how the sun formed in the center of the solar nebula. 8.2.g

The Structure of the Sun

The sun's diameter is more than 100 times that of Earth. Its surface temperature is approximately 5,500°C. The interior of the sun is composed of the core, where the sun's energy is generated; the radiative zone; and the convective zone. The photosphere, chromosphere, and corona make up the exterior, or atmosphere, of the sun. **Figure 4** shows the layers of the sun.

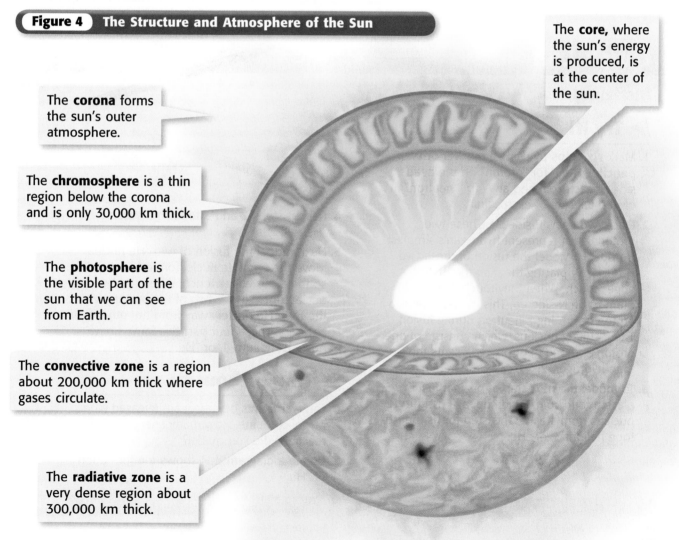

Figure 4 The Structure and Atmosphere of the Sun

The **core,** where the sun's energy is produced, is at the center of the sun.

The **corona** forms the sun's outer atmosphere.

The **chromosphere** is a thin region below the corona and is only 30,000 km thick.

The **photosphere** is the visible part of the sun that we can see from Earth.

The **convective zone** is a region about 200,000 km thick where gases circulate.

The **radiative zone** is a very dense region about 300,000 km thick.

Energy Production in the Sun

The sun has been shining on Earth for about 4.6 billion years. How can the sun stay hot for so long? What makes it shine?

At the beginning of the 20th century, Albert Einstein calculated that matter and energy are interchangeable. Matter can change into energy according to his famous formula: $E = mc^2$. (E is energy, m is mass, and c is the speed of light.) Because c is such a large number relative to, say, distances in the solar system, tiny amounts of matter can produce a huge amount of energy. By using Einstein's equation, astronomers were able to explain the huge quantities of energy produced by the sun.

Nuclear Fusion

Scientists now know that the sun generates energy through the process of nuclear fusion. *Nuclear fusion* is the process by which two or more low-mass nuclei fuse to form another nucleus. When hydrogen nuclei fuse to form helium, ignition begins in stars. The balance between gravity and pressure in the nuclear fusion process is what gives a star its spherical shape.

Standards Check Describe the process of nuclear fusion. 8.4.d

Quick Lab

Modeling Fusion

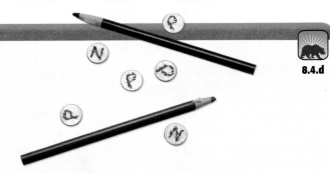

8.4.d

▶ Try It!

1. Mark **six coins** by using a **marker or wax pencil.** Put a *P* for "proton" on the head side of each coin and an *N* for "neutron" on the tail side of each coin.

2. Place two coins P-side up. These two protons each represent hydrogen's simplest isotope, H. Model the fusion of these two H nuclei by placing them so that their flat edges touch. When they touch, flip one of them to be N-side up. This flip represents a proton becoming a neutron during fusion. The resulting nucleus, which consists of one proton and one neutron, represents the isotope hydrogen-2, ^{2}H, called *deuterium.*

3. To model the next step of nuclear fusion, place a third coin, P-side up, against the ^{2}H nucleus from step 2. This step forms the isotope helium-3, or ^{3}He.

4. Repeat steps 2 and 3 to form a second ^{3}He nucleus.

5. Next, model the fusion of two ^{3}He nuclei. Move the two ^{3}He nuclei formed in step 3 so that their edges touch. When the two ^{3}He nuclei touch, move two of the protons in the two ^{3}He nuclei away from the other four particles. These four particles form a new nucleus: helium-4, or ^{4}He.

▶ Think About It!

6. Large amounts of energy are released when nuclei combine. How many energy-producing reactions did you model?

7. Create a diagram that shows the formation of ^{4}He.

🕐 5 min

Conditions Required for Fusion

Under normal conditions, the nuclei of hydrogen atoms never get close enough to join. The reason is that they are positively charged. Like charges repel each other, as shown in **Figure 5.** In the center of the sun, however, the temperature and pressure are very high. As a result, the hydrogen nuclei are forced close enough together to overcome the repulsive force, and hydrogen fuses into helium.

Figure 5 *Like charges repel just as similar poles on a pair of magnets do.*

Fusion in the Sun

Fusion of hydrogen in the sun consists of three steps, as shown in **Figure 6.** In the first step, two hydrogen nuclei, or *protons,* collide and fuse. In this step, one proton becomes a neutron and changes the original two protons into a proton-neutron pair. In the second step, another proton combines with the proton-neutron pair. This process produces a nucleus made up of two protons and one neutron. In the third step, two nuclei made up of two protons and one neutron collide and fuse. As this fusion happens, two protons are released. The remaining two protons and two neutrons fuse and form a helium nucleus. During each step of the reaction, energy is released.

Figure 6 **Fusion of Hydrogen in the Sun**

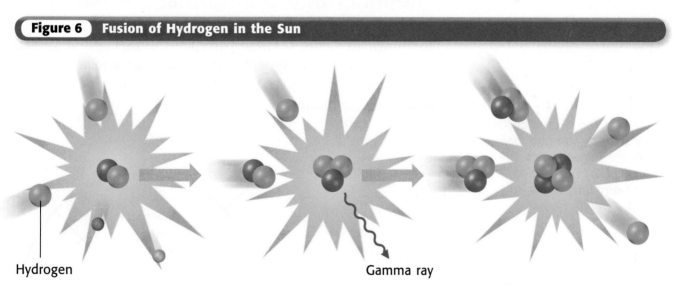

Hydrogen

Gamma ray

❶ **Deuterium** Two hydrogen nuclei (protons) collide. One proton emits particles and energy and then becomes a neutron. The proton and neutron combine to produce a heavy form of hydrogen called *deuterium.*

❷ **Helium-3** Deuterium combines with another hydrogen nucleus to form a variety of helium called *helium-3.* More energy, including gamma rays, is released.

❸ **Helium-4** Two helium-3 atoms combine to form ordinary helium-4, which releases more energy and a pair of hydrogen nuclei (protons).

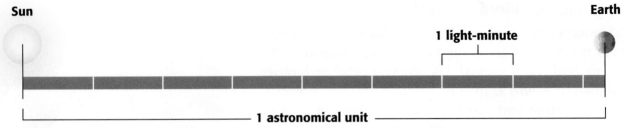

Sun

Earth

1 light-minute

1 astronomical unit

Figure 7 *One astronomical unit (AU) equals about 8.3 light-minutes.*

Measuring Interplanetary Distances

One way that scientists measure distances in space is by using the astronomical unit. One **astronomical unit** (AU) is the average distance between the sun and Earth, or approximately 150,000,000 km. Another way to measure distances in space is by using the speed of light. Light travels at about 300,000 km/s in space. Thus, in 1 s, light travels 300,000 km.

In 1 min, light travels nearly 18,000,000 km. This distance is called a *light-minute*. Look at **Figure 7**. Light from the sun takes 8.3 min to reach Earth. So, the distance from Earth to the sun, or 1 AU, is 8.3 light-minutes. Distances in the solar system can be measured in light-minutes and light-hours.

Standards Check How far is one astronomical unit? 🐾 **8.4.c**

astronomical unit (As truh NAHM i kuhl YOON it) the average distance between Earth and the sun; approximately 150 million kilometers (symbol, AU)

The Inner and Outer Solar Systems

Astronomers divide the solar system into two main parts. As shown in **Figure 8,** these parts are the inner solar system and the outer solar system. The *inner solar system* contains the four planets that are located closest to the sun. The *outer solar system* contains the four planets that are located farthest from the sun.

Figure 8 *The planets of the inner solar system and their orbits are shown at left. The planets of the outer solar system and their orbits are shown at right.*

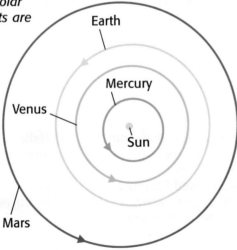

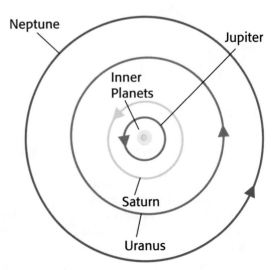

Summary

- For a nebula to be stable, outward pressure and the inward force of gravity must be balanced.
- The solar system formed out of a vast cloud of dust and gas called the *solar nebula.* The core of the nebula became the sun. Planets formed from material in the rotating disk.
- Energy is produced in the sun's core by the process of nuclear fusion.
- The sun consists of six layers: the core, the radiative zone, the convective zone, the photosphere, the chromosphere, and the corona.
- Distances in the solar system are measured in astronomical units, light-minutes, and light-hours.
- The inner solar system contains the planets closest to the sun. The outer solar system contains the planets farthest from the sun.

Using Vocabulary

1. Use *nebula* and *solar nebula* in separate sentences.

Understanding Concepts

2. **Analyzing** Explain the roles of gravity and pressure in the formation of the solar system.

3. **Applying** Explain how the solar nebula may have formed.

4. **Listing** List the steps in the formation of the solar system in the order they happened.

5. **Listing** List the layers of the sun, starting with the innermost layer.

6. **Summarizing** Summarize the three-step process of nuclear fusion in the sun.

7. **Identifying** Identify the relationship between astronomical units and light-minutes.

Critical Thinking

8. **Applying Concepts** Why did gravitational attraction in the solar nebula pull matter into spheres?

9. **Making Inferences** Why would astronomers be unlikely to use light-hours to measure distances outside the solar system?

INTERPRETING GRAPHICS Use the illustration below to answer the next question.

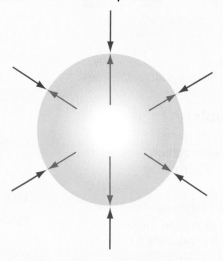

10. **Applying Concepts** What is the force that is indicated by the blue lines that point inward?

Math Skills

11. **Making Calculations** If Mercury is an average of 3.2 light-minutes from the sun, how many kilometers is Mercury from the sun?

Challenge

12. **Making Inferences** Why do all of the planets travel around the sun in the same direction, and why do the planets lie on a fairly flat plane?

The Inner Planets

Key Concept The four planets of the inner solar system are small, dense, and rocky and are close to the sun.

What You Will Learn

- The inner planets, or terrestrial planets, include Mercury, Venus, Earth, and Mars.
- The inner planets tend to be small and composed of rock.

Why It Matters

The inner planets contain the only known inhabited planet in the solar system.

Vocabulary

- terrestrial planet
- prograde rotation
- retrograde rotation

READING STRATEGY

Graphic Organizer In your **Science Journal,** make a Comparison Table that compares the inner planets' period of rotation, period of revolution, diameter, density, surface gravity, and interesting facts.

terrestrial planet (tuh RES tree uhl PLAN it) one of the highly dense planets nearest to the sun; Mercury, Venus, Mars, and Earth

In the inner solar system, you will find one of the hottest places in our solar system as well as the only planet known to support life. Mercury, Venus, Earth, and Mars are called **terrestrial planets** because they are very dense and rocky. They are smaller, denser, and rockier than the outer planets. In this section, you will learn more about the individual characteristics of the four planets that make up the inner solar system.

Mercury: Closest to the Sun

Mercury, shown in **Figure 1,** is the planet that is located closest to the sun. After Earth, Mercury is the densest body in the solar system. This high density is due to the fact that the majority of Mercury's interior is composed of a large, iron core. The atmosphere of Mercury is very thin. The gases that made up the atmosphere were boiled off into space by the sun.

Days and Years on Mercury

The amount of time that an object takes to rotate once is the object's *period of rotation*. Because of Mercury's slow rotation, a day on Mercury is approximately equal to 59 Earth days! Another curious thing about Mercury is that its year is only equal to 88 Earth days. A *year* is the time that a planet takes to go around the sun once. The motion of a body orbiting another body in space is called *revolution*. The time that an object takes to revolve around the sun once is the object's *period of revolution*. Every 88 Earth days—or 1.5 Mercurian days—Mercury revolves around the sun once.

Standards Check What is Mercury's period of rotation? 🐻 **8.4.e**

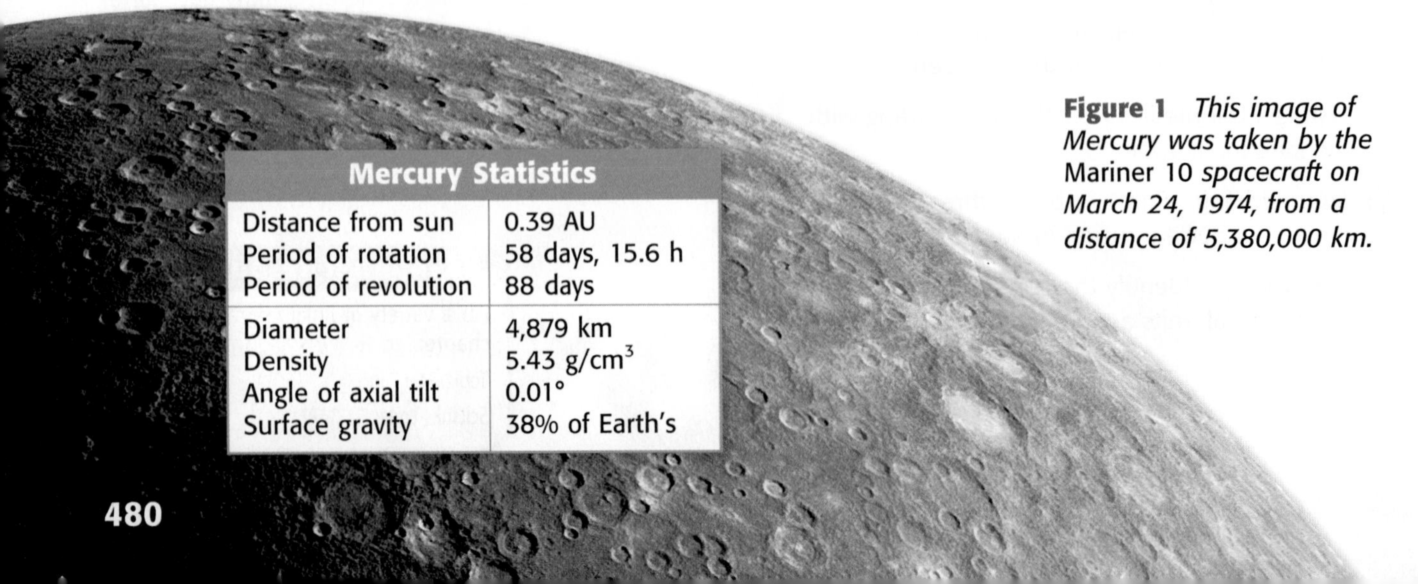

Figure 1 *This image of Mercury was taken by the Mariner 10 spacecraft on March 24, 1974, from a distance of 5,380,000 km.*

Mercury Statistics	
Distance from sun	0.39 AU
Period of rotation	58 days, 15.6 h
Period of revolution	88 days
Diameter	4,879 km
Density	5.43 g/cm^3
Angle of axial tilt	0.01°
Surface gravity	38% of Earth's

Figure 2 *This image of Venus was made from a mosaic of images taken from the* Magellan *spacecraft in 1991.*

Venus Statistics	
Distance from sun	0.72 AU
Period of rotation	243 days, 2.4 h (R)*
Period of revolution	224 days, 17 h
Diameter	12,104 km
Density	5.24 g/cm³
Angle of axial tilt	2.6°
Surface gravity	91% of Earth's

*R = retrograde rotation

Venus: Earth's Twin?

The second planet from the sun is Venus, which is shown in **Figure 2.** In some ways, Venus is more like Earth than like any other planet. Venus is only slightly smaller, less massive, and less dense than Earth. But in other ways, Venus is very different from Earth. On Venus, the sun rises in the west and sets in the east. In other words, Venus and Earth rotate in opposite directions. Earth is said to have **prograde rotation** because it appears to spin in a *counterclockwise* direction when it is viewed from above its North Pole. If a planet appears to spin in a *clockwise* direction when it is viewed from above its North Pole, the planet is said to have **retrograde rotation.**

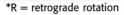

prograde rotation (PRO GRAYD roh TAY shuhn) the counterclockwise spin of a planet or moon as seen from above the planet's North Pole; rotation in the same direction as the sun's rotation
Wordwise The prefix *pro-* means "forward."

retrograde rotation (RE truh GRAYD roh TAY shuhn) the clockwise spin of a planet or moon as seen from above the planet's North Pole

The Atmosphere of Venus

Of the terrestrial planets, Venus has the densest atmosphere. Venus's atmosphere has 90 times the pressure of Earth's atmosphere—a pressure that would instantly crush a human! The atmosphere on Venus contains mainly carbon dioxide. The atmosphere also has clouds that are made up of droplets of sulfuric acid. Because of Venus's dense atmosphere, surface temperatures average 464°C. At this temperature, metals such as lead melt and flow.

Mapping Venus's Surface

Between 1990 and 1992, the *Magellan* spacecraft mapped the surface of Venus using radar waves. The radar waves traveled through the Venusian clouds and bounced off the planet's surface. Data gathered from the radar waves showed that Venus has impact craters, mountains, lava plains, and volcanoes.

8.4.e Students know the appearance, general composition, relative position and size, and motion of objects in the solar system, including planets, planetary satellites, comets, and asteroids.

Standards Check List four features of Venus's surface. 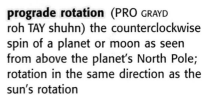8.4.e

Earth: An Oasis in Space

As viewed from space, Earth appears to be the sparkling blue oasis that, in fact, it is. During the course of Earth's history, many types of plants and animals, such as the birds shown in **Figure 3,** have inhabited Earth in numbers that are almost too large to comprehend.

A Constantly Changing Planet

Earth is the only planet in the solar system that is known to have the combination of factors that are needed to support life. Life as we know it requires water and an energy source. Earth is very geologically active. Landmasses slowly move around on the surface of Earth, so the shapes of the continents are continuously changing. Forces such as weathering and erosion also constantly reshape Earth's surface.

Studying Earth from Space

The picture of Earth shown in **Figure 4** was taken from space. You may think that the only goal of space exploration is to make discoveries beyond Earth. But the National Aeronautics and Space Administration (NASA) has a program to study Earth by using satellites in the same way that scientists study other planets. This program is called the *Earth Science Enterprise*. Its goal is to study Earth as an interrelated global system. Interrelated aspects of the global system include the atmosphere, land, ice, the oceans, and living things. The program will also help us understand how humans affect the global environment.

Figure 3 *Earth is the only planet known to support life.*

Earth Statistics	
Distance from sun	1.0 AU
Period of rotation	23 h, 56 min
Period of revolution	365 days, 6 h
Diameter	12,756 km
Density	5.52 g/cm³
Angle of axial tilt	23.5°
Surface gravity	100% of Earth's

Figure 4 *This image of Earth was taken on December 7, 1972, by members of the crew of* Apollo 17 *while on their way to the moon.* **Which interrelated aspects of the global system can you find in this image?**

Mars Statistics	
Distance from sun	1.52 AU
Period of rotation	24 h, 37 min
Period of revolution	1 year, 322 days
Diameter	6,794 km
Density	3.93 g/cm³
Angle of axial tilt	25.2°
Surface gravity	38% of Earth's

Figure 5 *This Viking orbiter image shows the eastern hemisphere of Mars. The large circular feature in the center is the impact crater Schiaparelli, which has a diameter of 450 km.*

Mars: The Red Planet

Mars, shown in **Figure 5,** is perhaps the most studied planet in the solar system other than Earth. Much of our knowledge of Mars has come from information gathered by spacecraft.

The Atmosphere of Mars

Because of its thinner atmosphere and greater distance from the sun, Mars is a cold planet. The *Mars Pathfinder* recorded midsummer temperatures ranging from –13°C to –77°C. The Martian atmosphere, which is composed mostly of carbon dioxide, is very thin. The air pressure on the surface of Mars is about the same as it is 30 km above Earth's surface. Because the temperature and air pressure in the Martian atmosphere are so low, liquid water cannot persist on Mars's surface.

Standards Check How do air temperature and air pressure on Mars differ from those on Earth? 📖**8.4.e**

Water on Mars

Even though liquid water cannot persist on Mars's surface today, evidence strongly suggests that liquid water existed on Mars's surface in the past. Mars has many surface features that are characteristic of erosion and deposition by water. **Figure 6** shows an area on Mars that has features that may have formed when water deposited sediments in a lake. These findings indicate that Mars may have been warmer and may have had a thicker atmosphere in the past.

Figure 6 *The origin of the features shown in this image is unknown. The features may have resulted from deposition of sediment in a lake.*

Where Is the Water Now?

Mars has two polar icecaps made of both frozen water and frozen carbon dioxide. Most of the water on Mars is trapped in these icecaps. However, data from the *Mars Global Surveyor* suggest that water may also exist either frozen or as a liquid just beneath Mars's surface. If liquid water does exist below Mars's surface, there is a possibility that life may exist on Mars.

Volcanoes on Mars

Mars has been geologically active in the past, which is shown in part by the presence of giant volcanoes. Unlike Earth, where volcanoes exist in many places, Mars has only two large volcanic systems. The largest, the Tharsis Montes, stretches 8,000 km across the planet.

The largest mountain in the solar system, Olympus Mons, is shown in **Figure 7.** It is a shield volcano that is similar to Mauna Kea on the island of Hawaii. Olympus Mons is nearly 24 km high—3 times as high as Mount Everest! At 600 km across, the base of the volcano is about the size of the state of Arizona. Olympus Mons may have grown so high because the volcano has erupted constantly for a longer period of time than corresponding volcanoes have on Earth. Other Martian volcanoes have 10 to 100 times the diameter of volcanoes on Earth.

Standards Check Explain how volcanoes on Mars differ from volcanoes on Earth. 🐻 **8.4.e**

Figure 7 *At a height of 24 km, Olympus Mons is the highest mountain in the solar system.*

Missions to Mars

Several recent missions to Mars were launched to gain a better understanding of the Martian world. **Figure 8** shows the *Mars Express Orbiter,* which reached Mars in December 2003. The spacecraft has been performing remote sensing of Mars. The *Orbiter*'s instruments are searching for traces of water both underground and on the planet's surface.

In January 2004, the exploration rovers *Spirit* and *Opportunity* landed on Mars. The instruments on this pair of wheeled robots have found strong evidence that water once existed on the surface of the planet. The evidence included finding sediments that had been rippled by water at the bottom of a shallow sea and rocks that had once been soaked with water.

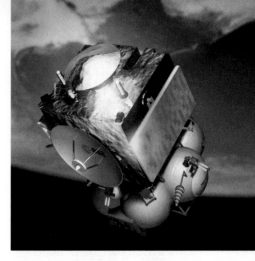

Figure 8 *The* Mars Express Orbiter *helps scientists map Mars and study Mars's atmosphere.*

SECTION Review

 8.4.e

Summary

- The inner planets include Mercury, Venus, Earth, and Mars.

- The inner planets differ from each other and from other bodies in the solar system in size and composition.

- Mercury is the closest planet to the sun. Mercury is small and rocky and revolves around the sun every 88 days.

- Venus is much like Earth, but Venus's atmosphere is much denser than Earth's.

- Earth is the only planet in the solar system known to support life.

- Evidence suggests that Mars had liquid water in the past and that Mars was geologically active in the past.

Using Vocabulary

① Explain how the meanings of *prograde rotation* and *retrograde rotation* differ.

Understanding Concepts

② **Comparing** Compare period of rotation with period of revolution.

③ **Analyzing** Why are surface temperatures on Venus so high?

④ **Identifying** Identify two factors that make Earth suitable for life.

⑤ **Analyzing** Why are surface temperatures on Mars low?

⑥ **Identifying** Identify three discoveries made by spacecraft that have been sent to study Mars.

Critical Thinking

⑦ **Making Inferences** How can satellites help us study Earth?

⑧ **Analyzing Ideas** Why do scientists think that Mars may have once been a warmer place and may have had a thicker atmosphere?

⑨ **Identifying Relationships** Earth is almost 3 times the size of Mercury. But Earth has an average density of 5.52 g/cm³, and Mercury has an average density of 5.43 g/cm³. Why does Mercury have an average density that is close to that of Earth even though Mercury is a much smaller planet?

⑩ **Identifying Relationships** Earth and Venus have a much higher surface gravity than Mercury and Mars do. How is surface gravity related to a planet's atmosphere?

Challenge

⑪ **Analyzing Ideas** Explain why Mercury, Venus, and Mars are not likely to support life as we know it.

Internet Resources

For a variety of links related to this chapter, go to www.scilinks.org

Topic: The Inner Planets
SciLinks code: HY70798

The Outer Planets

Key Concept The planets of the outer solar system have deep, massive gas atmospheres.

▶ The outer planets are very large planets that are made mostly of gas or rock. These planets are called gas giants. **Gas giants** are planets that have deep, massive gas atmospheres.

Jupiter: A Giant Among Giants

Jupiter, shown in **Figure 1,** is the largest planet in our solar system. It is also the most massive planet and has a mass that is twice that of the other eight planets combined. Jupiter is made mainly of hydrogen.

Jupiter's atmosphere consists of molecular hydrogen, helium, and trace amounts of ammonia, methane, and water. Violent disturbances occur in the planet's atmosphere. These disturbances include winds of up to 540 km/h and enormous areas of high pressure. Astronomers think that the Great Red Spot is a storm that is 3 times as large as Earth. The Great Red Spot has been viewed by astronomers for at least 350 years.

Jupiter—like Saturn and Neptune—radiates much more energy into space than it receives from the sun. The reason is that Jupiter's interior is very hot. Temperatures in the planet's interior can be as high as 30,000°C.

The Exploration of Jupiter

In 1995, the spacecraft *Galileo* arrived at Jupiter and began monitoring an atmospheric probe that *Galileo* had launched earlier. The data transmitted by the probe showed that Jupiter has thunderstorms that are much larger than the thunderstorms on Earth. *Galileo* also discovered that Jupiter has rings that are composed of small dust grains.

Figure 1 *This* Voyager 2 *image of Jupiter was taken at a distance of 28.4 million kilometers. Io, one of Jupiter's largest moons, can also be seen in this image.*

Jupiter Statistics	
Distance from sun	5.20 AU
Period of rotation	9 h, 55 min
Period of revolution	11 years, 314 days
Diameter	142,984 km
Density	1.33 g/cm³
Angle of axial tilt	3.1°
Gravity	236% of Earth's

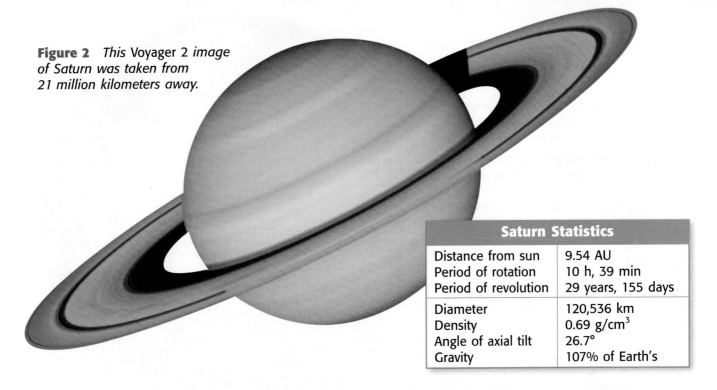

Figure 2 *This* Voyager 2 *image of Saturn was taken from 21 million kilometers away.*

Saturn Statistics	
Distance from sun	9.54 AU
Period of rotation	10 h, 39 min
Period of revolution	29 years, 155 days
Diameter	120,536 km
Density	0.69 g/cm^3
Angle of axial tilt	26.7°
Gravity	107% of Earth's

Saturn: The Ringed World

Saturn, shown in **Figure 2,** is the second-largest planet in the solar system. Saturn has roughly 764 times the volume of Earth and is 95 times as massive as Earth. Saturn is the least dense of all the planets. Its density—0.69 g/cm^3—is less than the density of water, or 1.0 g/cm^3. Like Jupiter, Saturn is made mainly of hydrogen. Saturn's atmosphere consists of molecular hydrogen, helium, traces of other gases, and water.

gas giant (GAS JIE uhnt) a planet that has a deep, massive atmosphere, such as Jupiter, Saturn, Uranus, or Neptune

The Rings of Saturn

Saturn is known for the spectacular rings that orbit its equator. Saturn's rings are more than 250,000 km in diameter (greater than the distance between Earth and the moon) but are less than 1 km thick. Trillions of particles of water ice and dust make up the rings of Saturn. The particles range from a centimeter to several meters across.

The origin of Saturn's rings is a mystery and a subject that is debated by scientists. Some scientists argue that the rings are the remains of a large cometlike body that entered Saturn's system and was ripped apart by gravitational forces.

Standards Check How do some scientists think that the rings of Saturn formed? **8.4.e**

The Exploration of Saturn

Scientists are learning about Saturn from the *Cassini* spacecraft. *Cassini* reached Saturn in July 2004. Since then, the spacecraft has provided information about the planet's rings, its northern polar region, and its storms.

8.4.e Students know the appearance, general composition, relative position and size, and motion of objects in the solar system, including planets, planetary satellites, comets, and asteroids.

Figure 3 *This image of Uranus was taken by* Voyager 2 *at a distance of 9.1 million kilometers.*

Uranus Statistics	
Distance from sun	19.218 AU
Period of rotation	17 h, 14 min (R)*
Period of revolution	83 years, 272 days
Diameter	51,118 km
Density	1.27 g/cm³
Angle of axial tilt	97.8°
Gravity	91% of Earth's

*R = retrograde rotation

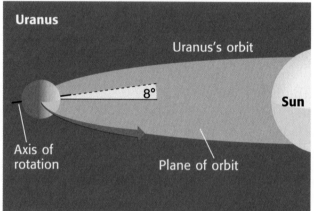

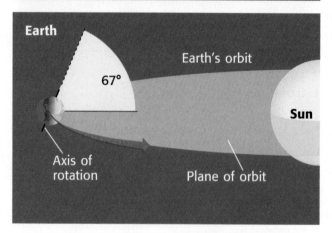

Figure 4 *Uranus's axis of rotation is tilted so that the axis is nearly parallel to the plane of Uranus's orbit. In contrast, the axes of most other planets are closer to being perpendicular to the plane of the planets' orbits.*

Uranus: A Small Giant

Uranus (YOOR uh nuhs) is the third-largest planet in the solar system. The planet is made mostly of rock and ices. Hydrogen, helium, and methane make up the planet's atmosphere. The methane in the atmosphere filters incoming sunlight. The scattering of light gives Uranus the greenish tinge that is seen in **Figure 3.**

A Tilted Planet

Unlike most other planets, Uranus is tipped over on its side. So, its axis of rotation is tilted almost 98° and lies almost in the plane of its orbit, as shown in **Figure 4.** For approximately half of a Uranian year, one pole points toward the sun while the other pole is in darkness. For the other part of the year, the poles are reversed. When *Voyager 2* visited Uranus in January 1986, the planet's south pole was tipped toward the sun. Some scientists think that Uranus may have been hit by a massive object that tipped the planet over.

Standards Check How does Uranus's axis of rotation differ from the axis of rotation of other planets in the solar system? 8.4.e

Neptune: The Blue World

Irregularities in the orbit of Uranus suggested to early astronomers that another planet must lie beyond Uranus. They thought that the gravity of this new planet pulled Uranus off its predicted path. By using the predictions of the new planet's orbit, astronomers discovered the planet Neptune in 1846.

Neptune, the fourth-largest planet in the solar system, is a beautiful blue planet, as shown in **Figure 5.** Neptune is about the same size as Uranus and is also made of rock and ices. The planet has an atmosphere that contains hydrogen, helium, and methane. Neptune's blue color is caused largely by the absorption of red light by methane in the atmosphere.

The Weather on Neptune

Unlike Uranus's, the deeper layers of Neptune's atmosphere are visible. Clouds and changes in weather can be seen. At the time *Voyager 2* visited Neptune in August 1989, Neptune had a Great Dark Spot in its southern hemisphere. The Great Dark Spot, a storm the size of Earth, was moving westward across the planet at a speed of approximately 300 m/s. By 1994, the Great Dark Spot had disappeared. Soon, however, another dark spot was located, this time in the planet's northern hemisphere. Neptune also has the fastest winds of any planet in the solar system. Neptune's winds travel at more than 1,000 km/h. No one knows what causes these winds to blow so hard.

Planetary Exploration

Plan an extraterrestrial science experiment. Go to **go.hrw.com,** and type in the keyword HY7FAMW.

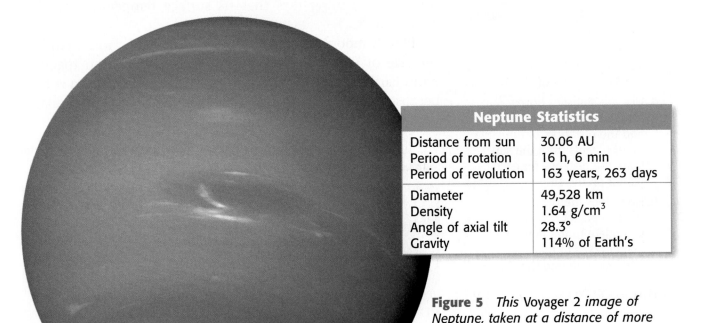

Neptune Statistics	
Distance from sun	30.06 AU
Period of rotation	16 h, 6 min
Period of revolution	163 years, 263 days
Diameter	49,528 km
Density	1.64 g/cm^3
Angle of axial tilt	28.3°
Gravity	114% of Earth's

Figure 5 *This* Voyager 2 *image of Neptune, taken at a distance of more than 7 million kilometers, shows the Great Dark Spot as well as some bright cloud bands.*

Figure 6 *This Hubble Space Telescope image is one of the clearest ever taken of Pluto (left) and its moon, Charon (right).*

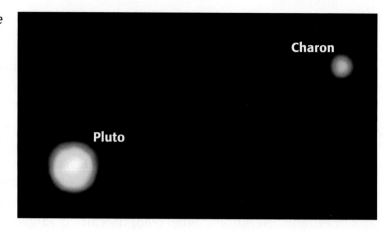

Pluto Statistics	
Distance from sun	39.5 AU (average)
Period of rotation	6 days, 9.3 h (R)*
Period of revolution	248 years, 4.5 days
Diameter	2,390 km
Density	1.75 g/cm³
Angle of axial tilt	122.5°
Surface gravity	6% of Earth's

*R = retrograde rotation

Quick Lab

Distances in the Outer Solar System

8.4.c

1. Use a **meterstick** and **scissors** to cut a **300 cm (3.00 m) strip of cash register tape or adding machine tape**.

2. Use **tape** to tape the strip to a flat surface, such as the floor of the classroom.

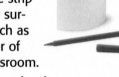

3. Using a scale of 10 cm = 1 AU, use a **marker** to mark off 30 AU.

4. Use the statistics boxes for the outer planets to find the distances of the outer planets from the sun. Mark the distance for each planet on the strip.

5. How does the distance of each planet from the sun relate to the time that planet takes to make a revolution around the sun?

 15 min

Figure 7 *An artist's view of the sun and Charon from Pluto shows just how little light and heat Pluto receives from the sun.*

Pluto: A Dwarf Planet

Since its discovery in 1930, Pluto has been called the ninth planet. However, in 2006, astronomers created a new definition of *planet*. Because Pluto does not fit all of the conditions necessary for it to be considered a planet, Pluto has been reclassified as a dwarf planet.

A Small World

Pluto differs a lot from the nearby gas giants. Pluto is less than half the size of Mercury and is made mainly of ice and rock. Scientists think that Pluto is covered by frozen nitrogen and has a thin atmosphere of methane. Pluto is located an average of 5.9 billion km from the sun. Pluto is so far from the sun's warming rays that its surface temperature reaches only −235°C.

Pluto's moon, Charon (KER uhn), is a little more than half the size of Pluto. **Figure 6** shows Pluto and Charon together. From Earth, separating the images of Pluto and Charon is hard because the bodies are so far away. From Pluto, the sun probably looks like a very distant bright star, as shown in **Figure 7**.

Standards Check Explain how Pluto differs from the outer planets.
8.4.e

Beyond Pluto

In recent years, scientists have discovered hundreds of objects in our solar system beyond Neptune's orbit. This region of the solar system contains small bodies that are made mostly of ice. The region is called the *Kuiper belt* (KIE puhr BELT). Some objects found in the Kuiper belt are larger than Pluto. Some scientists consider Pluto to be a Kuiper belt body.

In October 2003, another object, 2003UB313, was discovered in the Kuiper belt. The object is located almost 16 billion kilometers from the sun. It is larger than Pluto and takes 560 years to orbit the sun

SECTION Review

 8.4.e

Summary

- Jupiter is the largest and most massive planet in the solar system.
- Saturn is the second-largest planet and the least dense planet in the solar system. The rings of Saturn are made of particles of water ice and dust.
- Uranus's axis of rotation is tilted almost 98°.
- The weather on Neptune includes storms and winds that travel at more than 1,000 km/h.
- Pluto is a dwarf planet. Its moon, Charon, is more than half Pluto's size.
- Hundreds of objects have been discovered in our solar system beyond Neptune's orbit.

Using Vocabulary

1. Write an original definition for the term *gas giant*.

Understanding Concepts

2. **Comparing** Compare the size of Jupiter to the size of other planets in the solar system.

3. **Summarizing** Briefly describe the rings of Saturn.

4. **Identifying** What is so unusual about Uranus's axis of rotation?

5. **Applying** How do scientists know that intense storms move across the surface of Neptune?

6. **Comparing** Compare Pluto to the outer planets.

Critical Thinking

7. **Evaluating Data** What conclusions can you draw about the properties of a planet just by knowing how far from the sun the planet is?

8. **Making Comparisons** How do the massive outer planets differ from the inner terrestrial planets?

INTERPRETING GRAPHICS Use the illustration below to answer the next question.

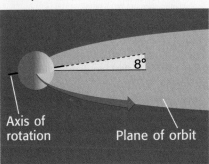

9. **Identifying Relationships** Which planet is illustrated? Explain your answer.

Math Skills

10. **Making Calculations** If Jupiter is 43.3 light-minutes from the sun and Neptune is 4.2 light-hours from the sun, how far from Jupiter is Neptune?

Internet Resources

For a variety of links related to this chapter, go to www.scilinks.org

Topic: The Outer Planets

SciLinks code: HY71091

Moons

Key Concept   Moons are bodies that are smaller than planets and that orbit planets.

What You Will Learn
- Earth's moon formed when an object collided with Earth.
- The moon's appearance changes as the moon revolves around Earth.
- Moons of other planets vary greatly from each other in size and composition.

Why It Matters
Moons have physical characteristics that astronomers find as interesting as those of planets.

Vocabulary
- satellite
- eclipse
- phase

READING STRATEGY

Asking Questions   Read this section silently. In your **Science Journal**, write down questions that you have about this section. Discuss your questions in a small group.

satellite (SAT'l IET) a natural or artificial body that revolves around a planet

Natural or artificial bodies that revolve around larger bodies such as planets are called **satellites.** Except for Mercury and Venus, all of the planets have natural satellites called *moons*. The moons in our solar system have volcanoes, craters, and possible underground oceans and would be interesting places to visit.

Luna: The Moon of Earth

Scientists have learned a lot from studying Earth's moon, which is also called *Luna*. The lunar rocks brought back during the Apollo missions were found to be almost 4.5 billion years old. Because these rocks have undergone few changes since they formed, scientists know that the solar system is at least 4.5 billion years old.

The Surface of the Moon

The moon's history is written on its surface. The surfaces of bodies that have no atmospheres and no erosion preserve a record of almost all of the impacts of objects that have struck them. About 3.8 billion years ago, all the planets and moons were struck repeatedly by objects left over from the formation of the solar system. The surfaces of the moon, of some of the moons of the outer planets, and of Mercury all record this bombardment.

The moon's surface is composed of highlands, or *terrae*, and plains, or *maria*. Terrae and maria are shown in **Figure 1.** Terrae are bright and cratered, and maria are dark and flat.

Figure 1   *This image of Earth's moon was taken by the Galileo spacecraft while on its way to Jupiter. **What are the bright, cratered areas on the moon's surface called?***

Moon Statistics	
Period of rotation	27 days, 7.7 hours
Period of revolution	27 days, 7.7 hours
Diameter	3,476 km
Density	3.35 g/cm^3
Surface temperature	−170°C to 130°C
Surface gravity	17% of Earth's

Lunar Origins

When rock samples of the moon were brought back from the Apollo mission, scientists studied them. Scientists found that the composition of the moon was similar to that of Earth's mantle. The evidence from the lunar rock samples supported none of the popular explanations for the moon's formation.

The current theory is that a large, Mars-sized object collided with Earth while Earth was still forming, as shown in **Figure 2.** The collision was so violent that material was blasted into orbit around Earth to form the moon.

Why did the moon become a sphere? A sphere forms when gravity pulls, or attracts, matter toward other matter. This gravitationally attracted matter arranges itself around a center. A sphere is the only geometric form in which every point on the surface is an equal distance from the center. There is no part of a sphere in which gravity call pull matter farther into the center of the sphere.

Standards Check Why is the moon spherical? **8.2.g**

8.2.g Students know the role of gravity in forming and maintaining the shapes of planets, stars, and the solar system.
8.4.d Students know that stars are the source of light for all bright objects in outer space and that the Moon and planets shine by reflected sunlight, not by their own light.
8.4.e Students know the appearance, general composition, relative position and size, and motion of objects in the solar system, including planets, planetary satellites, comets, and asteroids.

Figure 2 **Formation of the Moon**

❶ Impact
Almost 4.5 billion years ago, when Earth was still mostly molten, a nearby body that had a mass similar to that of Mars collided with Earth. The collision caused enough material from both objects to be ejected into Earth's orbit to form the moon.

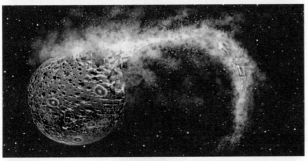

❷ Ejection
The resulting debris began to revolve around Earth within a few hours of the impact. Some debris consisted of mantle material from Earth. In large part, the debris consisted of mantle material from the impacting body as well as part of the iron core of the impacting body.

❸ Formation
Soon after the giant impact, the clumps of material ejected into orbit around Earth began to join to form the moon. Much later, as the moon cooled, additional impacts created deep basins and fractured the moon's surface. Lunar lava flowed from those cracks and flooded the basins to form the lunar maria that we see today.

Moonlight

Unlike the sun, the moon does not generate energy that can be emitted as light. Like the planets and other bodies in the solar system, the moon shines because it reflects light from the sun. The total amount of sunlight that the moon gets always remains the same. Half of the moon is always in sunlight, just as half of Earth is always in sunlight. But the moon's period of rotation is the same as its period of revolution. Therefore, you always see the same side of the moon from Earth.

Standards Check What is the source of the moon's light? 🐾 8.4.d

Phases of the Moon

Within a month, the moon's Earthward face changes from a fully lit circle to a thin crescent and then back to a circle. These different appearances of the moon result from its changing position relative to Earth and the sun. As the moon revolves around Earth, the amount of sunlight on the side of the moon that faces Earth changes. The different appearances of the moon are called **phases.** The phases of the moon are shown in **Figure 3.** When the moon is *waxing,* the sunlit fraction that we can see from Earth is getting larger. When the moon is *waning,* the sunlit fraction is getting smaller.

phase (FAYZ) the change in the sun-lit area of one celestial body as seen from another celestial body

eclipse (i KLIPS) an event in which the shadow of one celestial body falls on another

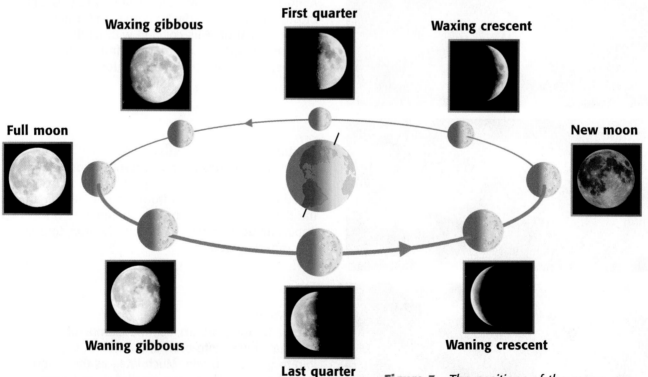

Waxing gibbous

First quarter

Waxing crescent

Full moon

New moon

Waning gibbous

Last quarter

Waning crescent

Figure 3 *The positions of the moon, sun, and Earth determine the phase of the moon. The photo insets show how the moon looks from Earth at each phase.*

Solar eclipse

NEVER look directly at the sun! You can permanently damage your eyes.

Figure 4 *On the left is a diagram of the positions of Earth and the moon during a solar eclipse. On the right is a picture of the sun's outer atmosphere, or* corona, *which is visible only when the entire disk of the sun is blocked by the moon.*

Eclipses

When the shadow of one celestial body falls on another, an **eclipse** occurs. A *solar eclipse* happens when the moon comes between Earth and the sun and the shadow of the moon falls on part of Earth. A *lunar eclipse* happens when Earth comes between the sun and the moon and the shadow of Earth falls on the moon.

Solar Eclipses

Because the moon's orbit is elliptical, the distance between the moon and Earth changes. During an *annular eclipse*, the moon is farther from Earth. The disk of the moon does not completely cover the disk of the sun. A thin ring of the sun shows around the moon's outer edge. When the moon is closer to Earth, the moon appears to be the same size as the sun. During a *total solar eclipse*, the disk of the moon completely covers the disk of the sun, as shown in **Figure 4.**

Quick Lab

Modeling Eclipses

An eclipse occurs when the shadow of one celestial body falls on another. In this lab, you will use different objects to model an eclipse.

▶ Try It!

1. Use **scissors** to cut out a circle of **heavy, white paper**. This circle represents Earth.

2. Find **two spherical objects** and **several other objects of different shapes**.

3. Hold up each object in front of a **lamp** (which represents the sun) so that the object's shadow falls on the white paper circle.

4. Record the shapes of the shadows that the objects make.

▶ Think About It!

5. Why does the moon cast a curved shadow on Earth during an eclipse?

8.4.d

15 min

Figure 5 *On the left, you can see that the moon can have a reddish color during a lunar eclipse. On the right, you can see the positions of Earth and the moon during a lunar eclipse.*

Lunar eclipse

Lunar Eclipses

As **Figure 5** shows, the view during a lunar eclipse is spectacular. Earth's atmosphere bends some of the sunlight into Earth's shadow. When sunlight hits the particles in the atmosphere, blue light is filtered out. As a result, most of the remaining light that reflects off the moon is red.

The Moon's Tilted Orbit

Why don't you see solar and lunar eclipses every month? The moon's orbit around Earth is tilted—by about 5°—relative to the orbit of Earth around the sun. This degree of tilt is enough to place the moon out of Earth's shadow for most full moons. It also places Earth out of the moon's shadow for most new moons.

The Moons of Other Planets

The moons of the other planets range in size from very small to as large as terrestrial planets. Venus and Mercury have no moons. All of the large outer planets have multiple moons, and scientists are still discovering new moons. Some moons have very elliptical orbits. Some moons even orbit their planet backward! Many of the very small moons may be captured asteroids. Moons may be some of the most bizarre and interesting places in the solar system.

Standards Check Describe the sizes of moons in the solar system.
■ 8.4.e

The Moons of Mars

Mars's two moons, Phobos and Deimos, are small, oddly shaped satellites. Both moons are very dark. Their surface materials are much like those of some asteroids—large, rocky bodies in space. One possibility is that these two moons are asteroids that were caught by Mars's gravity.

Observing the Phases of the Moon

With a parent, observe the moon. Follow it through its 28-day cycle. In your **Science Journal**, draw the moon as it appears in the sky each night. Label each drawing with the correct phase that you observed.

The Moons of Jupiter

Jupiter has more than 60 moons. The four largest moons—Ganymede, Callisto, Io, and Europa—were discovered in 1610 by Galileo. They are known as the *Galilean satellites*. The largest moon, Ganymede, is even larger than the planet Mercury! Many of the smaller moons probably are captured asteroids.

The Galilean satellite closest to Jupiter is Io (I OH), a truly bizarre world. Io, which is shown in **Figure 6,** is the most volcanically active body in the solar system. There are at least 100 volcanoes on the moon's surface that are presently active. In fact, volcanic eruptions on Io happen so continuously that impact craters on the moon are buried under the constantly erupting material.

Recent pictures and other information for the moon Europa, shown in **Figure 7,** support the idea that liquid water may lie beneath the moon's icy surface. This discovery would make Europa—along with Callisto, Ganymede, and possibly Titan—one of few bodies in the solar system other than Earth to have an ocean. Scientists wonder if, as on Earth, life could exist in the ocean of Europa.

The Moons of Saturn

Saturn has at least 47 moons. Most of these moons are small bodies that are made mostly of frozen water but contain some rocky material. At 5,150 km in diameter, Titan, shown in **Figure 8,** is Saturn's largest moon. Unlike other satellites in the solar system, Titan has an atmosphere 700 km thick, which is made mostly of molecular nitrogen.

Figure 6 *The yellow and yellow-red colors on the surface of Io are sulfur and sulfur dioxide that are contained in erupted volcanic material.*

Figure 7 *Europa, Jupiter's fourth-largest moon, has a smooth surface with very few impact craters. Thus, Europa's surface must be very young.*

Figure 8 *Titan is Saturn's largest moon. Complex chemicals that occur in small quantities in Titan's atmosphere are thought to account for Titan's orange color as seen from space.*

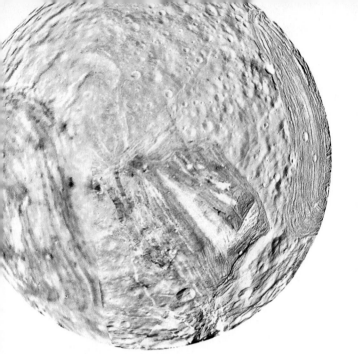

Figure 9 *This* Voyager 2 *image shows Miranda, the most unusual moon of Uranus. Its patchwork terrain indicates that Miranda has had a violent history.*

The Moons of Uranus

Uranus has at least 27 moons, most of which are small. These moons have been discovered by using spacecraft and orbiting observatories, such as the *Hubble Space Telescope*. Like the moons of Saturn, Uranus's largest moons are made of ice and rock and are heavily cratered.

Uranus's small moon Miranda, shown in **Figure 9,** has some of the strangest features in the solar system. Scientists think that a huge impact has nearly turned Miranda inside out. The impact shattered the moon and caused it to re-form in a mixed-up state. Rock and ice from the deep interior of Miranda are spread out on the moon's surface.

The Moons of Neptune

Neptune has 13 known moons. The largest moon of Neptune is named *Triton*. Triton revolves around Neptune in a retrograde orbit. This orbit suggests that Triton may have been caught by Neptune's gravity after forming elsewhere in the solar system and then coming too close to the planet. Triton has a very thin atmosphere made mostly of nitrogen gas. Triton's surface is mostly frozen nitrogen and methane. *Voyager 2* images reveal that Triton is geologically active. "Ice volcanoes," or geysers, eject nitrogen gas high into the atmosphere. Neptune's other moons are small, ice-and-rock worlds much like the smaller moons of Jupiter and Saturn.

The Moon of Pluto

Charon, Pluto's moon, has a period of revolution that is the same as Pluto's period of rotation—about 6.4 days. So, one side of Pluto always faces Charon. In other words, if you stood on the surface of Pluto, Charon would always occupy the same place in the sky. Charon's orbit around Pluto is tilted relative to Pluto's orbit around the sun. As a result, Pluto, as seen from Earth, is sometimes eclipsed by Charon. But don't hold your breath; this eclipse happens only once every 120 years!

In 2005, astronomers discovered two tiny objects, S/2005 P1 and S/2005 P2, near Pluto. If these objects are moons of Pluto, the planet would have three confirmed moons.

Standards Check How does Charon's orbit around Pluto differ from the orbits of most moons around their planets? 8.4.e

Period of Revolution

The period of revolution of Pluto's moon, Charon, is 6.4 days. The period of revolution of Earth's moon is 27.3 days. How many revolutions does Charon make in the time Earth's moon takes to make one revolution? Round your answer to the nearest tenth of a revolution. Record your work in your **Science Journal.**

Summary

- Scientists think that Earth's moon formed from debris that was ejected into space after a large body collided with Earth.
- Moons appear to shine because they reflect the light of the sun.
- As the moon revolves around Earth, the amount of sunlight on the side of the moon that faces Earth changes. Changes in the appearance of the moon are called *phases*.
- An eclipse occurs when the shadow of one celestial body falls on another.
- Mercury and Venus have no moons. Earth has one moon. Mars has two moons.
- Jupiter has more than 60 moons. The largest four are called the *Galilean moons*.
- Saturn has more than 50 moons. The largest, Titan, has an atmosphere that is 700 km thick.
- Uranus has 27 moons and Neptune has 13 moons.
- Pluto has only one confirmed moon, Charon. One side of Pluto always faces its moon.

Using Vocabulary

1 Use *phase* and *eclipse* in separate sentences.

Understanding Concepts

2 Summarizing Explain the role gravity played in the formation of the moon.

3 Analyzing What is the source of moonlight?

4 Applying Explain how the shading of the direct light of the sun causes a lunar eclipse.

5 Identifying Identify the characteristic that makes Io a unique moon in the solar system.

6 Identifying How does the orbit of Neptune's moon Triton differ from that of other satellites?

7 Analyzing Explain why Pluto is sometimes eclipsed by Charon when seen from Earth.

Critical Thinking

8 Analyzing Methods How can astronomers use the age of a lunar rock to estimate the age of the surface of a planet such as Mercury?

9 Applying Concepts Can the mass of a planet affect how many moons a planet has? Explain your answer.

INTERPRETING GRAPHICS Use the diagram below to answer the next three questions.

10 Evaluating Data What type of eclipse is shown in the diagram?

11 Applying Concepts What is the source of the light shown in the diagram?

12 Identifying Relationships Make a sketch of the type of eclipse that is not shown in the diagram.

Math Skills

13 Making Conversions The surface temperature of Neptune's moon Triton is approximately −391°F. Convert −391°F to its equivalent in degrees Celsius.

Challenge

14 Applying Concepts A lunar eclipse occurs when the moon moves through Earth's shadow. During which phase of the moon can a lunar eclipse occur? Explain your answer.

Small Bodies in the Solar System

Key Concept   Comets, asteroids, and meteoroids are small bodies in our solar system that orbit the sun.

▶ The solar system contains not only planets and moons but also large numbers of smaller bodies. These small bodies include comets, asteroids, and meteoroids. Scientists study these objects to learn about the formation and composition of the solar system.

Comets

A small, loosely packed body of ices, rock, and cosmic dust is called a **comet.** The core, or nucleus, of a comet is made mostly of rock, metals, and water ice. The nucleus of a comet is between 1 km and 100 km in diameter. A spherical cloud of gas and dust, called a *coma,* surrounds the nucleus and may extend as far as 1 million kilometers from the nucleus.

Comet Tails

The most spectacular parts of a comet are its tails. Tails form when sunlight causes the comet's ice to change to gas. The ion tail of a comet is gas that has been ionized, or stripped of electrons, by the sun. The solar wind—electrically charged particles expanding away from the sun—pushes the gas away from the comet's head. Thus, regardless of the direction the comet travels, its ion tail points away from the sun. The comet's second tail is made of dust and gas and curves backward along the comet's orbit. Some comets have dust tails that are tens of millions of kilometers long. **Figure 1** shows both the ion tail and the dust tail of a comet.

comet (KAHM it) a small body of ice, rock, and cosmic dust that follows an elliptical orbit around the sun and that gives off gas and dust in the form of a tail as it passes close to the sun

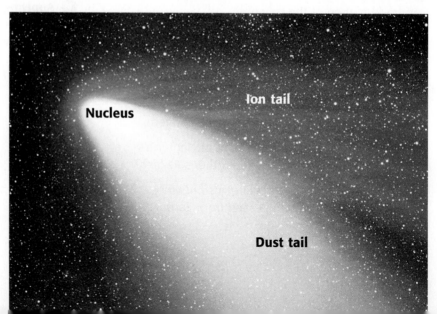

Figure 1   *This image shows the physical features of a comet when the comet is close to the sun. The nucleus of a comet is hidden by its gases and dust.*

Nucleus

Ion tail

Dust tail

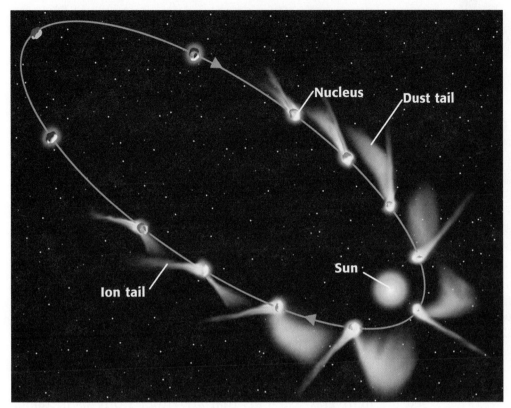

Figure 2 *Comets have very elongated orbits. Their orbits take them close to the sun to well beyond the orbit of Pluto. When a comet gets close to the sun, the comet can develop one or two tails.*

Labels in figure: Nucleus, Dust tail, Sun, Ion tail

Comet Origins

Many scientists think that comets come from the Oort (OHRT) cloud. The Oort cloud is a spherical cloud of dust and ice that surrounds the solar system far beyond Pluto's orbit. When the gravity of a passing star disturbs this cloud, comets may fall into an elliptical orbit around the sun, as shown in **Figure 2.** The orbits of comets that pass by Jupiter may also be changed by Jupiter's gravitational pull. Another region where comets are found is the Kuiper belt. The Kuiper belt is a flat ring of objects located just beyond Neptune's orbit.

Scientists think that comets are made of matter that was left over from the formation of the solar system. Therefore, scientists want to learn more about comets to understand the early history of the solar system. In 2004, material was collected by the spacecraft *Stardust* from a comet named Wild 2.

Standards Check Describe the orbit of comets. **8.4.e**

Long- and Short-Period Comets

Comets that take more than 200 years to complete one orbit of the sun are called a *long-period comets.* Comets that take less than 200 years to orbit the sun are called *short-period comets.* In recent years, astronomers have discovered that most short-period comets come from the Kuiper belt. Halley's comet, which has a period of 76 years, is a well-known short-period comet.

8.4.e Students know the appearance, general composition, relative position and size, and motion of objects in the solar system, including planets, planetary satellites, comets, and asteroids.

Asteroids

Small, rocky bodies that revolve around the sun are called **asteroids.** They range in size from a few meters to almost 1,000 km in diameter. Astronomers have discovered more than 50,000 asteroids. Most asteroids orbit the sun in the *asteroid belt.* The asteroid belt is a region 300 million kilometers wide between the orbits of Mars and Jupiter. Astronomers think that asteroids are material that Jupiter's gravity prevented from forming into a planet. **Figure 3** shows the asteroid Eros.

Standards Check Where in the solar system is the asteroid belt located? **8.4.e**

Figure 3 *NASA's NEAR spacecraft landed on the asteroid Eros in 2001. This view of the cratered surface of Eros was taken from an altitude of 200 km.*

Composition of Asteroids

The composition of asteroids varies depending on where they are located within the asteroid belt. In the outermost region of the asteroid belt, asteroids have dark reddish brown to black surfaces. This coloring may indicate that the asteroids are rich in organic material. Asteroids that have dark gray surfaces are rich in carbon. In the innermost part of the asteroid belt are light gray asteroids that are either stony or metallic.

Quick Lab

Modeling Crater Formation

▶ Try It!

1. Spread a mixture of **plaster of Paris** and **water** 4 cm thick in the bottom of a **plastic tub.** The surface should be as smooth as possible. Allow the plaster to dry until it is no longer soupy.

2. Drop a **large marble** onto the plaster from a height of 50 cm above the surface. Quickly remove the marble with **tweezers,** but do not damage the crater that formed. Label the crater "A."

3. Repeat step 2 by using a **small marble** dropped from a height of 25 cm and **another small marble** dropped from a height of 50 cm. Label the craters "B" and "C."

4. Repeat step 2 by using a small marble dropped from a height of 1 m. Label the crater "D."

8.4.e

5. Allow the plaster of Paris to harden. Write a description of each crater and the surrounding area.

▶ Think About It!

6. Which crater was formed by the marble that had the highest velocity? What is the effect of velocity on the characteristics of the crater?

7. Compare craters A, C, and D. How do they differ from each other? What caused this difference? Are the differences in the masses of the objects a factor? Explain your answer.

 30 min

Near-Earth Asteroids

More than a thousand asteroids have wide, elliptical orbits that bring them close to Earth. They are called *near-Earth asteroids*. Interest in near-Earth asteroids has increased in recent years with the realization that these asteroids could cause great damage if they were to strike Earth. Barringer Meteorite Crater, shown in **Figure 4,** formed when an asteroid that had a diameter of less than 50 m struck Earth about 40,000 years ago. Several recently established asteroid-detection programs have begun identifying asteroids whose orbits may bring them near Earth. By identifying and monitoring these asteroids, scientists hope future collisions can be avoided.

Meteoroids

The space within our solar system contains dust and debris from asteroids and comets. These pieces of dust and debris are called **meteoroids.** Most meteoroids are about the size of sand grains. Meteoroids that enter Earth's atmosphere reach speeds of between 35,000 and 250,000 km/h. Friction heats the meteoroids to thousands of degrees Celsius, which causes them to glow brightly. The atmosphere around the meteoroid's path also heats and glows because of friction between the meteoroid and air molecules. The glowing trails that result when meteoroids burn up in Earth's atmosphere are called **meteors.** A meteor trail can be a few hundred meters in diameter and tens of kilometers long before it fades.

Once every few days, larger bodies enter our atmosphere. The largest of these bodies can pass through Earth's atmosphere without burning up and can strike Earth. The bodies that reach Earth's surface are called **meteorites.**

asteroid (AS tuhr OYD) a small, rocky object that orbits the sun; most asteroids are located in a band between the orbits of Mars and Jupiter

meteoroid (MEET ee uhr OYD) a relatively small, rocky body that travels through space

meteor (MEET ee uhr) a bright streak of light that results when a meteoroid burns up in Earth's atmosphere

meteorite (MEET ee uhr IET) a meteoroid that reaches Earth's surface without burning up completely

Figure 5 **Three Major Types of Meteorites**

Stony meteorite
rocky material

Metallic meteorite
iron and nickel

Stony-iron meteorite
rocky material, iron, and nickel

Composition of Meteorites

Meteorites can be classified into three major types: stony, metallic, and stony-iron. These three types of meteorites are shown in **Figure 5.** *Stony meteorites* are similar in composition to rocks on Earth. Some stony meteorites contain carbon-bearing compounds that are similar to the carbon compounds in living organisms. Although most meteorites are stony, *metallic meteorites* are easier to find. They are easier to find because they have a distinctive metallic appearance. This distinctive appearance makes metallic meteorites easy to distinguish from common Earth rocks. *Stony-iron meteorites*, the third type of meteorite, contain iron and stone. Stony-iron meteorites are the rarest type of meteorite.

Standards Check Describe the compositions of the three types of meteorites. 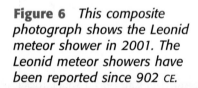 8.4.e

Figure 6 *This composite photograph shows the Leonid meteor shower in 2001. The Leonid meteor showers have been reported since 902 CE.*

Meteor Showers

Meteors can be seen on almost any night if you are far enough from a city to avoid the glare of its lights. When a large number of small meteoroids enter Earth's atmosphere in a short period of time, a meteor shower occurs. During the most spectacular of these showers, several meteors are visible every minute. A composite photo of the Leonid meteor shower is shown in **Figure 6.**

Meteor showers happen at the same time each year. These showers happen because Earth intersects the orbits of comets that have left behind a trail of dust. In the case of the Leonid meteor showers, Earth crosses the path of Comet P/Tempel-Tuttle. As these particles burn up in Earth's atmosphere, meteors streak across the sky.

Impacts on Earth

Most objects that come close to Earth are small and usually burn up in the atmosphere. Larger objects are more likely to strike Earth's surface. Scientists estimate that impacts that are powerful enough to cause a natural disaster might happen once every few thousand years. An impact that is large enough to cause a global catastrophe is estimated to happen once every 50 million to 100 million years.

About 65 million years ago, a meteor 10 km wide struck Earth. The debris sent into the atmosphere may have left the planet in darkness for months and dropped temperatures to near freezing for years. This impact may have contributed to the extinction of 15% to 20% of all species on Earth, including the dinosaurs.

SECTION Review

8.4.e

Summary

- Comets are small bodies of ice, rock, and cosmic dust that follow elliptical orbits around the sun. Comets originate in the Oort cloud and the Kuiper belt.
- Asteroids are small, rocky objects that are located in a band between Mars and Jupiter. Asteroids have nearly circular orbits around the sun.
- Near-Earth asteroids have wide, elliptical orbits that bring them close to Earth.
- Meteoroids are dust and debris from asteroids and comets.
- Meteoroids that burn up in Earth's atmosphere are meteors. Bodies that reach Earth are called *meteorites*.

Using Vocabulary

For each pair of terms, explain how the meanings of the terms differ.

1 *comet* and *asteroid*

2 *meteor* and *meteorite*

Understanding Concepts

3 **Analyzing** Why is the study of comets, asteroids, and meteoroids important in understanding the formation of the solar system?

4 **Identifying** Identify the two regions in space where comets originate.

5 **Analyzing** How do astronomers think that the asteroid belt formed?

6 **Comparing** Compare the orbits of comets and asteroids.

7 **Listing** List the composition of three types of meteorites.

8 **Applying** Distinguish between a meteoroid, a meteor, and a meteorite.

9 **Identifying** Identify the cause of meteor showers.

Critical Thinking

10 **Making Inferences** You find a meteorite on the ground. What kind of meteorite did you most likely find? Explain your answer.

Math Skills

11 **Making Calculations** A particluar short-period comet orbits the sun every 76 years. A long-period comet orbits the sun in three times this period. How long does the long-period comet take to orbit the sun?

Challenge

12 **Making Inferences** How might the study of meteorites help astronomers determine the origin of meteoroids?

Internet Resources

For a variety of links related to this chapter, go to www.scilinks.org

Topic: Space Science in California

SciLinks code: HY7CO1

Inquiry Lab

Weighing In

Have you ever seen movies of astronauts walking on the surface of the moon? If so, perhaps you watched the astronauts pick up and move large pieces of scientific equipment. Although this equipment may weigh more than 1,000 N (225 lb) on Earth, it weighs less than 167 N (38 lb) on the moon's surface.

This difference in weight is caused by a difference in gravity. The moon has 1/6 the gravity of Earth, so objects weigh much less on the moon than on Earth. This difference in weight is due to the fact that the moon and Earth have different masses. In the following activity, you'll infer how much a 12-oz. soft-drink can might weigh on different solar system bodies.

OBJECTIVES

Compare and contrast various weights.

Infer the weight of an object on different solar system bodies based on the bodies' mass.

MATERIALS

- pennies (150)
- soft-drink can, 12 oz., empty
- soft-drink can, 12 oz., full
- soft-drink cans, "weighted," (10, prepared by teacher)

Procedure

1. Pick up a full soft-drink can in one hand. Pick up an empty soft-drink can in the other hand. Without using any tools, compare and contrast the weights of the two cans.

2. Add pennies to the empty can until both cans feel as if they are the same weight.

3. From what you know about gravity, imagine how the weight of your soft-drink can might change if its weight were measured on different solar system bodies.

4. Make a table similar to the one shown below.

Body in solar system	Mass (kg)	Can (letter)
Mercury	3.3×10^{23}	
Venus	4.9×10^{24}	
Earth	5.97×10^{24}	
Moon	7.35×10^{22}	
Mars	6.42×10^{23}	
Jupiter	1.9×10^{27}	
Saturn	5.7×10^{26}	
Uranus	8.7×10^{25}	
Neptune	1.02×10^{26}	
Pluto	1.27×10^{22}	

DO NOT WRITE IN BOOK

8.4.e Students know the appearance, general composition, relative position and size, and motion of objects in the solar system, including planets, planetary satellites, comets, and asteroids.

5 Examine the set of cans supplied by your teacher. Without using any tools, compare and contrast their weights.

6 Match each can with the body whose gravity would produce the can's current weight. Record each prediction in the table that you made.

Analyze the Results

7 Analyzing Results On which body would the soft-drink can feel the heaviest?

8 Analyzing Results On which body would the soft-drink can feel the lightest?

Draw Conclusions

9 Drawing Conclusions How does a body's mass affect the weight of an object on that body?

Big Idea Question

10 Drawing Conclusions What is the relationship between a body's mass and its gravity?

Science Skills Activity

Investigation and Experimentation
8.9.d Recognize the slope of the linear graph as the constant in the relationship $y = kx$ and apply this principle in interpreting graphs constructed from data.

Finding the Slope of a Graph

▶ Tutorial

A graph that is linear is a graph whose data points form a straight line. A linear graph forms a relationship that fits the formula $y = kx$, where k is a number that is represented by the slope of the linear graph.

1 The slope of a linear graph, k, is a ratio. For any part of the graph, the ratio between the difference in y and the difference in x will be equal to k. The slope and ratio k is always the y difference ("rise") divided by the x difference ("run"). An easy way to remember this rule is to remember the phrase "rise over run."

2 Examine the graph at right. It represents the amount of mass per unit volume, or density, of lead. This relationship is linear, so it forms a linear graph.

3 For any linear graph that passes through (0,0), you can find the slope by dividing any y value by the x value that corresponds to it ("rise over run"). In the graph at right, you can take the y value of volume, divide it by the corresponding x value of mass, and calculate the slope, k.

4 Once you know the slope, k, of the graph, you will be able to find out what y will be for any x value, or the other way around, by using the equation $y = kx$.

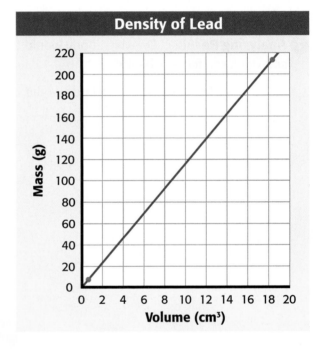

Density of Lead — graph with Mass (g) on the y-axis (0 to 220) and Volume (cm³) on the x-axis (0 to 20).

▶ You Try It!

According to Kepler's third law, the cube of the average distance, a, of a planet from the sun is proportional to the square of the planet's period, p. The mathematical formula that describes this relationship is $K \times a^3 = p^2$, where K is a constant. In this lab, you will calculate a^3 and p^2 for three planets and then find the slope of the graph, K.

1 **Making Calculations** In the table at right, you are given the values a and p for Earth, Mars, and Jupiter. Use these values to calculate a^3 and p^2 for each planet. Plot the p^2 value on the x-axis and the a^3 value on the y-axis. Then, calculate the slope, K, for each planet by using Kepler's third law, $K = p^2/a^3$.

2 **Analyzing Data** What is the slope of your graph? What measurement does the slope represent?

3 **Analyzing Data** How can scientists use the values a and p to calculate the distance of planets from the sun?

Astronomical Data				
Planet	**a**	**p**	**a³**	**p²**
Earth	1.0	1.0		
Mars	1.52	1.88		
Jupiter	5.2	11.86		

Chapter Summary

The Big Idea
The solar system contains a variety of objects that differ in size, appearance, and composition.

Section	Vocabulary

1 A Solar System Is Born

Key Concept The solar system formed as a result of gravitational attraction in the solar nebula.

- Gravity and pressure were major factors in the formation of the solar system.
- The sun is a star that produces energy by nuclear fusion.
- Astronomers use the astronomical unit to measure distances in the solar system.

Vocabulary:
nebula p. 472
solar nebula p. 473
astronomical unit p. 478

2 The Inner Planets

Key Concept The four planets of the inner solar system are small, dense, and rocky and are close to the sun.

- The inner planets, or terrestrial planets, include Mercury, Venus, Earth, and Mars.
- The inner planets tend to be small and composed of rock.

Vocabulary:
terrestrial planet p. 480
prograde rotation p. 481
retrograde rotation p. 481

3 The Outer Planets

Key Concept The planets of the outer solar system have deep, massive gas atmospheres.

- Jupiter, Saturn, Uranus, and Neptune are large planets that have deep gas atmospheres.
- Pluto is made of rock and ice and is a dwarf planet.

Vocabulary:
gas giant p. 486

4 Moons

Key Concept Moons are bodies that are smaller than planets and that orbit planets.

- Earth's moon formed when an object collided with Earth.
- The moon's appearance changes as the moon revolves around Earth.
- Moons of other planets vary greatly in size and composition.

Vocabulary:
satellite p. 492
phase p. 494
eclipse p. 495

5 Small Bodies in the Solar System

Key Concept Comets, asteroids, and meteoroids are small bodies in our solar system that orbit the sun.

- Comets are small bodies of ice and rock that have very elliptical orbits.
- Most asteroids are located in a belt between Mars and Jupiter.
- Meteoroids are dust and debris from asteroids and comets.

Vocabulary:
comet p. 500
asteroid p. 502
meteoroid p. 503
meteor p. 503
meteorite p. 503

Chapter Review

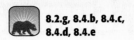

Organize

Booklet Review the FoldNote that you created at the beginning of the chapter. Add to or correct the FoldNote based on what you have learned.

Using Vocabulary

1. **Academic Vocabulary** Which of the following words means "the thing from which something else comes"?
   a. fusion
   b. source
   c. attraction
   d. force

For each pair of terms, explain how the meanings of the terms differ.

2. *nebula* and *solar nebula*

3. *prograde rotation* and *retrograde rotation*

4. *terrestrial planet* and *gas giant*

5. *phase* and *eclipse*

6. *comet* and *asteroid*

7. *meteorite* and *meteor*

Understanding Concepts

Multiple Choice

8. In the process of nuclear fusion, four hydrogen nuclei fuse to form a nucleus of
   a. calcium.
   b. sodium.
   c. helium.
   d. magnesium.

9. In which layer of the sun does nuclear fusion take place?
   a. corona
   b. photosphere
   c. convective zone
   d. core

10. Which of the following planets is located one astronomical unit from the sun?
    a. Mercury
    b. Earth
    c. Mars
    d. Jupiter

11. Which of the following terrestrial planets has retrograde rotation?
    a. Mercury
    b. Venus
    c. Earth
    d. Mars

12. Which of the following planets in the outer solar system is tipped on its side?
    a. Jupiter
    b. Saturn
    c. Uranus
    d. Neptune

13. Which of the following moons of Jupiter is volcanically active?
    a. Callisto
    b. Io
    c. Ganymede
    d. Europa

14. Small, rocky bodies that orbit the sun in nearly circular orbits are called
    a. asteroids.
    b. meteoroids.
    c. comets.
    d. meteorites.

INTERPRETING GRAPHICS The diagram below models the moon's orbit around Earth as viewed from above the South Pole. Use the diagram to answer the next question.

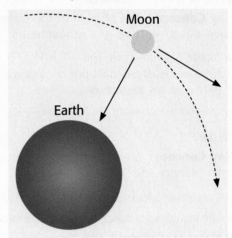

15. What term describes the motion of the moon that is shown in the diagram?
    a. prograde rotation
    b. prograde revolution
    c. retrograde rotation
    d. retrograde revolution

Short Answer

16. **Applying** Explain the role that gravity played in the formation of the planets.

17 **Summarizing** Briefly summarize the steps in the process of nuclear fusion in the sun.

18 **Identifying** Identify the unit that astronomers use to measure distances in the solar system.

19 **Listing** List the names of the planets in the order that they orbit the sun.

20 **Comparing** Compare the terrestrial planets with the gas giant planets by size, composition, and distance from the sun.

21 **Summarizing** Examine how the phases of the moon relate to the amount of lunar surface that is shaded from the direct light of the sun.

22 **Comparing** Compare the orbits of comets and asteroids around the sun.

Writing Skills

23 **Creative Writing** Imagine that you are the first astronaut to set foot on Mars. You are searching for life on that planet. Explain where you are going to look for life on Mars and why you chose to look there.

Critical Thinking

24 **Concept Mapping** Use the following terms to create a concept map: *solar system, terrestrial planets, gas giants, moons, comets, asteroids,* and *meteoroids.*

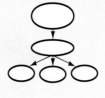

25 **Analyzing Ideas** Why does fusion occur in the sun's core but not in other layers?

26 **Analyzing Ideas** Explain why observers on Earth always see the same side of the moon.

27 **Analyzing Ideas** Explain why you don't see solar and lunar eclipses every month.

28 **Identifying Relationships** How did variations in the orbit of Uranus help scientists discover Neptune?

29 **Evaluating Conclusions** Explain whether scientists should consider Pluto to be a planet.

INTERPRETING GRAPHICS The graph below shows density versus mass for Earth, Uranus, and Neptune. Mass is given in Earth masses—the mass of Earth is equal to 1 Earth mass. The relative volumes for the planets are shown by the size of each circle. Use the graph to answer the next two questions.

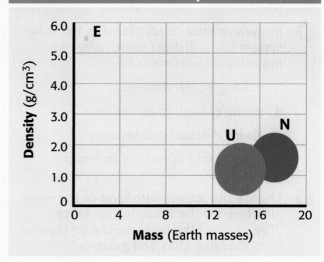

Density Vs. Mass for Earth, Uranus, and Neptune

30 **Evaluating Data** Which planet is denser: Uranus or Neptune? How can you tell?

31 **Making Inferences** You can see that although Earth has the smallest mass, it has the highest density of the three planets. How can Earth be the densest of the three when Uranus and Neptune have so much more mass than Earth does?

Math Skills

32 **Making Calculations** Pluto is 5.5 light-hours from the sun. How far is Pluto from the sun in AU? (Hint: 1 AU = 8.3 light-minutes)

Challenge

33 **Making Inferences** How does studying other planets help us better understand geological processes on Earth?

Standards Assessment

REVIEWING ACADEMIC VOCABULARY

1 **Which of the following words means "to keep the same"?**

A maintain

B persevere

C improve

D replenish

2 **In the sentence "Each planet in the solar system has a distinct orbit," what does the word *distinct* mean?**

A making a clear impression

B strong enough to be noticed

C clearly different and separate

D very great in degree, as an honor

3 **Choose the appropriate form of the word *structure* for the following sentence: "The _____ of the universe can be learned from studying stars and galaxies."**

A structured

B structural

C structure

D structuring

4 **Choose the set of words that best completes the following sentence: "Stars are _____ light for all bright objects in outer space."**

A a source by

B sources on

C the sources in

D the source of

REVIEWING CONCEPTS

5 **Which of the following will most likely occur inside a cold nebula?**

A Rapid collisions will push particles apart.

B Particles will slowly move closer to one another because of gravity.

C Gravity and pressure will push particles rapidly together.

D No forces will act on the particles, and the particles will drift apart.

6 **Why do scientists think that liquid water may have once existed on Mars?**

A Surface features on Mars suggest erosion and deposition by water.

B Mars had an atmosphere that contained clouds.

C Mars has two polar icecaps that contain frozen carbon dioxide.

D Fossils of marine organisms have been discovered on the surface of Mars.

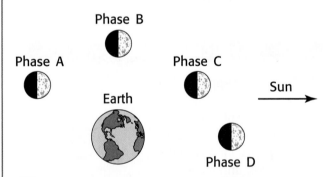

7 **The diagram above shows different phases of the moon in relation to Earth and the sun. In which phase will an observer on Earth see a crescent moon?**

A Phase A

B Phase B

C Phase C

D Phase D

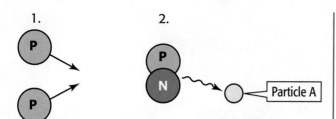

1.

2.

Particle A

8 The diagram above depicts nuclear fusion. If particles labeled "P" are protons and particles labeled "N" are neutrons, what kind of particle is Particle A?

A positron

B electron

C hydrogen nucleus

D helium nucleus

9 What is unusual about the rotation of Uranus?

A Uranus rotates more slowly than other planets.

B Uranus rotates more quickly than other planets.

C Uranus's axis of rotation lies almost in the plane of its orbit.

D Uranus's axis of rotation lies 90° to the plane of its orbit.

10 The distance from Earth to the sun is 1 astronomical unit, or 8.3 light-minutes. If a planet is located 20 astronomical units away from the sun, how many light-minutes or light-hours from the sun is it?

A 16.6 light-minutes

B 20.0 light-minutes

C 2.76 light-hours

D 166 light-hours

11 How is energy from the sun transferred to Earth?

A fusion

B radiation

C conduction

D convection

12 How does an asteroid impact primarily affect life on Earth?

A by disturbing tectonic plate motion

B by causing earthquakes

C by reducing the amount of sunlight that reaches Earth

D by causing volcanoes to erupt

13 Which of the following provides evidence of environmental change on Earth over time?

A radioactive decay

B the fossil record

C magnetic reversals

D earthquakes

14 What evidence shows that a large landmass broke up into smaller landmasses to form Earth's continents?

A the locations of glaciers on different continents

B the shape of the coastlines on different continents

C the climate pattern on different continents

D the rates of weathering on different continents

Standards Assessment

Science in Action

Science Fiction

"The Mad Moon"
by Stanley Weinbaum

The third-largest moon of Jupiter, called *Io*, can be a hard place to live. Grant Calthorpe is finding this out the hard way. Although living comfortably is possible in the small cities at the polar regions of Io, Grant has to spend most of his time in the moon's hot and humid jungles. Grant treks into the jungles of Io to gather ferva leaves so that they can be converted into useful medications for humans. During Grant's quest, he encounters loonies and slinkers; and he has to avoid blancha, a kind of tropical fever that causes hallucinations, weakness, and vicious headaches. Without proper medication, a person with blancha can go mad or even die. In "The Mad Moon," you'll discover a dozen adventures with Grant Calthorpe as he struggles to stay alive—and sane.

Language Arts ACTIVITY

Read "The Mad Moon" by Stanley Weinbaum. Write a short story that describes the adventures that you would have on Io if you were chosen as Grant Calthorpe's assistant.

Science, Technology, and Society

Light Pollution and Astronomical Observation

For astronomers, light pollution has become an important issue. Clear, dark skies are necessary for astronomers to study the cosmos. Because of city sprawl, there are few sites in the United States today where astronomers can observe the sky without the lights from nearby cities being a problem.

Lick Observatory was built on top of Mount Hamilton near the city of San Jose in the 1880s. As San Jose grew, stray light from the city made the study of the cosmos more difficult for astronomers at the observatory. In response to astronomers' concerns, city officials in San Jose replaced white light in their street lamps with low-pressure sodium lamps. Low-pressure sodium lamps produce light in a single color, or narrow range of wavelengths. Because it is easy for astronomers at Lick Observatory to filter this color out of their observations, light pollution is becoming less of an issue at Lick.

Math ACTIVITY

The efficacy of the low-pressure sodium lamp has increased from 50 lumen/watts since its introduction in 1932 to 200 lumen/watts in 2005. What is the percentage increase in efficacy over this period?

Adriana C. Ocampo

Planetary Geologist   Sixty-five million years ago, in what is now Mexico, a giant meteor at least 10 km wide struck Earth. The meteor made a hole 15 km deep and more than 160 km wide. The meteor sent billions of tons of dust into Earth's atmosphere. This dust formed thick clouds. After forming, these clouds may have left the planet in total darkness for six months and the temperature near freezing for 10 years. Some scientists think that this meteorite impact and its effect on Earth's climate contributed to the extinction of the dinosaurs.

Adriana Ocampo studies the site in Mexico where the meteorite hit. This site is known as the *Chicxulub* (cheeks OO loob) *impact crater*. Ocampo is a planetary geologist and has been interested in space exploration since she was young. Ocampo's specialty is studying impact craters. "Impact craters are formed when an asteroid or a comet collides with the Earth or any other terrestrial planet," explains Ocampo. Ocampo visits crater sites around the world to collect data. She also uses computers to create models of how the impacts affected the planet. Ocampo has worked for NASA and has helped plan space-exploration missions to Mars, Jupiter, Saturn, and Mercury. Ocampo currently works for the European Space Agency (ESA).

Social Studies ACTIVITY

Research information about impact craters. Find the different locations around the world where impact craters have been found. Make a world map that highlights these locations.

The circle on the map shows the site in Mexico of the Chicxulub impact crater.

Internet Resources

- To learn more about careers in science, visit www.scilinks.org and enter the SciLinks code HY70225.

- To learn more about these Science in Action topics, visit go.hrw.com and type in the keyword HY7FAMF.

- Check out articles related to this chapter by visiting go.hrw.com. Just type in the keyword HY7FAMC.

Appendix

Contents

Study Skills 517
    Making and Using FoldNotes 517
    Making and Using Graphic Organizers 521
Understanding Word Parts 530
Common Words with Multiple Meanings 532
Math Refresher 534
Making Graphs 538
Physical Science Refresher 541
Physical Science Laws and Principles 543
Useful Equations 546
    Useful Equations for Heat and Work 549
Scientific Methods 550
SI Measurement 554
Measuring Skills 555
Using the Microscope 556
Periodic Table of the Elements 558
Solar System Data 560
Temperature Scales 562

Ask a Question

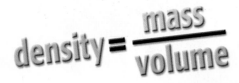

$$density = \frac{mass}{volume}$$

Study Skills: Making and Using FoldNotes

Have you ever tried to study for a test or quiz but didn't know where to start? Or have you read a chapter and found that you can remember only a few ideas? Well, FoldNotes are a fun and exciting way to help you learn and remember the ideas you encounter as you learn science!

FoldNotes are tools that you can use to organize concepts. One FoldNote focuses on a few main concepts. FoldNotes help you learn and remember how the concepts fit together. FoldNotes can help you see the "big picture." Below, you will find instructions for building 10 different FoldNotes.

Pyramid

A pyramid provides a unique way for taking notes. The three sides of the pyramid can summarize information into three categories. Use the pyramid as a tool for studying information in a chapter.

1. Place a **sheet of paper** in front of you. Fold the lower left-hand corner of the paper diagonally to the opposite edge of the paper.

2. Cut off the tab of paper created by the fold (at the top).

3. Open the paper so that it is a square. Fold the lower right-hand corner of the paper diagonally to the opposite corner to form a triangle.

4. Open the paper. The creases of the two folds will have created an X.

5. Using **scissors,** cut along one of the creases. Start from any corner, and stop at the center point to create two flaps. Use **tape** or **glue** to attach one of the flaps on top of the other flap.

Double-Door Fold

A double-door fold is useful when you want to compare the characteristics of two topics. The double-door fold can organize characteristics of the two topics side by side under the flaps. Similarities and differences between the two topics can then be easily identified.

1. Fold a **sheet of paper** in half from the top to the bottom. Then, unfold the paper.

2. Fold the top and bottom edges of the paper to the center crease.

Booklet

A booklet is a useful tool for taking notes as you read a chapter. Each page of the booklet can contain a main topic from the chapter. Write details of each main topic on the appropriate page to create an outline of the chapter.

1. Fold a **sheet of paper** in half from left to right. Then, unfold the paper.

2. Fold the sheet of paper in half again from the top to the bottom. Then, unfold the paper.

3. Refold the sheet of paper in half from left to right.

4. Fold the top and bottom edges to the center crease.

5. Completely unfold the paper.

6. Refold the paper from top to bottom.

7. Using **scissors,** cut a slit along the center crease of the sheet from the folded edge to the creases made in step 4. Do not cut the entire sheet in half.

8. Fold the sheet of paper in half from left to right. While holding the bottom and top edges of the paper, push the bottom and top edges together so that the center collapses at the center slit. Fold the four flaps to form a four-page book.

Layered Book

A layered book is a useful tool for taking notes as you read a chapter. The four flaps of the layered book can summarize information into four categories. Write details of each category on the appropriate flap to create a summary of the chapter.

1. Lay one **sheet of paper** on top of **another sheet.** Slide the top sheet up so that 2 cm of the bottom sheet is showing.

2. Holding the two sheets together, fold down the top of the two sheets so that you see four 2 cm tabs along the bottom.

3. Using a stapler, staple the top of the FoldNote.

Key-Term Fold

A key-term fold is a useful for studying definitions of key terms in a chapter. Each tab can contain a key term on one side and its definition on the other. Use the key-term fold to quiz yourself on the definitions of the key terms in a chapter.

1. Fold a **sheet of lined notebook paper** in half from left to right.

2. Using **scissors,** cut along every third line from the right edge of the paper to the center fold to make tabs.

Four-Corner Fold

A four-corner fold is useful when you want to compare the characteristics of four topics. The four-corner fold can organize the characteristics of the four topics side by side under the flaps. Similarities and differences between the four topics can then be easily identified.

1. Fold a **sheet of paper** in half from left to right. Then, unfold the paper.

2. Fold each side of the paper to the crease in the center of the paper.

3. Fold the paper in half from the top to the bottom. Then, unfold the paper.

4. Using **scissors,** cut the top flap creases made in step 3 to form four flaps.

Three-Panel Flip Chart

A three-panel flip chart is useful when you want to compare the characteristics of three topics. The three-panel flip chart can organize the characteristics of the three topics side by side under the flaps. Similarities and differences between the three topics can then be easily identified.

1. Fold a **piece of paper** in half from the top to the bottom.

2. Fold the paper in thirds from side to side. Then, unfold the paper so that you can see the three sections.

3. From the top of the paper, cut along each of the vertical fold lines to the fold in the middle of the paper. You will now have three flaps.

Table Fold

A table fold is a useful tool for comparing the characteristics of two or three topics. In a table fold, all topics are described in terms of the same characteristics so that you can easily make a thorough comparison.

1. Fold a **piece of paper** in half from the top to the bottom. Then, fold the paper in half again.

2. Fold the paper in thirds from side to side.

3. Unfold the paper completely. Carefully trace the fold lines by using a pen or pencil.

Two-Panel Flip Chart

A two-panel flip chart is useful when you want to compare the characteristics of two topics. The two-panel flip chart can organize the characteristics of the two topics side by side under the flaps. Similarities and differences between the two topics can then be easily identified.

1. Fold a **piece of paper** in half from the top to the bottom.

2. Fold the paper in half from side to side. Then, unfold the paper so that you can see the two sections.

3. From the top of the paper, cut along the vertical fold line to the fold in the middle of the paper. You will now have two flaps.

Tri-Fold

A tri-fold is a useful tool that helps you track your progress. By organizing the chapter topic into what you know, what you want to know, and what you learn, you can see how much you have learned after reading a chapter.

1. Fold a piece a paper in thirds from the top to the bottom.

2. Unfold the paper so that you can see the three sections. Then, turn the paper sideways so that the three sections form vertical columns.

3. Trace the fold lines by using a **pen** or **pencil.** Label the columns "Know," "Want," and "Learn."

Study Skills: Making and Using Graphic Organizers

Have you ever wished that you could "draw out" the many concepts you learn in your science class? Sometimes, being able to see how concepts are related really helps you remember what you've learned. Graphic Organizers do just that! They give you a way to draw or map out concepts.

All you need to make a Graphic Organizer is a piece of paper and a pencil. Below you will find instructions for nine different Graphic Organizers designed to help you organize the concepts you'll learn in this book.

Concept Map

How to Make a Concept Map

1. Identify main ideas from the text, and write the ideas as short phrases or single words.

2. Select a main concept. Place this concept at the top or center of a piece of paper.

3. Place other ideas under or around the main concept based on their relationship to the main concept. Draw a circle around each idea.

4. Draw lines between the concepts, and add linking words to connect the ideas.

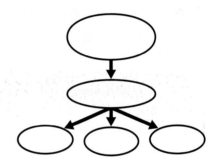

When to Use a Concept Map

Concept maps are useful when you are trying to identify how several ideas are connected to a main concept. Concept maps may be based on vocabulary terms or on main topics from the text. As you read about science, look for terms that can be organized in a concept map.

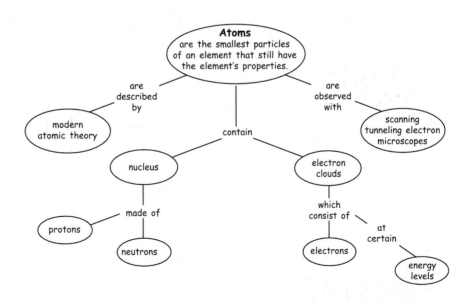

Cause-and-Effect Map

How to Make a Cause-and-Effect Map

1. Draw a box, and write a cause in the box. You can have as many cause boxes as you want. The diagram shown here is one example of a cause-and-effect map.

2. Draw another box to the right of the cause box to represent an effect. You can have as many effect boxes as you want. Draw arrows from each cause box to the appropriate effect boxes.

3. In the cause boxes, explain the process that makes up the cause. In the effect boxes, write a description of the effect or details about the effect.

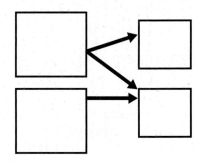

When to Use a Cause-and-Effect Map

A cause-and-effect map is a useful tool for illustrating a specific type of scientific process. Use a cause-and-effect map when you want to describe how, when, or why one event causes another event. As you read, look for events that are either causes or results of other events, and draw a cause-and-effect map that shows the relationships between the events.

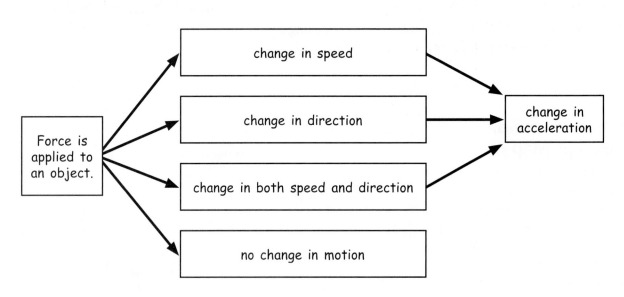

Spider Map

How to Make a Spider Map

1. Draw a diagram like the one shown here. In the circle, write the main topic.

2. From the circle, draw legs to represent the main ideas or characteristics of the topic. Draw as many legs as you want to draw. Write an idea or characteristic along each leg.

3. From each leg, draw horizontal lines. As you read the chapter, write details about each idea on the idea's horizontal lines. To add more details, make the legs longer and add more horizontal lines.

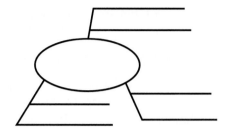

When to Use a Spider Map

A spider map is an effective tool for classifying the details of a specific topic in science. A spider map divides a topic into ideas and details. As you read about a topic, look for the main ideas or characteristics of the topic. Within each idea, look for details. Use a spider map to organize the ideas and details of each topic.

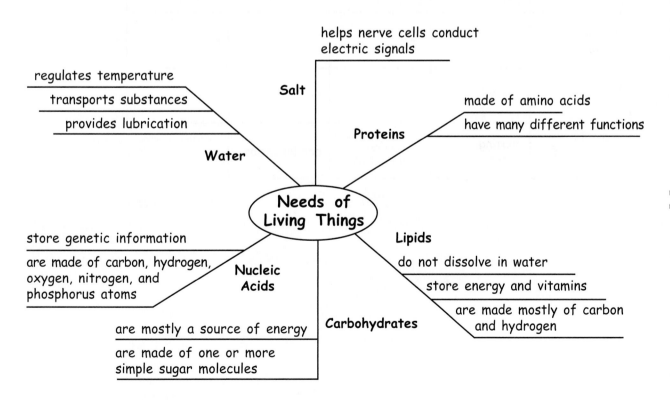

Comparison Table

How to Make a Comparison Table

1. Draw a table like the one shown here. Draw as many columns and rows as you want to draw.

2. In the top row, write the topics that you want to compare.

3. In the left column, write the general characteristics that you want to compare. As you read the chapter, fill in the characteristics for each topic in the appropriate boxes.

When to Use a Comparison Table

A comparison table is useful when you want to compare the characteristics of two or more topics in science. Organizing information in a table helps you compare several topics at one time. In a table, all topics are described in terms of the same list of characteristics, which helps you make a thorough comparison. As you read, look for topics whose characteristics you may want to compare in a table.

	Solid	Liquid	Gas	Plasma
Definite volume	yes	yes	no	no
Definite shape	yes	no	no	no
Possible changes of state	melting, sublimation	freezing, evaporation	condensation	

Venn Diagram

How to Make a Venn Diagram

1. Draw a diagram like the one shown here. Draw one circle for each topic. Make sure that each circle partially overlaps the other circles.

2. In each circle, write a topic that you want to compare with the topics in the other circles.

3. In the areas of the diagram where circles overlap, write the characteristics that the topics in the overlapping circles share.

4. In the areas of the diagram where circles do not overlap, write the characteristics that are unique to the topic of the particular circle.

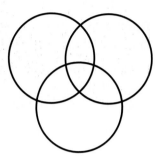

When to Use a Venn Diagram

A Venn diagram is a useful tool for comparing two or three topics in science. A Venn diagram shows which characteristics the topics share and which characteristics are unique to each topic. Venn diagrams are ideal when you want to illustrate relationships in a pair or small group of topics. As you read, look for topics that have both shared and unique characteristics, and draw a Venn diagram that shows how the topics are related.

Physical Properties
- can be observed or measured without changing the identity of a substance
- color, odor, mass, volume, weight, density, strength, flexibility, magnetism, and electrical conductivity

- help describe and define matter
- can be characteristic properties

Chemical Properties
- describe matter based on its ability to change into new matter that has different properties
- cannot always be observed
- reactivity, including flammability

Process Chart

How to Make a Process Chart

1. Draw a box. In the box, write the first step of a process, chain of events, or cycle.

2. Under the box, draw another box, and draw an arrow to connect the two boxes. In the second box, write the next step of the process or the next event in the timeline.

3. Continue adding boxes until each step of the process, chain of events, or cycle is written in a box. For cycles only, draw an arrow to connect the last box and the first box.

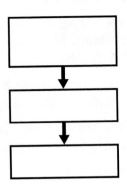

When to Use a Process Chart

Science is full of processes. A process chart shows the steps that a process takes to get from one point to another point. Timelines, chains of events, and cycles are examples of the kinds of information that can be organized well in a process chart. As you read, look for information that is described in steps or in a sequence, and draw a process chart that shows the progression of the steps or sequence.

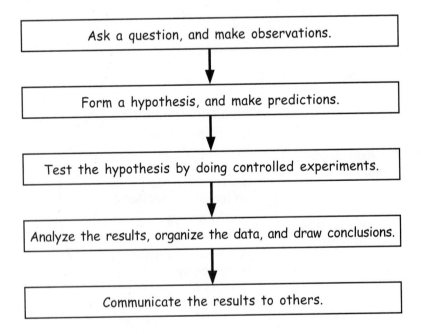

Idea Wheel

How to Make an Idea Wheel

1. Draw a circle. Draw a larger circle around the first circle. Divide the ring between the circles into sections by drawing lines from one circle to the other across the ring. Divide the ring into as many sections as you want.

2. Write a main idea or topic in the smaller circle. Label each section in the ring with a category or characteristic of the main idea.

3. In each section of the ring, include details that are unique to the topic.

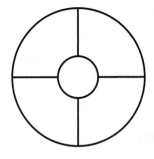

When to Use an Idea Wheel

An idea wheel is an effective type of visual organization in which ideas in science can be divided into categories or parts. It is also a useful way to illustrate characteristics of a main idea or topic. As you read, look for topics that are divided into ideas or categories that can be organized around an idea wheel.

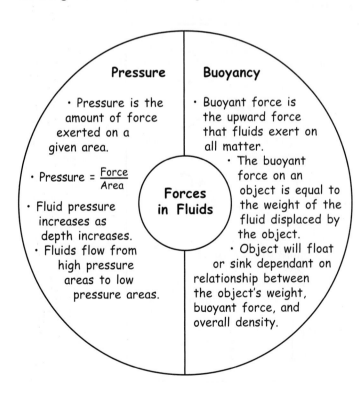

Combination Notes

How to Make Combination Notes

1. Draw a table like the one shown here. Draw the columns to be as long as you want them to be.

2. Write the topic of your notes in the section at the top of the table.

3. In the left column, write important phrases or sentences about the topic. In the right column, draw diagrams or pictures that illustrate the information in the left column.

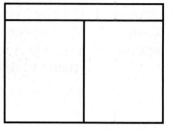

When to Use Combination Notes

Combination notes let you express scientific information in words and pictures at the same time. Use combination notes to express information that a picture could help explain. The picture could be a diagram, a sketch, or another useful visual representation of the written information in your notes.

Forces and Motion	

Gravity
 	
 Mass and **distance** affect the magnitude of gravitational force.
 	
 Gravitational force tends to be small when
   •masses are small
   •distances are large
 Gravitational force tends to be large when
   •masses are large
   •distances are small
 	
 Force and Motion
 • Objects move according to the net force exerted on them.
 	
 • Net force is the sum of all forces acting on an object.
 	
 • Newton's laws of motion describe how forces and motion relate.
	Mass
	
	 Distance
	
	 Example of net force
	 Air resistance
	 Gravity Net force

Pyramid Chart

How to Make a Pyramid Chart

1. Draw a triangle that is divided into sections like the one shown here. Draw as many sections as you need to draw.

2. Draw a box to the left of the triangle, as shown in the example. Write the topic of your pyramid chart in the box.

3. In each section of your triangle, write information about the topic in the appropriate level of the pyramid.

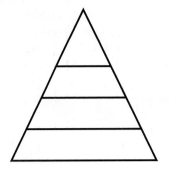

When to Use a Pyramid Chart

A pyramid chart is used to organize information in a hierarchy of importance, detail, or magnitude. As the shape of the pyramid suggests, the pyramid's bottom level contains information that is largest in terms of magnitude and broadest, or least specific, in terms of detail. As you read about science, look for information that you can organize into a hierarchy.

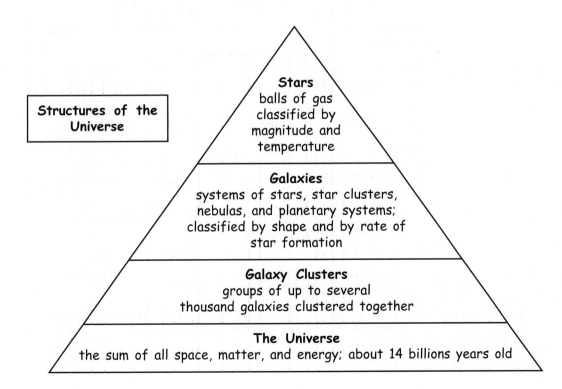

Structures of the Universe

Stars
balls of gas classified by magnitude and temperature

Galaxies
systems of stars, star clusters, nebulas, and planetary systems; classified by shape and by rate of star formation

Galaxy Clusters
groups of up to several thousand galaxies clustered together

The Universe
the sum of all space, matter, and energy; about 14 billions years old

Understanding Word Parts

Many scientific words are made up of parts based on Greek and Latin languages. Understanding the meaning of the parts will help you understand the meaning of the scientific words. The table below provides a definition and an example of prefixes, roots, and suffixes that you will see in this textbook.

Prefix	Definition	Example
bio-	life	biochemical: an organic compound that is made by living things
co-	with; together	covalent compound: a chemical compound that is formed by the sharing of electrons
com-	with; together	compression: a force that is exerted when matter is pushed or squeezed together
counter-	opposite; contrary to	counterclockwise: in a direction opposite to that in which the hands of a clock move
dis-	away; in different directions	displace: to move out of place; to move away from
endo-	in; within	endothermic reaction: a chemical reaction in which heat flows into the system from the surroundings
exo-	outside; external	exothermic reaction: a chemical reaction in which heat flows out of the system to the surroundings
infra-	below; beneath	infrared: describes invisible rays just beyond, or below, the red end of the visible spectrum
ir-	not	irregular galaxy: a small galaxy that has no identifiable shape and that contains a great amount of dust and gas
iso-	equal	isotope: an atom that has the same number of protons (or the same atomic number) as other atoms of the same element do but that has a different number of neutrons (and thus a different atomic mass)
non-	not	nonmetal: an element that conducts heat and electricity poorly and that does not form positive ions in an electrolytic solution; not a metal
retro-	backward	retrograde rotation: the clockwise, or backward, spin of a planet or moon as seen from above the planet's North Pole
super-	above; over	supernova: a gigantic, or oversized, explosion in which a massive star collapses and throws its outer layers into space
trans-	across; through	transmission: the passing of light or another form of energy through matter
ultra-	beyond; exceedingly	ultraviolet: a band of electromagnetic radiation that has wavelengths that are shorter than the wavelengths of violet light; beyond violet
uni	one	universe: the sum of all space, matter, and energy that exist, that have existed in the past, and that will exist in the future; the sum of all things as one unit

Appendix

Word root	Definition	Example
astr	star	astronomy: the scientific study of the universe
flamm	to burn, flame	flammability: the ability of a substance to burn
ject	to throw	projectile motion: the curved path that an object follows when thrown, launched, or otherwise projected near the surface of Earth
lip	fat	lipid: a fat molecule or a molecule that has similar properties; examples include oils, waxes, and steroids
mer	part	polymer: a large molecule that is formed by more than five monomers, or small units; a molecule made of many parts
poly	many	polymer: a large molecule that is formed by more than five monomers, or small units; a molecule made of many parts
solute	to free, to loosen	solubility: the ability of one substance to dissolve when in contact with another substance at a given temperature and pressure; as the substance dissolves, each of its particles becomes free from the surrounding particles
spec	to look	spectrum: the band of colors produced when white light passes through a prism
therm	heat	exothermic reaction: a chemical reaction in which heat flows out of the system to the surroundings
thesis	proposition	hypothesis: a testable idea or explanation that leads to scientific investigation
vapor	gaseous form of any substance	evaporation: the change of state from a liquid to a gas

Suffix	Definition	Example
-cule	little	molecule: the smallest unit of a substance that can exist by itself and retain all of the substance's chemical properties
-gram	thing written	H-R diagram: Hertzsprung-Russell diagram, a graph that shows the relationship between a star's surface temperature and absolute magnitude
-ic	pertaining to	periodic: describes something that occurs or repeats at regular intervals; pertaining to periods
-ion	the act of	compression: a force that is exerted when matter is pushed or squeezed together; the act of squeezing
-meter	to measure	thermometer: an instrument that measures and indicates temperature
-nomy	the science of	astronomy: the scientific study of the universe
-oid	resembling	metalloids: elements that have properties of both metals and nonmetals; they resemble metals more than nonmetals do
-scope	an instrument for seeing or observing	telescope: an instrument that collects light from the sky and concentrates it for better observation

Common Words with Multiple Meanings

Scientific words may have common meanings that you already know. Understanding the difference between common meanings and scientific meanings will help you develop a scientific vocabulary. The table below provides common and scientific meanings for words that you will see in this textbook.

Word	Common meaning	Scientific meaning
base	the lowest part	any compound that increases the number of hydroxide ions when dissolved in water
concentration	the act of focusing one's attention on something	the amount of a particular substance in a given quantity of a mixture or solution
condensation	the droplets of liquid on the outside of a glass or window	the change of state from a gas to a liquid
element	a fundamental constituent part	a substance that cannot be separated or broken down into simpler substances by chemical means
fluid	smooth; graceful (for example, fluid movement)	a nonsolid state of matter in which the atoms or molecules are free to move past each other, as in a gas or liquid
force	violence used to compel a person or thing	an action exerted on a body in order to change the body's state of rest or motion; force has magnitude and direction
friction	conflict between people who have opposing views	a force that opposes motion between two surfaces that are in contact
gas	short for *gasoline*; a liquid fuel used by vehicles, such as cars and buses	a form of matter that does not have a definite volume or shape
gravity	seriousness (for example, the gravity of the situation)	a force of attraction between objects that is due to their masses and that decreases as the distance between the objects increases
group	a number of people gathered together	a vertical column of elements in the periodic table; elements in a group share chemical properties
inertia	resistance to change	the tendency of an object to resist being moved or, if the object is moving, to resist a change in speed or direction until an outside force acts on the object
mass	a quantity of material that has an unspecified shape	a measure of the amount of matter in an object

Word	Common meaning	Scientific meaning
matter	a subject of concern or topic of discussion	anything that has mass and takes up space
medium	an intermediate measurement between small and large	a physical environment in which phenomena occur
model	a miniature representation of a larger object	a pattern, plan, representation, or description designed to show the structure or workings of an object, system, or concept
motion	movement	an object's change in position relative to a reference point
organic	describes an organism or object that is produced without the use of synthetic drugs, fertilizers, or hormones	describes a material that is derived from living organisms and that contains carbon
period	a punctuation mark used to indicate the end of a sentence	a horizontal row of elements in the periodic table
phase	a distinguishable stage in a cycle	in astronomy, the change in the illuminated area of one celestial body as seen from another celestial body
pressure	the burden of mental stress	the amount of force exerted per unit area of a surface
product	something available for sale (for example, a computer product)	a substance that forms in a chemical reaction
reaction	a response to a stimulus	the process by which one or more substances change to produce one or more different substances
revolution	the overthrow of one government and the substitution of that government with another (for example, the American Revolution)	the motion of a body that travels around another body in space; one complete trip along an orbit
solution	the answer to a problem	a homogeneous mixture throughout which two or more substances are uniformly dispersed
star	a person who is highly celebrated in a particular field	a large celestial body that is composed of gas and that emits light
table	a piece of furniture that has a flat, horizontal surface	an orderly arrangement of data
theory	an assumption based on limited knowledge	a system of ideas that explains many related observations and is supported by a large body of evidence acquired through scientific investigation
volume	a measure of how loud a sound is	a measure of the size of a body or region in three-dimensional space

Appendix

Math Refresher

Science requires an understanding of many math concepts. The following pages will help you review some important math skills.

Averages

An **average,** or **mean,** simplifies a set of numbers into a single number that *approximates* the value of the set.

> **Example:** Find the average of the following set of numbers: 5, 4, 7, and 8.

Step 1: Find the sum.

$$5 + 4 + 7 + 8 = 24$$

Step 2: Divide the sum by the number of numbers in your set. Because there are four numbers in this example, divide the sum by 4.

$$\frac{24}{4} = 6$$

The average, or mean, is **6.**

Ratios

A **ratio** is a comparison between numbers, and it is usually written as a fraction.

> **Example:** Find the ratio of thermometers to students if you have 36 thermometers and 48 students in your class.

Step 1: Make the ratio.

$$\frac{36 \text{ thermometers}}{48 \text{ students}}$$

Step 2: Reduce the fraction to its simplest form.

$$\frac{36}{48} = \frac{36 \div 12}{48 \div 12} = \frac{3}{4}$$

The ratio of thermometers to students is **3 to 4,** or $\frac{3}{4}$. The ratio may also be written in the form 3:4.

Proportions

A **proportion** is an equation that states that two ratios are equal.

$$\frac{3}{1} = \frac{12}{4}$$

To solve a proportion, first multiply across the equal sign. This is called *cross-multiplication.* If you know three of the quantities in a proportion, you can use cross-multiplication to find the fourth.

> **Example:** Imagine that you are making a scale model of the solar system for your science project. The diameter of Jupiter is 11.2 times the diameter of Earth. If you are using a plastic-foam ball that has a diameter of 2 cm to represent Earth, what must the diameter of the ball representing Jupiter be? $\frac{11.2}{1} = \frac{x}{2 \text{ cm}}$

Step 1: Cross-multiply.

$$\frac{11.2}{1} \diagdown\!\!\!\!\diagup \frac{x}{2}$$

$$11.2 \times 2 = x \times 1$$

Step 2: Multiply.

$$22.4 = x \times 1$$

Step 3: Isolate the variable by dividing both sides by 1.

$$x = \frac{22.4}{1}$$

$$x = 22.4 \text{ cm}$$

You will need to use a ball that has a diameter of **22.4** cm to represent Jupiter.

Percentages

A **percentage** is a ratio of a given number to 100.

Example: What is 85% of 40?

Step 1: Rewrite the percentage by moving the decimal point two places to the left.

0.85

Step 2: Multiply the decimal by the number that you are calculating the percentage of.

0.85 × 40 = 34

85% of 40 is **34.**

Decimals

To **add** or **subtract decimals,** line up the digits vertically so that the decimal points line up. Then, add or subtract the columns from right to left. Carry or borrow numbers as necessary.

Example: Add the following numbers: 3.1415 and 2.96.

Step 1: Line up the digits vertically so that the decimal points line up.

```
  3.1415
+ 2.96
```

Step 2: Add the columns from right to left, and carry when necessary.

```
  1 1
  3.1415
+ 2.96
-------
  6.1015
```

The sum is **6.1015.**

Fractions

Numbers tell you how many; **fractions** tell you *how much of a whole*.

Example: Your class has 24 plants. Your teacher instructs you to put 5 plants in a shady spot. What fraction of the plants in your class will you put in a shady spot?

Step 1: In the denominator, write the total number of parts in the whole.

$\dfrac{?}{24}$

Step 2: In the numerator, write the number of parts of the whole that are being considered.

$\dfrac{5}{24}$

So, $\dfrac{5}{24}$ of the plants will be in the shade.

Reducing Fractions

It is usually best to express a fraction in its simplest form. Expressing a fraction in its simplest form is called *reducing* a fraction.

Example: Reduce the fraction $\dfrac{30}{45}$ to its simplest form.

Step 1: Find the largest whole number that will divide evenly into both the numerator and denominator. This number is called the *greatest common factor* (GCF).

Factors of the numerator 30:
1, 2, 3, 5, 6, 10, **15,** 30

Factors of the denominator 45:
1, 3, 5, 9, **15,** 45

Step 2: Divide both the numerator and the denominator by the GCF, which in this case is 15.

$$\frac{30}{45} = \frac{30 \div 15}{45 \div 15} = \frac{2}{3}$$

Thus, $\dfrac{30}{45}$ reduced to its simplest form is $\dfrac{2}{3}$.

Adding and Subtracting Fractions

To **add** or **subtract fractions** that have the **same denominator,** simply add or subtract the numerators.

Examples:

$$\frac{3}{5} + \frac{1}{5} = ? \text{ and } \frac{3}{4} - \frac{1}{4} = ?$$

Step 1: Add or subtract the numerators.

$$\frac{3}{5} + \frac{1}{5} = \frac{4}{} \text{ and } \frac{3}{4} - \frac{1}{4} = \frac{2}{}$$

Step 2: Write the sum or difference over the denominator.

$$\frac{3}{5} + \frac{1}{5} = \frac{4}{5} \text{ and } \frac{3}{4} - \frac{1}{4} = \frac{2}{4}$$

Step 3: If necessary, reduce the fraction to its simplest form.

$\frac{4}{5}$ cannot be reduced, and $\frac{2}{4} = \frac{1}{2}$.

To **add** or **subtract fractions** that have **different denominators,** first find the least common denominator (LCD).

Examples:

$$\frac{1}{2} + \frac{1}{6} = ? \text{ and } \frac{3}{4} - \frac{2}{3} = ?$$

Step 1: Write the equivalent fractions that have a common denominator.

$$\frac{3}{6} + \frac{1}{6} = ? \text{ and } \frac{9}{12} - \frac{8}{12} = ?$$

Step 2: Add or subtract the fractions.

$$\frac{3}{6} + \frac{1}{6} = \frac{4}{6} \text{ and } \frac{9}{12} - \frac{8}{12} = \frac{1}{12}$$

Step 3: If necessary, reduce the fraction to its simplest form.

The fraction $\frac{4}{6} = \frac{2}{3}$, and $\frac{1}{12}$ cannot be reduced.

Multiplying Fractions

To **multiply fractions,** multiply the numerators and the denominators together, and then reduce the fraction to its simplest form.

Example:

$$\frac{5}{9} \times \frac{7}{10} = ?$$

Step 1: Multiply the numerators and denominators.

$$\frac{5}{9} \times \frac{7}{10} = \frac{5 \times 7}{9 \times 10} = \frac{35}{90}$$

Step 2: Reduce the fraction.

$$\frac{35}{90} = \frac{35 \div 5}{90 \div 5} = \frac{7}{18}$$

Dividing Fractions

To **divide fractions,** first rewrite the divisor (the number you divide by) upside down. This number is called the *reciprocal* of the divisor. Then multiply and reduce if necessary.

Example:

$$\frac{5}{8} \div \frac{3}{2} = ?$$

Step 1: Rewrite the divisor as its reciprocal.

$$\frac{3}{2} \rightarrow \frac{2}{3}$$

Step 2: Multiply the fractions.

$$\frac{5}{8} \times \frac{2}{3} = \frac{5 \times 2}{8 \times 3} = \frac{10}{24}$$

Step 3: Reduce the fraction.

$$\frac{10}{24} = \frac{10 \div 2}{24 \div 2} = \frac{5}{12}$$

Scientific Notation

Scientific notation is a short way of representing very large and very small numbers without writing all of the place-holding zeros.

Example: Write 653,000,000 in scientific notation.

Step 1: Write the number without the place-holding zeros.

653

Step 2: Place the decimal point after the first digit.

6.53

Step 3: Find the exponent by counting the number of places that you moved the decimal point.

6.53000000

The decimal point was moved eight places to the left. Therefore, the exponent of 10 is positive 8. If you had moved the decimal point to the right, the exponent would be negative.

Step 4: Write the number in scientific notation.

$$6.53 \times 10^8$$

Finding Area

Area is the number of square units needed to cover the surface of an object.

Formulas:
$area\ of\ a\ square = side \times side$
$area\ of\ a\ rectangle = length \times width$
$area\ of\ a\ triangle = \frac{1}{2} \times base \times height$

Examples: Find the areas.

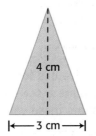

Triangle
$area = \frac{1}{2} \times base \times height$
$area = \frac{1}{2} \times 3\ cm \times 4\ cm$
$area = \textbf{6 cm}^2$

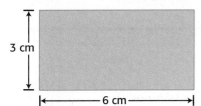

Rectangle
$area = length \times width$
$area = 6\ cm \times 3\ cm$
$area = \textbf{18 cm}^2$

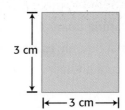

Square
$area = side \times side$
$area = 3\ cm \times 3\ cm$
$area = \textbf{9 cm}^2$

Finding Volume

Volume is the amount of space that something occupies.

Formulas:
$volume\ of\ a\ cube = side \times side \times side$

$volume\ of\ a\ prism = area\ of\ base \times height$

Examples:
Find the volume of the solids.

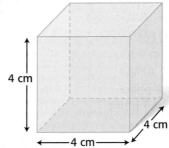

Cube
$volume = side \times side \times side$
$volume = 4\ cm \times 4\ cm \times 4\ cm$
$volume = \textbf{64 cm}^3$

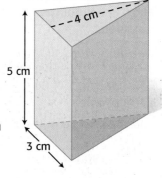

Prism
$volume = area\ of\ base \times height$
$volume = (area\ of\ triangle) \times height$
$volume = (\frac{1}{2} \times 3\ cm \times 4\ cm) \times 5\ cm$
$volume = 6\ cm^2 \times 5\ cm$
$volume = \textbf{30 cm}^3$

Making Graphs

Line Graphs

Line graphs are most often used to demonstrate continuous change. For example, Mr. Smith's students analyzed the population records for their hometown, Appleton, between 1900 and 2000. Examine the data at right.

Because the year and the population change, they are the *variables*. The population is determined by, or dependent on, the year. Therefore, the population is called the **dependent variable**, and the year is called the **independent variable.** Each set of data is called a **data pair.** To prepare a line graph, you must first organize data pairs into a table like the one at right.

Population of Appleton, 1900–2000	
Year	**Population**
1900	1,800
1920	2,500
1940	3,200
1960	3,900
1980	4,600
2000	5,300

How to Make a Line Graph

1 Place the independent variable along the horizontal (*x*) axis. Place the dependent variable along the vertical (*y*) axis.

2 Label the *x*-axis "Year" and the *y*-axis "Population." Look at your largest and smallest values for the population. For the *y*-axis, determine a scale that will provide enough space to show these values. You must use the same scale for the entire length of the axis. Next, find an appropriate scale for the *x*-axis.

3 Choose reasonable starting points for each axis.

4 Plot the data pairs as accurately as possible.

5 Choose a title that accurately represents the data.

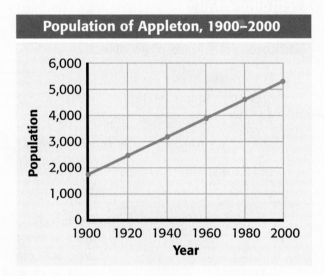

How to Determine Slope

Slope is the ratio of the change in the *y*-value to the change in the *x*-value, or "rise over run."

1 Choose two points on the line graph. For example, the population of Appleton in 2000 was 5,300 people. Therefore, you can define point *a* as (2000, 5,300). In 1900, the population was 1,800 people. You can define point *b* as (1900, 1,800).

2 Find the change in the *y*-value. (*y* at point *a*) − (*y* at point *b*) = 5,300 people − 1,800 people = 3,500 people

3 Find the change in the *x*-value. (*x* at point *a*) − (*x* at point *b*) = 2000 − 1900 = 100 years

4 Calculate the slope of the graph by dividing the change in *y* by the change in *x*.

$$slope = \frac{change\ in\ y}{change\ in\ x}$$

$$slope = \frac{3,500\ people}{100\ years}$$

$$slope = 35\ people\ per\ year$$

In this example, the population in Appleton increased by a fixed amount each year. The graph of these data is a straight line. Therefore, the relationship is **linear.** When the graph of a set of data is not a straight line, the relationship is **nonlinear.**

Using Algebra to Determine Slope

The equation in step ❹ may also be arranged to be

$$y = kx$$

where y represents the change in the y-value, k represents the slope, and x represents the change in the x-value.

$$slope = \frac{change\ in\ y}{change\ in\ x}$$

$$k = \frac{y}{x}$$

$$k \times x = \frac{y \times x}{x}$$

$$kx = y$$

Bar Graphs

Bar graphs are useful for comparing data values. For example, if you want to compare the amounts of several types of municipal solid waste, you might use a bar graph. The table at right contains the data used to make the bar graph below.

How to Make a Bar Graph

❶ Use an appropriate scale and a reasonable starting point for each axis.

❷ Label the axes, and plot the data.

❸ Choose a title that accurately represents the data.

United States Municipal Solid Waste	
Material	**Percentage of total waste**
Paper	38.1
Yard waste	12.1
Food waste	10.9
Plastics	10.5
Metals	7.8
Rubber, leather, and textiles	6.6
Glass	5.5
Wood	5.3
Other	3.2

Appendix

Pie Graph

A pie graph shows how each group of data relates to all of the data. Each part of the circle forming the graph represents a category of the data. The entire circle represents all of the data. For example, a biologist studying a hardwood forest found that there were five types of trees. The data table at right summarizes the biologist's findings.

Hardwood Trees	
Type of tree	**Number found**
Oak	600
Maple	750
Beech	300
Birch	1,200
Hickory	150
Total	3,000

How to Make a Pie Graph

1 To make a pie graph of these data, first find what percentage all of the trees of each type of tree represents. Divide the number of trees of each type by the total number of trees, and multiply by 100.

$$\frac{600 \text{ oak}}{3,000 \text{ trees}} \times 100 = 20\%$$

$$\frac{750 \text{ maple}}{3,000 \text{ trees}} \times 100 = 25\%$$

$$\frac{300 \text{ beech}}{3,000 \text{ trees}} \times 100 = 10\%$$

$$\frac{1,200 \text{ birch}}{3,000 \text{ trees}} \times 100 = 40\%$$

$$\frac{150 \text{ hickory}}{3,000 \text{ trees}} \times 100 = 5\%$$

2 Now, determine the size of the wedges that make up the pie graph. Multiply each percentage by 360°. Remember that a circle contains 360°.

20% × 360° = 72°   25% × 360° = 90°

10% × 360° = 36°   40% × 360° = 144°

5% × 360° = 18°

3 Check that the sum of the percentages is 100 and that the sum of the degrees is 360.

20% + 25% + 10% + 40% + 5% = 100%

72° + 90° + 36° + 144° + 18° = 360°

4 Use a compass to draw a circle and mark the center of the circle.

5 Then, use a protractor to draw angles of 72°, 90°, 36°, 144°, and 18° in the circle.

6 Finally, label each part of the graph, and choose an appropriate title.

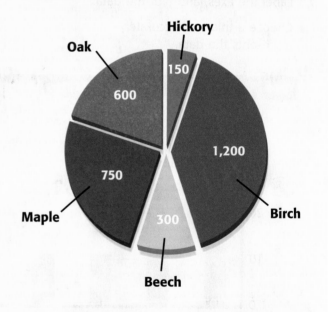

A Community of Hardwood Trees

Physical Science Refresher

Atoms and Elements

Every object in the universe is made up of particles of some kind of matter. **Matter** is anything that takes up space and has mass. All matter is made up of elements. An **element** is a substance that cannot be separated into simpler components by ordinary chemical means. The reason is that each element consists of only one kind of atom. An **atom** is the smallest unit of an element that maintains the properties of that element.

Atomic Structure

Atoms are made up of small particles called **subatomic particles.** The three major types of subatomic particles are **electrons, protons,** and **neutrons.** Electrons have a negative electric charge, protons have a positive electric charge, and neutrons have no electric charge. The protons and neutrons are packed close to one another to form the **nucleus.** The protons give the nucleus a positive charge. Electrons are most likely to be found in regions around the nucleus called **electron clouds.** The negatively charged electrons are attracted to the positively charged nucleus. An atom may have several energy levels in which electrons are located.

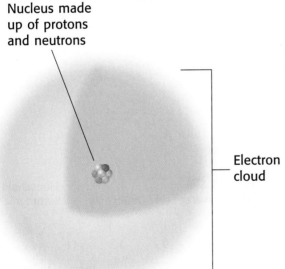

Nucleus made up of protons and neutrons

Electron cloud

Atomic Number

To help in the identification of elements, scientists have assigned an **atomic number** to each kind of atom. The atomic number is the number of protons in the atom. Atoms that have the same number of protons are the same kind of element. In an uncharged, or electrically neutral, atom, the numbers of protons and electrons are equal. Therefore, the atomic number equals the number of electrons in an uncharged atom. The number of neutrons, however, can vary for a given element. Atoms of the same element that have different numbers of neutrons are called **isotopes.**

Periodic Table of the Elements

In the periodic table, the elements are arranged from left to right in order of increasing atomic number. Each element in the table is in a separate box. An uncharged atom of each element has one more electron and one more proton than does an uncharged atom of the element to its left. Each horizontal row of the table is called a **period.** Changes in chemical properties of elements across a period correspond to changes in the electron arrangements of the atoms of the elements. Each vertical column of the table, known as a **group,** lists elements that have similar properties. The elements in a group have similar chemical properties because their atoms have the same number of electrons in their outer energy level. For example, the elements helium, neon, argon, krypton, xenon, and radon have similar properties and are known as the *noble gases.*

Molecules and Compounds

When two or more elements are joined chemically, the resulting substance is called a **compound.** A compound is a new substance whose properties differ from the properties of the elements that compose the compound. For example, water, H_2O, is a compound formed when hydrogen, H, and oxygen, O, combine. The smallest complete unit of a compound that has the properties of that compound is called a **molecule.** A chemical formula indicates the elements in a compound. It also indicates the relative number of atoms of each element present. The chemical formula for water is H_2O, which indicates that each water molecule consists of two atoms of hydrogen and one atom of oxygen. The subscript number after the symbol for an element indicates how many atoms of that element are in a single molecule of the compound.

Acids, Bases, and pH

An **ion** is an atom or group of atoms that has an electric charge because it has lost or gained one or more electrons. When an acid, such as hydrochloric acid, HCl, is mixed with water, it separates into ions. An **acid** is a compound that produces hydrogen ions, H^+, in water. The hydrogen ions then combine with water molecules to form hydronium ions, H_3O^+. A **base,** on the other hand, is a substance that produces hydroxide ions, OH^-, in water.

To determine whether a solution is acidic or basic, scientists use pH. The **pH** is a measure of the hydronium ion concentration in a solution. The pH scale ranges from 0 to 14. The middle point, pH = 7, is neutral—neither acidic nor basic. Acids have a pH less than 7; bases have a pH greater than 7. The lower the number is, the more acidic the solution. The higher the number is, the more basic the solution.

Chemical Equations

A chemical reaction occurs when a chemical change takes place. (In a chemical change, new substances that have new properties form.) A chemical equation is a useful way of describing a chemical reaction by means of chemical formulas. The equation indicates what substances react and what the products are. For example, when carbon and oxygen combine, they can form carbon dioxide. The equation for the reaction is as follows: $C + O_2 \rightarrow CO_2$.

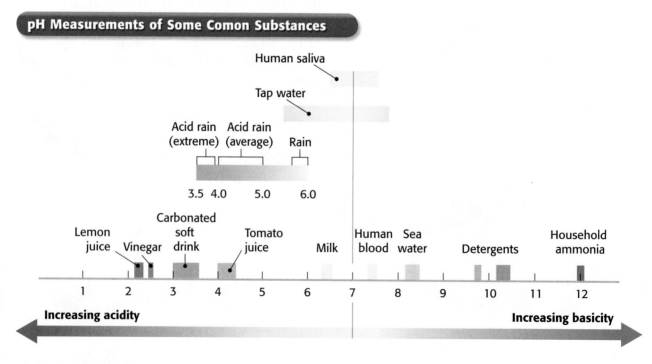

pH Measurements of Some Comon Substances

Physical Science Laws and Principles

Newton's Laws of Motion

> **Newton's first law of motion** states that an object at rest remains at rest and an object in motion remains in motion at constant speed and in a straight line unless acted on by an unbalanced force.

The first part of the law explains why a football will remain on a tee until it is kicked off or until a gust of wind blows it off.

The second part of the law explains why a bike rider will continue moving forward after the bike comes to an abrupt stop. Gravity and the friction of the sidewalk will eventually stop the rider.

> **Newton's second law of motion** states that the acceleration of an object depends on the mass of the object and the amount of force applied.

The first part of the law explains why the acceleration of a 4 kg bowling ball will be greater than the acceleration of a 6 kg bowling ball if the same force is applied to both balls.

The second part of the law explains why the acceleration of a bowling ball will be larger if a larger force is applied to the bowling ball.

The relationship of acceleration (a) to mass (m) and force (F) can be expressed mathematically by the following equation:

$$acceleration = \frac{force}{mass}, \text{ or } a = \frac{F}{m}$$

This equation is often rearranged to the form

$$force = mass \times acceleration, \text{ or } F = m \times a$$

> **Newton's third law of motion** states that whenever one object exerts a force on a second object, the second object exerts an equal and opposite force on the first.

This law explains that a runner is able to move forward because of the equal and opposite force that the ground exerts on the runner's foot after each step.

Law of Conservation of Mass

> **Mass cannot be created or destroyed during ordinary chemical or physical changes.**

The total mass in a closed system is always the same no matter how many physical changes or chemical reactions occur.

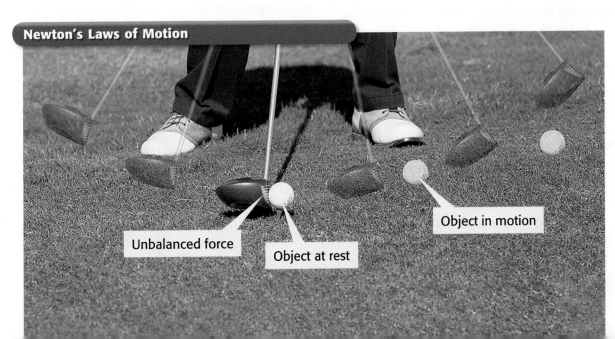

Newton's Laws of Motion

Unbalanced force

Object at rest

Object in motion

Law of Universal Gravitation

All objects in the universe attract each other by a force called *gravity*. The size of the force depends on the masses of the objects and the distance between the objects.

The first part of the law explains why lifting a bowling ball is much harder than lifting a marble. Because the bowling ball has a much larger mass than the marble does, the amount of gravity between Earth and the bowling ball is greater than the amount of gravity between Earth and the marble.

The second part of the law explains why a satellite can remain in orbit around Earth. The satellite is carefully placed at a distance great enough to prevent Earth's gravity from immediately pulling the satellite down but small enough to prevent the satellite from completely escaping Earth's gravity and wandering off into space.

Law of Conservation of Energy

Energy can be neither created nor destroyed.

The total amount of energy in a closed system is always the same. Energy can be changed from one form to another, but all of the different forms of energy in a system always add up to the same total amount of energy no matter how many energy conversions occur.

Charles's Law

Charles's law states that for a fixed amount of gas at a constant pressure, the volume of the gas increases as the temperature of the gas increases. Likewise, the volume of the gas decreases as the temperature of the gas decreases.

If a basketball that was inflated indoors is left outside on a cold winter day, the air particles inside the ball will move more slowly. They will hit the sides of the basketball less often and with less force. The ball will get smaller as the volume of the air decreases.

Boyle's Law

Boyle's law states that for a fixed amount of gas at a constant temperature, the volume of a gas increases as the pressure of the gas decreases. Likewise, the volume of a gas decreases as its pressure increases.

If an inflated balloon is pulled down to the bottom of a swimming pool, the pressure of the water on the balloon increases. The pressure of the air particles inside the balloon must increase to match that of the water outside, so the volume of the air inside the balloon decreases.

Pascal's Principle

Pascal's principle states that a change in pressure at any point in an enclosed fluid will be transmitted equally to all parts of that fluid.

When a mechanic uses a hydraulic jack to raise an automobile off the ground, he or she increases the pressure on the fluid in the jack by pushing on the jack handle. The pressure is transmitted equally to all parts of the fluid-filled jacking system. As fluid presses the jack plate against the frame of the car, the car is lifted off the ground.

Archimedes' Principle

Archimedes' principle states that the buoyant force on an object in a fluid is equal to the weight of the volume of fluid that the object displaces.

A person floating in a swimming pool displaces 20 L of water. The weight of that volume of water is about 200 N. Therefore, the buoyant force on the person is 200 N.

Bernoulli's Principle

Bernoulli's principle states that as the speed of a moving fluid increases, the fluid's pressure decreases.

The lift on an airplane wing can be explained in part by using Bernoulli's principle. Because of the shape of the wing, the air moving over the top of the wing is moving faster than the air below the wing. This faster-moving air above the wing exerts less pressure than the slower-moving air below it does. The resulting increased pressure below exerts an upward force and pushes the wing up.

Law of Reflection

The law of reflection states that the angle of incidence is equal to the angle of reflection. This law explains why light reflects off a surface at the same angle that the light strikes the surface.

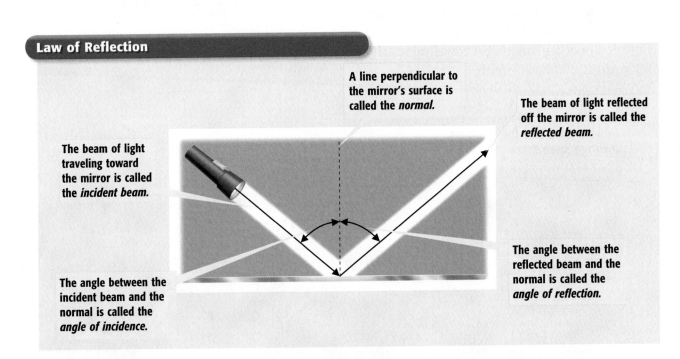

Law of Reflection

A line perpendicular to the mirror's surface is called the *normal*.

The beam of light reflected off the mirror is called the *reflected beam*.

The beam of light traveling toward the mirror is called the *incident beam*.

The angle between the reflected beam and the normal is called the *angle of reflection*.

The angle between the incident beam and the normal is called the *angle of incidence*.

Useful Equations

Average Speed

The rate at which an object moves is its *speed*. Speed depends on the distance traveled and the time taken to travel that distance. **Average speed** is calculated using the following equation:

$$average\ speed = \frac{total\ distance}{total\ time}$$

> **Example:** A bicycle messenger traveled a distance of 136 km in 8 h. What was the messenger's average speed?
>
> $$\frac{136\ km}{8\ h} = 17\ km/h$$
>
> The messenger's average speed was **17 km/h.**

Velocity

The speed of an object in a particular direction is **velocity.** Speed and velocity are not the same even though they are calculated by using the same equation. Velocity must include a direction, so velocity is described as speed in a certain direction. For example, the speed of a plane that is traveling south at 600 km/h is 600 km/h. The velocity of a plane that is traveling south at 600 km/h is 600 km/h south.

Velocity can also be thought of as the rate of change of an object's position. An object's velocity remains constant only if its speed and direction don't change. Therefore, constant velocity occurs only along a straight line.

Average Acceleration

The rate at which velocity changes is called *acceleration.* **Average acceleration** can be calculated by using the following equation:

$$average\ acceleration = \frac{final\ velocity - starting\ velocity}{time\ it\ takes\ to\ change\ velocity}$$

> **Example:** Calculate the average acceleration of an Olympic sprinter who reached a velocity of 20 m/s south at the finish line of a 100 m dash. The race was in a straight line and lasted 10 s.
>
> $$\frac{20\ m/s - 0\ m/s}{10\ s} = 2\ m/s/s$$
>
> The sprinter's average acceleration was **2 m/s/s south.**

The winner of this race is the athlete who has the greatest average speed.

Net Force

Forces in the Same Direction

When forces are in the same direction, add the forces together to determine the net force.

Example: Calculate the net force on a stalled car that is being pushed by two people. One person is pushing with a force of 13 N northwest, and the other person is pushing with a force of 8 N in the same direction.

$$13\ N + 8\ N = 21\ N$$

The net force is **21 N northwest.**

Forces in Opposite Directions

When forces are in opposite directions, subtract the smaller force from the larger force to determine the net force. The net force will be in the direction of the larger force.

Example: Calculate the net force on a rope that is being pulled on each end. One person is pulling on one end of the rope with a force of 12 N south. Another person is pulling on the opposite end of the rope with a force of 7 N north.

$$12\ N - 7\ N = 5\ N$$

The net force is **5 N south.**

The forces exerted by the dogs on the rope are in opposite directions. The net force is found by subtracting the smaller force from the larger force.

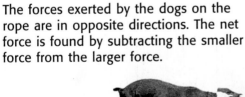

Pressure

Pressure is the force exerted over a given area. The SI unit for pressure is the pascal (Pa).

$$pressure = \frac{force}{area}$$

Example: Calculate the pressure of the air in a soccer ball if the air exerts a force of 25,000 N over an area of 0.15 m².

$$pressure = \frac{25{,}000\ N}{1\ m^2} = \frac{167{,}000\ N}{m^2} = 167{,}000\ Pa$$

The pressure of the air inside the soccer ball is **167,000 Pa.**

Density

The mass per unit volume of a substance is **density.** Thus, a material's density is the amount of matter it contains in a given space. To find density, you must measure both mass and volume. Density is calculated by using the following equation:

$$density = \frac{mass}{volume}$$

Example: Calculate the density of a sponge that has a mass of 10 g and a volume of 40 cm³.

$$\frac{10\ g}{40\ cm^3} = \frac{0.25\ g}{cm^3}$$

The density of the sponge is $\frac{0.25\ g}{cm^3}$.

Concentration

A measure of the amount of one substance that is dissolved in another substance is **concentration.** The substance that is dissolved is the solute. The substance that dissolves another substance is the solvent. Concentration is calculated by using the following equation:

$$concentration = \frac{mass\ of\ solute}{volume\ of\ solvent}$$

Example: Calculate the concentration of a solution in which 10 g of sugar is dissolved in 125 mL of water.

$$\frac{10\ g\ of\ sugar}{125\ mL\ of\ water} = \frac{0.08\ g}{mL}$$

The concentration of this solution is $\frac{0.08\ g}{mL}$.

These solutions were made by using the same volume of water. But less solute was dissolved in the beaker on the left. So, the concentration of the solution on the left is lower than the concentration of the solution on the right.

Work

Work is done by exerting a force through a distance. Work is expressed in joules (J), which are equivalent to newton-meters (N•m).

$$work = force \times distance$$

Example: Calculate the amount of work done by a man who lifts a 100 N toddler 1.5 m off the floor.

$$work = 100\ N \times 1.5\ m = 150\ N•m = 150\ J$$

The man did **150 J** of work.

Power

Power is the rate at which work is done. Power is expressed in watts (W), which are equivalent to joules per second (J/s).

$$power = \frac{work}{time}$$

Example: Calculate the power of a weight-lifter who raises a 300 N barbell 2.1 m off the floor in 1.25 s.

$$work = 300\ N \times 2.1\ m = 630\ N•m = 630\ J$$

$$power = \frac{30\ J}{1.25\ s} = \frac{504\ J}{s} = 504\ W$$

The weightlifter's power is **504 W.**

Heat

Heat is the energy transferred between objects that are at different temperatures. Heat is expressed in joules (J). In general, if you know an object's mass, change in temperature, and specific heat, you can calculate heat. Specific heat is the amount of energy needed to change the temperature of 1 kg of a substance by 1°C. Specific heat is expressed in joules per kilogram-degree Celsius (J/kg•°C).

heat = specific heat × mass × *change in temperature*

Example: Calculate the heat transferred to a mass of 0.2 kg of water to change the temperature of the water from 25°C to 80°C. The specific heat of water is 4,184 J/kg•°C.

heat = 4,184 J/kg•°C × 0.2 kg × (80°C − 25°C) = 46,024 J

The heat transferred is **46,024 J.**

Work and Heat

James Joule, an English scientist, performed experiments to explore the relationship between **work** and **heat.** He found that a given amount of work always generated the same amount of heat. By applying the law of conservation of energy, we know that the amount of heat generated can never be larger than the work done.

Example: What is the maximum amount of heat that can be generated from the work done if a force of 75 N is exerted over a distance of 5 m?

work = 75 N × 5 m = 375 N•m = 375 J

The maximum amount of heat that can be generated is **375 J.**

Example: A force of 299 N is exerted through a distance of 210 m. The resulting work is converted into heat and absorbed by 2.0 kg of water. What is the maximum change in temperature if the specific heat of water is 4,184 J/kg•°C?

work = 299 N × 210 m = 62,790 N•m = 62,790 J

$$\frac{change\ in}{temperature} = \frac{heat}{mass \times specific\ heat}$$

$$\frac{change\ in}{temperature} = \frac{62,790\ J}{2.0\ kg \times 4,184\ J/kg•°C} = 7.5°C$$

The maximum change in temperature is **7.5°C.**

As the air in this balloon absorbs heat, the temperature of the air rises.

Scientific Methods

The ways in which scientists answer questions and solve problems are called **scientific methods.** The same steps are often used by scientists as they look for answers. However, there is more than one way to use these steps. Scientists may use all of the steps or just some of the steps during an investigation. They may even repeat some of the steps. The goal of using scientific methods is to come up with reliable answers and solutions.

Six Steps of Scientific Methods

 Good questions come from careful **observations.** You make observations by using your senses to gather information. Sometimes, you may use instruments, such as microscopes and telescopes, to extend the range of your senses. As you observe the natural world, you will discover that you have many more questions than answers. These questions drive investigations.

Questions beginning with *what, why, how,* and *when* are important in focusing an investigation. Here is an example of a question that could lead to an investigation.

> **Question:** How does acid rain affect plant growth?

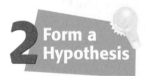 After you ask a question, you need to form a **hypothesis.** A hypothesis is a clear statement of what you expect the answer to your question to be. Your hypothesis will represent your best "educated guess" based on what you have observed and what you already know. A good hypothesis is testable. Otherwise, the investigation can go no further. Here is a hypothesis based on the question "How does acid rain affect plant growth?"

> **Hypothesis:** Acid rain slows plant growth.

The hypothesis can lead to predictions. A prediction is what you think the outcome of your experiment or data collection will be. Predictions are usually stated in an if-then format. Here is a sample prediction for the hypothesis that acid rain slows plant growth.

> **Prediction:** If a plant is watered with only acid rain (which has a pH of 4), then the plant will grow at half its normal rate.

3 Test the Hypothesis

After you have formed a hypothesis and made a prediction, your hypothesis should be tested. One way to test a hypothesis is with a controlled experiment. A **controlled experiment** tests only one factor at a time. In an experiment to test the effect of acid rain on plant growth, the **control group** would be watered with normal rainwater. The **experimental group** would be watered with acid rain. All of the plants should receive the same amount of sunlight and water each day. The air temperature should be the same for all groups. However, the acidity of the water will be a variable. In fact, any factor that differs from one group to another is a **variable.** If your hypothesis is correct, then the acidity of the water and plant growth are *dependant variables.* The amount that a plant grows is dependent on the acidity of the water. However, the amount of water and the amount of sunlight received by each plant are *independent variables.* Either of these factors could change without affecting the other factor.

Sometimes, the nature of an investigation makes a controlled experiment impossible. For example, Earth's core is surrounded by thousands of meters of rock. Under such circumstances, a hypothesis may be tested by making detailed observations.

4 Analyze the Results

After you have completed your experiments, made your observations, and collected your data, you must analyze all of the information that you have gathered. Tables and graphs are often used in this step to organize the data.

5 Draw Conclusions

After analyzing your data, you can determine if your results support your hypothesis. If your hypothesis is supported, you (or others) might want to repeat the observations or experiments to verify your results. If your hypothesis is not supported by the data, you may have to check your procedure for errors. You may even have to reject your hypothesis and make a new one. If you cannot draw a conclusion from your results, you may have to try the investigation again or carry out further observations or experiments.

6 Communicate Results

After any scientific investigation, you should report your results. By preparing a written or oral report, you let others know what you have learned. They may repeat your investigation to see if they get the same results. Your report may even lead to another question and then to another investigation.

Appendix

Scientific Methods in Action

Scientific methods contain loops in which several steps may be repeated over and over again. In some cases, certain steps are unnecessary. Thus, there is not a "straight line" of steps. For example, sometimes scientists find that testing one hypothesis raises new questions and new hypotheses to be tested. And sometimes, testing the hypothesis leads directly to a conclusion. Furthermore, the steps in scientific methods are not always used in the same order. Follow the steps in the diagram, and see how many different directions scientific methods can take you.

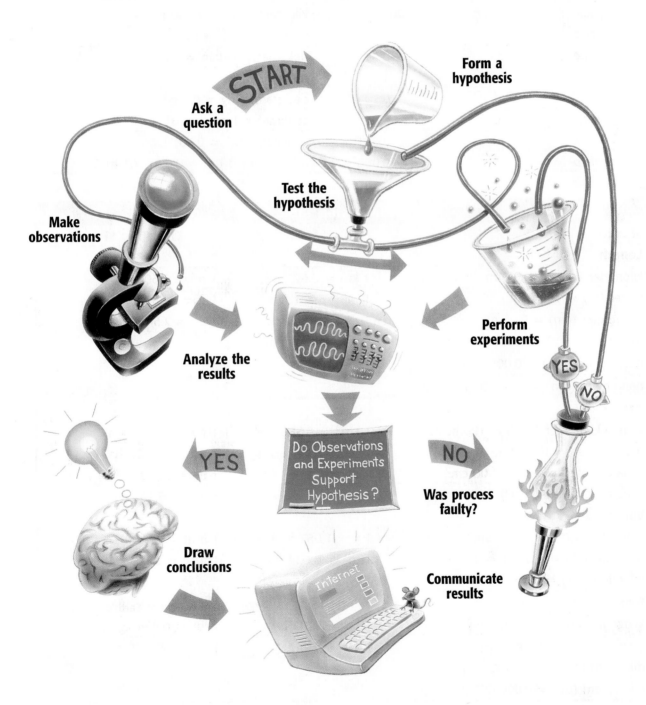

SI Measurement

The International System of Units, or SI, is the standard system of measurement used by many scientists. Using the same standards of measurement makes it easier for scientists to communicate with one another.

SI works by combining prefixes and base units. Each base unit can be used with different prefixes to define smaller and larger quantities. The table below lists common SI prefixes.

SI Prefixes			
Prefix	Symbol	Factor	Example
kilo-	k	1,000	kilogram, 1 kg = 1,000 g
hecto-	h	100	hectoliter, 1 hL = 100 L
deka-	da	10	dekameter, 1 dam = 10 m
		1	meter, liter, gram
deci-	d	0.1	decigram, 1 dg = 0.1 g
centi-	c	0.01	centimeter, 1 cm = 0.01 m
milli-	m	0.001	milliliter, 1 mL = 0.001 L
micro-	μ	0.000 001	micrometer, 1 μm = 0.000 001 m

SI Conversion Table		
SI units	From SI to English	From English to SI
Length		
kilometer (km) = 1,000 m	1 km = 0.621 mi	1 mi = 1.609 km
meter (m) = 100 cm	1 m = 3.281 ft	1 ft = 0.305 m
centimeter (cm) = 0.01 m	1 cm = 0.394 in.	1 in. = 2.540 cm
millimeter (mm) = 0.001 m	1 mm = 0.039 in.	
micrometer (μm) = 0.000 001 m		
nanometer (nm) = 0.000 000 001 m		
Area		
square kilometer (km^2) = 100 hectares	1 km^2 = 0.386 mi^2	1 mi^2 = 2.590 km^2
hectare (ha) = 10,000 m^2	1 ha = 2.471 acres	1 acre = 0.405 ha
square meter (m^2) = 10,000 cm^2	1 m^2 = 10.764 ft^2	1 ft^2 = 0.093 m^2
square centimeter (cm^2) = 100 mm^2	1 cm^2 = 0.155 in.^{2}	1 in.^{2} = 6.452 cm^2
Volume		
liter (L) = 1,000 mL = 1 dm^3	1 L = 1.057 fl qt	1 fl qt = 0.946 L
milliliter (mL) = 0.001 L = 1 cm^3	1 mL = 0.034 fl oz	1 fl oz = 29.574 mL
microliter (μL) = 0.000 001 L		
Mass	*Equivalent weight at Earth's surface	
kilogram (kg) = 1,000 g	1 kg = 2.205 lb*	1 lb* = 0.454 kg
gram (g) = 1,000 mg	1 g = 0.035 oz*	1 oz* = 28.350 g
milligram (mg) = 0.001 g		
microgram (μg) = 0.000 001 g		

Measuring Skills

Using a Graduated Cylinder

When using a graduated cylinder to measure volume, keep the following procedures in mind:

1. Place the cylinder on a flat, level surface before measuring liquid.
2. Move your head so that your eye is level with the surface of the liquid.
3. Read the mark closest to the liquid level. On glass graduated cylinders, read the mark closest to the center of the curve in the liquid's surface.

Using a Meterstick or Metric Ruler

When using a meterstick or metric ruler to measure length, keep the following procedures in mind:

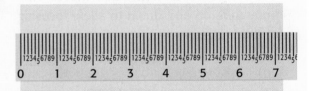

1. Place the ruler firmly against the object that you are measuring.
2. Align one edge of the object exactly with the 0 end of the ruler.
3. Look at the other edge of the object to see which of the marks on the ruler is closest to that edge. (Note: Each small slash between the centimeters represents a millimeter, which is one-tenth of a centimeter.)

Using a Triple-Beam Balance

When using a triple-beam balance to measure mass, keep the following procedures in mind:

1. Make sure the balance is on a level surface.
2. Place all of the countermasses at 0. Adjust the balancing knob until the pointer rests at 0.
3. Place the object to be measured on the pan. **Caution:** Do not place hot objects or chemicals directly on the balance pan.
4. Move the largest countermass along the beam to the right until it is at the last notch that does not tip the balance. Follow the same procedure with the next-largest countermass. Then, move the smallest countermass until the pointer rests at 0.
5. Add the readings from the three beams together to determine the mass of the object.
6. When determining the mass of crystals or powders, first find the mass of a piece of filter paper. Then, add the crystals or powder to the paper, and remeasure. The actual mass of the crystals or powder is the total mass minus the mass of the paper. When finding the mass of liquids, first find the mass of the empty container. Then, find the combined mass of the liquid and container. The mass of the liquid is the total mass minus the mass of the container.

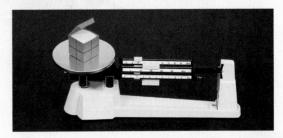

Using the Microscope

Parts of the Compound Light Microscope

- The **ocular lens** magnifies the image 10×.
- The **low-power objective** magnifies the image 10×.
- The **high-power objective** magnifies the image either 40× or 43×.
- The **revolving nosepiece** holds the objectives and can be turned to change from one magnification to the other.
- The **body tube** maintains the correct distance between the ocular lens and objectives.
- The **coarse-adjustment knob** moves the body tube up and down to allow focusing of the image.

- The **fine-adjustment knob** moves the body tube slightly to bring the image into sharper focus. It is usually located in the center of the coarse-adjustment knob.
- The **stage** supports a slide.
- **Stage clips** hold the slide in place for viewing.
- The **diaphragm** controls the amount of light coming through the stage.
- The light source provides a **light** for viewing the slide.
- The **arm** supports the body tube.
- The **base** supports the microscope.

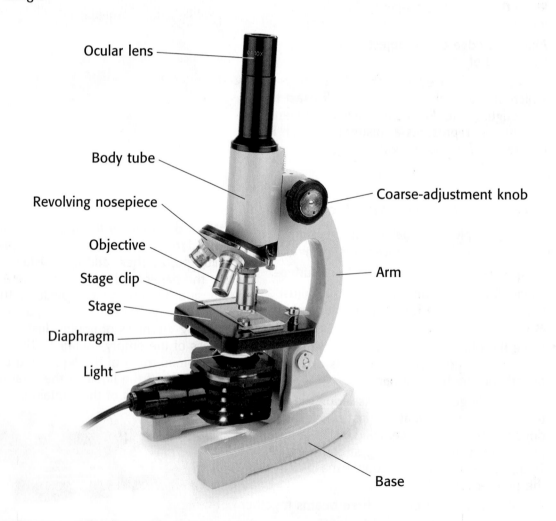

Ocular lens

Body tube

Revolving nosepiece

Objective

Stage clip

Stage

Diaphragm

Light

Coarse-adjustment knob

Arm

Base

Appendix

Proper Use of the Compound Light Microscope

1. Use both hands to carry the microscope to your lab table. Place one hand beneath the base, and use the other hand to hold the arm of the microscope. Hold the microscope close to your body while carrying it to your lab table.

2. Place the microscope on the lab table at least 5 cm from the edge of the table.

3. Check to see what type of light source is used by your microscope. If the microscope has a lamp, plug it in and make sure that the cord is out of the way. If the microscope has a mirror, adjust the mirror to reflect light through the hole in the stage.
   Caution: If your microscope has a mirror, do not use direct sunlight as a light source. Direct sunlight can damage your eyes.

4. Always begin work with the low-power objective in line with the body tube. Adjust the revolving nosepiece.

5. Place a prepared slide over the hole in the stage. Secure the slide with the stage clips.

6. Look through the ocular lens. Move the diaphragm to adjust the amount of light coming through the stage.

7. Look at the stage from eye level. Slowly turn the coarse adjustment to lower the objective until the objective almost touches the slide. Do not allow the objective to touch the slide.

8. Look through the ocular lens. Turn the coarse adjustment to raise the low-power objective until the image is in focus. Always focus by raising the objective away from the slide. Never focus the objective downward. Use the fine adjustment to sharpen the focus. Keep both eyes open while viewing a slide.

9. Make sure that the image is exactly in the center of your field of vision. Then, switch to the high-power objective. Focus the image by using only the fine adjustment. Never use the coarse adjustment at high power.

10. When you are finished using the microscope, remove the slide. Clean the ocular lens and objectives with lens paper. Return the microscope to its storage area. Remember to use both hands when carrying the microscope.

Making a Wet Mount

1. Use lens paper to clean a glass slide and a coverslip.

2. Place the specimen that you wish to observe in the center of the slide.

3. Using a medicine dropper, place one drop of water on the specimen.

4. Hold the coverslip at the edge of the water and at a 45° angle to the slide. Make sure that the water runs along the edge of the coverslip.

5. Lower the coverslip slowly to avoid trapping air bubbles.

6. Water might evaporate from the slide as you work. Add more water to keep the specimen fresh. Place the tip of the medicine dropper next to the edge of the coverslip. Add a drop of water. (You can also use this method to add stain or solutions to a wet mount.) Remove excess water from the slide by using the corner of a paper towel as a blotter. Do not lift the coverslip to add or remove water.

Periodic Table of the Elements

Each square on the table includes an element's name, chemical symbol, atomic number, and atomic mass.

The color of the chemical symbol indicates the physical state at room temperature. Carbon is a solid.

6	Atomic number
C	Chemical symbol
Carbon	Element name
12.0	Atomic mass

The background color indicates the type of element. Carbon is a nonmetal.

Background

Metals	
Metalloids	
Nonmetals	

Chemical symbol

Solid	
Liquid	
Gas	

Period 1

| 1 |
| **H** |
| Hydrogen |
| 1.0 |

	Group 1	Group 2		Group 3	Group 4	Group 5	Group 6	Group 7	Group 8	Group 9
Period 2	3 **Li** Lithium 6.9	4 **Be** Beryllium 9.0								
Period 3	11 **Na** Sodium 23.0	12 **Mg** Magnesium 24.3								
Period 4	19 **K** Potassium 39.1	20 **Ca** Calcium 40.1		21 **Sc** Scandium 45.0	22 **Ti** Titanium 47.9	23 **V** Vanadium 50.9	24 **Cr** Chromium 52.0	25 **Mn** Manganese 54.9	26 **Fe** Iron 55.8	27 **Co** Cobalt 58.9
Period 5	37 **Rb** Rubidium 85.5	38 **Sr** Strontium 87.6		39 **Y** Yttrium 88.9	40 **Zr** Zirconium 91.2	41 **Nb** Niobium 92.9	42 **Mo** Molybdenum 95.9	43 **Tc** Technetium (98)	44 **Ru** Ruthenium 101.1	45 **Rh** Rhodium 102.9
Period 6	55 **Cs** Cesium 132.9	56 **Ba** Barium 137.3		57 **La** Lanthanum 138.9	72 **Hf** Hafnium 178.5	73 **Ta** Tantalum 180.9	74 **W** Tungsten 183.8	75 **Re** Rhenium 186.2	76 **Os** Osmium 190.2	77 **Ir** Iridium 192.2
Period 7	87 **Fr** Francium (223)	88 **Ra** Radium (226)		89 **Ac** Actinium (227)	104 **Rf** Rutherfordium (261)	105 **Db** Dubnium (262)	106 **Sg** Seaborgium (266)	107 **Bh** Bohrium (264)	108 **Hs** Hassium (277)	109 **Mt** Meitnerium (268)

A row of elements is called a *period*.

A column of elements is called a *group* or *family*.

Values in parentheses are the mass numbers of those radioactive elements' most stable or most common isotopes.

These elements are placed below the table to allow the table to be narrower.

Lanthanides	58 **Ce** Cerium 140.1	59 **Pr** Praseodymium 140.9	60 **Nd** Neodymium 144.2	61 **Pm** Promethium (145)	62 **Sm** Samarium 150.4
Actinides	90 **Th** Thorium 232.0	91 **Pa** Protactinium 231.0	92 **U** Uranium 238.0	93 **Np** Neptunium (237)	94 **Pu** Plutonium (244)

Topic: **Periodic Table**
Go To: **go.hrw.com**
Keyword: **HN0 PERIODIC**
Visit the HRW Web site for updates on the periodic table.

Group 18

| 2 |
| **He** |
| Helium |
| 4.0 |

This zigzag line reminds you where the metals, nonmetals, and metalloids are.

Group 13	Group 14	Group 15	Group 16	Group 17
5 **B** Boron 10.8	6 **C** Carbon 12.0	7 **N** Nitrogen 14.0	8 **O** Oxygen 16.0	9 **F** Fluorine 19.0	10 **Ne** Neon 20.2
13 **Al** Aluminum 27.0	14 **Si** Silicon 28.1	15 **P** Phosphorus 31.0	16 **S** Sulfur 32.1	17 **Cl** Chlorine 35.5	18 **Ar** Argon 39.9

Group 10	Group 11	Group 12					
28 **Ni** Nickel 58.7	29 **Cu** Copper 63.5	30 **Zn** Zinc 65.4	31 **Ga** Gallium 69.7	32 **Ge** Germanium 72.6	33 **As** Arsenic 74.9	34 **Se** Selenium 79.0	35 **Br** Bromine 79.9	36 **Kr** Krypton 83.8
46 **Pd** Palladium 106.4	47 **Ag** Silver 107.9	48 **Cd** Cadmium 112.4	49 **In** Indium 114.8	50 **Sn** Tin 118.7	51 **Sb** Antimony 121.8	52 **Te** Tellurium 127.6	53 **I** Iodine 126.9	54 **Xe** Xenon 131.3
78 **Pt** Platinum 195.1	79 **Au** Gold 197.0	80 **Hg** Mercury 200.6	81 **Tl** Thallium 204.4	82 **Pb** Lead 207.2	83 **Bi** Bismuth 209.0	84 **Po** Polonium (209)	85 **At** Astatine (210)	86 **Rn** Radon (222)
110 **Ds** Darmstadtium (281)	111 **Uuu** Unununium (272)	112 **Uub** Ununbium (285)	113 **Uut** Ununtrium (284)	114 **Uuq** Ununquadium (289)	115 **Uup** Ununpentium (288)			

The discovery of elements 113, 114, and 115 has been reported but not confirmed.

The names and three-letter symbols of elements are temporary. They are based on the atomic numbers of the elements. Official names and symbols will be approved by an international committee of scientists.

63 **Eu** Europium 152.0	64 **Gd** Gadolinium 157.2	65 **Tb** Terbium 158.9	66 **Dy** Dysprosium 162.5	67 **Ho** Holmium 164.9	68 **Er** Erbium 167.3	69 **Tm** Thulium 168.9	70 **Yb** Ytterbium 173.0	71 **Lu** Lutetium 175.0
95 **Am** Americium (243)	96 **Cm** Curium (247)	97 **Bk** Berkelium (247)	98 **Cf** Californium (251)	99 **Es** Einsteinium (252)	100 **Fm** Fermium (257)	101 **Md** Mendelevium (258)	102 **No** Nobelium (259)	103 **Lr** Lawrencium (262)

Appendix

Solar System Data

The diagram at top shows the relative sizes of the nine planets. The order of the planets from the sun is the following: Mercury, Venus, Earth, Mars, Jupiter, Saturn, Uranus, Neptune, and Pluto. The diagrams at bottom show the orbits of the planets around the sun.

Mercury
Venus
Earth
Mars
Jupiter
Saturn
Uranus
Neptune
Pluto

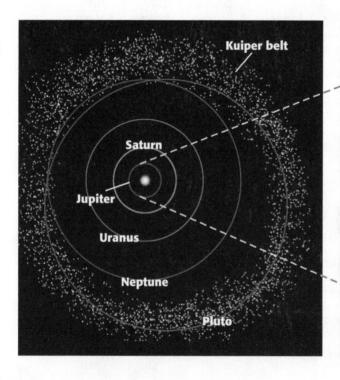

Kuiper belt
Saturn
Jupiter
Uranus
Neptune
Pluto

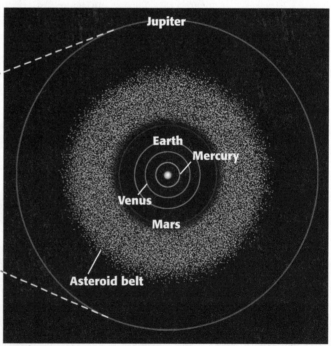

Jupiter
Earth
Mercury
Venus
Mars
Asteroid belt

Planetary Data

Planet	Distance from sun (AU)	Orbital period (Earth years)	Mean orbital speed (km/s)	Inclination of orbit to ecliptic (°)
Mercury	0.39	0.24	47.9	7.0
Venus	0.72	0.62	35.0	3.4
Earth	1.00	1.00	29.8	0.0
Mars	1.52	1.88	24.1	1.8
Jupiter	5.20	11.86	13.1	1.3
Saturn	9.54	29.46	9.6	2.5
Uranus	19.22	84.07	6.8	0.8
Neptune	30.06	164.82	5.4	1.8
Pluto	39.53	248.6	4.7	17.2

Planetary Data in Relation to Earth

Planet	Diameter	Mass	Surface gravity
Mercury	0.38	0.06	0.38
Venus	0.95	0.82	0.91
Earth	1.00	1.00	1.00
Mars	0.53	0.11	0.38
Jupiter	11.2	317.8	2.36
Saturn	9.41	94.3	1.07
Uranus	4.11	14.6	0.91
Neptune	3.81	17.2	1.14
Pluto	0.17	0.003	0.06

Data for the Sun

	Sun	Earth	Sun/Earth ratio
Mean diameter (km)	1,392,000	12,756	109
Mass (10^{24} kg)	1,989,100	5.9736	333,000
Surface gravity (m/s²)	274	9.8	28
Mean density (kg/m³)	1,408	5,515	0.255
Rotation period (h)	609.12	23.9345	25.4

Data for the Moon

	Moon	Earth	Moon/Earth ratio
Equatorial diameter (km)	3,476.2	12,756.2	0.2725
Mass (10^{24} kg)	0.07349	5.9736	0.0123
Surface gravity (m/s²)	1.70	9.8	0.165
Mean density (kg/m³)	3,350	5,515	0.607
Rotation period (h)	655.728	23.9345	27.4

Temperature Scales

Temperature can be expressed by using three scales: the Fahrenheit, Celsius, and Kelvin scales. The SI unit for temperature is the kelvin (K). Although 0 K is much colder than 0°C, a change of 1 K is equal to a change of 1°C.

Three Temperature Scales

Water boils — Fahrenheit 212° — Celsius 100° — Kelvin 373

Body temperature — 98.6° — 37° — 310

Room temperature — 68° — 20° — 293

Water freezes — 32° — 0° — 273

Temperature Conversion Table		
Conversion	Equation	Example
degrees Celsius to degrees Fahrenheit °C → °F	$°F = \left(\dfrac{9}{5} \times °C\right) + 32$	Convert 45°C to °F. $°F = \left(\dfrac{9}{5} \times 45°C\right) + 32 = 113°F$
degrees Fahrenheit to degrees Celsius °F → °C	$°C = \dfrac{5}{9} \times (°F - 32)$	Convert 68°F to °C. $°C = \dfrac{5}{9} \times (68°F - 32) = 20°C$
degrees Celsius to kelvins °C → K	$K = °C + 273$	Convert 45°C to K. $K = 45°C + 273 = 318\ K$
kelvins to degrees Celsius K → °C	$°C = K - 273$	Convert 32 K to °C. $°C = 32K - 273 = -241°C$

English and Spanish Glossary

with Academic Vocabulary

A

absolute magnitude (AB suh LOOT MAG nuh TOOD) the brightness that a star would have at a distance of 32.6 light-years from Earth (440)

magnitud absoluta el brillo que una estrella tendría a una distancia de 32.6 años luz de la Tierra (440)

acceleration (ak SEL uhr AY shuhn) the rate at which velocity changes over time; an object accelerates if its speed, direction, or both change (341)

aceleración la tasa a la que la velocidad cambia con el tiempo; un objeto acelera si su rapidez cambia, si su dirección cambia, o si tanto su rapidez como su dirección cambian (341)

*accuracy (AK yur uh see) the quality or state of being correct; free of error (5)

exactitud la cualidad o el estado de ser correcto; libre de errores (5)

*achieve (uh CHEEV) to do; to carry out (367)

lograr hacer; llevar a cabo (367)

acid (AS id) any compound that increases the number of hydronium ions when dissolved in water (286)

ácido cualquier compuesto que aumenta el número de iones de hidrógeno cuando se disuelve en agua (286)

alkali metal (AL kuh LIE MET uhl) one of the elements of Group 1 of the periodic table (lithium, sodium, potassium, rubidium, cesium, and francium) (202)

metal alcalino uno de los elementos del Grupo 1 de la tabla periódica (litio, sodio, potasio, rubidio, cesio y francio) (202)

alkaline-earth metal (AL kuh LIEN UHRTH MET uhl) one of the elements of Group 2 of the periodic table (beryllium, magnesium, calcium, strontium, barium, and radium) (203)

metal alcalinotérreo uno de los elementos del Grupo 2 de la tabla periódica (berilio, magnesio, calcio, estroncio, bario y radio) (203)

apparent magnitude (uh PER uhnt MAG nuh TOOD) the brightness of a star as seen from Earth (440)

magnitud aparente el brillo de una estrella como se percibe desde la Tierra (440)

*appropriate (uh PROH pree it) correct for the use; proper (39)

apropiado correcto para un determinado uso; adecuado (39)

Archimedes' principle (AHR kuh MEE DEEZ PRIN suh puhl) the principle that states that the buoyant force on an object in a fluid is an upward force equal to the weight of the volume of fluid that the object displaces (413)

principio de Arquímedes el principio que establece que la fuerza flotante de un objeto que está en un fluido es una fuerza ascendente cuya magnitud es igual al peso del volumen del fluido que el objeto desplaza (413)

*area (ER ee uh) a measure of the size of a surface or a region (39)

área una medida del tamaño de una superficie o región (39)

asteroid (AS tuhr OYD) a small, rocky object that orbits the sun; most asteroids are located in a band between the orbits of Mars and Jupiter (502)

asteroide un objeto pequeño y rocoso que se encuentra en órbita alrededor del Sol; la mayoría de los asteroides se ubican en una banda entre las órbitas de Marte y Júpiter (502)

* Academic Vocabulary

astronomical unit (AS truh NAHM i kuhl YOON it) the average distance between the Earth and the sun; approximately 150 million kilometers (symbol, AU) (478)

unidad astronómica la distancia promedio entre la Tierra y el Sol; aproximadamente 150 millones de kilómetros (símbolo: UA) (478)

atmospheric pressure (AT muhs FIR ik PRESH uhr) the pressure caused by the weight of the atmosphere (407)

presión atmosférica la presión producida por el peso de la atmósfera (407)

atom (AT uhm) the smallest unit of an element that maintains the properties of that element (164)

átomo la unidad más pequeña de un elemento que conserva las propiedades de ese elemento (164)

atomic mass (uh TAHM ik MAS) the mass of an atom expressed in atomic mass units (177)

masa atómica la masa de un átomo, expresada en unidades de masa atómica (177)

atomic mass unit (uh TAHM ik MAS YOON it) a unit of mass that describes the mass of an atom or molecule (173)

unidad de masa atómica una unidad de masa que describe la masa de un átomo o una molécula (173)

atomic number (uh TAHM ik NUHM buhr) the number of protons in the nucleus of an atom; the atomic number is the same for all atoms of an element (175)

número atómico el número de protones en el núcleo de un átomo; el número atómico es el mismo para todos los átomos de un elemento (175)

average speed (AV uhr ij SPEED) the total distance traveled divided by the total time taken (338)

rapidez promedio la distancia total recorrida dividida entre el tiempo total transcurrido (338)

axis (AK sis) one of two or more reference lines that mark the borders of a graph (52)

eje una de dos o más líneas de referencia que marcan los bordes de una gráfica (52)

B

base (BAYS) any compound that increases the number of hydroxide ions when dissolved in water (289)

base cualquier compuesto que aumenta el número de iones de hidróxido cuando se disuelve en agua (289)

big bang theory (BIG BANG THEE uh ree) the theory that all matter and energy in the universe was compressed into an extremely small volume that 13 billion to 15 billion years ago exploded and began expanding in all directions (455)

teoría del Big Bang la teoría que establece que toda la materia y la energía del universo estaban comprimidas en un volumen extremadamente pequeño que explotó hace aproximadamente 13 a 15 mil millones de años y empezó a expandirse en todas direcciones (455)

boiling (BOYL ing) the conversion of a liquid to a vapor when the vapor pressure of the liquid equals the atmospheric pressure (116)

ebullición la conversión de un líquido en vapor cuando la presión de vapor del líquido es igual a la presión atmosférica (116)

buoyant force (BOY uhnt FAWRS) the upward force that keeps an object immersed in or floating on a liquid (412)

fuerza boyante la fuerza ascendente que hace que un objeto se mantenga sumergido en un líquido o flotando en él (412)

Glossary

C

carbohydrate (KAHR boh HIE drayt) a class of energy-giving nutrients that includes sugars, starches, and fiber; contains carbon, hydrogen, and oxygen (314)

carbohidrato una clase de moléculas entre las que se incluyen azúcares, almidones y fibra; contiene carbono, hidrógeno y oxígeno (314)

change of state (CHAYNJ UHV STAYT) the change of a substance from one physical state to another (114)

cambio de estado el cambio de una sustancia de un estado físico a otro (114)

*chemical (KEM i kuhl) of or having to do with the properties or actions of substances (75, 107, 131, 223, 253)

químico perteneciente o relativo a las propiedades o acciones de las sustancias (75, 107, 131, 223, 253)

chemical bond (KEM i kuhl BAHND) an interaction that holds atoms or ions together (226, 282)

enlace químico una interacción que mantiene unidos los átomos o los iones (226, 282)

chemical bonding (KEM i kuhl BAHND ing) the combining of atoms to form molecules or ionic compounds (226)

formación de un enlace químico la combinación de átomos para formar moléculas o compuestos iónicos (226)

chemical change (KEM i kuhl CHAYNJ) a change that occurs when one or more substances change into entirely new substances with different properties (92)

cambio químico un cambio que ocurre cuando una o más sustancias se transforman en sustancias totalmente nuevas con propiedades diferentes (92)

chemical equation (KEM i kuhl ee KWAY zhuhn) a representation of a chemical reaction that uses symbols to show the relationship between the reactants and the products (264)

ecuación química una representación de una reacción química que usa símbolos para mostrar la relación entre los reactivos y los productos (264)

chemical formula (KEM i kuhl FAWR myoo luh) a combination of chemical symbols and numbers to represent a substance (262)

fórmula química una combinación de símbolos químicos y números que se usan para representar una sustancia (262)

chemical property (KEM i kuhl PRAHP uhr tee) a property of matter that describes a substance's ability to participate in chemical reactions (90)

propiedad química una propiedad de la materia que describe la capacidad de una sustancia de participar en reacciones químicas (90)

chemical reaction (KEM i kuhl ree AK shuhn) the process by which one or more substances change to produce one or more different substances (256)

reacción química el proceso por medio del cual una o más sustancias cambian para producir una o más sustancias distintas (256)

comet (KAHM it) a small body of ice, rock, and cosmic dust that follows an elliptical orbit around the sun and that gives off gas and dust in the form of a tail as it passes close to the sun (500)

cometa un cuerpo pequeño formado por hielo, roca y polvo cósmico que sigue una órbita elíptica alrededor del Sol y que libera gas y polvo, los cuales forman una cola al pasar cerca del Sol (500)

compound (KAHM POWND) a substance made up of atoms of two or more different elements joined by chemical bonds (138)

compuesto una sustancia formada por átomos de dos o más elementos diferentes unidos por enlaces químicos (138)

Glossary

concentration (KAHN suhn TRAY shuhn) the amount of a particular substance in a given quantity of a mixture, solution, or ore (146)

concentración la cantidad de una cierta sustancia en una cantidad determinada de mezcla, solución o mena (146)

condensation (KAHN duhn SAY shuhn) the change of state from a gas to a liquid (117)

condensación el cambio de estado de gas a líquido (117)

* **conduct** (kuhn DUHKT) to carry out; to do (5)

realizar llevar a cabo; hacer (5)

* **consist** (kuhn SIST) to be made up of (307)

consistir estar compuesto de (307)

* **constant** (KAHN stuhnt) a quantity whose value does not change (39)

constante una cantidad cuyo valor no cambia (39)

* **constituent** (kuhn STICH oo uhnt) serving as part of a whole (131, 223, 253, 279)

constitutivo que funciona como parte de un todo (131, 223, 253, 279)

* **construct** (kuhn STRUHKT) to build; to make from parts (39)

construir armar; hacer con partes (39)

* **correspond** (KAWR uh SPAHND) to match (191)

corresponder coincidir (191)

covalent bond (KOH vay luhnt BAHND) a bond formed when atoms share one or more pairs of electrons (236)

enlace covalente un enlace formado cuando los átomos comparten uno o más pares de electrones (236)

covalent compound (KOH vay luhnt KAHM POWND) a chemical compound that is formed by the sharing of electrons (284)

compuesto covalente un compuesto químico que se forma al compartir electrones (284)

crystal lattice (KRIS tuhl LAT is) the regular pattern in which a crystal is arranged (234)

red cristalina el patrón regular en el que un cristal está ordenado (234)

D

data (DAYT uh) any pieces of information acquired through observation or experimentation (18)

datos cualquier parte de la información que se adquiere por medio de la observación o experimentación (18)

* **define** (dee FIEN) to state or explain the meaning or properties of (333)

definir mencionar o explicar el significado o las propiedades de algo (333)

density (DEN suh tee) the ratio of the mass of a substance to the volume of the substance (44, 85)

densidad la relación entre la masa de una sustancia y su volumen (44, 85)

dependent variable (dee PEN duhnt VER ee uh buhl) in an experiment, the factor that changes as a result of manipulation of one or more other factors (the independent variables) (51)

variable dependiente en un experimento, el factor que cambia como resultado de la manipulación de uno o más factores (las variables independientes) (51)

* **displace** (dis PLAYS) to take the place of; to move aside (403)

desplazar tomar el lugar de; mover a un lado (403)

* Academic Vocabulary

E

eclipse (i KLIPS) an event in which the shadow of one celestial body falls on another (495)

eclipse un suceso en el que la sombra de un cuerpo celeste cubre otro cuerpo celeste (495)

electron (ee LEK TRAHN) a subatomic particle that has a negative charge (166)

electrón una partícula subatómica que tiene carga negativa (166)

electron cloud (ee LEK TRAHN KLOWD) a region around the nucleus of an atom where electrons are likely to be found (169)

nube de electrones una región que rodea al núcleo de un átomo en la cual es probable encontrar a los electrones (169)

element (EL uh muhnt) a substance that cannot be separated or broken down into simpler substances by chemical means (134)

elemento una sustancia que no se puede separar o descomponer en sustancias más simples por medio de métodos químicos (134)

endothermic reaction (EN doh THUHR mik ree AK shuhn) a chemical reaction that requires heat (260)

reacción endotérmica una reacción química que necesita calor (260)

*evaluate (ee VAL yoo AYT) to judge the worth of (5)

evaluar juzgar el valor de algo (5)

evaporation (ee VAP uh RAY shun) the change of state from a liquid to a gas (116)

evaporación el cambio de estado de líquido a gas (116)

exothermic reaction (EK soh THUHR mik ree AK shuhn) a chemical reaction in which heat is released to the surroundings (259)

reacción exotérmica una reacción química en la que se libera calor a los alrededores (259)

F

first aid (FUHRST AYD) emergency medical care for someone who has been hurt or who is sick (26)

primeros auxilios atención médica de emergencia para una persona que se lastimó o está enferma (26)

fluid (FLOO id) a nonsolid state of matter in which the atoms or molecules are free to move past each other, as in a gas or liquid (406)

fluido un estado no sólido de la materia en el que los átomos o moléculas tienen libertad de movimiento, como en el caso de un gas o un líquido (406)

force (FAWRS) a push or a pull exerted on an object in order to change the motion of the object; force has size and direction (344)

fuerza una acción de empuje o atracción que se ejerce sobre un objeto con el fin de cambiar su movimiento; la fuerza tiene magnitud y dirección (344)

free fall (FREE FAWL) the motion of a body when only the force of gravity is acting on the body (379)

caída libre el movimiento de un cuerpo cuando la única fuerza que actúa sobre él es la fuerza de gravedad (379)

friction (FRIK shuhn) a force that opposes motion between two surfaces that are in contact (350)

fricción una fuerza que se opone al movimiento entre dos superficies que están en contacto (350)

G

galaxy (GAL uhk see) a collection of stars, dust, and gas bound together by gravity (450)

galaxia un conjunto de estrellas, polvo y gas unidos por la gravedad (450)

gas (GAS) a form of matter that does not have a definite volume or shape (112)

gas un estado de la materia que no tiene volumen ni forma definidos (112)

gas giant (GAS JIE uhnt) a planet that has a deep, massive atmosphere, such as Jupiter, Saturn, Uranus, or Neptune (486)

gigante gaseoso un planeta con una atmósfera masiva y profunda, como por ejemplo, Júpiter, Saturno, Urano o Neptuno (486)

gravity (GRAV i tee) a force of attraction between objects that is due to their masses (370)

gravedad una fuerza de atracción entre dos objetos debido a sus masas (370)

group (GROOP) a vertical column of elements in the periodic table; elements in a group share chemical properties (200)

grupo una columna vertical de elementos de la tabla periódica; los elementos de un grupo comparten propiedades químicas (200)

H

halogen (HAL oh juhn) one of the elements of Group 17 of the periodic table (fluorine, chlorine, bromine, iodine, and astatine); halogens combine with most metals to form salts (206)

halógeno uno de los elementos del Grupo 17 de la tabla periódica (flúor, cloro, bromo, yodo y ástato); los halógenos se combinan con la mayoría de los metales para formar sales (206)

H-R diagram (AYCH AHR DIE uh GRAM) Hertzsprung-Russell diagram, a graph that shows the relationship between a star's surface temperature and absolute magnitude (446)

diagrama H-R diagrama de Hertzsprung-Russell; una gráfica que muestra la relación entre la temperatura de la superficie de una estrella y su magnitud absoluta (446)

hypothesis (hie PAHTH uh sis) a testable idea or explanation that leads to scientific investigation (16)

hipótesis una idea o explicación que conlleva a la investigación científica y que se puede probar (16)

I

*identify (ie DEN tuh FIE) to point out or pick out (191, 223, 253, 367)

identificar señalar o elegir (191, 223, 253, 367)

independent variable (IN dee PEN duhnt VER ee uh buhl) in an experiment, the factor that is deliberately manipulated (51)

variable independiente el factor que se manipula deliberadamente en un experimento (51)

indicator (IN di KAYT uhr) a compound that can reversibly change color depending on conditions such as pH (287)

indicador un compuesto que puede cambiar de color de forma reversible dependiendo de condiciones tales como el pH (287)

inertia (in UHR shuh) the tendency of an object to resist being moved or, if the object is moving, to resist a change in speed or direction until an outside force acts on the object (386)

inercia la tendencia de un objeto a no moverse o, si el objeto se está moviendo, la tendencia a resistir un cambio en su rapidez o dirección hasta que una fuerza externa actúe en el objeto (386)

*interact (IN tuhr AKT) to act upon one another (75, 131, 223, 253)

interactuar influirse mutuamente (75, 131, 223, 253)

*interpret (in TUHR pruht) to figure out the meaning of (39, 333)

interpretar entender el significado (39, 333)

*investigation (in VES tuh GAY shuhn) a detailed search for answers (5)

investigación búsqueda cuidadosa de respuestas (5)

*involve (in VAHLV) to have as a part of (333)

consistir tener como parte (333)

*Academic Vocabulary

Glossary

ion (IE AHN) a charged particle that forms when an atom or group of atoms gains or loses one or more electrons (230)

ion una partícula cargada que se forma cuando un átomo o grupo de átomos gana o pierde uno o más electrones (230)

ionic bond (ie AHN ik BAHND) the attractive force between oppositely charged ions, which form when electrons are transferred from one atom to another (230)

enlace iónico la fuerza de atracción entre iones con cargas opuestas, que se forman cuando se transfieren electrones de un átomo a otro (230)

ionic compound (ie AHN ik KAHM POWND) a compound made of oppositely charged ions (282)

compuesto iónico un compuesto formado por iones con cargas opuestas (282)

isotope (IE suh TOHP) an atom that has the same number of protons (or the same atomic number) as other atoms of the same element do but that has a different number of neutrons (and thus a different atomic mass) (175)

isótopo un átomo que tiene el mismo número de protones (o el mismo número atómico) que otros átomos del mismo elemento, pero que tiene un número diferente de neutrones (y, por lo tanto, otra masa atómica) (175)

L

law (LAW) a descriptive statement or equation that reliably predicts events under certain conditions (48)

ley una ecuación o afirmación descriptiva que predice sucesos de manera confiable en determinadas condiciones (48)

law of conservation of energy (LAW UHV KAHN suhr VAY shuhn UHV EN uhr jee) the law that states that energy cannot be created or destroyed but can be changed from one form to another (261)

ley de la conservación de la energía la ley que establece que la energía ni se crea ni se destruye, sólo se transforma de una forma a otra (261)

law of conservation of mass (LAW UHV KAHN suhr VAY shuhn UHV MAS) the law that states that mass cannot be created or destroyed in ordinary chemical and physical changes (265)

ley de la conservación de la masa la ley que establece que la masa no se crea ni se destruye por cambios químicos o físicos comunes (265)

***liberate** (LIB uhr AYT) to release; to set free (75, 253)

liberar soltar; poner en libertad (75, 253)

light-year (LIET YIR) the distance that light travels in one year; about 9.46 trillion kilometers (441)

año luz la distancia que viaja la luz en un año; aproximadamente 9.46 trillones de kilómetros (441)

lipid (LIP id) a fat molecule or a molecule that has similar properties; examples include oils, waxes, and steroids (315)

lípido una molécula de grasa o una molécula que tiene propiedades similares; algunos ejemplos son los aceites, las ceras y los esteroides (315)

liquid (LIK wid) the state of matter that has a definite volume but not a definite shape (111)

líquido el estado de la materia que tiene un volumen definido, pero no una forma definida (111)

M

main sequence (MAYN SEE kwuhns) the location on the H-R diagram where most stars lie; it has a diagonal pattern from the lower right (low temperature and luminosity) to the upper left (high temperature and luminosity) (445)

secuencia principal la ubicación en el diagrama H-R donde se encuentran la mayoría de las estrellas; tiene un patrón diagonal de la parte inferior derecha (baja temperatura y luminosidad) a la parte superior izquierda (alta temperatura y luminosidad) (445)

Glossary

*maintain (mayn TAYN) to keep the same (433, 469)

mantener conservar igual (433, 469)

mass (MAS) a measure of the amount of matter in an object (43, 82, 374)

masa una medida de la cantidad de materia que tiene un objeto (43, 82, 374)

mass number (MAS NUHM buhr) the sum of the numbers of protons and neutrons in the nucleus of an atom (176)

número de masa la suma de los números de protones y neutrones que hay en el núcleo de un átomo (176)

matter (MAT uhr) anything that has mass and takes up space (78)

materia cualquier cosa que tiene masa y ocupa un lugar en el espacio (78)

mean (MEEN) the number obtained by adding up the data for a given characteristic and dividing this sum by the number of individuals (58)

media el número que se obtiene sumando los datos de una característica dada y dividiendo esa suma entre el número de individuos (58)

median (MEE dee uhn) the value of the middle item when data are arranged in order by size (58)

mediana el valor del elemento del medio cuando los datos se ordenan por tamaño (58)

melting (MEHLT ing) the change of state in which a solid becomes a liquid by adding heat (115)

fusión el cambio de estado en el que un sólido se convierte en líquido al añadirse calor (115)

meniscus (muh NIS kuhs) the curve at a liquid's surface by which one measures the volume of the liquid (79)

menisco la curva que se forma en la superficie de un líquido, la cual sirve para medir el volumen de un líquido (79)

metal (MET uhl) an element that is shiny and that conducts heat and electricity well (136)

metal un elemento que es brillante y conduce bien el calor y la electricidad (136)

metallic bond (muh TAL ik BAHND) a bond formed by the attraction between positively charged metal ions and the electrons around them (239)

enlace metálico un enlace formado por la atracción entre iones metálicos cargados positivamente y los electrones que los rodean (239)

metalloid (MET uh LOYD) an element that has properties of both metals and nonmetals (136)

metaloide un elemento que tiene propiedades tanto de metales como de no metales (136)

meteor (MEET ee uhr) a bright streak of light that results when a meteoroid burns up in Earth's atmosphere (503)

meteoro un rayo de luz brillante que se produce cuando un meteoroide se quema en la atmósfera de la Tierra (503)

meteorite (MEET ee uhr IET) a meteoroid that reaches Earth's surface without burning up completely (503)

meteorito un meteoroide que llega a la superficie de la Tierra sin quemarse por completo (503)

meteoroid (MEET ee uhr OYD) a relatively small, rocky body that travels through space (503)

meteoroide un cuerpo rocoso relativamente pequeño que viaja en el espacio (503)

mixture (MIKS chuhr) a combination of two or more substances that are not chemically combined (142)

mezcla una combinación de dos o más sustancias que no están combinadas químicamente (142)

*Academic Vocabulary

mode (MOHD) the most frequently occurring value in a data set (58)

moda el valor que se repite con más frecuencia en un conjunto de datos (58)

model (MAHD'l) a pattern, plan, representation, or description designed to show the structure or workings of an object, system, or concept (45)

modelo un diseño, plan, representación o descripción cuyo objetivo es mostrar la estructura o funcionamiento de un objeto, sistema o concepto (45)

molecule (MAHL i KYOOL) a group of atoms that are held together by chemical forces; a molecule is the smallest unit of matter that can exist by itself and retain all of a substance's chemical properties (237)

molécula un conjunto de átomos que se mantienen unidos por acción de las fuerzas químicas; una molécula es la unidad más pequeña de la materia capaz de existir en forma independiente y conservar todas las propiedades químicas de una sustancia (237)

motion (MOH shuhn) an object's change in position relative to a reference point (336)

movimiento el cambio en la posición de un objeto respecto a un punto de referencia (336)

N

nebula (NEB yu luh) a large cloud of gas and dust in interstellar space; a region in space where stars are born (452, 472)

nebulosa una nube grande de gas y polvo en el espacio interestelar; una región en el espacio donde las estrellas nacen (452, 472)

net force (NET FAWRS) the combination of all of the forces acting on an object (345)

fuerza neta la combinación de todas las fuerzas que actúan sobre un objeto (345)

*neutral (NOO truhl) being neither acidic nor basic (279)

neutro que no es ácido ni básico (279)

neutralization reaction (noo truhl i ZAY shuhn ree AK shuhn) the reaction of an acid and a base to form a neutral solution of water and a salt (293)

reacción de neutralización la reacción de un ácido y una base que forma una solución neutra de agua y una sal (293)

neutron (NOO TRAHN) a subatomic particle that has no charge and that is located in the nucleus of an atom (173)

neutrón una partícula subatómica que no tiene carga y que está ubicada en el núcleo de un átomo (173)

newton (NOOT uhn) the SI unit for force (symbol, N) (344)

newton la unidad de fuerza del sistema internacional de unidades (símbolo: N) (344)

noble gas (NOH buhl GAS) one of the elements of Group 18 of the periodic table (helium, neon, argon, krypton, xenon, and radon); noble gases are unreactive (207)

gas noble uno de los elementos del Grupo 18 de la tabla periódica (helio, neón, argón, criptón, xenón y radón); los gases nobles son no reactivos (207)

nonmetal (NAHN met uhl) an element that conducts heat and electricity poorly (136)

no metal un elemento que es mal conductor del calor y la electricidad (136)

nucleic acid (noo KLEE ik AS id) a molecule made up of subunits called *nucleotides* (317)

ácido nucleico una molécula formada por subunidades llamadas *nucleótidos* (317)

nucleus (NOO klee uhs) in physical science, an atom's central region, which is made up of protons and neutrons (168)

núcleo en ciencias físicas, la región central de un átomo, la cual está constituida por protones y neutrones (168)

Glossary

O

observation (ahb zuhr VAY shuhn) the process of obtaining information by using the senses (15)

observación el proceso de obtener información por medio de los sentidos (15)

organic compound (awr GAN ik KAHM POWND) a covalently bonded compound that contains carbon (311)

compuesto orgánico un compuesto enlazado de manera covalente que contiene carbono (311)

P

parallax (PAR uh LAKS) an apparent shift in the position of an object when viewed from different locations (441)

paralaje un cambio aparente en la posición de un objeto cuando se ve desde lugares distintos (441)

*parameter (puh RAM uht uhr) any factor that sets the limit of a possible value (5)

parámetro cualquier factor que fija el límite de un valor posible (5)

pascal (pas KAL) the SI unit of pressure (symbol, Pa) (406)

pascal la unidad de presión del sistema internacional de unidades (símbolo: Pa) (406)

period (PIR ee uhd) in chemistry, a horizontal row of elements in the periodic table (200)

período en química, una hilera horizontal de elementos en la tabla periódica (200)

periodic (PIR ee AHD ik) describes something that occurs or repeats at regular intervals (195)

periódico término que describe algo que ocurre o que se repite a intervalos regulares (195)

periodic law (PIR ee AHD ik LAW) the law that states that the repeating chemical and physical properties of elements change periodically with the atomic numbers of the elements (200)

ley periódica la ley que establece que las propiedades químicas y físicas repetitivas de un elemento cambian periódicamente en función del número atómico de los elementos (200)

pH (PEE AYCH) a value that is used to express the acidity or basicity (alkalinity) of a system (293)

pH un valor que expresa la acidez o la basicidad (alcalinidad) de un sistema (293)

phase (FAYZ) the change in the sunlit area of one celestial body as seen from another celestial body (494)

fase el cambio en el área iluminada de un cuerpo celeste según se ve desde otro cuerpo celeste (494)

*physical (FIZ i kuhl) of or having to do with matter or the body (75, 107)

físico perteneciente o relativo a la materia o el cuerpo (75, 107)

physical change (FIZ i kuhl CHAYNJ) a change of matter from one form to another without a change in chemical properties (88)

cambio físico un cambio de materia de una forma a otra sin que ocurra un cambio en sus propiedades químicas (88)

physical property (FIZ i kuhl PRAHP uhr tee) a characteristic of a substance that does not involve a chemical change, such as density, color, or hardness (84)

propiedad física una característica de una sustancia que no implica un cambio químico, tal como la densidad, el color o la dureza (84)

plasma (PLAZ muh) in physical science, a state of matter that starts as a gas and then becomes ionized; it consists of free-moving ions and electrons, it takes on an electric charge, and its properties differ from the properties of a solid, liquid, or gas (113)

plasma en ciencias físicas, un estado de la materia que comienza como un gas y luego se vuelve ionizado; está formado por iones y electrones que se mueven libremente, tiene carga eléctrica y sus propiedades difieren de las propiedades de un sólido, líquido o gas (113)

precipitate (pree SIP uh tit) a solid that is produced as a result of a chemical reaction in solution (257)

precipitado un sólido que se produce como resultado de una reacción química en una solución (257)

* **predict** (pree DIKT) to say ahead of time (403)

predecir saber antes de que ocurra (403)

pressure (PRESH uhr) the amount of force exerted per unit area of a surface (406)

presión la cantidad de fuerza ejercida en una superficie por unidad de área (406)

* **principle** (PRIN suh puhl) basic law, rule, or belief (39)

principio ley, regla o creencia básica (39)

* **process** (PRAH ses) a set of steps, events, or changes (75, 107)

proceso una serie de pasos, sucesos o cambios (75, 107)

product (PRAHD uhkt) a substance that forms in a chemical reaction (264)

producto una sustancia que se forma en una reacción química (264)

prograde rotation (PROH GRAYD roh TAY shuhn) the counterclockwise spin of a planet or moon as seen from above the planet's North Pole; rotation in the same direction as the sun's rotation (481)

rotación progresiva el giro en contra de las manecillas del reloj de un planeta o de una luna según lo veía un observador ubicado encima del Polo Norte del planeta; rotación en la misma dirección que la rotación del Sol (481)

projectile motion (proh JEK tuhl MOH shuhn) the curved path that an object follows when thrown, launched, or otherwise projected near the surface of Earth (380)

movimiento proyectil la trayectoria curva que sigue un objeto cuando es aventado, lanzado o proyectado de cualquier otra manera cerca de la superficie de la Tierra (380)

protein (PROH TEEN) a molecule that is made up of amino acids and that is needed to build and repair body structures and to regulate processes in the body (315)

proteína una molécula formada por aminoácidos que es necesaria para construir y reparar estructuras corporales y para regular procesos del cuerpo (315)

proton (PROH TAHN) a subatomic particle that has a positive charge and that is located in the nucleus of an atom; the number of protons in the nucleus is the atomic number, which determines the identity of an element (173)

protón una partícula subatómica que tiene una carga positiva y que está ubicada en el núcleo de un átomo; el número de protones que hay en el núcleo es el número atómico, y éste determina la identidad del elemento (173)

pure substance (PYOOR SUHB stuhns) a sample of matter, either a single element or a single compound, that has definite chemical and physical properties (134)

sustancia pura una muestra de materia, ya sea un solo elemento o un solo compuesto, que tiene propiedades químicas y físicas definidas (134)

R

reactant (ree AK tuhnt) a substance or molecule that participates in a chemical reaction (264)

reactivo una sustancia o molécula que participa en una reacción química (264)

*reaction (ree AK shuhn) a response or change (75, 107, 253)

reacción una respuesta o un cambio (75, 107, 253)

*region (REE juhn) an area (191)

región área (191)

retrograde rotation (RE truh GRAYD roh TAY shuhn) the clockwise spin of a planet or moon as seen from above the planet's North Pole (481)

rotación retrógrada el giro en el sentido de las manecillas del reloj de un planeta o de una luna según lo vería un observador ubicado encima del Polo Norte del planeta (481)

*role (ROHL) a part or function; purpose (307, 433, 469)

papel parte o función; propósito (307, 433, 469)

S

salt (SAWLT) an ionic compound that forms when a metal atom replaces the hydrogen of an acid (295)

sal un compuesto iónico que se forma cuando un átomo de un metal reemplaza el hidrógeno de un ácido (295)

satellite (SAT uhl IET) a natural or artificial body that revolves around a planet (492)

satélite un cuerpo natural o artificial que gira alrededor de un planeta (492)

science (SIE uhns) the knowledge obtained by observing natural events and conditions in order to discover facts and formulate laws or principles that can be verified or tested (8)

ciencia el conocimiento que se obtiene por medio de la observación natural de acontecimientos y condiciones con el fin de descubrir hechos y formular leyes o principios que puedan ser verificados o probados (8)

scientific methods (SIE uhn TIF ik METH uhdz) a series of steps followed to solve problems (14)

métodos científicos una serie de pasos que se siguen para solucionar problemas (14)

slope (SLOHP) a measure of the slant of a line; the ratio of rise over run (59)

pendiente una medida de la inclinación de una línea; la relación entre la elevación y la distancia (59)

solar nebula (SOH luhr NEB yu luh) a rotating cloud of gas and dust from which the sun and planets formed (473)

nebulosa solar una nube de gas y polvo en rotación a partir de la cual se formaron el Sol y los planetas (473)

solid (SAHL id) the state of matter in which the volume and shape of a substance are fixed (111)

sólido el estado de la materia en el cual el volumen y la forma de una sustancia están fijos (111)

solubility (SAHL yoo BIL uh tee) the ability of one substance to dissolve in another at a given temperature and pressure (146)

solubilidad la capacidad de una sustancia de disolverse en otra a una temperatura y una presión dadas (146)

solute (SAHL YOOT) in a solution, the substance that dissolves in the solvent (144)

soluto en una solución, la sustancia que se disuelve en el solvente (144)

solution (suh LOO shuhn) a homogeneous mixture throughout which two or more substances are uniformly dispersed (144)

solución una mezcla homogénea en la cual dos o más sustancias se dispersan de manera uniforme (144)

solvent (SAHL vuhnt) in a solution, the substance in which the solute dissolves (144)

solvente en una solución, la sustancia en la que se disuelve el soluto (144)

*source (SAWRS) the thing from which something else comes (433, 469)

fuente el lugar de donde viene una cosa (433, 469)

*specific (spuh SIF ik) unique; peculiar to or characteristic of; exact (161, 191)

específico singular; peculiar o característico; exacto (161, 191)

*specify (SPES uh FIE) to state or tell clearly (333)

especificar expresar o decir claramente (333)

spectrum (SPEK truhm) the band of colors produced when white light passes through a prism (437)

espectro la banda de colores que se produce cuando la luz blanca pasa a través de un prisma (437)

states of matter (STAYTS UHV MAT uhr) the physical forms of matter, which include solid, liquid, and gas (110)

estados de la materia las formas físicas de la materia, que son sólida, líquida y gaseosa (110)

*structure (STRUHK chuhr) the arrangement of the parts of a whole (161, 223); a whole that is built or put together from parts (223, 279, 307)

estructura la forma en que se distribuyen las partes de un todo (161, 223); un todo que se construye o se arma con partes (223, 279, 307)

sublimation (SUHB luh MAY shuhn) the process in which a solid changes directly into a gas (118)

sublimación el proceso por medio del cual un sólido se transforma directamente en un gas (118)

supernova (SOO puhr NOH vuh) a gigantic explosion in which a massive star collapses and throws its outer layers into space (448)

supernova una explosión gigantesca en la que una estrella masiva se colapsa y lanza sus capas externas hacia el espacio (448)

T

temperature (TEM puhr uh chuhr) a measure of how hot (or cold) something is; specifically, a measure of the average kinetic energy of the particles in an object (45)

temperatura una medida de qué tan caliente (o frío) está algo; específicamente, una medida de la energía cinética promedio de las partículas de un objeto (45)

*tension (TEN shuhn) stress that happens when forces act to stretch an object (367)

tensión estrés que se produce cuando distintas fuerzas actúan para estirar un objeto (367)

terminal velocity (TUHR muh nuhl vuh LAHS uh tee) the constant velocity of a falling object when the force of air resistance is equal in magnitude and opposite in direction to the force of gravity (378)

velocidad terminal la velocidad constante de un objeto en caída cuando la fuerza de resistencia del aire es igual en magnitud y opuesta en dirección a la fuerza de gravedad (378)

terrestrial planet (tuh RES tree uhl PLAN it) one of the highly dense planets nearest to the sun; Mercury, Venus, Mars, and Earth (480)

planeta terrestre uno de los planetas muy densos que se encuentran más cerca del Sol; Mercurio, Venus, Marte y la Tierra (480)

theory (THEE uh ree) a system of ideas that explains many related observations and is supported by a large body of evidence acquired through scientific investigation (48)

teoría un sistema de ideas que explica muchas observaciones relacionadas y que está respaldado por una gran cantidad de pruebas obtenidas mediante la investigación científica (48)

Glossary

V

valence electron (VAY luhns ee LEK TRAHN) an electron that is found in the outermost shell of an atom and that determines the atom's chemical properties (227)

electrón de valencia un electrón que se encuentra en el orbital más externo de un átomo y que determina las propiedades químicas del átomo (227)

*variable (VER ee uh buhl) a factor that changes in an experiment in order to test a hypothesis (5, 39)

variable factor que se cambia en un experimento para poner a prueba una hipótesis (5, 39)

*vary (VER ee) to differ; to have more than one possible state (333)

variar ser distinto; tener más de un estado posible (333)

velocity (vuh LAHS uh tee) the speed of an object in a particular direction (340)

velocidad la rapidez de un objeto en una dirección dada (340)

volume (VAHL yoom) a measure of the size of a body or region in three-dimensional space (44, 78)

volumen una medida del tamaño de un cuerpo o región en un espacio de tres dimensiones (44, 78)

W

weight (WAYT) a measure of the gravitational force exerted on an object; its value can change with the location of the object in the universe (82, 374)

peso una medida de la fuerza gravitacional ejercida sobre un objeto; su valor puede cambiar en función de la ubicación del objeto en el universo (82, 374)

Glossary

*Academic Vocabulary

Index

Boldface page numbers refer to illustrative material, such as figures, tables, margin elements, photographs, and illustrations.

A

absolute magnitude, 440, 446–447, **446–447**
absorption lines, 437–438, **437, 438**
acceleration, 341–342
    in circular motion, 341, **341**
    definition of, 341, **341**
    detecting, 356–357
    equation for, 546
    forces and, 344
    on graphs of speed vs. time, 342, **342**
    due to gravity, 377, **377**
    inertia and, 386, **386**, 392–393
    mass and, 387, **387**
    in Newton's second law of motion, 387–388, **387, 388**
    terminal velocity and, 378
accelerometers, 356–357
accident procedures, 26–27, **27**
accuracy
    in chemical equations, 265
    of data measurements, 19, 44, 57, 64, 79
    data reproducibility and, 19, 57, 64
acetic acid, 288, 292
acetylene (ethyne), 311, **311**
acid rain, pH of, 294
acids. *See also under names of individual acids*
    antacids and, 292, **292**, 293
    hydronium ions from, 286, 292
    indicators for, 287, **287**, 293–294
    neutralization reactions, 293
    pH scale, 293, **293**, 542
    properties of, 286–288, **286, 287, 288**
    reaction with metals, 287, **287**
    strength of, 292
    uses of, 288, **288**
actinides, 204, 217
action and reaction force pairs, 389–390, **389, 390**
age of the universe, 456
AIDS/HIV research, 329

air pressure, 406–407, **406**
air resistance, 378–379, **378, 379**
alchemists, 218
alkali metals, 202, **202**
alkaline-earth metals, 203, **203**
alloys, 145
aluminum
    foil, 170, **170**
    ions, 231, **231**
    properties of, 204
    scanning tunneling electron micrograph of, 164, **164**
aluminum hydroxide, 291
amino acids, 315, 317
ammonia, 291, 486
amu (atomic mass unit), 173
Andromeda galaxy, 450, **450**
annular eclipses, 495
antacids, 292, **292**, 293
Antares, 445, **445, 447**
Apollo missions, **370, 482,** 492
apparent magnitude, 440, **440**
Arcata to Ferndale Kinetic Sculpture Race, 365
Archimedes, 104
Archimedes' principle, 413–414, 545
area, formula of, 80
argon, 207
Aristotle, 376
arrows, in chemical equations, **264**
arson investigators, 277, **277**
artists, nature, 129, **129**
ascorbic acid (vitamin C), 288
asteroid belt, 502
asteroids
    composition of, 502, **502**
    moons captured from, 496, 497
    near-Earth, 503
astronomers, 467, **467**
astronomical unit (AU), 478, **478**
astronomy, light pollution and, 514
atmosphere
    on Jupiter, 486
    on Mars, 483
    on Mercury, 480
    on Titan, 497, **497**
    on Venus, 481
atmospheric pressure, 117, 407–408, **407, 408**
atomic mass, 177
atomic mass unit (amu), 173
atomic number, 175, 200, **200,** 227, 541

atomic structure, 168–169, **169,** 172–175, **172, 174,** 541
atomic theory, 164–170
    ancient Greek, 164
    atom sizes, 170, **170**
    Dalton's, 165, **165**
    electron energy levels in, 169, **169**
    Rutherford's discovery of the nucleus, 167–168, **167, 168**
    Thomson's discovery of electrons, 166, **166**
atoms, 162–189, 541
    in a bubble chamber, **162–163**
    building models of, 177, 228
    changes of state and, 114–118, **116, 119**
    Dalton's atomic theory, 165, **165**
    definition of, 164
    Democritus's thoughts on, 164
    electron-dot diagrams of, **237**
    electron energy levels in, 169, **169,** 227–229, **227, 229**
    of elements, 134
    forces in, 178, **178**
    isotopes, 175–177, **175, 176**
    magnetic atomic models, 177
    mass number of, 176–177, **176**
    observing, 170, **170**
    parts of, 172–173, **172**
    Rutherford's discovery of the nucleus, 167–168, **167, 168**
    size of, 170, **170**
    states of matter and, 110–113, **110, 112**
    Thomson's discovery of electrons, 166, **166**
    valence electrons in, 227–228, **227, 228**
AU (astronomical unit), 478, **478**
average speed, 338–339, **338,** 546
axes (singular, *axis*), 52, **52**
axis of rotation, 488, **488**
    of Uranus, 488, **488**

B

bacteria, on plant roots, 141, **141**
baking cakes, 93, **93**
baking powder, **256**
baking soda, **289**

Index

balanced forces
   examples of, **347**
   net force and, 345–346, **345, 346**
   Newton's first law of motion and, 384
   no motion from, 347, **347**
   static friction from, 353, **353**
   weight and buoyant forces, 414, **414**
balancing equations, 265–266, **266**
ballast tanks, 418, **418**
ball bearings, 354
bar graphs, **19,** 539
Barringer Meteorite Crater (Arizona), 503, **503**
bases
   in antacids, 291
   examples of, **289**
   indicators for, 290, **290,** 293–294
   neutralization reactions, 293
   pH scale, 293, **293,** 542
   properties of, 289–290
   strong vs. weak, 293
   uses of, 291, **291**
batteries, 92, 288
Betelgeuse, 436, **436, 447,** 459
Bernoulli's principle, 545
big bang theory, 46, 454–455, **454**
Big Dipper constellation, 439, **439, 442**
biochemistry, 308–329
   carbohydrates, 141, 314, **314**
   carbon bonds, 310–311, **310, 311**
   enzymes, 320–321
   labs on, 312, 316, 320–321
   lipids, 315, **315**
   nucleic acids, 317, **317**
   other elements in, 312–313, **312, 313**
   proteins, 315–316, **316**
   salt in, 319, **319**
bitterness, of bases, 289
black holes, 449, 453, 466
bleach, 289
blue stars, **446,** 452, 466, **466**
boat propulsion, 15–20, **17, 19, 20**
Bohr, Niels, 169
boiling, 116–117, **116,** 118, 119
boiling point, 116–118, **116, 119**
booklet instructions (FoldNote), 518, **518**
boron group elements, 204
Boyle's law, 544
branched-chain molecules, **310**

brass, 145
breathing, pressure differences and, 410, **410**
bridge design, 400, **400**
brightness, of stars, 439–440, **439, 440,** 446–447, **446–447**
brittleness, of ionic compounds, 282
bromine, **206**
bromthymol blue, 287, **287,** 290, **290**
bubble chambers, **162–163**
bubbles, pressure and, 407
buckyballs, 216, **216**
buoyancy, 412–418
   buoyant force, 412–414, **412, 413, 414**
   changing overall density, 417–418, **417, 418**
   density and, 86, **86,** 405, 415, **415**
   labs on, 410, 413, 416, 417, 420–421
   in scuba diving, 429
   weight and, 414, **414**
buoyant force
   definition of, 412
   determining, 413, **413**
   fluid pressure and, 412, **412**
   lab on, 420–421
   weight and, 414, **414**
buoying up, 414, **414**
burns, 27, **27**

C

cabbage, pH indicators in, 296–297
calcium carbonate, **280–281**
calcium hydroxide, 291, 293
calcium sulfate, 295
California
   Arcata to Ferndale Kinetic Sculpture Race, 365
   fireworks in, 156, **156**
   gold in, 192, **192–193**
   hot springs in, 304, **304**
   Lick Observatory, 514
   Light Gas Gun Chamber, NASA Ames Research Center, **40–41**
   Mono Lake, **280–281**
   Sea Lions, 308, **308–309**
   Stanford Linear Acceleration Center, 104
   University of Southern California Plasma Accelerator Lab, 128, **128**

Californium, 188, **188**
Callisto (moon of Jupiter), 497
car batteries, 288
carbohydrates, 141, 314, **314**
carbon
   in asteroids, 502
   atoms of, **170,** 174
   backbones, 310, **310**
   chemical bonding of, 310–311, **310, 311**
   in living organisms, 310–313, **310, 311, 312, 313**
   in meteorites, 504
   in molecules, 239, **239**
   properties of, 205, **205**
carbon backbones, 310, **310**
carbon dioxide
   as dry ice, 118, **118**
   on Mars, 484
   properties of, **265**
   on Venus, 481
carbon group elements, 205, **205**
carbonic acid, 288, 292
carbon monoxide, **265**
careers
   arson investigators, 277, **277**
   astronomers, 467, **467**
   ecologists, 12, **12**
   electronics engineers, 37, **37**
   experimental physicists, 189, **189**
   forensic scientists, 305, **305**
   gemologists, 105, **105**
   geochemists, 12, **12**
   jewelry designers, 105, **105**
   kinetic sculptors, 365, **365**
   metallurgists, 157, **157**
   meteorologists, 11, **11**
   molecular biologists, 329, **329**
   nature artists, 129, **129**
   oceanographers, 71, **71**
   planetary geologists, 515, **515**
   roller coaster designers, 401, **401**
   science illustrators, 13, **13**
   scuba instructors, 429, **429**
   volcanologists, 12, **12**
   wastewater managers, 251, **251**
Cascade Mountains, 304, **304**
Cassini spacecraft, 470–471, 487
cathode-ray tube experiment, 166, **166**
cause-and-effect map instructions (Graphic Organizer), 252, 333, 522, **522**
cellulose, 314, **314**
Celsius temperature scale, **43,** 45, **45**

Index

centrifuges, **143**
centripetal acceleration, 341, **341**
centripetal force, 382, **382**
CFCs (chlorofluorocarbons), 11
changes of state, 114–119
    condensation, 117, **117**
    definition of, 114
    energy and, 114, **114**
    evaporation, 116–117, **116, 143**
    freezing, 115, **115**
    melting, 115, **115**, 118, **119**
    sublimation, 118, **118**
    temperature and, 115–118, **118, 119**, 120–121
characteristic properties, 91, 135
charges
    of ions, 173, 230–232, **231, 232**
    of protons and electrons, 173, **178**
Charles's law, 544
Charon (moon of Pluto), 490, **490**, 498
chemical bond, definition of, 226, 258. *See also* chemical bonding
chemical bonding, 224–251
    of carbon atoms, 310–311, **310, 311**
    in chemical reactions, 258–259, **258**
    covalent bonds, 236–239, **236, 237, 238, 239**
    covalent compounds, 263, **263**, 284–285, **285**
    definition of, 226
    double bonds, 243, 311, **311**
    electron-dot diagrams, 237
    energy level filling in, 228–229, **229**
    ionic bonds, 230–232, **231, 232**
    ionic compounds, 233–235, **233, 234, 235**
    labs on, 225, 228, 234, 238, 242–243
    metallic bonds, 239–240, **240, 241**
    role of electrons in, 226–229, **227, 228, 229**, 240
chemical burns, 27, **27**
chemical changes, 92–95, **92, 93, 94**, 140
chemical compounds, 138–141, 280–305
    acids, properties of, 286–288, **286, 287, 288**
    acid strength, 292
    bases, properties of, 289–291, **289, 290, 291**

base strength, 293
breaking down, 140, **140**
classifying, 284
covalent compounds, 263, **263**, 284–285, **285**
definition of compound, 138
elements in, 138, **138**
flame tests of, 148–149
in industry, 140
ionic compounds, 233–235, **233, 234, 235**, 282–283
labs on, 139, 148–149, 284, 290
mixtures compared with, **144**
in nature, 141, **141**
neutralization reactions, 293
organic, 311, **311** (*see also* organic molecules)
pH scale, 293, **293**
properties of, 139–140, **139**, 282–285, **282, 283, 284, 285**
solutions of acids and bases, 292–295, **293, 294**
specific ratios of elements in, 140
chemical energy, 259–260, **259, 260**
chemical equations, 262–267, 542
    balancing, 265–266, **266**
    chemical formulas in, 262–263, **262, 263**
    definition of, 264
    describing reactions with, 264, **264**
chemical formulas, 262–263, **262, 263**
    model, 255
chemical names, **263**
chemical properties, 90–95
    chemical changes, 92–95, **92, 93, 94**
    definition of, 90
    labs on, 94, 96–97
    physical properties compared to, 91, **91**
chemical reactions, 254–277
    chemical bonding in, 258–259, **258, 259**
    compounds from, 138
    definition of, 256
    endothermic, 260, **260**
    energy and, 259–260
    examples of, **256**
    exothermic, 259, **259**
    labs on, 259, 260, 267, 268–269
    law of conservation of energy and, 261
    modeling, 255
    neutralization reactions, 293

signs of, 257–258, **257, 258**
synthesis reactions, 268–269
chemical symbols, 199
chemistry of living things, 308–329
    carbohydrates, 314, **314**
    carbon bonds, 310–311, **310, 311**
    elements other than carbon in the, 312–313, **312, 313**
    enzymes, 320–321
    labs on, 312, 316, 320–321
    lipids, 315, **315**
    nucleic acids, 317, **317**
    proteins, 315–316, **316**
Chicxulub impact crater (Mexico), 515
Chihuly, Dale, **108–109**
chlorine
    properties of, **206**, 233, **233**, 259
    in sodium chloride, **233**
chlorofluorocarbons (CFCs), 11
chlorophyll, 256
chocolate chip ice-cream model, 166, **166**
chromium, **90**
chromosphere, 475, **475**
circular motion, 341, **341**, 349
citric acid, 286, 288, 292
cleaning up, 25
cloning, 329
clusters of galaxies, 456, **456**
clusters of stars, 452, **452**
cobalt, **135, 265**
coefficients, in chemical equations, 266, **266**
coin-in-a-cup procedure, 393
collisions
    of galaxies, 451
    of particles in solar system formation, 474, **474**
    Uranus's axis of rotation and, 488
colors
    of fireworks, 216
    of leaves, 256, **256**
    of pH indicators, 287, **287**, 290, **290**, 294
    in the spectrum, 437, **437**
    of stars, 436, **436, 439**
comas of comets, 500
combination notes instructions (Graphic Organizer), 38, 366, 529, **529**
Comet P/Tempel-Tuttle, 504
comets, 500–501, **500, 501**
common words with multiple meanings, **532–533**
communicating results, 20
companion stars, 438

comparison table instructions (Graphic Organizer), 106, 222, 524, **524**
complex carbohydrates, 314, **314**
compounds, 138–141, 280–305, 542
  acids, properties of, 286–288, **286, 287, 288**
  acid strength, 292
  bases, properties of, 289–291, **289, 290, 291**
  base strength, 293
  breaking down, 140, **140**
  classifying, 284
  covalent compounds, 263, **263,** 284–285, **285**
  definition of, 138
  elements in, 138, **138**
  flame tests of, 148–149
  in industry, 140
  ionic compounds, 233–235, **233, 234, 235,** 282–283
  labs on, 139, 148–149, 268–269
  mixtures compared with, **144**
  in nature, 141, **141**
  neutralization reactions, 293
  organic, 311, **311** (see also organic molecules)
  pH scale, 293, **293**
  properties of, 139–140, **139**
  solutions of acids and bases, 292–295, **293, 294**
  specific ratios of elements in, 140
compression, 347, **347**
computers, in data organization, 55, **55**
concentration, 146, **146, 147,** 292, 548
concept map instructions (Graphic Organizer), 160, 468, 521, **521**
conceptual models, 46, **46**
conclusions, in scientific methods, 19–20, **20**
condensation, 117, **117**
condensation point, 117
conduction, electrical, **198**
conduction, thermal, 198, **198**
conductivity, electrical
  of acids, 288
  of bases, 290
  of covalent compounds, 285, **285**
  of ionic compounds, 283, **283**
conductivity, thermal, **85**
conservation of energy, law of, 261, 544

conservation of mass, law of, 48, **48,** 265, 267, 543
conservation of matter, 48, **48,** 265, 267
continuous spectrum, 437, **437**
controlled experiments, 17
controlled parameters, 51, 150, 270
controls, 51, 270
convective zone, in the sun, 475, **475**
copper, **92,** 177
core, of the sun, 475, **475**
corona, 475, **475**
corrosivity, 286, 289
cosmic background radiation, 455
cosmology, 454
covalent bonds, 236–239
  in covalent compounds, 284
  definition of, 236, **236**
  electron-dot diagrams of, 237, **237**
  marshmallow models of, 242–243
  in molecules, 237, **237,** 238, **238**
covalent compounds
  formulas for, 263, **263**
  properties of, 284–285, **285**
craters, impact
  on Earth, 503, **503,** 515
  on Io, 497
  on Mars, **483**
  modeling formation of, 502
  on the moon, 492, **492**
  studying, **40–41**
crescent moon, **494**
crystal lattice, 234, **234,** 282, **282**
  crystal-growing lab, 234
crystals, 234, **234,** 282, **282**
cubes, volume of, 80, **80**
cubic centimeters, **43,** 44, 80
cubic meters, **43,** 44, 80
current, electric
  in acids in water, 288
  in bases in water, 290
  in ionic compounds in salt water, 283, **283**
  metallic bonding and, 240
Czarnowski, James, 14–20, **15**

D

Dalton's atomic theory, 165, **165**
dark energy, 457
dark matter, 457
data, 40–71. See also data analysis
  accuracy of, 19, 44, 57, 64, 79

collection of, 18, 42–45, **42, 43, 45**
  data points, 53, **53**
  data tables, 50–51, **51, 180**
  mean, median, and mode in, 58, **58**
  organization of, 50–55, **51, 52–53, 54, 55**
  reproducibility of, 19, 57, 64
  in scientific methods, 19, **19**
  tools for collection of, 42–45, **42, 43, 45**
data accuracy, 19, 44, 57, 64, 79
data analysis
  constructing and interpreting graphs, 52–53, **52–53,** 212, 358, 460
  creating data tables, 50–51, **51, 180**
  finding missing quantities, 394, 422
  finding slopes of graphs, 59–61, **59, 60,** 322, 508
  linear and nonlinear relationships, 60–61, **60,** 122, **122,** 322, 508
  mean, median, and mode in, 58, **58**
  reproducibility of data, 19, 57, 64
  in scientific methods, 19, **19**
  tools for organization, 55, **55**
data collection
  creating tables during, 50–51, **51, 180**
  in scientific methods, 18
  tools for, 42–45, **42, 43, 45**
data organization, 50–55
  data tables, 50–51, **51, 180**
  graphs, 52–54, **52–53, 54** (see also graphs)
  tools for, 55, **55**
data points, 53, **53**
data reproducibility, 19, 57, 64
data tables, 50–51, **51, 190**
days, on Mercury, 480
deceleration, 341
Deep Flight 1, 428, **428**
deep-sea diving, 128, **128**
Deimos (moon of Mars), 496
Democritus, thoughts on atoms of, 164
density
  buoyancy and, 415, **415,** 417–418, **417, 418**
  calculating, 44, 85, 86, 98, 415
  changing, 417–418, **417, 418**
  of common substances, **86**
  definition of, 85, **85**

Index

equation for, 44, 547
floating and, 87, 405, 415, **415**
identifying substances by using, 86
liquid layers and, 87, **87**
measuring, 44, 416
overall, 417–418, **417, 418**
of pennies, 62–63
of solids, 86, **86**
units of, 85
water pressure and, 409
deoxyribonucleic acid (DNA)
models of, **224–225**
nucleic acids in, 317, **317**
polymerase chain reaction and, 328
dependent variables, 51
deposition, on Mars, 483
depth
atmospheric pressure and, 408, **408**
water pressure and, 409, **409**
deskunking formula, 328
detergents, **289**
deuterium, 208, **477**
diatomic elements, 238
diatomic molecules, 238
dilute solutions, 146
direction of force, 345–346, **345, 346**
direct relationships, 54, **54**
displacement measurements, 81, **81**, 413, **413**
dissolving, 88, **143**
distance
gravitational force and, 373, **373**
interplanetary, 478, **478**, 484, 490
inverse square of, 440
to stars, 441, **441**
units of, 441, 478, **478**
distillation, **143**
DNA (deoxyribonucleic acid)
models of, **224–225**
nucleic acids in, 317, **317**
polymerase chain reaction and, 328
dolphins, in the navy, 70, **70**
domino derby, 335
double bonds, 243, 311, **311**
double-door instructions (FoldNote), 517, **517**
drag, **404–405**
dry cleaning, 156
dry ice, 118, **118**
ductility, **85, 137, 198,** 240
dust tails, 500, **500, 501**

E

Eagle nebula, 452, **452**
ears, "popping" in, 408
Earth
distance to sun, 478, **478**
properties of, **482**
revolution of, 442, **442**
rotation of, 441–442, **442**
from space, 482, **482**
Earth Science Enterprise, 482
echolocation, 70
eclipses, 495, **495**
ecologists, 12
effervescent tablets, **92**
efficiency, 15, 16
Einstein, Albert, 476
Einstein's formula, 476
electrical conductivity
of acids, 288
of bases, 290
of covalent compounds, 285, **285**
of elements, 136, **137**
of ionic compounds, 283, **283**
of metals, 240
electrical energy, from chemical reactions, **259**
electromagnetic force, in atoms, 178, **178**
electron clouds, 169, **169**
electron-dot diagrams, 237
electronegativity, 212, **212**
electronics engineers, 37, **37**
electrons
in atoms, 174, **174, 175**
in covalent bonds, 236–237, **236, 237**
definition of, 166
discovery of, 166, **166**
grouping elements by, 202–208
in energy levels, 169, 169, 227–229, **227, 229**
in ionic compounds, **232**, 233–235, **233, 234**
in ions, 230–232, **231, 232**
in metallic bonds, 240, **240**
in orbitals, 169, **169**
properties of, **172,** 173
valence, 227–228, **227, 228**
elements, 134–137, 541. *See also* periodic table of the elements
alkali metals, 202, **202**
alkaline-earth metals, 203, **203**
arrangement in periodic table, 194–195, **194, 195**

atomic number of, 175, 200, **200,** 227
atoms in, 134
boron group, 204
carbon group, 205, **205**
categories of, 136–137, **137**
changing from one to another, 188
characteristic properties of, 91, 135
classes of, 198–199, **198, 199**
classifying by properties, 135, **135,** 210–211
combining in certain proportions, 165
definition of, 134
diatomic, 238
emission and absorption lines of, 437–438, **437, 438**
halogens, 206, **206,** 232
isotopes, 175–177, **175, 176,** 200
labs on, 135, 180–181, 268–269
making, 217
mass number of, 176–177, **176**
nitrogen group, 205, **205**
noble gases, 207, **207,** 228
oxygen group, 206, **206**
predicting properties of, 195, **195**
transition metals, 203–204, **203, 204**
elevation, atmospheric pressure and, 408, **408**
ellipses, 382
elliptical galaxies, 451, **451**
elliptical orbits, 501, 503
emission lines, 437, **437**
endothermic reactions, 260, **260**
energy
changes of state and, 114–118, **114**
in chemical reactions, 259–260, **259, 260**
dark, 457
efficiency of, 15
in Einstein's formula, 476
electron energy levels, 169, **169,** 227–229, **227, 229**
in forming ions, 231, 232
law of conservation of, 261
from nuclear fusion in the sun, 476–477, **477**
from quasars, 453
stored in lipids, 315, **315**
from sunlight, 318, **318**
energy levels, electrons in, 169, **169,** 227–229, **227, 229**
enzymes, 320–321

equations, useful, 546–548
Erie, Lake, 79
Eros, 502, **502**
erosion, on Mars, 483
ethene, 311, **311**
ethyne, 311, **311**
Europa (moon of Jupiter), 497, **497**
evaporation, 116–117, **116, 143**
Everest, Mount, atmospheric pressure on, 408, **408**
exothermic reactions, 259, **259**
expansion of the universe, 455, 457
experimental physicists, 189, **189**
experimentation
  in scientific methods, 9, 17–18, **17, 18**
  variable and controlled parameters in, 17, 51, 150, 270
extinction, 505
eyes, washing, 27

F

Fahrenheit temperature scale, 45, **45**
falling objects
  action and reaction force pairs in, 390, **390**
  air resistance and, 378–379, **378, 379**
  free fall, 379, **379**
  gravity and, 376–377, **376, 377**
  lab on, 369
  projectile motion in, 380–381, **380, 381**
families of elements, 200, 228, **228**
fats, 315, **315**
filtering, **143**
finding a missing quantity, 98, 394, 422
fire retardants, 276, **276**
fireworks
  chemical compounds in, 156, **156**
  flame tests and, 148–149
  photographs of, **254–255**
first aid, 26–27, **27**
first energy level, **227**
first-magnitude stars, 439
fish, buoyancy of, 418, **418**
flame tests, 148–149
flammability, 90, **91**
flipchart movies of stars, 445
flippers, efficiency of, **6–7**
floating
  buoyant force and, 412–414, **412, 413, 414**

changing overall density, 417–418, **417, 418**
  density and, 86, **86,** 405, 415, **415**
  determining density, 415, 416
  predicting, 414–415, **414, 415,** 416
  weight and, 414, **414**
flow, pressure differences and, 410–411, **410, 411**
fluids, 404–429
  atmospheric pressure, 407–408, **407, 408**
  buoyant forces in, 412–414, **412, 413, 414**
  definition of, 404
  floating and, 86, 405, 415–418, **415, 418**
  lab on, 405
  pressure differences and flow of, 410–411, **410, 411**
  pressure from, 406–407, **406, 407**
  water pressure, 409, **409**
foils, **17**
FoldNote instructions, 517–520, **517, 518, 519, 520**
following directions, 24
forces, 344–349
  action and reaction force pairs, 389–390, **389, 390**
  air resistance, 378–379, **378, 379**
  atmospheric pressure, 117, 407–408, **407, 408**
  in atoms, 178, **178**
  balanced, 347, **347,** 353, 384, 414
  buoyant, 412–414, **412, 413, 414**
  centripetal, 382, **382**
  compression, 347
  definition of, 344
  direction of, 345–346, **345, 346**
  distance and, 373, **373**
  fluid flow and, 410–411, **410, 411**
  friction, 350–355, **350, 351, 352, 353**
  gravitational, 370–375, **371, 372, 373**
  motion and, 344, **344**
  net, 345–346, **345, 346**
  in Newton's first law of motion, 384–386, **384, 385, 386**
  in Newton's second law of motion, 387–388, **387, 388**
  in Newton's third law of motion, 389–390, **389, 390**
  pressure and, 406–407

tension, 347
  unbalanced, 348–349, **348, 349,** 353, **353**
  van der Waals, 250
  water pressure, 409, **409**
  weight and, 82–83, **82, 83,** 374, **374**
forensic scientists, 305, **305**
formation of the moon, 493, **493**
formation of the solar system, 474, **474**
four-corner fold instructions (FoldNote), 519, **519**
free fall, 379, **379.** See also falling objects
freezing, 115, **115**
freezing point, 115
friction, 350–355
  harmful and helpful, 353–355, **354, 355**
  definition of, 350
  feeling, 351
  kinetic, 352, **352**
  Newton's first law and, 385
  sources of, 350–351, **350, 351**
  static, 353, **353**
full moon, **494**
fusion, 444, 476–477, **477**

G

galaxies, 450–453
  clusters of, 456, **456**
  contents of, 452, **452**
  definition of, 450
  exploring movement of, 435
  irregular, 451, **451**
  modeling, 451
  oldest, 456, **457**
  origin of, 453, **453**
  spiral, 450, **450**
  types of, 450–451, **450, 451**
galaxy clusters, 456, **456**
Galilean satellites, 497
Galileo Galilei, 376
Galileo spacecraft, 486, **492**
gallium, 115, **115**
gamma rays, 477
Ganymede (moon of Jupiter), 497
gas chromatographs, 277
gases
  condensation of, 117, **117**
  definition of, 112
  inert, 207
  noble, 207, **207,** 228
  shape and volume of, 112, **112**
  in solution, 145, **145**
  as state of matter, 112, **112**

Index

gas giants
  definition of, 486
  Jupiter, 486, **486**, 497
  Neptune, 489, **489**, 498
  Saturn, **470–471**, 487, **487**, 497
  Uranus, 488, **488**, 498
gas lubricants, 354
gasoline, 311
geckos, 250, **250**
gemologists, 105, **105**
genetic information, 317
geochemists, 12, **12**
germanium, 195, **195**, 205
gibbous moon, **494**
glass sculpture, **108–109**
global positioning system (GPS),
    364, **364**
globular clusters, 452, **452**
gloves, 25, **25**
glucose, 260, **262**, 314, **314**
glue, chemical bonding in, 225
glycogen, 314, **314**
gold, **204**
gold-foil experiment, 167, **167**
GPS (global positioning system),
    364, **364**
GPS watch systems, 364, **364**
graduated cylinders
  accuracy of, 57, **57**
  liquid volume measurements in,
    44, 79, **79**
  use of, 28–29, 79, **79**
grams, 43, **43**
granite, 144, **144**
Graphic Organizer instructions,
    521–529, **521, 522, 523, 524,
    525, 526, 527, 528, 529**
graphs
  acceleration on, 342, **342**
  axes of, 52, **52**
  bar, **19**, 539
  constructing and interpreting,
    52–53, **52–53**, 212, 358, 460,
    538–540
  line, **19**, 212, 460, **460**,
    538–539
  linear and nonlinear relation-
    ships on, 54, **54**, 60–61, **60**,
    122, **122**, 508, **508**
  patterns shown by, 54, **54**
  pie, 540
  of position vs. time, 338–339,
    339, 358
  reference points on, 337, **337**
  slopes of, 59–61, **59, 60**, 322,
    508
  of speed vs. time, 342, **342**
gravitational forces
  action and reaction force pairs,
    390, **390**

in atoms, 178, **178**
distance and, 373, **373**
Earth's, 371
effects on matter, **370–371**
mass and, 372, **372**
pressure from, 407, 408
weight and, 82–83, **82, 83,**
    374, **374**
gravity
  acceleration due to, 377, **377**
  air resistance and, 378–379,
    378, 379
  definition of, 370
  falling objects and, 376–377,
    376, 377
  lab on weight on different
    planets, 506–507
  law of universal gravitation, 371,
    372–373, **372, 373**, 544
  on the moon, 370, **370**
  orbiting and, 381–382, **381, 382**
  projectile motion and, 380–381,
    380, 381
  role in solar system orbits,
    372–373, **372, 373**, 382
  size and shape of universe and,
    456
  spherical shapes and, 474, 493
  star and planet formation and,
    472–474, **473, 474**
  static objects and, 375
Great Dark Spot (Neptune),
    489, **489**
Great Red Spot (Jupiter), 486
groups of elements, 200, 228, **228**
gunpowder, 216

H

hailstones, terminal velocity of, 378
hairlets, on geckos, 250, **250**
Halley's comet, 501
halogens, 206, **206**, 232
halos, galaxy, 452
Hawkes, Graham, 428
heat, equation for, 549
heat burns, 27, **27**
heat of chemical reactions, **257,**
    259–260, **259, 260**
Heisenberg, Werner, 169
heliox, 128
helium
  atoms of, 174, **174**
  in balloons, 207
  deep-sea diving with, 128, **128**
  isotopes of, 188

from nuclear fusion, 445,
    476–477, **477**
  valence electrons in, **228**, 229
helium-3, 188
hemoglobin, 316
Hertzsprung, Ejnar, 446
Hertzsprung-Russell diagrams
    (H-R diagrams), 446–447,
    446–447
HIV/AIDS research, 329
horizontal motion, 380
hormones, 316
Horsehead Nebula, 472, **472**
hot springs, 304, **304**
H-R diagrams (Hertzsprung-Russell
    diagrams), 446–447, **446–447**
Hubble Space Telescope, **434–435,**
    467, **490**, 498
human body, atmospheric pressure
    and, 407, 408
humpback whales, **315**
hydrangeas, 294, **294**
hydrochloric acid, 287, **287**, 288,
    292
hydrofluoric acid, 288, **288**
hydrogen
  absorption spectrum for,
    437, **437**
  atoms of, 174
  deuterium, 208, **477**
  as diatomic element, 238
  in gas giants, 486, 487, 488,
    489
  hydronium ions, 286, 292
  isotopes of, 175, **175**, 177, 208
  in living organisms, 310–311,
    310, 311, 313
  molecular, 486, 487
  from nuclear fusion in the sun,
    476–477, **477**
  properties of, 208, **208**, 259
hydrogen chloride, **258**, 259
hydrogen peroxide, 328
hydrogen sulfide, 304
hydronium ions, 286, 292
hydrothermal water, 304, **304**
hydroxide ions, 289, 290, 293
hypotheses (singular, *hypothesis*)
  developing, 16–17
  testing, 17–18, 30, 182, 298,
    459

I

ice palaces, 36, **36**
ice sculpture, **76–77**
ice volcanoes, 498

Index

idea wheel instructions (Graphic Organizer), 278, 402, 527, **527**
impact craters
 on Earth, 503, **503,** 505, 515
 on Io, 497
 on Mars, **483**
 modeling formation of, 502
 on the moon, 492, **492**
 studying, **40–41**
impacts, on Earth, 503, **503,** 505, 515
independent variables, 51, 150, 270
indicators
 acids and, 287, **287,** 293–294
 bases and, 290, **290,** 293–294
 lab on, 296–297
 pH scale and, 293
 in plants, 294, **294,** 296–297
 using, 294, **294**
inert gases, 207, **207,** 228
inertia, 386, **386,** 392–393
injuries, 27. *See also* first aid
inner solar system, 480–485
 distances in, 484
 Earth, 482, **482**
 Mars, 483–485, **483, 484, 485,** 496
 Mercury, 480, **480**
 planets in, 478, **478**
 Venus, 481, **481**
insoluble materials, 144
insulin, 316
International System of Units (SI), 43–45, **43, 45,** 554. *See also* units
inverse relationships, 54, **54**
inverse square of the distance, 440
investigations. *See also* data
 applying answers of, 10–11
 collecting data, 18, 42–45, **42, 43, 45**
 communicating results, 20
 creating a scientific plan, 41
 developing hypotheses, 16–17
 experimental design in, 150, 270
 finding missing quantities, 394, 422
 methods used in, 9
 planning and conducting, 182, 244, 298
 testing hypotheses, 17–18, 30, 182, 298, 459
 variable and controlled parameters in, 150, 270
Io (moon of Jupiter), **486,** 497, **497,** 514

iodine, 206, **206**
ionic bonds, 230–235
 lab on crystal-growing, 234
 definition of, 230
 forming, 230
 in ionic compounds, 233–235, **233, 234, 235,** 282
 negative ions, 232, **232**
 positive ions, 231, **231**
ionic compounds, 233–235
 chemical formulas for, 263, **263**
 crystal lattices in, 234, **234,** 282, **282**
 forming, 233, **233**
 properties of, 235, 282–283, **282, 283**
 salts, 295, **295**
ions
 charges of, 173, 230–232, **231, 232**
 definition of, 230
 electrical conductivity and, 283, 285, 288, 290
 forming negative, 232, **232**
 forming positive, 231, **231,** 239
 names of, 232
ion tails, 500, **500, 501**
iron
 in meteorites, 504, **504**
 properties of, **90, 91, 135, 204**
irregular galaxies, 451, **451**
isotopes, 175–177, **175, 176,** 200

J

jai alai, 364, **364**
jewelry designers, 105, **105**
Jupiter, 486, **486,** 497

K

kelvins, **43,** 45
Kepler's third law, 508
key-term fold instructions (FoldNote), 519, **519**
kilograms, 43, **43**
kilojoules, 322
kilo- prefix, 43, **43**
kinetic friction, 352, **352**
kinetic sculptors, 365
Kuiper belt, 491, 501

L

labels
 on data tables, 51
 on graphs, 53, **53**
Lake Erie, 79
lanthanides, 204
Large Magellanic Cloud, 451, **451**
lasers, 37
lava lamps, **132–133**
Lavoisier, Antoine, 265
law of conservation of energy, 261, 544
law of conservation of mass, 48, **48,** 265, 267, 543
law of universal gravitation, 371, 372–373, **372, 373,** 544
laws, scientific, 48, **48**
laws of motion
 Kepler's third law, 508
 Newton's first law, 384–386, **384, 385, 386,** 543
 Newton's second law, 387–388, **387, 388,** 543
 Newton's third law, 389–390, **389, 390,** 543
layered book instructions (FoldNote), 518, **518**
LBV 1806-20, 466, **466**
leaves, color changes in, 256, **256**
length, units of, 43, **43**
Leonid meteor shower, 504, **504**
Lick Observatory (California), 514
Lidar system, 37
life, in the solar system, 484, 497
lifting, power suits for, 400, **400**
light
 from chemical reactions, **259**
 colors of, 437, **437**
 emission and absorption lines, 437–438, **437, 438**
 from the moon, 494
 pollution, 514
 scattering by particles, 145, **145,** 488
 speed of, 476, 478
 from stars, 436–437, **437,** 439, 440
light bulbs, 207
light energy, from chemical reactions, **259**
Light Gas Gun Chamber, NASA Ames Research Center (California), **40–41**
light-minutes, 478, **478**
lightning, 113, **113**
light pollution, 514

light scattering, 145, **145,** 488
light sticks, 276, **276**
light-years, 441
linear graphs, *See also* line graphs
  comparing with nonlinear
    graphs, 61
  equations of, 322, 508
  slopes of, 59–61, **59, 60,** 322,
    508
linear relationships, 60–61, **60,** 122
line graphs, 538–539
  constructing, 212, 460
  linear relationships on, 60–61,
    60, 122
  nonlinear relationships on,
    54, **54,** 61
  slopes on, 59–61, **59, 60,** 322,
    508
  of test results, **19**
lines, equations for, 60, **60,** 322,
    508
lipids, 315, **315**
liquid layers, 87, **87**
liquids
  boiling of, 116–117, **116,** 118,
    119
  definition of, 111
  density and layers of, 87, **87**
  evaporation of, 116–117, **116**
  freezing of, 115, **115**
  shape and volume of, 111, **111**
  in solution, 145, **145**
  volume of, 79, **79**
liquid volume, 28–29, 79, **79**
liters, **43,** 79
litmus, 287, 290
living organisms, chemistry of,
    308–329
  carbohydrates, 314, **314**
  carbon bonds, 310–311,
    310, 311
  enzymes, 320–321
  labs on, 312, 316, 320–321
  lipids, 315, **315**
  noncarbon elements in,
    312–313, **312, 313**
  nucleic acids, 317, **317**
  proteins, 315–316, **316**
  salt in, 319, **319**
  water in, 318, **318**
long-period comets, 501
lubricants, friction reduction from,
    354, **354**
luminous blue variable stars,
    466, **466**
Luna (moon of Earth), 492–496
  eclipses and, 495–496, **496**

formation of, 493, **493**
mining on, 188
orbit of, 382, **382**
phases of, 494, **494**
reduced gravity on, 370, **370**
reflected light from, 494
surface of, 492, **492**
tilted orbit of, 496
lunar eclipses, 495–496, **496**
lunar rocks, 492–493

M

M87 galaxy, **451**
Magellanic Clouds, 451, **451**
Magellan spacecraft, 481, **481**
magic eggs lab, 392–393
magic thread lab, 393
magnesium, **229**
magnesium hydroxide, 291
magnesium oxide, 138, **138**
magnetic atomic models, 177
magnets, separation of mixtures by,
    143
magnitude, absolute, 440,
    446–447, **446–447**
magnitude, apparent, 440, **440**
magnitude of force, 345–346,
    345, 346
main sequence, 445, **446–447,** 447
main-sequence stars, 445,
    446–447, 447
malleability, **85, 137, 198,** 240
marbles, circling, 382
maria, lunar, **492**
Marine Mammal Program, 70
Mars, 483–485, **483, 484, 485,** 496
Mars Express Orbiter, 485, **485**
Mars Global Surveyor, 484
marshmallows, bond models using,
    242–243
Mars Pathfinder, 483
mass
  atomic, 177
  buoyancy and, 405, 418, **418**
  definition of, 43, 82, 374
  density and, 44, 85–86, 415
  of electrons, 173
  gravitational force and, 372, **372,**
    376–377, **376**
  inertia and, 386, **386**
  law of conservation of, 265, 543
  motion and, 386, **386,** 392–393
  of neutron stars, 448
  in Newton's second law of
    motion, 387, **387**

of protons and neutrons, 173
units of, 43, **43,** 83
weight and, 82–83, **82, 83,**
    374, **374**
mass number, 176–177, **176**
mathematical models, 46
mathematic relationships
  in density calculations, 44, 85,
    86, 415
  direct and inverse relationships,
    54, **54**
  in force and pressure
    calculations, 406–407
  linear and nonlinear, 60–61, **60,**
    122, 322
  mathematical models, 46
  mean, median, and mode,
    58, **58**
  in speed calculations, 338
  in volume calculations, 80, **80**
mathematics, as the language of
    science, 56
Math Refresher, 534–537
matter
  characteristic properties of, 91,
    135
  chemical changes in, 92–95,
    92, 93, 94
  dark, 457
  definition of, 78
  density of, 85–87, **86, 87**
  in Einstein's formula, 476
  identifying physical properties of,
    84–87, **85, 86, 87**
  law of conservation of, 48, **48,**
    265, 267
  mass and, 82–83, **82, 83**
  molecular motion and changes
    of state, 114–119, **116, 119**
  molecular motion and states of,
    110–113, **110, 112**
  physical changes in, 88–89,
    88, 89
  physical properties of, 84–87,
    85, 86, 87
  physical vs. chemical changes,
    91, **91,** 94–95, **94, 95**
mean, 58, **58**
measurements
  accuracy of, 44, 57, **57,** 64, 79
  of density, 44, 416
  of displacement, 81, **81,**
    413, **413**
  ruler positions, 337
  tools for, 42–45, **42, 43, 45**
  units of, 42–45, **43, 45**
  of volume, 28–29, 79–81,
    79, 80, 81

measuring skills, 555
median, 58, **58**
melting, 115, **115**, 118, **119**
melting point
    change of state and, 118, **119**
    of covalent compounds, 285
    definition of, 115
    of ionic compounds, 235,
      283, **283**
Mendeleev, Dmitri, 194–195, **194**
    periodic table of, 195, **195**
meniscus, 79, **79**
mercury (element), 198, **204**
Mercury (planet), 480, **480**
metallic bonds, 239–240, **240, 241**
metallic meteorites, 504, **504**
metalloids, 136, **137**, 199, **199**, 205
metallurgists, 157, **157**
metals. *See also names of*
    individual metals
    active, 287
    alkali, 202, **202**
    alkaline-earth, 203, **203**
    alloys, 145
    bending of, 241, **241**
    density of, 86–87, **86**
    in fireworks, 216
    ions of, 231, **231**, 239
    metallic bonds in, 239–240,
      240, 241
    in the periodic table, **196–197,**
      198
    properties of, 136, **137**, 198, **198**
    reaction with acids, 287, **287**
    transition, 203–204, **203, 204**
meteorites, 503–504, **504**
meteoroids, 503–505, **504**
meteorologists, 11, **11**
meteors, 503
meteor showers, 504, **504**
meters, 43, **43**
methane, 486, 488, 489
metric system, 43
metric tons, 43
microscopes, using, 556–557
Milky Way galaxy, 451, 452
Millennium Bridge (England),
    400, **400**
milliliters, **43,** 44, 79
millimeters, 43, **43**
milli- prefix, 43, **43**
mining on the moon, 188
Miranda (moon of Uranus),
    498, **498**
missing quantities, finding, 394,
    422

mixtures, 142–147
    compounds compared to, **144**
    definition of, 142
    lab on, 146
    properties of, 142–144, **142,**
      143, 144
    separating, 142, **143**
    solutions as, 144–146, **145, 146,**
      147
mode, 58, **58**
models in science, 45–48
    conceptual, 46, **46**
    limits of, 47
    mathematical, 46
    physical, 45, **45**
    sizes of, 46, **46**
    using, 47, **47**
molecular biologists, 329, **329**
molecular photocopying, 328
molecules, 542
    branched-chain, **310**
    changes of state and, 114–118,
      116, 119
    covalent bonding in, 237, **237,**
      238, **238,** 284
    in crystal lattices, 234, **234,** 282,
      282
    definition of, 237
    diatomic, 238
    electron-dot diagrams of, **237**
    organic, 308–329 (*see also*
      organic molecules)
    states of matter and, 110–113,
      110, 112
Mono Lake (California), **280–281**
moon (of Earth), 492–496
    eclipses and, 495–496, **496**
    formation of, 493, **493**
    mining on, 188
    orbit of, 382, **382**
    phases of, 494, **494**
    reduced gravity on, 370, **370**
    reflected light from, 494
    surface of, 492, **492**
    tilted orbit of, 496
moons, of other planets, 496–498,
    497, 498, 514
Moseley, Henry, 195
motion, 368–401
    acceleration, 341–342, **341, 342,**
      546 (*see also* acceleration)
    average speed, 338–339, **338,**
      546
    balanced forces and, 347, **347**
    circular, 341, **341,** 349
    definition of, 336
    graphs of position vs. time,
      338–339, **339,** 358

    graphs of speed vs. time,
      342, **342**
    horizontal, 380
    Kepler's third law of, 508
    kinetic friction and, 352, **352**
    Newton's first law of, 384–386,
      384, 385, 386, 543
    Newton's second law of,
      387–388, **387, 388,** 543
    Newton's third law of, 389–390,
      389, 390, 543
    projectile, 380–381, **380, 381**
    reference points and, 336–337,
      336, 337
    of stars, 441–442, **441, 442**
    in a two-dimensional system,
      337, **337**
    unbalanced forces and,
      348–349, **348, 349,** 353, **353**
    velocity, 340, **340,** 348–349,
      348, 349
    vertical, 381, **381**

N

National Aeronautics and Space
    Administration (NASA), 482
National Oceanic and Atmospheric
    Administration (NOAA), 71
near-Earth asteroids, 503
NEAR spacecraft, **502**
neatness, importance of, 24, **24**
nebulas
    birth of the sun from, **474,** 475
    star birth in, 452, **452,** 472–473,
      474, 475
negative acceleration, 341
negative ions, 232, **232**
Neptune, 489, **489,** 498
net force
    air resistance and gravity,
      378, **378**
    definition of, 345
    equation for, 547
    examples of, **347**
    forces in different directions,
      346, **346**
    forces in the same direction,
      345, **345**
    Newton's first law of motion
      and, 384
    no motion from, 347, **347**
    static friction from, 353, **353**
    weight and buoyant forces,
      414, **414**
neutralization reactions, 293

neutral solutions, 293, **293**
neutrons
  in atoms, 174, **174, 175**
  in nuclear fusion in the sun, 477, **477**
  properties of, **172**, 173
neutron stars, 448
new moon, **494**
Newton, Isaac, 371, **371**, 384
newtons, 83, 344, 374
Newton's laws of motion, 543
  first law, 384–386, **384, 385, 386**
  second law, 387–388, **387, 388**
  third law, 389–390, **389, 390**
nickel
  in meteorites, 504, **504**
  properties of, **135**
nickel(II) oxide, **283**
nitric acid, 288, 292
nitrogen
  in living organisms, 312, **312, 313**
  properties of, 205
  in proteins, 141, 312, **312**
nitrogen group elements, 205, **205**
nitrogen narcosis, 128
NOAA (National Oceanic and Atmospheric Administration), 71
noble gases, 207, **207**, 228
nonlinear graphs, 54, **54**, 61, 122
  (*see also* line graphs)
nonlinear relationships, 54, 54, 61, 122
nonmetals
  ions of, 232, **232**
  on the periodic table, **196–197**, 199
  properties of, 136, **137**, 199, **199**
nonreactivity with oxygen, 90, **90**
nuclear fusion, 444, 476–477, **477**
nucleic acids, 317, **317**
nucleotides, 317, **317**
nucleus, of a comet, 500, **500**
nucleus, of an atom
  definition of, 168
  protons and neutrons in, **172**, 173
  relative size of, 168, **168**
  Rutherford's discovery of, 167–168, **167, 168**
  strong force in, **178**

O

observations, 7, 9
oceanographers, 71, **71**
oils, 315
Olympus Mons (Mars), 484, **484**
Omega Centauri, 452
Oort cloud, 501
open clusters, 452, **452**
Opportunity rover, 485
oral presentations, 20
orbitals, 169, **169**
orbits
  of asteroids, 502
  of comets, 501
  gravity and, 381–382, **381, 382**
  of the moon, 496
organic molecules, 308–329
  building models of, 309
  carbohydrates, 314, **314**
  carbon backbones in, 310, **310**
  enzymes, 320–321
  importance of salt, 319, **319**
  importance of water, 318, **318**
  lipids, 315, **315**
  manufacturing, 313
  noncarbon elements in, 312–313, **312, 313**
  nucleic acids, 317, **317**
  proteins, 141, 315–316, **316**, 317
Orion constellation, 436, **436**
outer solar system
  distances in, 490
  Jupiter, 486, **486**, 497, **497**
  Neptune, 489, **489**, 498
  planets in, 478, **478**
  Pluto, 490, **490**, 498
  Saturn, **470–471**, 487, **487**, 497, **497**
  Uranus, 488, **488**, 498, **498**
overall density, 417–418, **417, 418**
oxide ions, 232, **232**
oxygen
  chemical formula for, **262**
  ions, 232, **232**
  isotopes, 176
  in living organisms, 312, **312, 313**
  properties of, 206
  reactivity with, 90, **90, 91**
oxygen group elements, 206, **206**
ozone layer, 11

P

paper bags, 104
parachutes, air resistance and, 379
parallax, 441, **441**
parameters
  controlled, 17, 20, 51, 150, 270
  variable, 17, 20, 51, 150, 270
particles
  changes of state and, 114–118, **116**
  charged, 230–232, **231, 232**
  light scattering by, 145, **145**, 488
  in planetary rings, **487**
  in solar system formation, 474, **474**
  states of matter and, 110–113, **110, 112**
  subatomic, 172–173, **172**
pascals, 406
Pascal's principle, 545
PCR (polymerase chain reaction), 328
penguins, **6–7**, 16–17, **16**
pennies
  density of, 62–63
  number of atoms in, 170
periodic law, 200
periodic table of the elements, 192–217, **196–197, 558–559**
  alkali metals, 202, **202**
  alkaline-earth metals, 203, **203**
  arrangement by Mendeleev, 194–195, **194, 195**
  arrangement by Moseley, 195
  atomic number on, 200, **200**
  boron group elements, 204
  carbon group elements, 205, **205**
  classes of elements on, 198–199, **198, 199**
  creating elements, 217
  determining number of valence electrons from, 228, **228**
  halogens, 206, **206**, 232
  hydrogen, 208, **208**
  isotopes on, 200
  labs on, 193, 198, 208, 210–211
  nitrogen group elements, 205, **205**
  noble gases, 207, **207**, 228
  oxygen group elements, 206, **206**

periodic table of the elements
  (*continued*)
    symbols on, 199–200
    transition metals, 203–204,
      203, 204
period of revolution, 480, 498
period of rotation, 480
periods, of elements, 200
petroleum, 311
pH. *See also* acids; bases
    determining, 294, **294**, 296–297
    indicators of, 287, **287**, 290, **290**,
      293–294
    lab on, 296–297
    pH scale, 293, **293**, 542
    plant requirements for, 294, **294**
phases of the moon, 494, **494**
pH indicators
    acids and, 287, **287**, 293–294
    bases and, 290, **290**, 293–294
    lab on, 296–297
    pH scale and, 293
    in plants, 294, **294**, 296–297
    using, 294, **294**
pH meters, 294
Phobos (moon of Mars), 496
phosphoric acid, 288
phosphorus, 205, **205**, 312, **312**
photosphere, 475, **475**
photosynthesis, 260, 318, **318**
pH scale, 293, **293**
physical changes, 88–89, **88, 89**,
      94–95, **94**
    changes of state as, 114–119
    compared with chemical
      changes, 94, **94**
    in separating mixtures, 142, **143**
physical models, 45, **45**
physical processes, 88–89, **88, 89**,
      94–95, **94**
    changes of state as, 114–119
    compared with chemical
      changes, 94, **94**
    in separating mixtures, 142, **143**
physical properties, 84–89
    density, 85–87, **86, 87**
    examples of, **85**
    identifying, 84–87, **85, 86, 87**
    lab on, 94, 96–97, **133**
    physical changes and, 88–89,
      88, 89, 94–95, **94**
physical science laws and
    principles, 544–545
Physical Science Refresher,
    541–542
physicists, experimental, 189
pie graphs, 540
pigments, 256
planetary geologists, 515, **515**

planetary nebula stage, 456
planetesimals, 474, **474**
planets
    Earth, 482, **482**
    formation of, 474, **474**
    Jupiter, 486, **486**, 497, **497**
    Mars, 483–485, **483, 484**, 496
    Mercury, 480, **480**
    Neptune, 489, **489**, 498
    orbits of, **478**
    role of gravity in, 373, **373**, 382
    Saturn, **470–471**, 487, **487**,
      497, **497**
    tenth planet, 491
    Uranus, 488, **488**, 498, **498**
    Venus, 481, **481**
    weight on different, 506–507
plants, pH range for, 294, **294**
plasmas, 113, 128, **128**
plastic bags, 104
Pleiades, **452**
plum-pudding model of atoms,
    166, **166**
plus signs, in chemical equations,
    264
Pluto, 490, **490**, 498
Polaris, 442, **442**
pollution, from light, 514
polymerase chain reaction (PCR),
    328
polymers, 314, **314**
position
    graphs of position vs. time,
      338–339, **339**, 358
    reference points and, 336–337,
      336
positive acceleration, 341
positive ions, 231, **231**, 239
potassium dichromate, **283**
potassium hydroxide, 293
potassium metal, **202**
power, equation for, 548
power suits, for lifting patients,
    400, **400**
precipitates, 257, **257**
prefixes
    in chemical names, **263**
    in units, 43, **43**, 408
pressure
    air, 406–407, **406**
    atmospheric, 117, 407–408,
      407, 408
    boiling point and, 117
    breathing and, 410, **410**
    bubbles and, 407
    buoyant force and, 412–414,
      412, 413, 414

    calculation of, 406–407, 422
    equation for, 547
    fluid flow and, 410–411,
      410, 411
    force and, 406–407
    star and planet formation and,
      473, **473**
    tornadoes and, 411, **411**
    units of, 406
    water, 409, **409**
process chart instructions (Graphic
    Organizer), 4, 526, **526**
products, in chemical equations,
    264, **264**
prograde rotation, 481
projectile motion, 380–381,
    380, 381
propane, 311, **311**
properties of matter, 76–103
    characteristic, 91, 135
    chemical, 90–95, **91, 92, 93, 94**
    chemical changes and, 92–95,
      92, 93, 94, 258
    classifying by, 133
    of compounds, 139–140, **139**
    density, 85–87, **86, 87**
    of elements, 91, 135, 195, **195**
    labs on, 77, 94, 96–97
    mass, 82–83, **82, 83**
    physical, 84–87, **85, 86, 87**
    physical changes and, 88–89,
      88, 89, 94–95, **94**
    physical vs. chemical, 91, **91**,
      94–95, **94, 95**
    volume, 78–81, **79, 80, 81, 82**
proteins, 141, 315–316, **316**, 317
protons
    atomic number and, 175, **200**
    in atoms, 174, **174, 175**
    in nuclear fusion in the sun,
      477, **477**
    properties of, **172**, 173
protoplanets, 474
P/Tempel-Tuttle, Comet, 504
pulsars, 448
pure substances, 134, 138. *See also*
    elements; compounds
pyramid chart instructions (Graphic
    Organizer), 432, 529, **529**
pyramid instructions (FoldNote),
    517, **517**

Q

quarks, 189
quasars, 453, **453**
questions, in scientific methods,
    8, **8**, 9, 15–16, **15**

Index

R

radar waves, 481
radiation, cosmic background, 455
radiative zone, in the sun, 475, **475**
radioactive isotopes, 176
rain, pH of, 294
range, of graphs, 52, **53**
reactants, in chemical equations, 264, **264**
reactions, 254–277
    chemical bonding in, 258–259, **258, 259**
    compounds from, 138
    definition of, 256
    endothermic, 260, **260**
    examples of, **256**
    exothermic, 259, **259**
    labs on, 259, 260, 267, 268–269
    law of conservation of energy and, 261
    modeling, 255
    neutralization reactions, 293
    signs of, 257–258, **257, 258**
    synthesis, 268–269
reactivity
    of alkali metals, 202
    of alkaline-earth metals, 203
    definition of, 90
    of halogens, 206
    of hydrogen, 208
    of noble gases, 207
    with oxygen, **90, 91**
    of transition metals, 203
rectangular solids, volume of, 80
recycling resources, 10, **10,** 104
red cabbage, indicators in, 296–297
red dwarf stars, 447, **447**
red giant stars, 445, 447, **447**
red supergiant stars, 445, **445,** 447, **447**
reference directions, 336–337, **337**
reference points, 336–337, **336**
reflected sunlight, 494
reflection, law of, 545
remote sensing, 485
reproducibility of data, 19, 57, 64
research, 9
resistance, air, 378–379, **378, 379**
retrograde rotation, 481, 488, 498
reversibility of changes, 95
revolution, of planets, 480, 498
ribonucleic acid (RNA), 317
Rigel, 436, **436**
rings, carbon, **310**
rings, of planets, 382, 487

rise, in slope, 59, **59,** 322, 508
"rise over run," 59, **59,** 322, 508
RNA (ribonucleic acid), 317
roller coaster designers, 401, **401**
rolling kinetic friction, 352, **352,** 354
rotation
    axis of, 488, **488**
    of Earth, 441–442, **442**
    period of, 480, 498
    prograde, 481
    retrograde, 481, 488, 498
rubbing alcohol, **91**
run, in slope, 59, **59,** 322, 508
Russell, Henry Norris, 446
rust, **90, 91**
Rutherford, Ernest, 167–168, **167, 168**

S

safety, 22–27
    accident procedures, 22, 26–27, **27**
    chemical burns, 27, **27**
    elements of, 23–25, **23, 24, 25**
    first aid, 26–27, **27**
    following directions, 24
    safety maps, 24
    spills in the laboratory, 26
    symbols, 23, 23
safety equipment, 25
safety goggles, 25, **25**
safety maps, 24
safety symbols, 23, **23**
salt (sodium chloride)
    building a model of, 281
    crystal lattice of, **234,** 282, **282**
    formation of, **139,** 233
    importance to living things, 319, **319**
    melting point of, 283
    uses of, 295, **295**
salts
    definition of, 295
    importance to living things, 319, **319**
    from neutralization reactions, 293, 295
    uses of, 295, **295**
salt water
    electrical conductivity of, 283, **283**
    sea water, 230, 235
    as a solution, 144
sandpaper, 354, 355

satellites, artificial, tracking plate motion with, 70
satellites, planetary (moons)
    of Earth, 492–496, **492, 493, 494, 495, 496**
    Galilean, 497
    of Jupiter, 497, **497,** 514
    of Mars, 496
    moons as satellites, 492
    of Neptune, 498
    of Pluto, 498
    of Saturn, 497, **497**
    of Uranus, 498, **498**
saturated fats, 315
Saturn, **470–471,** 487, **487,** 497
scale, on graphs, 53, **53**
scanning tunneling electron microscopes (STMs), 164, **164,** 170, **170**
scattering of light, 145, **145,** 488
Schiaparelli (Mars), **483**
Schrödinger, Erwin, 169
science. See also scientific methods
    definition of, 8
    role of questions in, 8, **8,** 9, **15,** 15–16
science illustrators, 13, **13**
Science Skills Activity
    accuracy and reproducibility of data, 64
    constructing and interpreting graphs, 358
    constructing line graphs, 212, 460
    finding missing quantities, 98, 394, 422
    finding slopes of graphs, 322, 508
    linear and nonlinear relationships, 122
    planning and conducting investigations, 244, 298
    testing hypotheses, 30, 182
    variable and controlled parameters, 150, 270
scientific investigations. See also data
    applying answers of, 10–11
    collecting data, 18, 42–45, **42, 43, 45**
    communicating results, 20
    creating a scientific plan, 41
    developing hypotheses, 16–17
    experimental design, 150, 270
    finding missing quantities, 98, 394, 422
    methods used in, 9

Index

scientific investigations (*continued*)
  planning and conducting, 182, 244, 298
  testing hypotheses, 17–18, 30, 182, 298, 459
  variable and controlled parameters in, 17, 20, 51, 150, 270
scientific laws, 48, **48**
scientific methods, 14–20, 550–553
  analyzing results, 19, **19**
  asking questions, 8, **8**, 9, 15–16, **15**
  communicating results, 20
  drawing conclusions, 19–20, **20**
  forming hypotheses, 16–17
  summary of steps in, 14, **14**
  testing hypotheses, 17–18, 30, 182, 459
scientific plans, 41
scientific theories, 48, **48**
scuba instructors, 429, **429**
Seaborg, Glenn T., 217, **217**
seating chart activity, 193
sea water, ionic bonds in, 230, 235
seeing without looking, 163
semiconductors, 205
semimetals (metalloids), 136, **137**, 199, **199**, 205
shape
  buoyancy and, 417, **417**
  as physical property, **91**
shininess, in metals, **198**
ships, buoyancy of, 417–418, **417, 418**
short-period comets, 501
silicon, 192, **192–193**, 205
Silly Putty™, 304, **304**
simple carbohydrates, 314
single bonds, 311, **311**
sinking
  buoyant force and, 412–414, **412, 413, 414**
  changing overall density, 417–418, **417, 418**
  density and, 86, **86**, 414, **414**, 415, **415**
  determining density, 415, 416
  predicting, 414–415, **414, 415**, 416
Sirius, 439, 459
SI units, 43–45, **43, 45,** 554. *See also* units
sixth-magnitude stars, 439
skateboard lab, 385
skunks, formula for eliminating odors from, 328
SLAC (Stanford Linear Acceleration Center), 104

sliding kinetic friction, 352, **352**
slopes, in equations, 60, **60**
slopes, of graphs, 59–61, **59, 60,** 322, 508
soaps, **289**
sodium
  metal, **202, 233**
  in sodium chloride, **233, 234**
sodium chloride
  building a model of, 281
  crystal lattice of, **234,** 282, **282**
  formation of, **139,** 233
  importance to living things, 319, **319**
  melting point of, 283
  uses of, 295, **295**
sodium hydroxide
  dissolved in water, 289
  as a strong base, 293
  uses of, 291, 295
sodium nitrate, 295
solar eclipses, 495, **495**
solar nebula, 472–474, **472, 473, 474**
solar system, 470–515, 560–561. *See also* sun
  asteroid belt, 502
  asteroids, 502–503, **502, 503**
  comets, 500–501, **500, 501**
  data, 560–561
  distances in, **471,** 478, 484, 490
  Earth, 441–442, 478, **478,** 482, **482**
  formation of planets, 474, **474**
  formation of sun, 474–475, **474**
  gravity in, 372–373, **372, 373,** 382
  inner and outer, 478, **478**
  Jupiter, 486, **486,** 497
  Kuiper belt, 491, 501
  life in, 482, 484
  Luna (moon of Earth), 492–496, **492, 493, 494, 495, 496**
  Mars, 483–485, **483, 484,** 496
  measuring interplanetary distances, 478, **478**
  Mercury, 480, **480,** 492
  meteoroids, 503
  Neptune, 489, **489,** 498
  Oort cloud, 501
  Pluto, 490, **490,** 498
  reason for spherical objects in, **474**
  Saturn, **470–471,** 487, **487,** 497
  solar nebula in formation of, 472–473, **472, 473**
  Uranus, 488, **488,** 498
  Venus, 481, **481**

solar wind, 500
solids
  definition of, 111
  density of, 86, **86**
  melting of, 115, **115,** 118, **119**
  in solution, 145, **145**
  sublimation of, 118, **118**
  volumes of, 80–81, **80, 81,** 111, **111**
solubility
  of covalent compounds, 384
  definition of, **85,** 146
  identifying solutes by, 146
  of ionic compounds, 235, 283
  of solids in water, **147**
soluble substances, 144
solutes, 144
solutions
  acidic, basic, and neutral, 292–295, **293, 294**
  concentration of, 146, **146, 147**
  dilute, 146
  lab on, 146
  properties of, 144–146, **145, 146, 147**
  states of matter in, 145, **145**
solvents, 144, 156
sourness, in acids, 286, **286**
space exploration
  Apollo missions, **370,** 492
  Cassini spacecraft, **470–471,** 487
  Galileo spacecraft, 486, **492**
  Magellan spacecraft, 481, **481**
  missions to Mars, 485, **485**
  NEAR spacecraft, **502**
  Opportunity rover, 485
  orbiting, 381–382, **381, 382**
  reduced gravity in, **368–369,** 370, **370**
  space shuttle, **381,** 381, 390, **390**
  Spirit rover, 485
  Stardust spacecraft, 501
  Viking missions, **483**
  Voyager missions, **486, 487,** 488, **489, 498**
SpaceShipOne, **56**
space shuttle, 381, **381,** 390, **390**
spectroscopes, 437, **437**
spectrum (plural, *spectra*), 437, **437**
speed
  average, 338–339, **338,** 546
  definition of, 338
  from GPS watch systems, 364, **364**
  on graphs of time and position, 338–339, **339**

of light, 441, 476, 478
unit of, 338
velocity compared with, 340
speeding cars lab, 339
speed skating, **334–335**
spheres, surface area per volume in, 474, 493
spider map instructions (Graphic Organizer), 190, 306, 523, 523
spills, in the laboratory, 26
spiral galaxies, 450, **450**, 451
Spirit rover, 485
spring scales, **42**
Stanford Linear Acceleration Center (SLAC), 104
star clusters, 452, **452**
Stardust spacecraft, 501
stargazing, 439
stars, 436–449. *See also* galaxies; sun
  brightest, 466, **466**
  brightness of, 439–440, **439**, 446–447, **446–447**
  classification of, 438–439, **438**
  clusters of, 452, **452**
  color and temperature of, 436, **436, 438**
  companion stars, 439
  composition of, 437–438, **437, 438**
  distances to, 441, **441**
  flipchart movies of, 445
  formation of, 475
  in galaxies, 450–452, **450, 451, 452**
  H-R diagrams of, 446–447, **446–447**
  life cycle of massive stars, 448–449, **448**
  life cycle of sunlike stars, 444–445, **444, 445**
  light from, 436–437, **437, 438**, 439, 440
  luminous blue variable stars, 466, **466**
  main-sequence stars, 445, 446, **446–447**
  motions of, 441–442, **441, 442**
  neutron stars, 448
  origin of elements in, **173**
  red dwarf stars, 447, **447**
  red giant stars, 445, 447, **447**
  red supergiant stars, 445, **445**, 447, **447**
  white dwarf stars, 445, 446, **446**, 456

states of matter, 108–129
  condensation and, 117, **117**
  definition of, **85**, 110
  energy and changes of, 114, **114**
  evaporation and, 116–117, **116**
  freezing and, 115, **115**
  gases, 112, **112**
  labs on, 109, 112, 120–121
  liquids, 111, **111**
  melting and, 115, **115**, 118, **119**
  molecular motion and, 110, **110**, 114–118, **116**
  as a physical property, **91**
  plasmas, 113, 128, **128**
  solids, 111, **111**
  in solutions, 145, **145**
  sublimation and, 118, **118**
  temperature and, 118, **119**
static friction, 353, **353**
static objects, 347–348, 375
statistics, 58, **58**
Statue of Liberty, **92**
steel, **10**, 145
STMs (scanning tunneling electron microscopes), 164, **164**, 170, **170**
stony-iron meteorites, 504, **504**
stony meteorites, 504, **504**
storms, on gas giants, **470–471**, 489
straight-chain molecules, **310**
straws, pressure differences and, 410
strong acids, 292
strong bases, 293
strong force in atoms, 178, **178**
subatomic particles, 172–173, **172**
sublimation, 118, **118**
submarines, 418, **418**
submersibles, 428, **428**
subscripts, 262, **262**
sugar
  as carbohydrate, 314, **314**
  glucose, 260, **262**, 314, **314**
  solubility in water, 285, **285**
sulfur
  in living organisms, 312, 328
  properties of, 206
  valence electrons in, **229**
sulfuric acid, 288, 292, 481
sun. *See also* stars
  absolute magnitude of, 440
  absorption lines from, 438, **438**
  eclipses of, 495, **495**
  energy production in, 476–477, **477**
  formation of, 475, **474**

gravitational force of, 373, **373**
life cycle of, 444–445, 447, **447**
location in Milky Way, 451
as main-sequence star, **446–447**, 447
size of, 475
structure of, 475, **475**
superglue, 250, **250**
supernovas, 448, **448**
surface-area-to-volume ratio, 474
swim bladders, 418, **418**
symbols
  chemical, 199
  for ions, 231
  safety, 23, **23**
synthesis reactions, 268–269

T

table fold instructions (FoldNote), 520, **520**
table salt (sodium chloride)
  building a model of, 281
  crystal lattice of, **234**, 282, **282**
  formation of, **139, 233**
  importance to living things, 319, **319**
  melting point of, 283
  uses of, 295, **295**
tails, of comets, 500, **500**, 501
temperature
  of boiling water, 118
  changes of state and, 115–118, **118**, 120–121
  classification of stars by, **438**, 439
  color of stars and, 436, **436, 438**
  in H-R diagrams, **446–447**
  in nebulas, 473, **473**
  scales, 562
  solubility in water and, **147**
  units of, **43**, 45, **45**
tension, 347, **347**
terminal velocity, 378
terrestrial planets
  definition of, 480
  Earth, 482, **482**
  Mars, 483–485, **483, 484**
  Mercury, 480, **480**
  Venus, 481, **481**
testing hypotheses, 17–18, 30, 182, 298, 459
testing ideas exercise, 7
Tharsis Montes (Mars), 484
theories, scientific, 48, **48**

thermal conductivity, **85**
   of elements, 136, **137**
thermal energy, in chemical
      reactions, 259–260, **259, 260**
thermometers, 45, **45**
third law, Kepler's, 508
Thomson, J. J., 166, **166**
three-panel flip chart instructions
      (FoldNote), 519, **519**
thumbs seen at arm's length, 441
time travel, 36
Titan (moon of Saturn), 497, **497**
titanium, **204**
tools for science, 42–45, **42, 43, 45**
tornadoes, pressure differences
      and, 411, **411**
total solar eclipses, 495, **495**
transition metals, 203–204,
      203, 204
trends, on graphs, 54
Triantafyllou, Michael, 14–20, **15**
tri-fold instructions (FoldNote),
      520, **520**
triple bonds, 311, **311**
tritium, 208
Triton (moon of Neptune), 498
two-panel flip chart instructions
      (FoldNote), 520, **520**

U

ultraviolet light (UV light), 11
unbalanced forces
   acceleration from, 377,
      387–388, **387, 388**
   in falling objects, 378, **378**
   net force and, 345–346,
      345, 346
   Newton's first law of motion
      and, 384–385, **384, 385**
   Newton's second law of motion
      and, 387–388, **387, 388**
   Newton's third law of motion
      and, 389–390, **389, 390**
   in orbits, 371, 382, **382**
   static friction and, 353, **353**
   velocity and, 348–349, **348, 349**
undersea vessels, 428, **428**
underwater mines, 70
units, **43**
   of acceleration, 341
   astronomical, 441, 478, **478**
   cubic, 80
   of density, 85
   of distance, 441, 478, **478**
   of force, 344

   of heat, 322
   of length, 43, **43**
   of mass, 43, **43**, 83
   of pressure, 406
   of speed, 338
   table of SI units, **43**, 554
   of temperature, **43**, 45, **45**
   of velocity, 340
   of volume, **43**, 44, 79, 80
   of weight, 83, 374
universal gravitation, law of, 371,
      372–373, **372, 373**, 544
universe
   age of, 456
   expansion of, 455, 457
   formation of, 454–455, **454**
   gravity and, 456
   structure of, 456, **456**
unsaturated fats, 315
Uranus, 488, **488**, 498, **498**
UV light (ultraviolet light), 11

V

vacuum
   free fall in, 379, **379**
   speed of light in, 476, 478
valence electrons
   in covalent bonds, 236–237,
      236, 237
   energy levels and, 227–228,
      227, 228
   in ions, 230–232, **231, 232**
   in metallic bonds, 240, **240**
van der Waals forces, 250
variable parameters, 17, 20, 51,
      150, 270
variables
   dependent, 51
   in experiments, 17
   independent, 51
velocity
   changes in, 340, **340**, 348–349,
      348, 349
   definition of, 340
   direction in, 340, **340**
   friction and, 352
   gravitational forces on, 377, **377**
   Newton's first law and, 385, **385**
   speed compared with, 340
   terminal, 378
   unbalanced forces and,
      348–349, **348, 349**
venn diagram instructions (Graphic
      Organizers), 74, 130, 525,
      525
Venus, 481, **481**

vertical motion, 381, **381**
Viking missions, **483**
vitamin C, 288
vitamins, 288, 315
volcanoes
   on Io, 497, **497**
   on Mars, 484, **484**
   on Triton, 498
volcanologists, 12, **12**
volume
   of an irregularly shaped solid
      object, 81, **81**, 416
   buoyancy and, 418, **418**
   calculations, 80, **80**
   definition of, 78
   of gases, 112, **112**
   lab on, 79
   liquid, 28–29, 79, **79**
   measuring by displacement,
      81, **81**, 416
   of a regularly shaped solid
      object, 80, **80**, 416
   units of, **43**, 44
"Vomit Comet," **368–369**
Voyager missions, **486, 487**, 488,
      489, 498

W

waning moon, 494, **494**
wastewater managers, 251, **251**
water
   buoyancy in, 412–418, **412, 413,
      414**
   chemical formula for, **262**
   covalent bonds in, **237**, 242–243
   electrical conductivity of,
      283, **283**
   on Europa, 497
   evaporation of, 116, **116**
   freezing of, 115, **115**
   hydronium ions in, 286
   hydroxide ions in, 289, 290, 293
   importance to living things, 318
   on Mars, 483–485, **483**
   pH of, 293, **293**
   in photosynthesis, 318, **318**
   pressure, 409, **409**
   pressure differences and flow of,
      410–411, **410, 411**
   salt water, 144, 230, 235,
      283, **283**
   sea water, 230, 235
   solubility of ionic compounds
      in, 283
   state changes in, 118, **119**
   wastewater treatment, 251

Index

water pressure, 409, **409**
waxing moon, 494, **494**
weak acids, 292
weak bases, 293
weak force in atoms, 178, **178**
weather
    on Jupiter, 486
    on Neptune, 489
weight
    buoyant force and, 414, **414**
    definition of, 374
    on different planets, 506–507
    gravitational forces and, 82–83,
        82, 83, 374, **374**
    mass and, 82–83, **82, 83**,
        374, **374**
    units of, 83, 374

white dwarf stars, 445, 446, **446,**
    456
White Knight carrier plane, **56**
Wide Field Planetary Camera, 467
wildfires, 276, **276**
winds, on gas giants, 486, 489
wind tunnels, **404–405**
word parts, understanding,
    530–531
work, equation for, 548
work and heat, equation for, 549
written reports, 20

X

X rays
    from black holes, 449
    reading ancient texts with, 104

Y

years, on Mercury, 480
yields sign in chemical reactions,
    264

Z

zinc, 287, **287**

Acknowledgments

continued from p. ii

James E. Marshall, Ph.D.
Professor of Science Education
Department of Curriculum and Instruction
California State University, Fresno
Fresno, California

Richard D. McCallum, Ph.D.
Research Specialist
Graduate School of Education
University of California, Berkeley
Berkeley, California

Advisors

Kristin L. Baker
Science Teacher
Starr King School
Carmichael, California

Laura L. Bauer
Department Chair
Toby Johnson Middle School
Elk Grove, California

Jack Bettencourt
Science Department Chair
Joseph Kerr Middle School
Elk Grove, California

Rebecca Buschang
Science Partner
University of California, Los Angeles;
    Los Angeles Unified School District
Los Angeles, California

Eddyce Pope Moore
Science Teacher
Daniel Webster Middle School
Los Angeles, California

Kim O'Donnell
Science Teacher
Earle E. Williams Middle School
Tracy, California

Theresa Pearse
Science Teacher
Fremont Middle School
Stockton, California

Manuel Sanchez
Science Department Chair
Greer Middle School
Galt, California

Chuck Schindler
Secondary Math and Science Coordinator
San Bernardino City Unified School District
San Bernardino, California

William W. Tarr Jr., Ed.D.
Coordinator, Secondary Periodic Assessments
Los Angeles Unified School District
Los Angeles, California

Hong Tran
Science Teacher
Westlake Middle School
Oakland, California

Academic Reviewers

Henry Alegria, Ph.D.
Stauffer Professor of Chemistry
Director of Environmental Science
California Lutheran University
Thousand Oaks, California

Simone Aloisio, Ph.D.
Assistant Professor of Chemistry
Department of Chemistry
California State University, Channel Islands
Camarillo, California

Susana E. Deustua, Ph.D.
Director of Educational Activities
American Astronomical Society
Washington, D.C.

Alexander Dzyubenko, Ph.D.
Associate Professor of Physics
Department of Physics
California State University, Bakersfield
Bakersfield, California

Alejandro L. Garcia, Ph.D.
Professor of Physics
Department of Physics
San Jose State University
San Jose, California

Andreas Gebauer, Ph.D.
Assistant Professor of Chemistry
Department of Chemistry
California State University, Bakersfield
Bakersfield, California

Timothy A. Heumier, Ph.D.
Associate Professor of Physics
Department of Mathematics and Physics
Azusa Pacific University
Azusa, California

Lisa M. Lindert, Ph.D.
Assistant Professor
Department of Chemistry and Biochemistry
California Polytechnic State University
San Luis Obispo, California

Hideo Mabuchi, Ph.D.
Associate Professor
Department of Physics
California Institute of Technology
Pasadena, California

Mark B. Moldwin, Ph.D.
Associate Professor of Space Physics
Department of Earth and Space Sciences
University of California, Los Angeles
Los Angeles, California

Christopher Nichols, Ph.D.
Associate Professor of Chemistry
Department of Chemistry
California State University, Chico
Chico, California

Cynthia Phillips, Ph.D.
Principal Investigator
Center for the Study of Life in the Universe
SETI Institute
Mountain View, California

David Stevenson, Ph.D.
*George van Osdol Professor of
    Planetary Science*
Division of Geological and Planetary Sciences
California Institute of Technology
Pasadena, California

Brian M. Stoltz, Ph.D.
Assistant Professor of Chemistry
Division of Chemistry and
    Chemical Engineering
California Institute of Technology
Pasadena, California

James White, Ph.D.
Professor
Department of Biology and Chemistry
Azusa Pacific University
Azusa, California

Teacher Reviewers

Karen Benitez
Science Teacher
George V. LeyVa Middle School
San Jose, California

Joel S. Brener
Science Teacher
Daniel Webster Middle School
Los Angeles, California

Dana Carrigan
Vice Principal
Cordova High School
Rancho Cordova, California

Brian Conrad
Science Teacher
George V. LeyVa Middle School
San Jose, California

Treena Joi
Science Teacher
Corte Madera Middle School
Portola Valley, California

Dan Judnick
Department Chair and Science Teacher
Bernal Intermediate School
San Jose, California

Sushma Kashyap, MSc
Science Teacher
Alvarado School
Diamond Bar, California

Carla M. Kuhn, MA
Physical Science Teacher
Morrill Middle School
San Jose, California

Frank D. Lucio
Science Teacher
Olive Peirce Middle School
Ramona, California

Anna Marcello
Science Teacher
Audubon Middle School
Los Angeles, California

Bama Medley
Department Chair and Teacher
Fesler Junior High School
Santa Maria, California

Jacqueline Montejano, MA
Science Teacher
Sylvandale Middle School
San Jose, California

Michael R. Wells
Science Teacher
Spring Valley Middle School
Spring Valley, California

Jane Yuster
Department Chair
Hoover Elementary School
Redwood City, California

Lab Development

Phillip G. Bunce
Former Physics Teacher
Austin, Texas

Kenneth E. Creese
Science Teacher
White Mountain Junior High School
Rock Springs, Wyoming

Michael A. DiSpezio
Professional Development Specialist
JASON Project
Cape Cod, Massachusetts

William G. Lamb, Ph.D.
Winningstad Chair in the Physical Sciences
Oregon Episcopal School
Portland, Oregon

Alyson M. Mike
Science Teacher
East Valley Middle School
East Helena, Montana

Joseph W. Price
Department Chair and Science Teacher
*Science and Math Instructor for
    Pre-College Program*
H. M. Browne Junior High School
Howard University
Washington, D.C.

Denise Lee Sandefur
Science Chairperson
Nucla High School
Nucla, Colorado

John Spadafino
Mathematics and Physics Teacher
Hackensack High School
Hackensack, New Jersey

Walter Woolbaugh
Science Teacher
Manhattan Junior High School
Manhattan, Montana

Lab Testing

Karen Benitez
Science Teacher
George V. LeyVa Middle School
San Jose, California

Joel S. Brener
Science Teacher
Daniel Webster Middle School
Los Angeles, California

Brian Conrad
Science Teacher
George V. LeyVa Middle School
San Jose, California

Anna Marcello
Science Teacher
Audubon Middle School
Los Angeles, California

Bama Medley
Department Chair and Teacher
Fesler Junior High School
Santa Maria, California

Jane Yuster
Department Chair
Hoover Elementary School
Redwood City, California

Feature Development

Katy Z. Allen
Hatim Belyamani
John A. Benner
David Bradford
Jennifer Childers
Mickey Coakley
Susan Feldkamp
Jane Gardner
Erik Hahn
Christopher Hess
Abby Jones

Deena Kalai
Charlotte W. Luongo, MSc
Michael May
Persis Mehta, Ph.D.
Eileen Nehme, MPH
Catherine Podeszwa
Dennis Rathnaw
Daniel B. Sharp
John M. Stokes
April Smith West
Molly F. Wetterschneider

Staff Credits

The people who contributed to **Holt California Physical Science** are listed below. They represent editorial, design, production, emedia, and permissions.

Chris Allison, Wesley M. Bain, Juan Baquera, Angela Beckmann, Ed Blake, Marc Burgamy, Rebecca Calhoun, Kimberly Cammerata, Soojinn Choi, Julie Dervin, Michelle Dike, Lydia Doty, Jen Driscoll, Diana Goetting, Angela Hemmeter, Tim Hovde, Wilonda Ieans, Elizabeth Ihry, Jevara Jackson, Simon Key, Jane A. Kirschman, Cathy Kuhles, Denise Mahoney, Michael Mazza, Kristen McCardel, Richard Metzger, Christina Murray, Micah Newman, Janice Noske, Dustin Ognowski, Joeleen Ornt, Laura Prescott, Bill Rader, Jim Ratcliffe, Peter Reid, Michael Rinella, Kelly Rizk, Jeff Robinson, Audrey Rozsypal, Beth Sample, Kay Selke, Chris Smith, Dawn Marie Spinozza, Sherry Sprague, Jeff Streber, Roshan Strong, Jeannie Taylor, Bob Tucek, Tam Voynick, Clay Walton, Kira J. Watkins, Ken Whiteside, Holly Whittaker, David Wisnieski, Monica Yudron

Credits

Abbreviations used: (t) top, (c) center, (b) bottom, (l) left, (r) right, (bkgd) background

PHOTOGRAPHY

Front Cover NASA

Table of Contents iii, Sam Dudgeon/HRW; iv, Howard B. Bluestein; v (bl), Peter Van Steen/HRW; v (br), Victoria Smith/HRW; vi, Sam Dudgeon/HRW; vii (t), Scott Van Osdol/HRW; vii (b), Richard Megna/Fundamental Photographs; ix, Jonathan Blair/CORBIS; x (tl), Victoria Smith/HRW; x (b), Jack Newkirk/HRW; xi, Royalty-Free/Corbis; xii, Steve Coleman/AP/Wide World Photos; xiii (b), Bruno P. Zehnder/Peter Arnold, Inc.; xiv (b), Bill & Sally Fletcher/Tom Stack & Associates; xv, NASA

Safety First! xxviii, Sam Dudgeon/HRW; xxix (t), John Langford/HRW; Xxix(b), xxx(br) & xxx(t), Sam Dudgeon/HRW; Xxx(bl), Stephanie Morris/HRW; xxxi(tl), Sam Dudgeon/HRW; xxxi(tr), Jana Birchum/HRW; Xxxi(b), Sam Dudgeon/HRW

Unit One 2 (t), Bettmann/CORBIS; 2 (bl), Enrico Tedeschi; 2 (c), UPI/CORBIS/Bettman; 3 (cl), Sam Dudgeon/HRW; 3 (tr), Brown Brothers/HRW Photo Library; 3 (bl), Natalie Fobes/Getty Images; 3 (br), REUTERS/Charles W. Luzier/NewsCom

Chapter One 6-7, Kevin Schafer/Getty Images; 8, Peter Van Steen/HRW; 9 (tr), PhotoObjects.net/PictureQuest; 09 (br), Peter Van Steen/HRW Photo; 10 (tl), Regis Bossu/Sygma; 10 (br), Richard R. Hansen/Photo Researchers, Inc.; 11, Howard B. Bluestein; 12 (tl & tr), Andy Christiansen/HRW; 12 (b), G. Brad Lewis/Getty Images; 15 (tr), Stephen Maclone; 15 (tl), Republished with permission of The Globe Newspaper Company, Inc. Photo by Barry Chin; 17, Donna Coveney/MIT; 18 (t), Donna Coveney/MIT; 18 (br), John Morrison/Morrison Photography; 22, Victoria Smith/HRW; 23 & 24, Sam Dudgeon/HRW; 24 (l), John Morrison/Morrison Photography; 25 & 26, Sam Dudgeon/HRW; 27, GARO/Photo Researchers, Inc.; 28, Sam Dudgeon/HRW; 29, Digital Image copyright © 2005 PhotoDisc; 31 (t), Peter Van Steen/HRW Photo; 36, MEEP; 37, Louis Fronkier/Art Louis Photographics/HRW

Chapter Two 40-41, Jonathan Blair/CORBIS; 41 (br), John Morrison/Morrison Photography; 42, Victoria Smith/HRW; 44, John Morrison/Morrison Photography; 45 (br), Peter Van Steen/HRW; 45 (bl), Digital Image copyright © 2005 PhotoDisc; 46 (t), JULIAN BAUM/Photo Researchers, Inc.; 46 (b), Victoria Smith/HRW; 47, Tom Pantages/Phototake; 48, Victoria Smith/HRW; 49, NASA; 52 (tl), Michael Newman/Photo Edit Inc.; 52 (bl), John Morrison/Morrison Photography; 55, Paul Barton/CORBIS; 56, Scaled Composites/Photo Researchers, Inc.; 59, David Madison Sports Images, Inc.; 60 (tl), John Morrison/Morrison Photography; 60 (b), Getty Images; 62 & 63, Scott Van Osdol/HRW; 65 (t), Tom Pantages/Phototake; 67, Victoria Smith/HRW; 70 (l), NASA/Science Photo Library/Photo Researchers, Inc.; 70 (r), U.S. Navy, Brien Aho, HO/AP/Wide World Photos; 71, Photo Courtesy of NOAA

Unit Two 72 (c), W.A. Mozart at the age of 7: oil on canvas, 1763, by P.A. Lorenzoni/The Granger Collection; 72 (bl), Photo Researchers, Inc.; 72 (t), SPL/Photo Researchers, Inc.; 73 (tc), The Vittoria, colored line engraving, 16th century/The Granger Collection; 73 (tr), Stock Montage, Inc.; 73 (cl), Getty Images; 73 (cr), Underwood & Underwood/Bettmann/CORBIS; 73 (br), AFP/CORBIS

Chapter Three 76-77, Mark Renders/Getty Images; 77 (br), John Morrison/Morrison Photography; 78 (br), Sam Dudgeon/HRW; 78 (bl), Digital Image copyright © 2005 PhotoDisc; 79 (cr), Sam Dudgeon/HRW; 79 & 81, John Morrison/Morrison Photography; 82, Sam Dudgeon/HRW; 83, John Langford/HRW; 84, Sam Dudgeon/HRW; 85 (tl), Victoria Smith/HRW; 85 (br), Sam Dudgeon/HRW; 85 (cr), Peter Van Steen/HRW; 85 (bl & cl), Sam Dudgeon/HRW; 85 (tr & b), John Morrison/Morrison Photography; 87 (tr), Richard Megna/Fundamental Photographs; 87 (br), John Morrison/Morrison Photography; 88 (t), John Langford/HRW; 88 (tr), Lance Schriner/HRW; 89, Victoria Smith/HRW; 90, Rob Boudreau/Getty Images; 91 (r), Charlie Winters/HRW; 91 (tl & tr), Sam Dudgeon/HRW; 92 (c & cr), John Morrison/Morrison Photography; 92 (l), Joseph Drivas/Getty Images; 92 (tr), SuperStock; 93, Sam Dudgeon/HRW; 94 (tl & tr), Charlie Winters/HRW; 94 (b), John Morrison/Morrison Photography; 95, CORBIS Images; 96, Sam Dudgeon/HRW; ,99 (c), Richard Megna/Fundamental Photographs; 99 (bl & br), Charlie Winters/HRW; 100, Richard Megna/Fundamental Photographs; 101, Lance Schriner/HRW; 104 (tl), David Young-Wolff/PhotoEdit; 104 (r & tr), The Walters Art Museum; 105 (r), Courtesy Mimi So; 105 (b, c, cr & r) Steve Cole/Photodisc/PictureQuest

Chapter Four 108-9, Teresa Nouri Rishel/Dale Chihuly Studio; 109 (br), John Morrison/Morrison Photography; 111, Victoria Smith/HRW; 112 (c), Scott Van Osdol/HRW; 112 (br), John Morrison/Morrison Photography; 113 (tr), Richard Kaylin/Getty Images; 115 (tr), Richard Megna/Fundamental Photographs; 115 (b), Scott Van Osdol/HRW; 117, Paul Zahl/National Geographic Image Collection; 118 (l), Omni Photo Communications, Inc./Index Stock Imagery, Inc.; 118 (br), John Morrison/Morrison Photography; 121, Victoria Smith/HRW; 128 (l), Scoones/SIPA Press; 128 (br & tr), Dr. Tom Katsouleas; 129 (r), Susanna Frohman/KRT/NewsCom; 129(l), Andrew Goldsworthy

Chapter Five 132-3, Scott Van Osdol/HRW; 133 (br), John Morrison/Morrison Photography; 134 (l), Jonathan Blair/Woodfin Camp & Associates, Inc.; 134 (br), Victoria Smith/HRW; 135 (br), Russ Lappa/Photo Researchers, Inc.; 135 (bl & bc), Charles D. Winters/Photo Researchers, Inc.; 135 (tr), Sam Dudgeon/HRW; 136 (l), Zack Burris/Zack Burris, Inc.; 136 (c), Yann Arthus-Bertrand/CORBIS; 136 (r), Walter Chandoha; 137 (tl), Victoria Smith/HRW; 137 (l, cl & tc), Sam Dudgeon/HRW; 137 (cr),Runk/Shoenberger/Grant Heilman Photography, Inc.; 137 (r), Joyce Photographics/Photo Researchers, Inc.; 137 (tr), Russ Lappa/Photo Researchers, Inc.; 137 (br), Charles D. Winters/Photo Researchers, Inc.; 137 (cl), Larry Stepanowicz; 138 & 139 (bl), Runk/Schoenberger/Grant Heilman Photography Inc.; 139 (bc), Richard Megna/Fundamental Photographs; 139 (br), Sam Dudgeon/HRW; 139 (tr), John Morrison/Morrison Photography; 140, Richard Megna/Fundamental Photographs; 141(tr), John Kaprielian/Photo Researchers, Inc.; 142, Sam Dudgeon/HRW; 143 (tl), Charles D. Winters; 143 (cl), Sam Dudgeon/HRW; 143 (bc), Charles D. Winters/Photo Researchers, Inc.; 143 (bl), Klaus Guldbrandsen/Science Photo Library/Photo Researchers, Inc.; 143 (tr, cr, br), John Langford/HRW; 144, Sam Dudgeon/HRW; 145, Richard Haynes/HRW; 146 (l), Sam Dudgeon/HRW; 146 (r), John Morrison/Morrison Photography; 149, Sam Dudgeon/HRW; 151 (b), Sam Dudgeon/HRW; 151 (c), Richard Megna/Fundamental Photographs; 151 (tl), Sam Dudgeon/HRW; 151 (tr), Larry Stepanowicz; 151 (tc), Russ Lappa/Photo Researchers, Inc.; 156 (l), Peter Van Steen/HRW; 156 (r), J. GUICHARD/CORBIS SYGMA; 157 (r), Courtesy of Aundra Nix; 157 (l), Astrid & Hans-Frieder Michler/SPL/Photo Researchers, Inc.

Unit Three 158 (t), The Granger Collection, New York; 158 (c), Bettmann/CORBIS; 158 (b), Conley Photography, Inc./American Solar Energy Society; 159 (tr), Phil Degginger/Color-Pic, Inc.; 159 (cl), Robert Wolf/HRW; 159 (c), The Granger Collection, New York; 159 (bc), David Madison; 159 (br), Courtesy of DEKA Research and Development/PRNewsFoto/NewsCom

Chapter Six 162-3 & (inset), Sandia National Laboratories; 163 (br), John Morrison/Morrison Photography; 164 (t), Courtesy JEOL; 164 (r), Carin Krasner/CORBIS; 165, Corbis-Bettmann; 167, John Morrison/Morrison Photography; 168 (b), John Zoiner; 168 (bl), Mavournea Hay/HRW; 169, Getty Images; 170 (l), Sam Dudgeon/HRW; 170(b), COLIN CUTHBERT/SCIENCE PHOTO LIBRARY; 173, NASA/PHOTO RESEARCHERS, INC.; 177, John Morrison/Morrison Photography; 180, Victoria Smith/HRW; 181, Sam Dudgeon/HRW; 188 (r), NASA; 188 (l), Aurora/Getty Images; 189 (cr), Fermi National Accelerator Laboratory/Corbis; 189 (tr), Stephen Maclone

Chapter Seven 192-3, Ken Lucas/Visuals Unlimited; 193 (br), John Morrison/Morrison Photography; 195 & 198 (br, bl, cr, & cl), Sam Dudgeon/HRW; 198 (tl), John Morrison/Morrison Photography; 199 (tr), Lester V. Bergman/Corbis-Bettmann; 199 (tl), Sally Anderson-Bruce/HRW; 201, HRW; 202 (bl), Charles D. Winters/Photo Researchers, Inc.; 202, Richard Megna/Fundamental Photographs; 203 (tr), Sam Dudgeon/HRW; 204 (tl & tc), Sam Dudgeon/HRW; 204 (tr), 1990 P. Petersen/Custom Medical Stock Photo; 204 (t), Victoria Smith/HRW; 205 (tr), Phillip Hayson/Photo Researchers, Inc.; 205, Sam Dudgeon/HRW; 206 (c & cl), Richard Megna/Fundamental Photographs; 206 (b), Charlie Winters/HRW; 206 (t), Stephen Frink/CORBIS; 207, Robert Landau/Corbis; 208 (tl), NASA; 208 (br), John Morrison/Morrison Photography; 210, John Langford/HRW; 211, Sam Dudgeon/HRW; 211 (c), Richard Megna/Fundamental Photographs; 211 (b), Charlie Winters/HRW; 218 (r), Giraudon/Art Resource, NY; 219 (r), LAWRENCE BERKELEY NATIONAL LABORATORY/PHOTO RESEARCHERS, INC.; 219 (l), Bettmann/CORBIS

Unit Four 220 (t), The Granger Collection, New York; 220 (bl), Science VU/ © IBM/Visuals Unlimited; 220 (l), SCIENCE PHOTO LIBRARY/Photo Researchers, Inc.; 221 (cr), J A Giordano/CORBIS SABA; 221 (tl), SuperStock; 221 (bl), B. Bisson/Sygma; 221 (br), AP Photo/The Albuquerque Tribune, KayLynn Deveney

Chapter Eight 224-5, Doug Struthers/Getty Images; 225 (br), John Morrison/Morrison Photography; 226, Charles Gupton/CORBIS; 228, John Morrison/Morrison Photography; 230, Konrad Wothe/Minden Pictures; 233 (bl), Runk/Shoenberger/Grant Heilman Photography; 233 (bc), Richard Megna/Fundamental Photographs; 233 (br), Sam Dudgeon/HRW; 234 (tr), Paul Silverman/Fundamental Photographs; 234, John Morrison/Morrison Photography; 238 (tr), Sam Dudgeon/HRW; 238 (br), John Morrison/Morrison Photography; 239 (tr), Sam Dudgeon/HRW; 239 (b), Jonathan Blair/CORBIS; 240, Victoria Smith/HRW; 241, John Langford/HRW; 243, Sam Dudgeon/HRW; 244 (cr), Paul Silverman/Fundamental Photographs; 244 (br), Sam Dudgeon/HRW; 244 (bl), Russ Lappa/Photo Researchers, Inc.; 246, Victoria Smith/HRW; 247 (tr & cr), Sam Dudgeon/HRW; 250 (r), Peter Oxford/Nature Picture Library; 250 (l), Diaphor Agency/Index Stock Imagery, Inc.; 251 (r), Neil Michel/Axiom